BABY

Late Quaternary Palaeoceanography of the North Atlantic Margins

Geological Society Special Publications
Series Editor A. J. FLEET

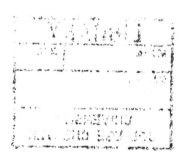

GEOLOGICAL SOCIETY SPECIAL PUBLICATION NO. 111

Late Quaternary Palaeoceanography of the North Atlantic Margins

EDITED BY

J. T. ANDREWS

INSTAAR and Department of Geological Sciences, University of Colorado,
Boulder, Colorado, USA

W. E. N. AUSTIN

Dept of Geology and Geophysics,
University of Edinburgh, UK

H. BERGSTEN

Dept of Oceanography,
University of Göteborg, Sweden

AND

A. E. JENNINGS

INSTAAR and Department of Geological Sciences, University of Colorado,
Boulder, Colorado, USA

1996

Published by

The Geological Society

London

THE GEOLOGICAL SOCIETY

The Society was founded in 1807 as The Geological Society of London and is the oldest geological society in the world. It received its Royal Charter in 1825 for the purpose of 'investigating the mineral structure of the Earth'. The Society is Britain's national society for geology with a membership of around 8000. It has countrywide coverage and approximately 1000 members reside overseas. The Society is responsible for all aspects of the geological sciences including professional matters. The Society has its own publishing house, which produces the Society's international journals, books and maps, and which acts as the European distributor for publications of the American Association of Petroleum Geologists, SEPM and the Geological Society of America.

Fellowship is open to those holding a recognized honours degree in geology or cognate subject and who have at least two years' relevant postgraduate experience, or who have not less than six years' relevant experience in geology or a cognate subject. A Fellow who has not less than five years' relevant postgraduate experience in the practice of geology may apply for validation and, subject to approval, may be able to use the designatory letters C Geol (Chartered Geologist).

Further information about the Society is available from the Membership Manager, The Geological Society, Burlington House, Piccadilly, London W1V 0JU, UK. The Society is a Registered Charity, No. 210161.

Published by The Geological Society from:
The Geological Society Publishing House
Unit 7
Brassmill Enterprise Centre
Brassmill Lane
Bath BA1 3JN
UK
(*Orders*: Tel. 01225 445046
Fax 01225 442836)

First published 1996

The publishers make no representation, express or implied, with regard to the accuracy of the information contained in this book and cannot accept any legal responsibility for any errors or omissions that may be made.

British Library Cataloguing in Publication Data
A catalogue record for this book is available from the British Library.

ISBN 1-897799-61-6

Typeset by Aarontype Ltd, Unit 47, Easton Business Centre, Felix Road, Bristol BS5 0HE, UK.

Printed in Great Britain by
The Alden Press, Osney Mead
Oxford, UK.

Distributors

USA
  AAPG Bookstore
  PO Box 979
  Tulsa
  OK 74101-0979
  USA
  (*Orders*: Tel. (918) 584-2555
       Fax (918) 560-2652)

Australia
  Australian Mineral Foundation
  63 Conyngham Street
  Glenside
  South Australia 5065
  Australia
  (*Orders*: Tel. (08) 379-0444
       Fax (08) 379-4634)

India
  Affiliated East-West Press PVT Ltd
  G-1/16 Ansari Road
  New Delhi 110 002
  India
  (*Orders*: Tel. (11) 327-9113
       Fax (11) 326-0538)

Japan
  Kanda Book Trading Co.
  Tanikawa Building
  3-2 Kanda Surugadai
  Chiyoda-Ku
  Tokyo 101
  Japan
  (*Orders*: Tel. (03) 3255-3497
       Fax (03) 3255-3495)

Contents

Preface

The papers published here are a selection of those presented at a meeting which was held at the Royal Society of Edinburgh and a series of workshops at the Department of Geology and Geophysics, University of Edinburgh between 5 and 7 January 1995. The meeting was organized by a steering committee comprising John Andrews, Bill Austin and Helene Bergsten. Anne Jennings was added to the list of editors of the current volume.

This volume includes many papers which deal with the palaeoceanography of North Atlantic continental margins and associated environments. It has been organized geographically with Part 1 including five papers dealing with the western margin of the Labrador Sea, Davis Strait and Baffin Bay. In Part 2, five papers deal with events on the East Greenland margin, together with papers examining records from the Arctic Ocean and North Atlantic deep-sea. The evidence from Northwest European margins with some emphasis on the region of the Barents Sea and Spitsbergen margin is dealt with in Part 3, which includes a total of ten papers. Finally, two papers are included in Part 4 that extend the coverage both geographically and conceptually, including for example research in the Mediterranean Basin.

Many people helped to make the meeting at Edinburgh a success and have assisted in the completion of this volume. In particular we would like to thank the following organisations (contact person named) who supported the meeting: Quaternary Research Association (Elaine Street-Perrot), the Marine Studies Group of the Geological Society (Dan Evans) and IGCP-253 North Atlantic Seaboard Project (John Lowe). Financial support was given by the University of Göteborg, the Quaternary Research Association and the University of Edinburgh. Bill Austin would like to thank all those who helped with the local organization of the meeting, in particular Heather Austin, Geoffrey Boulton, Shirley Derrick and Cecilia Taylor. Thanks also to the staff at the Royal Society of Edinburgh, the Department of Geology and Geophysics at the University of Edinburgh, the Edinburgh Tourist Office, the Royal Bank of Scotland, the Roxburgh Hotel and *Le Bistro* caterers

In the completion of this volume the editors are particularly indebted to David Ogden, Andrew Fleet and Angharad Hills, who have steered and encouraged us through the publication process at the Geological Society. John Andrews and Anne Jennings would like to thank Wendy Freeman for her assistance during the editing process and the National Science Foundation for their support. Finally, we thank the authors and reviewers of the manuscripts for adhering to the deadlines imposed and making this volume what it is. We hope that their efforts will encourage and inspire further innovative research at the continental margins of the North Atlantic Ocean and elsewhere.

John Andrews, Bill Austin, Helene Bergsten, Anne Jennings
November 1995

The Late Quaternary palaeoceanography of North Atlantic margins: an introduction

JOHN T. ANDREWS[1], WILLIAM E. N. AUSTIN[2],
HELENE BERGSTEN[3] & ANNE E. JENNINGS[1]

[1] *INSTAAR and Department of Geological Sciences, Box 450, University of Colorado, Boulder, CO 80309, USA*
[2] *Department of Geology and Geophysics, University of Edinburgh, Edinburgh EH9 3JW, UK (Present address: Environmental Research Centre, Department of Geography, University of Durham, South Road, Durham DH1 3LE, UK)*
[3] *Department of Oceanography, University of Goteborg, PO Box 4038, S-400 40 Goteborg, Sweden*

The inspiration for this volume on the 'Late Quaternary palaeoceanography of North Atlantic margins' came from a meeting of the 'North Atlantic Seaboard Programme' (NASP), a subproject of the International Geological Correlation Program (IGCP) No. 253 on 'Termination of the Pleistocene' which was held at Royal Holloway, University of London, in the spring of 1991. The majority of the talks given at that meeting were later put together in a special issue of the *Journal of Quaternary Science*, under the guidance of J. J. Lowe (Lowe *et al.* 1994). At the Royal Holloway meeting, which had a significant focus on terrestrial records of late glacial change, Andrews, Austin and Bergsten proposed that the marine records from the continental margins around the North Atlantic required 'equal' consideration, and thus proposed to convene a meeting to evaluate the palaeoceanographic marine records from the North Atlantic. A particular goal was to obtain new information from both the northeastern North Atlantic (i.e. the region between east Greenland and NW Europe), but also data from the northwestern North Atlantic, particularly the eastern margins of North America. These objectives have largely been achieved (Fig. 1).

The papers published here are a selection of those presented at a meeting which was held at the Royal Society of Edinburgh and a series of workshops at the Department of Geology and Geophysics, University of Edinburgh during January 1995.

Why continental margins?

In tracing the history of the evolution of both data and thought on the last deglacial transition (say 8 to 18 ka BP) during the last two decades, it is clear that there have been three major sources of data. The first is the wealth of information on terrestrial deglacial sequences (i.e. from glacial margins, lakes, bogs, and raised beach sequences) (see Lowe 1994, for example). The second is the rich information that has been derived from a study of marine cores from 'blue water' (i.e. deep sea) and the third concerns the newly emerging ice-core records, in particular those from the Greenland ice sheet.

Although the study of terrestrial sequences has a history on both sides of the Atlantic going back for a century or more, the vital importance of the deep sea records largely became apparent in the 1970s and 1980s, and owes much to the pioneer efforts of the CLIMAP Project; in particular to the work of Ruddiman & McIntyre (Ruddiman 1977, 1987; Ruddiman & Glover 1975; Ruddiman & McIntyre 1981; 1982), and Kellogg (Kellogg 1980, 1984), who established key links in ice sheet/ ocean interactions and, in the context of the North Atlantic, demonstrated how rapidly the Polar Front migrated back and forth during the last deglaciation. Of considerable significance was the development of transfer functions which predict palaeoceanographic parameters, such as temperature and salinity, from foraminiferal assemblages (Imbrie & Webb 1981), and the focus on improved chronologies.

Another major international development that has had an enormous impact on research has been the Deep Sea Drilling Project and its successor, the Ocean Drilling Programme (ODP). Although much of the early DSDP and ODP work focused on drilling in the deep-sea *per se*, more recently operations have shifted toward continental margins and other sites of rapid sediment accumulation. For example, during ODP Leg 152 the margin of East Greenland was drilled (Larsen *et al.* 1994), while ODP Leg 162 recently drilled the expanded sediment drifts of

From Andrews, J. T., Austin, W. E. N., Bergsten, H. & Jennings, A. E. (eds), 1996, *Late Quaternary Palaeoceanography of the North Atlantic Margins*, Geological Society Special Publication No. 111, pp. 1–6.

the North Atlantic. Hopefully, future ODP expeditions will 'routinely' sample the thick sequences of Quaternary sediments that lie within high latitude glaciated continental margins, such as the major trough and fjord sequences, some of which contain 800 m or so of sediment (Andrews *et al.* 1994). ODP has led the way in technological improvements for onboard core logging and the description of physical properties; such techniques are bound to play an increasingly important role in the future development and study of high resolution stratigraphies.

However, the intermediate environment between that of the land-based glacial systems and the deep-sea sedimentary environments, the continental shelves and slopes, entered the debate rather late and only became potentially important in the 1980s and to the present day (Rowe & Baldauf 1995). The reason was simple and consisted of two major elements: the first was that many deep sea palaeoceanographers were distrustful of the integrity of the records on shelves and slopes and frequently asserted, in private conversations, that sedimentation rates varied during deglaciation, that hiatuses were probable, and that reworking would be common, hence the records could not be trusted! By contrast, many palaeoceanographers continue to assume that deep sea records do accumulate continuously, which as we now know is not the case. The second main problem was that most sediments from glaciated continental margins were extremely difficult, if not impossible to date, because of the relative paucity of marine carbonates (i.e. foraminifera or marine molluscs) (Fillon *et al.* 1981; Vilks & Mudie 1978). The latter was significantly alleviated by the advent of AMS ^{14}C dating, such that reliable dates can now be obtained from milligrams of marine carbonate materials, rather than the grams needed by conventional decay counting.

The AMS ^{14}C dating method started to become more widely available in the mid-1980s (Andrews *et al.* 1985). One of the big beneficiaries of this technology were glaciated continental margins where a combination of high rates of sediment accumulation (metres per 1000 years), often coupled with low foraminiferal concentrations (10^0–10^3 foraminifera/gram), had restricted radiocarbon dating to the chance recovery of marine bivalves (Fillon & Harmes 1982; Hald & Vorren 1987*a*; Scott *et al.* 1984) or to the dubious approach of dating the acid-insoluble organic fraction (Andrews *et al.* 1985). However, as Nielsen *et al.* (1995) have discussed, the mollusc shells which do occur in continental shelf sequences may provide more reliable age

control than the more readily reworked tests of foraminifera (Austin & McCarroll 1992).

The ability to document changing ages in relatively short depth increments from glacial marine sediments indicated that rates of sediment accumulation were in themselves important conveyors of palaeoenvironmental information (Andrews 1990; Jennings 1993) and could be used to infer changes in the location of the ice margin relative to the cored site. The depositional environments of the continental shelves are therefore highly dynamic and often exhibit significant facies changes, particularly in response to regional deglaciation (Boulton 1990).

Another parallel and important tool that became generally available to researchers working on continental margins from the 1970s onwards was the development of high-resolution acoustic systems of various kinds. One of the best known systems was the Huntec Deep-Tow System (DTS) and this was rapidly used to develop regional mapping of sub-seafloor stratigraphy in the 1 to 100 m range, depending on the acoustic characteristics of the sediment (Fillon & Harmes 1982; Josenhans *et al.* 1986; King & Fader 1986; King *et al.* 1987; Praeg *et al.* 1986). Coring from research vessels frequently extracted cores of 5 to 15 m in length, and the pre-acquisition of acoustic stratigraphy meant that judicious coring at sites where sediment units thinned could be used to extend the records. In turn, the ability to date these sediments was now improved, although not guaranteed, by AMS ^{14}C technology (Linick *et al.* 1986; Slota *et al.* 1987). Models of glacial and glacial marine sedimentation were advanced on the basis of the acoustic stratigraphy and core chronology (Vorren *et al.* 1983).

In the 1970s palaeoceanographic information from marine cores was frequently restricted to analysis of changes in the assemblage of planktic foraminifera and in their stable isotopic composition. The work of CLIMAP members was especially noteworthy and significant gains were made in our understanding of the palaeoceanography of the Atlantic and Pacific oceans (Imbrie & Webb 1981; Kellogg 1986; Ruddiman & McIntyre 1981; Ruddiman & others 1994; Shackleton 1977). However, the development of information about continental margin benthic foraminifera and the changes in isotopic composition of shelf near-surface waters was slower to evolve (Aksu & Mudie 1985; Feyling-Hanssen 1982; Hald & Vorren 1987*b*; Osterman 1984; Scott *et al.* 1984; Vilks *et al.* 1984). In the last decade major changes include a better understanding of the ecology of benthic foraminifera, better chronology, and a multivariate approach to environmental reconstructions (Andrews *et al.* 1991; Hald & Steinsund 1992*a*, *b*; Jennings & Helgadottir 1994; Poole *et al.* in press; Vilks & Deonarine 1988). Although much of the palaeoceanographic literature is based on an interpretation of foraminiferal assemblages or geochemical changes in foraminifera (Duplessy *et al.* 1993), it should not be forgotten that other groups, such as diatoms, are playing an increasingly important role in our understanding of past oceanographic conditions (Koç & Jansen 1992, Koç *et al.* 1993; Williams 1993).

One of the most exciting new developments in palaeoceanography has been the realization that, in cores with adequate temporal resolution, marine conditions changed very rapidly during the last glacial/interglacial transition (Bard *et al.* 1987; Lehman & Keigwin 1992; Koç *et al.* 1993, Duplessy *et al.* 1993).

The present volume and future perspectives

One strength of this collection is evident from Fig. 1 which shows the location (sometimes specifically, at other times more generally) of the papers included in this volume. This is the first time that papers from the northeastern North American continental margin have been included together with papers dealing with the East Greenland margin, the margins of northwest

Europe, the northwest European Arctic, the Arctic and North Atlantic oceans.

One of the most important issues in this volume, which has been re-emphasized because of newly emerging data from the GISP2 and GRIP ice cores from central Greenland, is the speed of environmental change in the North Atlantic, especially during the last deglacial transition (Johnsen *et al.* 1992; Taylor *et al.* 1993). Many of the papers in this volume present high-resolution stratigraphic data which support these reconstructions and demonstrate the advantages of continental margin records, not only in resolving the palaeoceanography of the North Atlantic Ocean, but also in regional reconstructions of climate change. However, changes within the North Atlantic during the late glacial period are complex and exhibit the apparent non-linearity of climate response to insolation driven changes. While we still do not fully understand what causes these millennial and shorter timescale changes, there is an ever-increasing body of evidence to demonstrate the link between all these climatic records and changes within the surface North Atlantic.

The evidence for abrupt climate change, such as the Younger Dryas event (see, for example, **Duplessy** *et al.*), is not totally unambiguous at all locations around the North Atlantic (**Andrews** *et al.*, East Greenland). The diachroneity of climatic events, or even their absence at certain

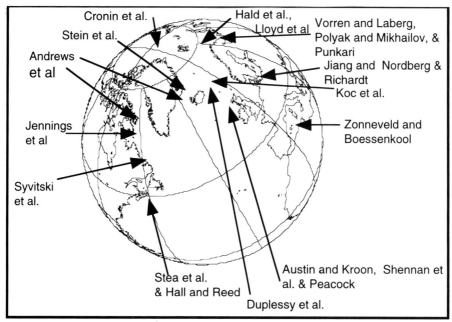

Fig 1. Map of the North Atlantic region with arrows pointing to the areas discussed in the various chapters of this volume.

locations, may relate to the fact that steep climate gradients are associated with features such as the North Atlantic Arctic Front and that such features are highly dynamic in both space and time. Polar or sub-polar waters, in particular, may register few of the minor climatic oscillations of the late glacial period which are observed at the mid-latitudes. Compare, for example, the timing of initial late glacial interstadial climate warming as it is recorded at many of the sites reported in this volume. This topic is discussed further in the paper by **Koç** *et al.*, while **Austin & Kroon** explore the stratigraphic significance of an oscillating North Atlantic Arctic Front as its latitudinal extent changes relative to a high temporal resolution continental shelf site from NW Scotland.

In addition, the observations of Heinrich (Heinrich 1988) that the North Atlantics pelagic regime was interrupted by dramatic iceberg rafting events, was confirmed by studies from the North American margin eastward toward Great Britain (Andrews *et al.* 1993; Bond *et al.* 1992; Broecker *et al.* 1992; Dowdeswell *et al.* 1995; Robinson *et al.* 1995; Keigwin & Lehman 1994). These events, called Heinrich or H-events, have dates of around 11 (H-0), 14.5 (H-1), 20.5 (H-2), 26 (H-3), 33 (H-4) ^{14}C ka BP, and at least two older events which are younger than marine isotope stage 5e but >40 ka BP (Grousset *et al.* 1993). Several papers in this volume discuss evidence for one or more Heinrich events, but the major issue for future study at the North Atlantic margins will be the extent to which ice sheets, other than the Laurentide, contributed to, or were influenced by, these major ice-rafting events (e.g. Fronval *et al.* 1995). Indeed, many of the papers which discuss the interaction of ice sheets and climates during the last deglacial period are a key aspect of this volume.

Finally, one aspect of the Edinburgh meeting which stimulated much debate, and which must certainly be a priority of future research, is the question of how well are we able to date these climatic changes? The role of AMS ^{14}C dating has been discussed above, but many problems remain to be resolved. For example, how reliable are the current comparisons between time series based on marine and terrestrial radiocarbon ages? Recent work, comparing the terrestrial and marine radiocarbon ages of isochronous deposits associated with the Vedde Ash (Austin *et al.* 1995) have demonstrated that marine radiocarbon reservoir ages nearly doubled during the Younger Dryas period. The reasons are complex and not yet fully understood (Bard *et al.* 1994), but the implications are obvious and particularly acute

when we want to compare climatic time series dated by [14]C. The clues to the causes of the deglacial climatic changes will probably come from precise determinations of leads between the time series obtained in the different compartments of the ocean–atmosphere system. During the last deglaciation, the major climatic changes occurred as very abrupt steps (within a few centuries) and it is now crucial to understand marine ^{14}C ages at this level of accuracy (Austin *et al.* 1995).

Future objectives for research at the continental margins of the North Atlantic and elsewhere are therefore numerous. In many respects, the great advantage that ocean margins have over the central, deep-ocean sites is the very fact that they provide strong local signals and therefore provide valuable insight into the interaction between marine and continental climate systems.

References

AKSU, A. E. & MUDIE, P. J. 1985. Late Quaternary stratigraphy and paleoecology of Northwest Labrador Sea. *Marine Micropaleontology*, **9**, 537–557.

ANDREWS, J. T. 1990. Fjord to Deep-Sea sediment transfers along the Northeastern Canadian Continental Margin: Models and Data. *Geographie Physique et Quaternaire*, **44**, 55–70.

——, JULL, A. J. T., DONAHUE, D. J., SHORT, S. K. & OSTERMAN, L. E. 1985. Sedimentation rates in Baffin Island fiord cores from comparative radiocarbon dates. *Canadian Journal of Earth Sciences*, **22**, 1827–1834.

——, ERLENKEUSER, H., EVANS, L., BRIGGS, W. & JULL, A. J. T. 1991. Meltwater and Deglaciation SE Baffin Shelf (NE margin Laurentide Ice Sheet) between 13.5 and 8 ka: From stable O and C data. *Paleoceanography*, **6**, 621–637.

——, TEDESCO, K. & JENNINGS, A. E. 1993. Heinrich events: Chronology and processes, east-central Laurentide Ice Sheet and NW Labrador Sea. *In*: PELTIER, W. R. (eds) *Ice in the Climate System*. Springer, Berlin, 167–186.

——, MILLIMAN, J. D., JENNINGS, A. E., RYNES, N. & DWYER, J. 1994. Sediment thicknesses and Holocene Glacial Marine Sedimentation Rates in Three East Greenland Fjords (ca. 68°N). *Journal of Geology*, **102**, 669–683.

AUSTIN, W. E. N. & MCCARROLL, D. 1992. Foraminifera from the Irish Sea glacigenic deposits at Aberdaron, western Lleyn, North Wales: palaeoenvironmental implications. *Journal of Quaternary Science*, **7**, 311–317.

——, BARD, E., HUNT, J. B., KROON, D. & PEACOCK, J. D. 1995. The ^{14}C age of the Icelandic Vedde Ash: implications for Younger Dryas marine reservoir age corrections. *Radiocarbon*, **37**, 53–62.

BARD, E., ARNOLD, M., MAURICE, P., DUPRAT, J., MOYES, J. & DUPLESSY, J. C. 1987. Retreat velocity of the North Atlantic polar front during the last deglaciation determined by ^{14}C accelerator mass spectrometry. *Nature*, **328**, 791–794.

——, ARNOLD, M., MANGERUD, J., PATERNE, M., LABEYRIE, L., DUPRAT, J., MELIERS, M.-A., SONSTEGAARD, E. & DUPLESSY, J. C. 1994. The North Atlantic atmosphere-sea surface ^{14}C gradient during the Younger Dryas climatic event. *Earth and Planetary Science Letters*, **126**, 275–287.

BOND, G., HEINRICH, H., BROECKER, W. S., LABEYRIE, L., McMANUS, J., ANDREWS, J. T., HUON, S., JANTSCHIK, R., CLASEN, S., SIMET, C., TEDESCO, K., KLAS, M., BONANI, G. & IVY, S. 1992. Evidence for massive discharges of icebergs into the glacial Northern Atlantic. *Nature*, **360**, 245–249.

BOULTON, G. S. 1990. Sedimentary and sea level changes during glacial cycles and their control on glacimarine facies architecture. *In*: DOWDESWELL, J. A. & SCOURSE, J. D. (eds) *Glacimarine Environments: Processes and Sediments*. Geological Society, London, Special Publication, **53**, 15–52.

BROECKER, W. S., BOND, G., McMANUS, J., KLAS, M. & CLARK, E. 1992. Origin of the Northern Atlantic's Heinrich events. *Climatic Dynamics*, **6**, 265–273.

DOWDESWELL, J. A., MASLIN, M. A., ANDREWS, J. T. & McCAVE, I. N. 1995. Iceberg production, debris rafting, and the extent and thickness of Heinrich layers (H-1, H-2) in North Atlantic sediments. *Geology*, **23**, 301–304.

DUPLESSY, J. C., BARD, E., LABEYRIE, L., DUPRAT, J. & MOYES, J. 1993. Oxygen isaotope records and salinity changes in the northeastern Atlantic Ocean during the last 18,000 years. *Paleoceanography*, **8**, 341–350.

FEYLING-HANSSEN, R. W. 1982. Foraminiferal zonation of a boring in Quaternary deposits of the northern North Sea. *Bull. Geol. Soc. Denmark*, **31**, 29–47.

FILLON, R. H. & HARMES, R. A. 1982. Northern Labrador Shelf glacial chronology and depositional environments. *Canadian Journal of Earth Sciences*, **19**, 162–192.

——, HARDY, I. W., WAGNER, F. J. E., ANDREWS, J. T. & JOSENHANS, H. 1981. Labrador Shelf: Shell and total organic matter ^{14}C date discrepancies. *Geological Survey of Canada*, Paper, **81-1B**, 105–111.

FRONVAL, T., JANSEN, E., BLOMENDAL, J. & JOHNSEN, S. 1995. Oceanic evidence for coherent fluctuations in Fennoscandian and Laurentide ice sheets on millenium timescales. *Nature*, **374**, 443–446.

GROUSSET, F. E., LABEYRIE, L., SINKO, J. A., CREMER, M., BOND, G., DUPRAT, J., CORTIJO, E. & HUON, S. 1993. Patterns of ice-rafted detritus in the glacial North Atlantic (40–55°N). *Paleoceanography*, **8**, 175–192.

HALD, M. & STEINSUND, P. I., 1992a. Distribution of Surface Sediment Benthic Foraminifera in the Southwestern Barents Sea. *Journal of Foraminiferal Research*, **22**, 347–362.

—— & ——1992b. Recent and Late Quaternary Benthic Foraminiferal Assemblages in the Southwestern Barents Sea. *Studies in Benthic Foraminifera*, Benthos '90, 255–264.

—— & VORREN, T. O. 1987a. Foraminiferal stratigraphy and environment of Late Weichselian deposits on the continental shelf off Troms, Northern Norway, *Marine Micropalaeontology*, **12**, 129–160.

—— & ——1987b: Stable isotope stratigraphy and paleoceanography during the last deglaciation on the continental shelf off Troms, Northern Norway. *Paleoceanography*, **2**, 583–599.

HEINRICH, H. 1988. Origin and consequences of cyclic ice rafting in the Northeast Atlantic Ocean during the past 130,000 years. *Quaternary Research*, **29**, 143–152.

IMBRIE, J. & WEBB, T., III 1981, Transfer func-tions: calibrating micropaleontological data in climatic terms. *In*: BERGER, A. (eds) *Climatic Variations and Variability: Facts and Theory*. Reidel, Dordrecht, 125–134.

JENNINGS, A. E. 1993. The quaternary history of Cumberland Sound, Southeastern Baffin Island: the marine evidence. *Geographie Physique et Quaternaire*, **47**, 21–42.

—— & HELGADOTTIR, G. 1994. Foraminiferal assemblages from the fjords and shelf of Eastern Greenland. *Journal of Foraminiferal Research*, **24**, 123–144.

JOHNSEN, S. J., CLAUSEN, H. B., DANSGAARD, W., FUHRER, K., GUNDESTRUP, N., HAMMER, C. U., IVERSEN, P., JOUZEL, J., STAUFFER, B. & STEFFENSEN, J. P. 1992. Irregular glacial interstadials recorded in a new Greenland ice core. *Nature*, **359**, 311–313.

JOSENHANS, H. W., ZEVENHUIZEN, J. & KLASSEN, R. A. 1986. The Quaternary geology of the Labrador Shelf. *Canadian Journal of Earth Sciences*, **23**, 1190–1214.

KEIGWIN, L. D. & LEHMAN, S. J. 1994. Deep circulation change linked to HEINRICH event 1 and Younger Dryas in a mid depth North Atlantic core. *Paleoceanography*, **9**, 185–194.

KELLOGG, T. B. 1980. Paleoclimatology and paleoceanography of the Norwegian and Greenland seas: glacial-interglacial contrasts. *Boreas*, **9**, 115–137.

——1984. Late-glacial/Holocene high-frequency climatic changes in deep-sea cores from the Denmark Strait. *In*: MÖRNER, N. A. & KARLEN, W. (eds) *Climatic Changes on a Yearly to Millennial Basis*. Reidel, Dordrecht, 123–133.

——1986. Late Quaternary paleoclimatology and paleoceanography of the Labrador Sea and Baffin Bay: an alternative viewpoint. *Boreas*, **15**, 331–343.

KING, L. H. & FADER, G. B. 1986. Wisconsinan glaciation of the continental shelf, southeastern Atlantic Canada. *Geological Survey of Canada Bulletin*, **363**.

——, ROKOENGEN, K. & GUNLEIKSRUD, T. 1987. *Quaternary Seismostratigraphy of the Mid Norwegian Shelf, 65°–67°30′N.—A Till Tongue Stratigraphy.* IKU Publication no 11.

KOÇ, N. & JANSEN, E. 1992. A high-resolution diatom record of the last deglaciation from the SE Norwegian Sea: Documentation of rapid climatic changes. *Paleoceanography,* 7, 499–520.

—— & ——1994. Response of the high-latitude Northern Hemisphere to orbital climate forcing: Evidence from the Nordic Seas. *Geology,* 22, 523–526.

——, —— & HAFLIDSON, H. 1993. Paleoceanographic reconstructions of surface ocean conditions in the Greenland, Iceland and Norwegian Seas through the last 14 ka based on diatoms. *Quaternary Science Reviews,* 12, 115–140.

LARSEN, H. C., SAUNDERS, A. D., CLIFT, P. D., BEGET, J., WEI, W., SPEZZAFERRI, S. & PARTY, O. S. 1994. Seven million years of glaciation in Greenland. *Science,* 264, 952-955.

LEHMAN, S. J. & KEIGWIN, L. D. 1992. Sudden changes in North Atlantic circulation during the last deglaciation. *Nature,* 356, 757–762.

——, ANDERSEN, E. S., BUTENKO, G., JONES, G. A., KELGWIN, L. D. & OSTMO, S.-R. 1991. Initiation of Fennoscandian ice-sheet retreat during the last deglaciation. *Nature,* 349, 513–516.

LINICK, T. W., JULL, A. J. T., TOOLIN, L. J. & DONAHUE, D. J. 1986. Operation of the NSF Arizona Accelerator Facility for Radioistope Analysis results from selective collaborative research projects. *Radiocarbon,* 28, 522–533.

LOWE, J. J., AMMANN, B., BIRKS, H. H., BJÖRKE, S., COOPE, G. R., CWYNAR, L., DE BEAULIEU, J.-L., MOTT, R. J., PETEET, D. M. & WALKER, M. J. C. 1994. Climatic changes in areas adjacent to the North Atlantic during the Last glacial-interglacial transition (14–9 ka BP): a contribution to IGCP-253. *Journal of Quaternary Science,* 9, 185–198.

NIELSEN, S. H., HEINEMEIER, J. & RUD, N. 1995. Comparative radiocarbon dating of shells and foraminifera: a systematic investigation. *Radiocarbon,* 37.

OSTERMAN, L. E. 1984. Benthic foraminiferal zonation of a glacial/interglacial transition from Frobisher Bay, Baffin Island, Northwest Territories, Canada. *Benthos '83.*

POOLE, D. A. R., DOKKEN, T. M., HALD, M. & POLYAK, L. 1996. Stable isotope fractionation in recent benthic foraminifera from the Barents and Kara Seas. *Paleoceanography.*

PRAEG, D. B., MACLEAN, B., HARDY, I. A. & MUDIE, P. J., 1986. *Quaternary Geology of the Southeast Baffin Island Continental Shelf.* Geological Survey of Canada. paper **85-14**.

ROBINSON, S. G., MASLIN, M. A. & MCCAVE, N. 1995. Magnetic Susceptibility Variations in Upper Pleistocene Deep-Sea Sediments of the N. E. Atlantic: Implications for Ice Rafting and Palaeocirculation at the Last Glacial Maximum. *Paleoceanography,* 10, 221–250.

ROWE, G. & BALDAUF, J. 1995. Biofeedback in the ocean in response to climate change. *In:* WOODWELL G. & MACKENSIE, F. (eds) *Biotic Feedbacks in the Global Climate System: Will the Warming Feed the Warming?* Oxford University Press, New York, 233–245.

RUDDIMAN, W. F. 1977. Late Quaternary deposition of ice-rafted sand in the sub-polar North Atlantic (40°–60°N). *Geological Society of America Bulletin,* **88**, 1813–1827.

——1987, Northern oceans. *In:* RUDDIMAN, W. F. & WRIGHT, H. E. J. (eds) *North America and Adjacent Oceans During the Last Deglaciation.* Geological Society of America, 137–154.

—— & GLOVER, L. K. 1975. Subpolar North Atlantic circulation at 9,300 yr B.P.: faunal evidence. *Quaternary Research,* 5, 361–389.

—— & MCINTYRE, A. 1981. The Mode and Mechanism of the Last Deglaciation: Oceanic Evidence. *Quaternary Research,* 16, 125–134.

—— & ——1982. Severity and speed of Northern Hemisphere glaciation pulses: The limiting case? *Geological Society of America Bulletin,* 93, 1273–1279.

—— & others 1994. Reconstructing the Last Glacial and Deglacial Ice Sheets. *Eos,* 82–84.

SCOTT, D. B., MUDIE, P. J., VILKS, G. & YOUNGER, D. C. 1984. Latest Pleistocene-Holocene paleoceanographic trends on the continental margin of Eastern Canada: Foraminifera, Dinoflagellate and Pollen evidence. *Marine Micropaleontology,* 9, 181–218.

SHACKLETON, N. J. 1977. The oxygen isotope stratigraphic record of the Late Pleistocene. *Philosophical Transactions of the Royal Society of London,* 280B, 169–182.

SLOTA, P. J., JULL, A. J. T., LINICK, T. W. & TOOLIN, L. J. 1987. Preparation of small samples for ^{14}C accelerator targets by catalytic reduction of CO. *Radiocarbon,* 29, 303–306.

TAYLOR, K. C., LAMOREY, G. W., DOYLE, G. A., ALLEY, R. B., GROOTES, P. M., MAYEWSKI, P. A., WHITE, J. W. C. & BARLOW, L. K. 1993. The "flickering switch" of late Pleistocene climate change. *Nature,* 361, 432–436.

VILKS, G. & DEONARINE, B. 1988. Labrador shelf benthic Foraminifera and stable oxygen isotopes of Cibicides lobatulus related to the Labrador Current. *Canadian Journal of Earth Sciences,* 25, 1240–1255.

—— & MUDIE, P. J. 1978. Early Deglaciation of the Labrador Shelf. *Science,* 15 December, 1181–1183.

——, HARDY, I. A. & JOSENHANS, H. W. 1984. Late Quaternary stratigraphy of the inner Labrador Shelf. Current Research, Part A, *Geological Survey of Canada.*

VORREN, T. O., HALD, M., EDVARDSEN, M. & LIND-HANSEN, O.-W. 1983. Glacigenic sediments and sedimentary environments on continental shelves: General principles with a case study from the Norwegian shelf. *In:* EHLERS, J. (ed) *Glacial Deposits in North-West Europe.* Balkema, Rotterdam, 61–73.

WILLIAMS, K. M. 1993. Ice Sheet and ocean interactions, margin of the East Greenland Ice Sheet (14 ka to present): Diatom evidence. *Paleoceanography,* 8, 69–83.

Late glacial foraminifera

KAREN LUISE KNUDSEN[1] & WILLIAM E. N. AUSTIN[2]

[1] *Department of Micropalaeontology, Institute of Earth Sciences,*
University of Aarhus, DK-8000 Århus C, Denmark
[2] *Department of Geology and Geophysics, University of Edinburgh,*
West Mains Road, Edinburgh EH9 3JW, UK
(Present address: Environmental Research Centre, Department of Geography,
University of Durham, South Road, Durham DH1 3LE, UK)

Foraminiferal Workshop
Late Quaternary Palaeoceanography of the North Atlantic Margins
Grant Institute, University of Edinburgh, Edinburgh, UK
7 January, 1995

Participants included: H. E. Bergsten (University of Göteborg), T. M. Cronin (US Geological Survey), M. Gustafsson (University of Göteborg), M. Hald (University of Tromsø), M. Houmark-Nielsen (University of Copenhagen), D. Huddart (Liverpool John Moores University), A. E. Jennings (University of Colorado), M. H. Jiang (Lund University), D. Klitgaard (University of Bergen), P. Kristensen (University of Aarhus), D. Kroon (University of Edinburgh) J. M. Lloyd (University of Durham), J. J. Lowe (University of London), K. Nordberg (University of Göteborg), L. Osterman (Smithsonian Institution), L. Polyak (Byrd Polar Research Centre), T. M. Rasmussen (Netherlands Institute for Sea Research), G. Scott (University of Wales), J. D. Scourse (University of Wales), R. F. Spielhagen (GEOMAR), C. Turney (University of London), M. Weinelt (University of Kiel).

The Foraminiferal Workshop was arranged in connection with the meeting Late Glacial Palaeoceanography of the North Atlantic Margins, held in Edinburgh, UK, on 5–7 January 1995. The meeting was open to all registered delegates and was run as one of three parallel workshops: Cores and Seismic, Tephra, and Foraminifera. Workshop participants were invited to bring along overheads to discuss specific points or microscope slides to discuss taxonomic problems. Those who attended the workshop ranged in ability from active researchers in the field to interested non-specialists.

The topics discussed, both formally and informally, were extremely diverse and demonstrated the wide range of foraminiferal projects currently being applied to late glacial stratigraphies. The main topics discussed were: preparation methods, palaeoecology and specific taxonomic determinations. These notes are intended to highlight some of the most relevant issues concerning late glacial foraminiferal studies and provide some guidance to those new to the subject.

Preparation methods

The wide range of geological settings from which foraminifera are derived means that there are many preparation methods which might be used in their extraction and concentration from their host sediments. Fortunately, in the case of the late glacial sediments surrounding the North Atlantic margins, simple wet sediment sieving is generally sufficient to concentrate foraminiferal numbers before picking or heavy liquid flotation (Feyling-Hanssen *et al.* 1971; Meldgaard & Knudsen 1979).

Although most of the workshop participants agreed that wet sieving on a 0.063 mm mesh size sieve was common practice, there was some debate about the appropriate mesh size from which to pick and count foraminifera. The 0.063 mm mesh size is particularly useful in the wet sieving stage as it provides valuable sedimentological information about the division of the sediment sample into clay/silt and sand/gravel fractions. The most commonly used mesh sizes for dry residue sieving before foraminiferal analyses

From Andrews, J. T., Austin, W. E. N., Bergsten, H. & Jennings, A. E. (eds), 1996, *Late Quaternary Palaeoceanography of the North Atlantic Margins*, Geological Society Special Publication No. 111, pp. 7–10.

Table 1. *Preferred mesh sizes used by workshop participants in foraminiferal analyses of Quaternary deposits*

	Mesh size (mm)				
	0.045	0.063	0.100	0.125	0.150
Benthic	1 (3.7)	7 (25.9)	9 (33.3)	9 (33.3)	1 (3.7)
Planktonic	0	4 (23.5)	3 (17.6)	6 (35.3)	4 (23.5)

First figure, number of participants commonly using the specified mesh size; figure in parentheses, percentage of total votes cast for benthic or planktonic group. Note that multiple votes were cast.

were: 0.063, 0.100, 0.125 and 0.150 mm. A quickly convened 'show of hands' from the workshop participants revealed that the 0.125 mm mesh size is the most commonly used for both planktonic and benthic work (Table 1).

This survey reveals that slightly different strategies are used in counting benthic and planktonic foraminifera, with generally larger mesh sizes used for planktonic foraminiferal analyses. The reasons why different mesh sizes have been used are complex, resulting either from tradition, the type of material being analysed, taxonomic uncertainty or the time available for counting. Certainly it is less time consuming and taxonomically less problematic to work with larger mesh sizes. However, as many studies have demonstrated, much assemblage information is lost if the foraminifera present on the smaller mesh sizes are ignored. For a useful discussion of this topic, including quantitative comparisons of assemblages from the >0.063 mm and >0.125 mm fractions of samples from the fjords and shelf of eastern Greenland, see Jennings & Helgadottir (1994).

The issue of mesh size generated considerable debate, particularly as direct comparisons between data sets are difficult to reconcile when based on different size fractions. The extensive use of planktonic foraminiferal sea surface temperature transfer functions (e.g. Imbrie & Kipp 1971) have resulted in greater consistency for planktonic counts and the 0.125 mm mesh size is widely used. However, following some discussion of benthic foraminiferal population size structure (e.g. Austin & McCarroll 1992), M. Weinelt and M. Hald described how many Subarctic planktonic foraminiferal species, e.g. *Turborotalia quinqueloba*, often do not attain test diameters of >0.125 mm. However, under normal circumstances a mesh size of 0.100 mm is adequate. It

was recognized that benthic deep-water assemblages from the high Arctic, in particular, should be examined at the smaller mesh size (occasionally at 0.045 mm).

In conclusion, it was agreed that this report should recommend the use of either the 0.100 or the 0.125 mm fractions for quantitative foraminiferal analysis. However, we strongly recommend that wet sieving is performed on a 0.063 mm mesh size and that residues are retained for subsequent analyses if necessary.

Palaeoecology

The value of benthic foraminifera in quantitative palaeoenvironmental reconstructions was widely discussed. M. Hald presented a wealth of new data on modern benthic foraminiferal distributions (>0.100 mm) from the surface sediments of the Barents Sea (Hald & Steinsund 1994; Steinsund *et al.* in press). The results were discussed in the light of attempts by the Tromsø group (e.g. Poole *et al.* 1994) to develop a summer bottom water temperature transfer function which accounts for variability not only in species abundance, but also bulk sediment properties such as organic carbon, calcium carbonate and pelite content. It appears that this new transfer function works well within a limited geographical area, but that results tend to become unreliable when it is applied elsewhere.

However, W. Austin presented an example of a late glacial sequence from the Hebridean Shelf, northwest Scotland (Austin & Kroon this volume) where the same transfer function had been used. The fluctuations in temperature agree with first axis principal component scores based on the same data and with benthic stable isotope records, but there was a problem with the absolute temperature results. This is probably because the Barents Sea data set is calibrated to a maximum bottom water temperature of 6°C, whereas modern values on the Hebridean Shelf are up to 10°C. These results were encouraging and it is hoped that the data set will be expanded to cover a wider geographical spread, including warmer summer bottom water temperatures.

The general consensus of opinion was that the 'modern analogue technique' provided more reliable palaeoenvironmental reconstructions, particularly when combined with other quantitative methods. Greater effort should, however, be made to find the so-called 'no analogue', perhaps better termed 'missing analogue', modern environments for many late glacial assemblages; see Murray (1991) for a useful review.

Late glacial occurrence of *Nonionellina labradorica*

Nonionellina labradorica (synonymous with *Nonion labradoricum*) often occurs in great numbers in Late Weichselian deposits both in the west and in northeast Atlantic, and in some instances it appears to peak at certain levels. Some examples of its late glacial occurrence were presented from the Skagerrak–Kattegat (K. L. Knudsen), from the Norwegian Channel (D. Klitgaard) and from the Scottish Shelf (W. Austin).

The palaeoecological significance of these high abundance peaks of *N. labradorica* are poorly understood, although they generally occur during the latter stages of deglaciation. After some discussion it seemed clear that there might be more than one reason for the abundance peaks, but that they might commonly be associated with periods of high organic carbon input to the sediments. Recent distribution studies from the Barents and Kara Seas (Hald & Steinsund 1992; Steinsund *et al.* in press) show a clear relationship between *Nonionellina labradorica* abundance maxima and the position of the polar front. The connection between the polar front and high organic carbon input to the sediment may be related to enhanced productivity at these sites. Therefore the proximity of the polar front in an area might be one of several possible explanations for a *Nonionellina labradorica* relative abundance peak in a glaciomarine sequence.

Depth distribution of *Elphidium excavatum*

Elphidium excavatum is one of the most commonly occurring late glacial benthic foraminiferal species and is generally recorded living in recent shallow water areas surrounding the North Atlantic margins. When it is recorded at depths deeper than about 200 m it is often supposed to be reworked. However, the depth range through which this species lives, particularly beyond the continental shelf break, is poorly known. In the Arctic, for example, H. Bergsten reported that it has been found living (up to 5% of the fauna) down to about 700 m.

Elphidium excavatum often occurs at an abundance of a few per cent in marine Weichselian assemblages from much greater water depths (see Hald *et al.* 1994). T. Rasmussen presented records from the Faeroe–Shetland Channel at water depths >1000 m, whereas A. Jenning illustrated the same phenomenon from the Labrador Sea. In both instances the occurrences seem to have some connection with the Heinrich Events, possibly suggesting a link between massive North Atlantic iceberg discharge and widespread downslope resedimentation. Monospecific foraminiferal AMS ^{14}C datings from the Labrador Sea suggest that *Elphidium excavatum* is actually redeposited in that area, but this has not yet been proved from any of the east Atlantic sites.

Given that the material available is often too sparse for monospecific AMS dating, K. L. Knudsen suggested that a comparison of oxygen isotope values from *Elphidium excavatum* and the known deep water species *Cassidulina neoteretis* from the same sample set might help to resolve the reworking problem. This approach would be possible from several of the Faeroe–Shetland Channel cores (T. Rasmussen).

Specific determinations

The participants also discussed specific taxonomic problems in smaller groups at the microscopes. Time was, however, much too short and it was agreed that a specialist workshop dealing with benthic foraminiferal taxonomy and relating to the determination of Quaternary shelf foraminifera was required. K. L. Knudsen offered the Micropalaeontology Department, University of Aarhus, Denmark, as a possible venue for any such future meeting.

General conclusions

Foraminifera, perhaps more than any other microfossil group, have played a key part in Quaternary palaeoceanography. Quantitative planktic foraminiferal sea surface temperature transfer function reconstructions, even with all their inherent problems of interpretation, have revolutionized the subject. As palaeo-oceanographers look increasingly to sites which offer greater temporal resolution, such as the continental margins, then benthic foraminifera will play an increasingly important part. Discussions at the Edinburgh workshop demonstrated that the potentials and problems of foraminiferal studies at such sites are being fully exploited by an active research community.

References

AUSTIN, W. E. N. & MCCARROLL, D. 1992. Foraminifera from the Irish Sea glacigenic deposits at Aberdaron, western Lleyn, North Wales: palaeoenvironmental implications. *Journal of Quaternary Science*, 7, 311–317.

AUSTIN, W. E. N. & KROON, D. 1996. The Lateglacial Palaeoceanography of the Hebridean Continental Shelf, N.W. Scotland based on foraminiferal analysis. *This volume*.

FEYLING-HANSSEN, R. W., JØRGENSEN, J. A., KNUDSEN, K. L. & ANDERSEN, A.-L. L. 1971. Late Quaternary foraminifera from Vendsyssel, Denmark and Sandnes, Norway. *Bulletin of the Geological Society of Denmark*, **21**, 67–317.

HALD, M. & STEINSUND, P.I. 1992. Distribution of surface sediment benthic foraminifera in the southwestern Barents Sea. *Journal of Foraminiferal Research*, **22**, 347–362.

——, STEINSUND, P. I., DOKKEN, T., KORSUN, S., POLYAK, L. & ASPELI, R. 1994. Recent and Late Quaternary Distribution of Elphidium excavatum f. clavatum in Arctic Seas. *Cushman Foundation Special Publication*, **32**, 141–153.

IMBRIE, J. & KIPP, N. 1971. A new micropalaeontological method of quantitative palaeoclimatology: application to a Late Pleistocene Carribean core.

In: TUREKIAN, K. K. (ed.) *The Late Cenozoic-Glacial Ages*. Yale University Press, New Haven, 71–181.

JENNINGS, A. E. & HELGADOTTIR, G. 1994. Foraminiferal assemblages from the fjords and shelf of Eastern Greenland. *Journal of Foraminiferal Research*, **24**, 123–144.

MURRAY, J. W. 1991. *Ecology and Palaeoecology of Benthic Foraminifera*. Longman, Harlow

MELDGAARD, S. & KNUDSEN, K. L. 1979. Metoder til indsamling og oparbejdning af prøver til foraminifer-analyser. *Dansk Natur Dansk Skole*, Årsskrift for 1979, 48–57.

POOLE, D. A. R., SÆTTEM, J. & VORREN, T. O. 1994. Foraminiferal stratigraphy, palaeoenvironments and sedimentation of the glacigenic sequence southwest of Bjørnøya. *Boreas*, **23**, 122–138.

STEINSUND, P. I., POLYAK, L., HALD, M., MIKHAILOV, V. & KORSUN, S. Distribution of calcareous benthic foraminifera in recent sediments of the Barents and Kara Seas. *Journal of Foraminiferal Research*, in press.

Abrupt changes in marine conditions, Sunneshine Fiord, eastern Baffin Island, NWT during the last deglacial transition: Younger Dryas and H-0 events

J. T. ANDREWS[1], L. E. OSTERMAN[2], A. E. JENNINGS[1],
J. P. M. SYVITSKI[3], G. H. MILLER[1] & N. WEINER[1]

[1] *INSTAAR and Department of Geological Sciences, Box 450, University of Colorado,
Boulder, CO 80309, USA*
[2] *Department of Paleobiology, NHB-121, Smithsonian Institution, Washington,
DC 20506, USA*
[3] *Atlantic Geoscience Center, Bedford Institute of Oceanography, Box 1006, Dartmouth,
Nova Scotia, Canada, B2Y 4A2*

Abstract: Sunneshine Fiord is a shallow fiord that lies at the easternmost tip of Baffin Island, NWT, *c.* 66°33′ N on the western end of Davis Strait, a 600 m deep sill that links Baffin Bay to the north with the Labrador Sea and the North Atlantic in the south. Offshore surface circulation today consists principally of the southward transport of Polar Water in the Baffinland Current. Raised marine deposits in the outer part of the fiord are radiocarbon dated at >57 ka and can be associated with large lateral moraines on both walls of the fiord; Holocene raised marine sediments appear to be absent. A gravity and piston core together (HU82–031-SU5) sample about 8.5 m of the sediment fill. Nine AMS ^{14}C dates on marine shells and foraminifera indicate that the coring recovered sediments that span around 14 calibrated (cal) of record. Seismic surveys indicate that the upper sediment is acoustically transparent and overlies acoustically stratified materials. There is a major reflector towards the base of the cored section. Analyses of physical properties, lithofacies and biofacies indicate that there is a very sharp break in the record at around 12.4 cal ka, which is interpreted as a change from relatively ice-distal conditions to one characterized by a dramatic increase in cold, ice-proximal foraminiferal benthic species, notably *Elphidium excavata* forma *clavata*. At the same time, there was an extremely abrupt increase in detrital carbonate, most of which is dolomite. Because there is no known local source of detrital carbonate within the fiord, this abrupt event signals an increase in the transport of detrital carbonate derived from icebergs and/or meltwater from sources further north in Baffin Bay, or immediately to the south from Cumberland Sound. The onset of this event at 12.4 cal ka is synchronous with evidence for an abrupt increase in detrital calcitic carbonate emanating from an ice re-advance within and probably across Hudson Strait. These events are the probable source of detrital calcitic carbonate in the northwestern North Atlantic associated with the Younger Dryas cold period and iceberg rafting event, H-0.

Across the Eastern Canadian Arctic, information on changes in the terrestrial and nearshore environments during the last glacial/interglacial transition are rare. Research over the last two decades has consistently indicated that materials which can be dated from raised marine sediments and basal lake sediments usually date from ≤11 or >30 ka (Andrews 1989). In fact, it is this distribution of ages that led in part to the notions of 'minimum' and 'maximum' ice sheet configurations (Denton & Hughes 1981).

As part of the programme 'Paleoclimate of Arctic Lakes and Estuaries' (PALE) (Andrews & Brubaker 1994), Miller and co-workers cored a series of lakes in the vicinity of Sunneshine and Mooneshine fiords, on the easternmost tip of Baffin Island (Fig. 1). Previous geological mapping and dating indicated that Sunneshine Fiord was probably largely ice-free during the late Foxe (Wisconsin) Glaciation (Hawkins 1980; Locke 1987). However, coring of a series of lake basins did not succeed in extracting basal sediments >9 ka in age, thus suggesting that a critical examination be conducted of the glacial history of this easternmost section of Cumberland Peninsula, in case the 'ruling hypothesis' of ice-free conditions was incorrect (Dyke *et al.* 1982).

This paper focuses on such a re-examination through the analysis of the seismo-stratigraphy of the outer portion of the fiord and an analysis of a marine piston core (HU82–031-SU5, hereafter SU5) from the outer fiord, taken as part of

From Andrews, J. T., Austin, W. E. N., Bergsten, H. & Jennings, A. E. (eds), 1996, *Late Quaternary Palaeoceanography of the North Atlantic Margins*, Geological Society Special Publication No. 111, pp. 11–27.

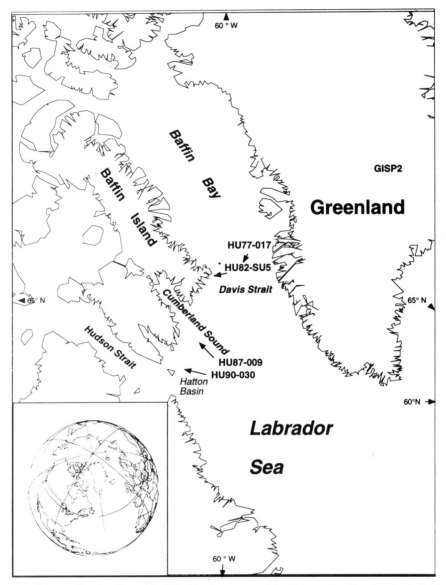

Fig. 1. Location map showing Sunneshine Fiord in the context of the Eastern Canadian Arctic; the inset shows the wider area of North America and the North Atlantic. Other core sites on this figure are referred to in the text.

the Sedimentology of Arctic Fjords Experiment (SAFE) (Syvitski and Blakeney 1983; Andrews *et al.* 1994*a*) (Fig. 2). In undertaking this research we were re-visiting data which were originally derived in the mid-1980s, but only partly published (Andrews *et al.* 1985*b*; 1989). In this paper, we have extended the chronology through an additional seven AMS ^{14}C dates and undertaken a detailed analysis of the foraminifera in a section of the core which is coeval with

the Younger Dryas chronozone of northwest Europe (Mangerud *et al.* 1974).

Background

Topography and bathymetry

Sunneshine Fiord is an average-sized fiord for Baffin Island (Dowdeswell & Andrews 1985) with an area of 130 km^2 and a length of 36 km

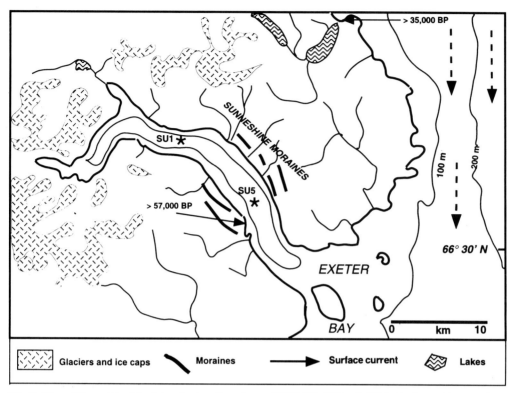

Fig. 2. Map of Sunneshine Fiord showing location of cores HU82-031-SU5 and -SU-1, the Sunneshine moraines (Locke 1987) and radiocarbon dates on marine shells.

(Gilbert & MacLean 1983) (Fig. 2). The drainage basin for the fiord is 460 km², of which 16% is covered by glaciers. Glaciers descend to tide water level towards the head of the fiord – that is, up-fiord from SU5. Lakes intercept about 35% of the drainage area from ice-covered areas, thus presumably reducing sediment transport into the fiord. The height of mountain summits increases from the outer coast, where steep cliffs lead to an upland with an elevation of *c.* 300–500 m asl (above sea level), to the head of the fiord where valley glaciers head into peaks that reach 1200 m asl. Fifty per cent of the land is >1000 m asl.

Based on acoustic surveys in 1982 with CSS *Hudson* and in 1985 with MV *Pandora II* with the manned submersible *Pisces IV* (Syvitski *et al.* 1985), the water depth in the inner basin of Sunneshine Fiord is 214 m. The outer fiord consists of an extended sill complex, typically <150 m deep, and a minimum sill depth of 64 m. The shelf to the east of the fiord mouth is shallow with depths of only 50–100 m (Krank 1966). About 20 km offshore the shelf abruptly deepens to depths of >300 m.

Bedrock geology

During the late Cretaceous/early Tertiary, Greenland and North America were rifted apart (Balkwill *et al.* 1990). Tertiary volcanic rocks associated with this rifting form the outermost uplands north of Sunneshine Fiord and extend offshore. They lie on Palaeocene terrestrial sediments in places, but elsewhere they extend on to Precambrian metamorphic rocks (MacLean 1985). The trends of the fiords suggest a structural control associated with the rifting episode.

Glacial geology and relative sea-level changes

Locke (1987) mapped the onshore area in the outer part of Sunneshine Fiord. Along the north wall of the fiord he described the Sunneshine Moraines (Fig. 2). On the basis of surface and soil weathering, radiocarbon ages and amino acid ratios, these features were assigned to the early Foxe Glaciation (Miller 1985; Locke 1986; 1987), possibly 110 ka in age (Funder 1990). Just to the north of Sunneshine Fiord, Hawkins (1980) and Miller (1975) argued that the late Foxe Glaciation was restricted in extent and within Sunneshine Fiord may have been exceeded by the re-advance of ice during Neoglaciation (cf. Miller 1976). Miller located a raised marine deposit along the outer, southern flank of Sunneshine Fiord which contained *in situ* molluscs. These molluscs were ^{14}C dated at >57 000 ka (CAMS-11337) (Fig. 2). Locke (1980) examined shells from the northern side of the fiord, associated with the Sunneshine Moraine, for their amino acid (D/L) ratios; on this basis they are correlative with the Kogulu aminozone of Baffin Island and northwest Greenland and judged to date from sometime between 80 and 115 ka (Funder 1990; Miller 1985).

The relative sea-level history of outer Cumberland Peninsula is currently one of submergence (Andrews 1980). Raised marine sediments of Holocene age have not been found. Radiocarbon dating of shells in older raised marine sediments which extend up to 30–40 m asl are >30 ka (Fig. 2). Numerical modelling of relative sea level across the Eastern Canadian Arctic (Quinlan 1985) led to the suggestion that the relative sea level in Sunneshine Fiord between 7 and 20 ka would have been *c.* −20 m.

Modern climate, glaciology and oceanography

The mean July temperature at the Cape Dyer DEW Line Site (376 m asl) is about 5°C, with January temperatures averaging *c.* −25°C and a mean annual temperature of −11°C. The area is anomalously snowy, with heavy snowfalls taking place in the autumn; the total precipitation is around 0.6 m H_2O/year. The glacier equilibrium line altitude rises from east to west from *c.* 400 to 600 m asl. Three glaciers have terminuses in the fiord; they retreated at about 8 m/year between 1949 and 1960 (Syvitski & Praeg 1987). The thermal bed conditions of the glaciers are unknown and may be polythermal. Landsat and aerial photographs indicate that meltwater plumes cover the inner fiord during the summer months. The annual discharge from runoff into the fiord is estimated to be 0.34 km³. This strong seaward advection includes suspended sediment from fluvial runoff and from lateral and sublateral meltwater streams along the subpolar glacier margins. Approximately 44 000 t of glacial flour is delivered to the fiord annually (LeBlanc *et al.* 1988).

The fiord and inner shelf are covered by landfast sea ice for nine months of the year and open

pack occurs offshore even in the winter months. Cold, low salinity water moves southwards along the shelf as the Baffinland or Canadian Current (Fig. 2). Extensive sea ice and icebergs are entrained in this flow and move southwards, frequently grounding and breaking up in their transit. The seaward flowing meltwater is mixed with waters from the Canadian Current by strong tidal mixing across the outer sill. The average tidal range in the fiord is 2.2 m, but large tides reach 4 m in amplitude. The highest sediment concentrations are in waters just above the seafloor, suggesting current resuspension (Winters *et al.* 1985).

Few oceanographic measurements are available from the fiord and adjacent shelf. The surface circulation on the shelf is principally southwards, although there is a counterclockwise gyre in the area of Exeter Bay (Kranck 1966). Icebergs track across the shelf and frequently ground in shallow depths; speeds of 8 to 50 cm/s have been noted for iceberg drift rates.

Oceanographic casts taken in autumn 1982 (Syvitski & Blakeney 1983) showed that temperatures were nearly −1.5°C at the sediment–water interface, with a salinity of 32.99‰. The upper 10 m of the water column had temperatures ranging from *c.* −0.2 to −0.6°C and fresher salinities (*c.* 30–30.34‰). The waters are well oxygenated, with the lowest dissolved values of 6.5 ml/l.

Data and results

Basin seismostratigraphy

Andrews *et al.* (1994*a*) provide detailed illustrations of the airgun and high-resolution Huntec deep-towed system. The systems could not be used west of SU5 because of the ice conditions. In this paper, we specifically concentrate on placing core SU5 in the context of the outer fiord seismic stratigraphy.

The Huntec deep-towed system results at the core site (Figs 3–5) reveal a 5 ± m upper acoustic unit (unit III), which is transparent to weakly stratified. In acoustic properties this unit is similar to post-glacial sediments identified in other regional surveys (e.g. Jennings 1993). It overlies an acoustically stratified unit (unit IIB) which is about 7 m thick and ends in a major reflector. Unit IIA extends below the reflector for *c.* 2 m and probably overlies bedrock (Fig. 3).

The contact between units III and IIB is sharp along the entire transect, although it does pinch out on slopes (Fig. 4). By and large the surface

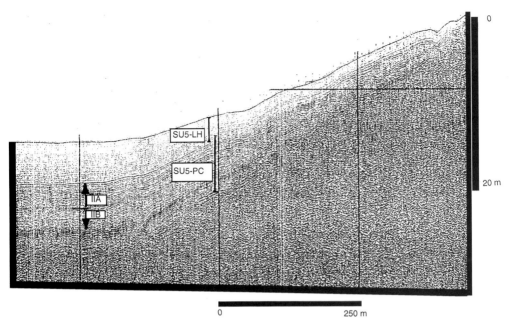

Fig. 3. High-resolution Huntec deep-tow seismic record from the site of core SU5.

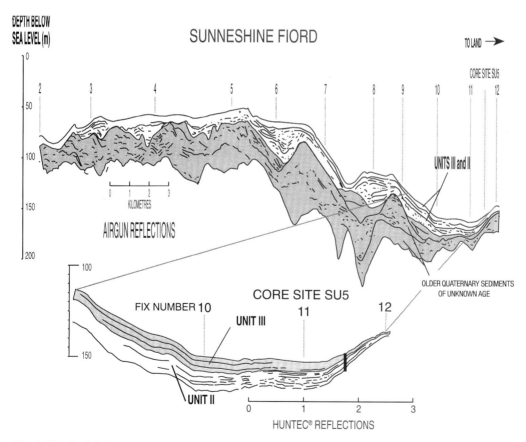

Fig. 4. Sketch of the interpretation of the seismic stratigraphy in the vicinity of core site SU5.

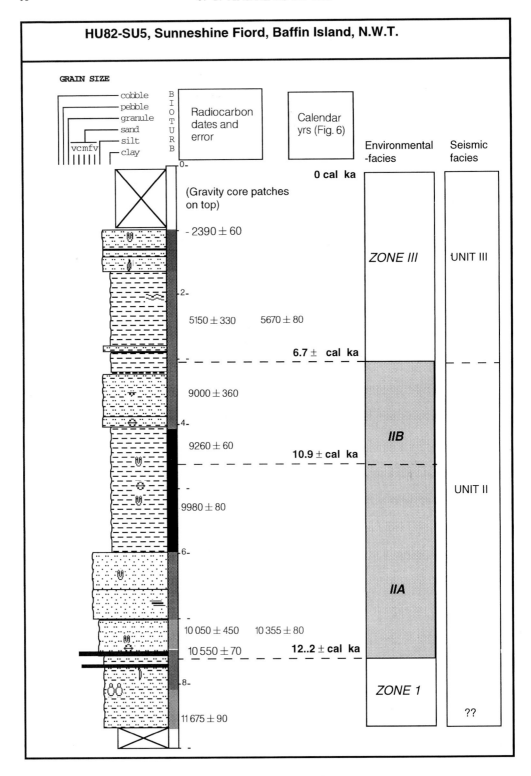

Fig. 5. Core log of SU5 and the position and results of the AMS ^{14}C assays.

of the seafloor and the III/IIB reflector is smooth, but to the east (seawards) there is some evidence of iceberg scouring of the modern seafloor and also at the III/IIB surface. During submersible dives onto the floor of Sunneshine Fiord, seismic unit II was investigated where it cropped out at the surface; Andrews *et al.* (1994*a*) describe it as '...shell rich and over-consolidated'.

Core description, physical properties and chronology

At site HU82-031-SU5 (66°33.4′ N 61°42.6′ W 155 m water depth) a 7.6 m Benthos 7 cm wide piston core and a 2 m × 11 cm diameter Lehigh gravity core were retrieved (Fig. 2). An analysis of the core properties indicates that the top of the piston core sampled about 1 m or so below the sediment surface (Syvitski *et al.* 1990). Thus the complete 8.6 m of recovered section includes the upper part of the gravity core patched on to the top of the piston core (Fig. 5).

We describe the piston core on the basis of the split core and X-radiographs (Syvitski & Blakeney 1983; Syvitski *et al.* 1990). The core log (Fig. 5) indicates that most of the sediments are bioturbated silty clays; small, arcticulated bivalves (mainly *Portlandia arctica*) can be seen on X-radiographs and have been extracted for AMS ^{14}C dates (see later). Ice-rafted pebbles are scattered throughout the core, but are not common and are concentrated in the lower 1–3 m. Individual graded sand beds at a reconstructed 7.5–7.8 m core, depth reflect local debris or turbidite flows (Andrews *et al.* 1994*a*).

The chronology for the core is based on AMS ^{14}C ages on marine shells and foraminifera (Linick *et al.* 1986; Slota *et al.* 1987). Three shell ages were originally published (Andrews *et al.* 1985*b*), but since then we have obtained an additional seven dates, including one from the Lehigh gravity core (Table 1). To develop an age–depth model (e.g. Bennett 1994), we use the program CALIB to convert radiocarbon years to sidereal years (Stuiver & Braziunas 1993; Stuiver and Reimer 1986; 1993). This program was run using an additional 50 years for the ocean reservoir model and a standard deviation on the reservoir of ±50 years. The resulting calibrated ages are given in Table 1 and are referred to in this paper as 'cal ka'. The age–depth relationship can be approximated by a fourth-order polynomial with the top of the gravity core having an assumed age of 0 cal years BP (Fig. 6). The basal ^{14}C age of 11.675 ± 0.09 ka (13.52–13.82 cal ka) at 860 cm reconstructed core depth, and ^{14}C dates of ≥10 and ≤10.5 ka from depths of 545–718 cm confirm that the sediments in the lowermost 3 m span the Younger Dryas chronozone (10–11 ka) (Mangerud *et al.* 1974). However, there is discussion of the dates on the 'event' boundaries in the 10–13 ka range (Broecker 1992); the ocean reservoir age correction is uncertain and may be larger than previously estimated (Bard *et al.* 1994).

Samples for physical property measurements were taken from the split core. We use here the measurements of the sediment bulk density and moisture content, the weight percentage of total organic carbon (TOC%) (Syvitski *et al.* 1990; Walkley 1947), grain-size spectra, the weight percentage total carbonate (calcite and dolomite) (Dreimanis 1962), and the percentages of

Table 1. *Radiocarbon dates from HU82-031-SU5 piston core (PC) and Lehigh gravity core (L) (66°33.4′ N, 61°42.6′ W, 155 m water depth)*

New sample No.	Old Sample No.	Depth (cm)†	Material	Date*	Error	Cal years
CAMS-13511		149 LH	Shell	2 390	60	2 480
	AA-0712	165 PC	Shell	5 150	330	5 960
CAMS-11814		165	Shell	5 670	80	6 540
	AA-0412	277	Shell	9 000	360	10 060
CAMS-11815		331	Shell	9 260	60	10 400
AA-13053		445	Shell	9 980	80	11 560
	AA-0264	618	Shell	10 040	450	11 670
AA-13054		618	Shell	10 340	80	12 305
CAMS-17398		640	Forams	10 560	70	12 590
CAMS-13511		760	Forams	11 680	90	13 670

* Corrected for 450 years ocean reservoir. Assumed δ^{13}C of 0‰.
† Add 100 cm to depths from the piston core (see Fig. 5) to conform with Figs 6 and 7 (see text).

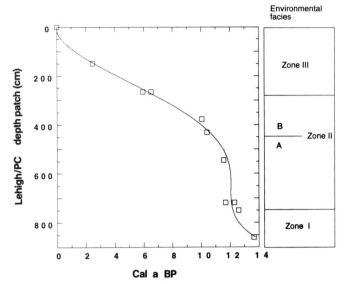

Fig. 6. Depth versus age of samples calibrated to calendar years and showing the fit to a fourth-order polynomial. Width of the individual data point is ±150 years.

silt- and clay-sized mineral species (Cook *et al.* 1975; Andrews *et al.* 1989).

Foraminifera were sieved onto >63 and >125 μm screens and the number of benthic and planktonic species were counted and expressed as no./g sediment dry weight and as percentages (Osterman 1984; Jennings 1993). The work on the pollen content of the cores was discussed in Short *et al.* (1989) and is summarized, in part, in this paper.

Physical properties and mineralogy

The sediment is typically a clayey silt with an average silt content of about 50% (Fig. 7). The sand content throughout the core is relatively low, apart from some intervals of sandy mud probably associated with sediment gravity flows. Minimum sand percentages occur between *c*. 500 and 650 cm. In the uppermost 2–3 m the percentage of clay increases and this change is

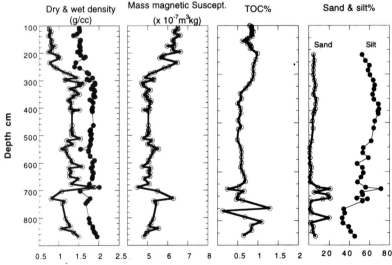

Fig. 7. Downcore changes in some of the physical attributes of the sediment in SU5, namely sediment density, mass magnetic susceptibility, total organic carbon (TOC) and changes in the weight percentage of sand and silt.

paralleled by a relatively sharp decrease in the dry sediment density.

A three-fold zonation is seen in Fig. 8 (see also Fig. 5), which illustrates some of the most dramatic changes in the core. The total detrital carbonate (principally dolomite) in zone III averages 4%, but then it increases abruptly between 730 and 740 cm to values between 15 and 20% carbonate by weight. In this fraction, dolomite remains the dominant detrital carbonate mineral. The peak in carbonate declines rapidly at 550 cm and by 300 cm values are ≤3% by weight and nearly entirely dolomite. X-ray diffraction (XRD) analyses of both the silt- and clay-sized fractions indicate that these changes are present in both these grain sizes, although the largest signal is carried in the silt-sized fraction.

Further examination of Fig. 7 also suggests three distinct facies, which correspond to changes in the detrital carbonate content: (1) a lowermost (860–750 cm) zone I, dated 13.7–12.2 cal ka; (2) a middle unit (750–300 cm) (zone II), divided into IIA and IIB, dated 12.4–6.7 cal ka with the IIA/IIB boundary at 10.9 cal ka; and (3) an uppermost (0–300 cm) (III) zone which covers the last 6.7 cal ka. Zones III and I have some similar characteristics, whereas zone II is different from both of these.

The importance of detrital carbonate in the sediments within Baffin Bay was emphasized by Aksu (1985) and Aksu & Piper (1987). The conclusion that dolomite is the major carbonate detrital mineral in the western Baffin Bay region is similar to that reached earlier on samples from both piston cores and the ODP Site 645B (Andrews et al. 1989; Andrews 1993). In addition to small amounts of calcite and dolomite in the clay-sized fraction, zones I and IIA have a large smectite peak. Smectite decreases rapidly upwards in zone IIB and there is a single-value peak in zone III. Further up-fiord, at site SU1 (Fig. 2), XRD analyses of this 2.4 m gravity core indicated values of smectite around 5–8% (Syvitski &

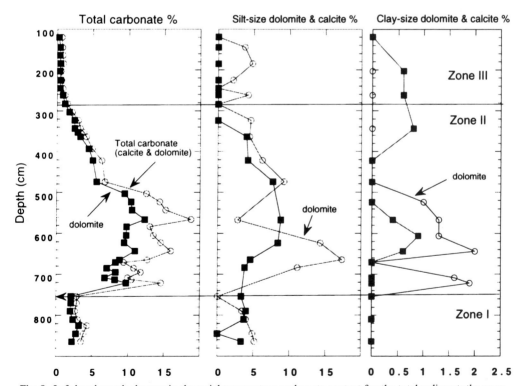

Fig. 8. Left-hand panel: changes in the weight percentage carbonate content for the total sediment; the open circles are the total carbonate content and the closed squares are the dolomite percentage. The centre and right-hand columns show the silt- and clay-sized carbonate compositions—dolomite is represented by the open circles and calcite by the closed squares.

Blakeney 1983). Locke (1980) noted some smectite in his XRD analyses of soils from the region.

Other indicators of sediment mineralogy include environmental magnetic parameters such as magnetic susceptibility and the intensity of natural remnant magnetism. The results of a palaeomagnetic study were reported earlier (Andrews & Jennings 1990). The mass magnetic susceptibility has an abrupt change at about 300 cm reconstructed core depth, which coincides with the onset of post-glacial sedimentation; however, the natural remnant magnetism intensity, which generally mimics the mass magnetic susceptibility, starts to decrease earlier at 550 cm (*c*. 11.5 cal ka).

Changes in the biological components

One of the key questions in palaeoenvironmental studies is whether changes in the physical composition of the sediment are mirrored by changes in various biotic components. We have three individual groups that can tell us something about the palaeo-oceanography of Sunneshine Fiord: the pollen and spores, diatoms, and foraminifera. The first two groups have been reported previously (Short *et al.* 1989; Williams 1990) and we summarize their results here (Fig. 9).

One of the major changes in the pollen assemblages retrieved from the sediments at SU5 is the percentages of pre-Quaternary palynomorphs. The occurrence of these taxa

indicates either (a) substantial reworking and erosion of Tertiary and Cretaceous offshore sediments, and the probable entrainment of these pollen grains in turbid meltwater plumes, or (b) a local outcrop of Tertiary sediment. The trends in the numbers of dinoflagellates and pre-Quaternary pollen are inverse (Fig. 9) with major changes paralleling those just described (Figs 5, 7 and 8). The maximum percentage of 'old' pollen types occurs at 750 cm, rising sharply from a lower, but still high, value at the base of the core. The dinoflagellates are either absent or present in very small numbers between 860 and 480 cm, but then rise and peak near 250 cm (6.4 cal ka). The numbers of diatoms are also extremely low in zones I and II, but then increase rapidly at the zone II/III transition and occur in moderate numbers in zone III.

The foraminifera were initially studied by Osterman; subsequently, with the addition of the new AMS ages (Table 1), a higher resolution survey was undertaken by Weiner between *c*. 500 and 860 cm (Table 2). In this paper we are particularly interested in the changes of the benthic species *Elphidium excavata* forma *clavata*, which is characteristic of ice-proximal, late Quaternary glacial marine sediments from eastern and northeastern Canada, and northwest Europe (Osterman 1984; Osterman *et al.* 1985; Osterman and Nelson 1989; Vilks *et al.* 1989; Jennings 1993). Its modern occurrence is restricted to cold polar seas (Hald & Steinsund 1992*a*; Hald & Steinsund 1992*b*; Jennings & Helgadottir 1994).

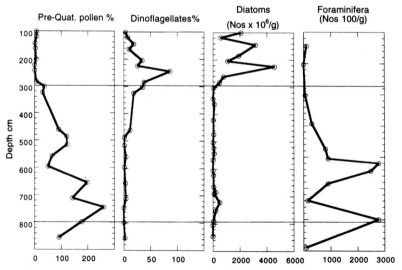

Fig. 9. Downcore changes in bitoic elements from SU5—namely, pollen, diatom numbers and foraminifera abundance.

Table 2. *Foraminiferal percentages and abundance (no./g) in patched HU82-SU5 (Fig. 5) across the major faunal change dated at c. 12.4 cal ka (Fig. 10)*

Depth (m)	No./g	Plank.	Aren.	Cr%	Ee%	Ff%	Ih%
550	95	3	0	27	34	31	3
580	70	2	0	22	30	40	5
610	59	2	0	31	21	29	9
640	91	0	0	28	64	3	1
670	56	0	28	28	36	8	6
685	13	0	3	22	42	16	10
700	70	0	3	19	68	1	6
730	133	2	0	16	71	6	5
745	111	4	0	6	75	7	11
760	22	25	0	39	18	1	21
790	7	0	0	12	12	0	47
820	17	0	0	11	11	1	75
850	45	0	0	13	56	0	18

Plank, no. planktonic foraminifera/g; Aren., no. of arenaceous foraminifera/g; Cr%, *Cassidulina reniform*; Ee%, *Elphidium excavatum* forma *clavata*; Ff%, *Fursenkoina fusiformis*; and Ih%, *Islaniella helenae.*

A striking feature of the record is the dramatic increase in *E. excavatum* forma *clavata* between 800 and 750 cm (Table 2). This coincides with a sharp decrease in foraminifera numbers per gram (Fig. 9). Numbers of *E. excavatum* forma *clavata* remain high throughout the interval between 750 and 600 cm and the percentage of

this species also remains high, but decreases rather abuptly above 600 cm. This decrease is associated with a rise in the occurrence of *Fursenkoina fusiformis* (Table 2), a deep water estuarine species often associated with anoxic conditions (Scott *et al.* 1984). It is the dominant species within the Younger Dryas chronozone on the southeast Baffin Island shelf (Andrews *et al.* 1990; Evans 1990). Zone 1 has moderate *E. excavatum* forma *clavata* percentages, but is noteworthy for the high percentages of *Islandiella helenae*, a species which is not usually considered as an ice-proximal indicator (Osterman 1984; Vilks *et al.* 1989).

Discussion and conclusions

The ^{14}C ages from the fiord sediments that lie within the Sunneshine moraines (Fig. 2) indicate that the 'basal' dates on lake sediments are indeed minimum ages. However, there is still a critical hiatus in our knowledge of palaeoenvironmental conditions ⩽ 57 ka and ⩾ 14 cal ka. It is far from clear why lakes, such as this on eastern Baffin Island and in northern Labrador (e.g. Clark *et al.* 1989), have basal ages that appear to be significantly younger than other estimates of deglaciation.

The downcore data from SU5 indicate that an abrupt change in the environment occurred about 1 m above the base of the piston core and a more

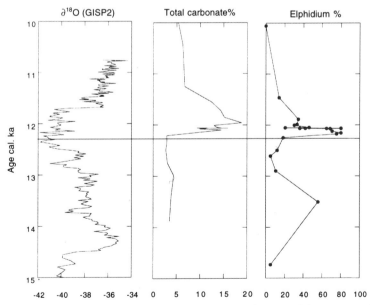

Fig. 10. Plot showing changes in the composition of the core SU5, carbonate weight percentage *Elphidium excavataum* forma *clavata* percentages and the GISP2 ^{18}O results.

gradual transition is noted at *c.* 300 cm. To assist in placing these changes in a regional and temporal framework, we show the downcore changes in carbonate percentage and *E. excavatum* forma *clavata* percentage plotted against the modelled calender years (Figs 6 and 10). The abruptness of the change in both records at *c.* 12.4 ± cal ka is obvious. Although we cannot resolve the absolute rate of change, our data indicate that the shift from low to high carbonate probably occurred over a space of >10 and <200 years. The records further show that the deglacial signal consisted of a decrease in carbonate and *E. excavatum* forma *clavata* percentage with the zone IIA/IIB boundary occurring at about 10.9 cal ka. Thereafter, during the next 4 cal ka (zone IIB), there is a gradual decline in carbonate and in the glacial marine foraminifera assemblages. At the II/III boundary the environment becomes essentially like the modern fiord environment with increases in TOC%, dinoflagellates and diatoms (Figs 7 and 9).

Stable isotopic records from various sites on the Greenland Ice Sheet, which lies to the northeast of Sunneshine Fiord (Fig. 1), show extremely rapid changes during the last glacial–interglacial transition. Changes across this transition have now been resolved to an annual resolution in the GISP2 and GRIP cores (Alley *et al.* 1993; Grootes *et al.* 1993). We compare the GISP2 record with the record from SU5 (Fig. 10). Our modelled age for the onset in the increase in detrital carbonate and in *E. excavatum* forma *clavata* percentage occurs at *c.* 12.4 ka or, within the errors in the radiocarbon ages (Table 1), essentially at the same time as the onset of a rapid change in $\delta^{18}O$ and rate of accumulation at the GISP2 and GRIP cores (Alley *et al.* 1993; Grootes *et al.* 1993; Meese *et al.* 1994). This change has been correlated with the Younger Dryas cooling across northwest Europe. However, the duration of the event in Sunneshine Fiord appears shorter than that from the ice-core record. This may be true or it may be an artifact of the problem of dating across an interval where there is a radiocarbon plateau (Ammann & Lotter 1989). At this time we can only point to the problem, but cannot resolve it.

Regional coeval carbonate events

The rapid rise in detrital carbonate ca. 12.4 cal ka in the sediments in Sunneshine Fiord leads on to a consideration of the evidence for other detrital carbonate events in the marine record from the margin of the Eastern Canadian Arctic and the northwest Labrador Sea and their relationship to a

Heinrich-like event, H-0, in the North Atlantic and southern Labrador Sea (Andrews & Tedesco 1992; Bond *et al.* 1993; Hillaire-Marcel *et al.* 1994; Bond and Lotti 1995; Andrews *et al.* 1995). In three cores north of Hatton Basin (Fig. 1), a rapid increase in total carbonate is dated close to 11 ^{14}C ka (Fig. 11), thus coeval with the carbonate rise in SU5. A key question is: where is the source for carbonate in the area west of Davis Strait? Two sources are possible—the first would be from the northern end of Baffin Bay (a southward transport) where limestones and dolostones crop out on the floor of the channels and on Devon Island and northwest Greenland (Aksu 1981, 1985), whereas the second would be from Palaeozoic carbonates in Cumberland Sound and on the southeast Baffin Shelf (a northern transport) (Fig. 1) (MacLean *et al.* 1977; Jennings 1993).

In surface grab samples, just offshore from Sunneshine Fiord, Krank (1966) noted the presence of limestone erratics. In the shallow waters of Exeter Bay (Fig. 2), limestone makes up generally <25% of the iceberg rafted detritus, but further offshore, at depths >200 m, the percentages of limestone (both calcitic and dolomitic) are frequently in the range 50–100%. These observations indicate that, even today, icebergs from northwest Greenland and the High Canadian Arctic bring carbonates along the eastern Baffin shelf. Further north, at the southern extremity of Baffin Bay, Aksu & Piper (1987) described several prominent detrital carbonate-rich units within the cored sequence, but the exact ages of these events has not yet been determined. However, at site HU77–027–017 in northern Davis Strait, Aksu (Andrews *et al.* 1985*b*) shows that the sediment above a date of 10.5 ± 0.7 ka is carbonate-rich. A small gastropod from 55 cm depth, below the carbonate facies in #017 (Fig. 1), has an AMS ^{14}C age of 10.35 ± .05 (CAMS-19389). Clay-sized XRD analyses of sediments from a suite of cores within Baffin Bay (Aksu 1981) indicates that dolomite exceeds calcite by factors of between two and five thus showing a similar carbonate mineralogy to that found in SU5 (Fig. 8).

However, Cumberland Sound is also a source for dolomitic-rich sediments. In HU87–033–009, from the southeast Baffin slope (Fig. 1), Jennings *et al.* (this volume) argue that ice moved seawards along Cumberland Sound out onto the shelf at 11 ka—therefore, icebergs and meltwater plumes from this ice source, only a few tens of kilometres south of SU5, could also account for the rapid changes in total carbonate content and carbonate mineralogy.

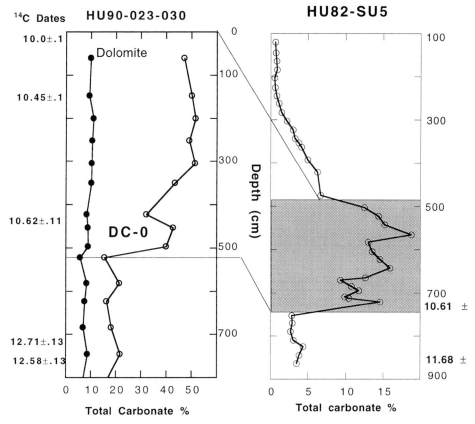

Fig. 11. Comparison of the carbonate records from SU5 compared with one from the Resolution Basin (e.g. HU90-030) (cf. Andrews *et al.* 1995). Note the differences in the relative contributions of calcite and dolomite in these records (see Fig. 1 for core locations).

The dominance of dolomite in sediments from SU5 represents a difference from the results from the southeast Baffin Shelf, where calcite is the dominant mineral in the total sediment and in the clay-sized fraction (Andrews *et al.* 1994*b*) (Fig. 11). Notwithstanding the probability that the cores from the area of Baffin Bay and those from Hudson Strait have a different carbonate signature, the timing of the last major pulse of detrital carbonate appears to be synchronous or essentially coeval with the onset of lighter $\delta^{14}O$ conditions at both the GISP2 and GRIP core sites of the central Greenland Ice Sheet (Grootes *et al.* 1993) (Figs 10 and 11). Interestingly, the carbonate record from HU87-033-009 (Andrews & Tedesco 1992) (Fig. 1) shows that the carbonate signal in event H-1 at *c.* 14.5 ka is dominated by calcite, whereas dolomite increases in importance in the upper section of the core (see Jennings *et al.* this volume).

The synchroneity of the increase in detrital carbonate in southern Baffin Bay, in Sunneshine Fiord, and on the shelf east of Hudson Strait (Fig. 1) suggests some common climate or glaciological thread between response of ice that lay over Palaeozoic bedrock at the northern end of Baffin Bay, which advanced down Cumberland Sound, and that which advanced northwards across Hudson Strait close to the onset of the Younger Dryas cold period (Stravers *et al.* 1992; Andrews *et al.* 1995).

The 'downstream' effect of the abrupt changes in carbonate content, which we link explicitly to ice sheet re-advance and iceberg discharge, is not only noted in the detrital carbonate content of event H-0 (Younger Dryas) in the Labrador Sea and North Atlantic (Hillaire-Marcel *et al.* 1994; Bond and Lotti 1995; Andrews *et al.* 1995), but may be the major cause for the widespread cooling event(s) that have been reported from the

Canadian Maritimes. Although a cooling event, approximately coeval with the northwest European Younger Dryas event, has been reported (Mott *et al.* 1986; Anderson & Macpherson 1994; Cwynar *et al.* 1994), there is no specific marine evidence (e.g. Rodrigues & Vilks 1995) that unambiguously links this with the meltwater discharge of Glacial Lake Agassiz through the St Lawrence drainage system (Teller 1987; Broecker *et al.* 1989). Although this latter explanation has become popular, the alternative or co-occurring event(s) 'upstream' along the east and northeast margins of the Laurentide and northwest Greenland ice sheets requires attention and widens the search for a source for the dramatic cooling that characterized the Younger Dryas period around the North Atlantic.

This paper is a contribution to several different projects and has been funded by grants from the National Science Foundation, Office of Polar Programs OPP-9321135 and the ARCSS program on the Paleoclimate of Arctic Lakes and Estuaries (ATM-9122974), and from the NOAA Consortium Program on Abrupt Climate Change. We are grateful to the NSF AMS Facility at the University of Arizona for providing some of the dates (AA-) and the others were obtained via T. Stafford (CAMS-). The Bedford Institute of Oceanography and the Core Curator, I. Hardy, are thanked for their assistance in providing of samples for this study. The paper was critically reviewed by B. MacLean and P. Clark; we thank them for their comments.

PALE contribution No. 27

References

AKSU, A. E. 1981. *Late Quaternary stratigraphy, paleoenvironmentology, and sedimentation history of Baffin Bay and Davis Strait.* PhD Thesis, Dalhousie University, Halifax, Nova Scotia.
——1985. Climatic and oceanographic changes over the past 400,000 years: evidence from deep-sea cores on Baffin Bay and David Strait. *In*: ANDREWS, J. T. (ed.) *Quaternary Environments: Eastern Canadian Arctic, Baffin Bay and Western Greenland,* Allen and Unwin, Boston, 181–209.
—— & PIPER, D. J. W. 1987. Late Quaternary sedimentation in Baffin Bay. *Canadian Journal of Earth Sciences,* 24, 1833–1846.
ALLEY, R. B., MEESE, D. A. & 9 others 1993. Abrupt increase in Greenland snow accumulation at the end of the Younger Dryas event. *Nature,* 362, 527–529.
AMMANN, B. & LOTTER, A. F. 1989. Late-glacial radiocarbon and palynostratigraphy on the Swiss Plateau. *Boreas,* 18, 109–126.
ANDERSON, T. W. & MACPHERSON, J. B. 1994. Wisconsinan Late-glacial environmental change in Newfoundland: a regional review. *Journal of Quaternary Science,* 9, 171–178.

ANDREWS, J. T. 1980. Progress in relative sea level and ice sheet reconstructions Baffin Island, N.W.T., for the last 125,000 years. *In*: MORNER, N.-A. (eds) *Earth Rheology, Isostasy, and Eustasy,* Wiley, London, 275–200.
——1989. Quaternary geology of the northeastern Canadian Shield. *In*: FULTON, R. J. (ed.) *Quaternary Geology of Canada and Greenland.* Geological Society of America, Boulder, 276–301.
——1993. Changes in the silt- and clay-size mineralogy of sediments at ODP Site 645B, Baffin Bay. *Canadian Journal of Earth Sciences,* 30, 2448–2452.
—— & BRUBAKER, L. 1994. The paleoclimates of Arctic lakes and estuaries (PALE): goals and rationale of an international research program. *Journal of Paleolimnology,* 10, 163–166.
—— & JENNINGS, A. E. 1990. Geomagnetic secular variations (inclination) of high latitude fiord cores: eastern Canadian Arctic. *Polar Research,* 8, 245–259.
—— & TEDESCO, K. 1992. Detrital carbonate-rich sediments, northwestern Labrador Sea: implications for ice-sheet dynamics and iceberg rafting (Heinrich) events in the North Atlantic. *Geology,* 20, 1087–1090.
——, AKSU, A., KELLY, M., KLASSEN, R., MILLER, G. H., MODE, W. N. & MUDIE, P. 1985a. Land/ocean correlations during the last interglacial/glacial transition, Baffin Bay, Northwestern North Atlantic: a review. *Quaternary Science Reviews,* 4, 333–355.
——, BOND, G., JENNINGS, A. E., KERWIN, M., KIRBY, M., MACLEAN, B., MANLEY, W. & MILLER, G. H. 1995. A Heinrich like-event, H-0 (DC-0): source(s) for detrital carbonate in the North Atlantic during the Younger Dryas chronozone. *Paleoceanography,* 10, 953–952.
——, EVANS, L. W., WILLIAMS, K. M., BRIGGS, W. M., ERLENKEUSER, H., HARDY, I. & JULL, A. J. T. 1990. Cryosphere/ocean interactions at the margin of the Laurentide Ice Sheet during the Younger Dryas Chron: SE Baffin Shelf, Northwest Territories. *Paleoceanography,* 5, 921–935.
——, GEIRSDOTTIR, A. & JENNINGS, A. E. 1989. Spatial and temporal variations in clay- and silt-size mineralogies of shelf and fiord cores, Baffin Island. *Continental Shelf Research,* 9, 445–463.
——, JULL, A. J. T., DONAHUE, D. J., SHORT, S. K. & OSTERMAN, L. E. 1985b. Sedimentation rates in Baffin Island fiord cores from comparative radiocarbon dates. *Canadian Journal of Earth Sciences,* 22, 1827–1834.
——, J. T., SYVITSKI, J. P. M., WILLIAMS, K. M., JENNINGS, A. E., SHORT, S. K., MODE, W. N. & KRAVITZ, J. 1994a. *Marine Geology of Sunneshine Fiord (Baffin Island).* Geological Survey of Canada Open File Report, 3034, 2 map sheets.
——, J. T., TEDESCO, K., BRIGGS, W. M. & EVANS, L. W. 1994b. Sediments, sedimentation rates, and environments, SE Baffin Shelf and NW Labrador Sea 8 to 26 KA. *Canadian Journal of Earth Sciences,* 31, 90–103.

BALKWILL, H. R., MCMILLAN, N. J., MACLEAN, B., WILLIAMS, G. L. & SRIVASTAVA, S. P. 1990. Geology of the Labrador Shelf, Baffin Bay, and Davis Strait, Chapter 7. *In*: KEEN, M. J. & WILLIAMS, G. L. (eds) *Geology of the Continental Margin of Eastern Canada.* Geological Survey of Canada, Queens Printer, Ottawa, 293–348.

BARD, E., ARNOLD, M. & 7 others 1994. The North Atlantic atmosphere-sea surface ^{14}C gradient during the Younger Dryas climatic event. *Earth and Planetary Science Letters*, 126, 275–287.

BENNETT, K. D. 1994. Confidence intervals for age estimates and deposition times in late-Quaternary sediment sequences. *Holocene*, 4, 337–348.

BOND, G. C. & LOTTI, R. 1995. Millennial-scale ice rafting cycles in the North Atlantic during the last glaciation. *Science*, 267, 1005–1009. .

——, BROECKER, W. S., JOHNSEN, S., MCMANUS, J., LABEYRIE, L., JOUZEL, J. & BONANI, G. 1993. Correlations between climate records from North Atlantic sediments and Greenland ice. *Nature*, 365, 143–147.

BROECKER, W. S. 1992. Defining the boundaries of the Late-Glacial isotope episodes. *Quaternary Research*, 38, 135–138.

——, W. S., KENNETT, J. P., FLOWER, B. P., TELLER, J. T., TRUMBORE, S., BONANI, G. & WOLFLI, W. 1989. Routing of meltwater from the Laurentide Ice Sheet during the Younger Dryas cold episode. *Nature*, 314, 318–321.

CLARK, P. U., SHORT, S. K., WILLIAMS, K. M. & ANDREWS, J. T. 1989. Late Quaternary chronology and environments of Square Lake, Torngat Mountains, Labrador. *Canadian Journal of Earth Sciences*, 26, 2130–2144.

COOK, H. E., JOHNSON, P. D., MATTI, J. C. & ZEMMELS, T. 1975. Methods of sample preparation, and X-ray diffraction data analysis, X-ray mineralogy laboratory, Deep-Sea Drilling Project, University of CA, Riverside. *In*: HAYES, D. E., FRAKES, L. A. ET AL. (eds) *Initial reports of the Deep Sea Drilling Project.* United States Government Printing Office, Washington, DC, 999–1007.

CWYNAR, L. C., LEVESQUE, A., MAYLE, F. E. & WALKER, I. 1994. Wisconsinan late-glacial environmental change in New Brunswick: a regional synthesis. *Journal of Quaternary Science*, 9, 161–164.

DENTON, G. H. & HUGHES, T. J. 1981. *The Last Great Ice Sheets.* Wiley, New York.

DOWDESWELL, E. K. & ANDREWS, J. T. 1985. The fiords of Baffin Island: description and classification. *In*: ANDREWS, J. T. (ed.) *Quaternary Environments: Eastern Canadian Arctic, Baffin Bay, and Western Greenland.* Allen and Unwin, Boston, 93–121.

DREIMANIS, A. 1962. Quantitative gasometric determination of calcite and dolomite by using Chittick apparatus. *Journal of Sedimentary Petrology*, 32, 520–529.

DYKE, A. S., ANDREWS, J. T. & MILLER, G. H. 1982. *Quaternary Geology of Cumberland Peninsula, Baffin Island, District of Franklin.* Geological Survey of Canada, Ottawa, Memoir, 403.

EVANS, L. W. 1990. *Late Quaternary stratigraphy of the Hatton and Resolution Basins, southeast Baffin Island Shelf, N.W.T., Canada.* MSc Thesis, University of Colorado, Boulder.

FUNDER, S. (ed.) 1990. Late Quaternary stratigraphy and glaciology in the Thule area, Northwest Greenland. *Meddelelser om Gronland, Geoscience*, 22.

GILBERT, R. & MACLEAN, B. 1983. *Geophysical Studies Based on Conventional Shallow and Huntec High Resolution Seismic Surveys of Fiords on Baffin Island.* Fisheries of Oceans, Canada Canadian Data report on Hydrography and Ocean Sciences, 12, Ch. 15.

GROOTES, P. M., STUIVER, M., WHITE, J. W. C., JOHNSEN, S. & JOUZEL, J. 1993. Comparison of oxygen isotope records from the GISP2 and GRIP Greenland ice cores. *Nature*, 366, 552–554.

HALD, M. & STEINSUND, P. I. 1992a. Distribution of surface sediment benthic foraminifera in the southwestern Barents Sea. *Journal of Foraminiferal Research*, 22, 347–362.

—— & —— 1992b. Recent and Late Quaternary benthic foraminiferal assemblages in the southwestern Barents Sea. *Studies in Benthic Foraminifera, Benthos '90*, 255–264.

HAWKINS, F. F. 1980. *Glacial geology and late Quaternary paleoenvironment in the Merchants Bay area, Baffin ISLAND, N.W.T., Canada.* MS Thesis, University of Colorado, Boulder.

HILLAIRE-MARCEL, C., DE VERNAL, A., BILODEAU, G. & WU, G. 1994. Isotope stratigraphy, sedimentation rates, deep circulation, and carbonate events in the Labrador Sea during the last ~200 kyr. *Canadian Journal of Earth Sciences*, 31, 63–89.

JENNINGS, A. E. 1993. The quaternary history of Cumberland Sound, southeastern Baffin Island: the marine evidence. *Geographie physique et Quaternaire*, 47, 21–42.

—— & HELGADOTTIR, G. 1994. Foraminiferal assemblages from the fjords and shelf of Eastern Greenland. *Journal of Foraminiferal Research*, 24, 123–144.

——, TEDESCO, K. A. & ANDREWS, J. T. Shelf erosion and glacial ice proximity in the Labrador Sea during and after Heinrich events as shown by foraminifera. *This volume*.

KRANCK, K. 1966. *Sediments of Exeter Bay, Baffin Island, District of Franklin.* Geological Survey of Canada Paper, 66-8.

LEBLANC, K. W., SYVITSKI, J. P. M. & MAILLET, L. 1988. *Examination of Suspended Particulate Matter Within Arctic Fiords.* Geological Survey of Canada, Open File Report, 1733.

LINICK, T. W., JULL, A. J. T., TOOLIN, L. J. & DONAHUE, D. J. 1986. Operation of the NSF Arizona accelerator facility for radioistope analysis results from selective collaborative research projects. *Radiocarbon*, 28, 522–533.

LOCKE, W. W., III 1980 *Quaternary geology of the Cape Dyer area, southwesternmost Baffin Island.* PhD. Thesis, University of Colorado, Boulder.

——1986. Fine particle translocation in soils developed on glacial deposits, southern Baffin Island, N.W.T., Canada. *Arctic and Alpine Research*, **18**, 33–43.

——1987. The late Quaternary geomorphic and paleoclimatic history of Cape Dyer area, easternmost Baffin Island, N.W.T. *Canadian Journal of Earth Sciences*, **24**, 1185–1198.

MacLean, B. 1985. Geology of the Baffin Island Shelf. *In*: ANDREWS, J. T. (ed.) *Quaternary Environments: Eastern Canadian Arctic, Baffin Bay, and Western Greenland*. Allen and Unwin, Boston, 154–177.

——, JANSA, L. F., FALCONER, R. K. H. & SRIVASTAVA, S. P. 1977. Ordovician strata on the southeastern Baffin Island shelf revealed by shallow drilling. *Canadian Journal of Earth Sciences*, **14**, 1925–1939.

MANGERUD, J., ANDERSON, S. T., BERGLUND, B. E. & DONNER, J. J. 1974. Quaternary stratigraphy of Norden, a proposal for terminology and classification. *Boreas*, **3**, 109–128.

MEESE, D. A., GOW, A. J. & 7 others 1994. An accumulation record from the GISP2 core and as indictor of climate change throughout the Holocene. *Science*, **266**, 1680–1682.

MILLER, G. H. 1975. *Glacial and climatic history of northern Cumberland Peninsula, Baffin Island, Canada, during the last 10,000 years*. PhD Thesis, University of Colorado, Boulder.

——1976. Anomalous local glacier activity, Baffin Island, Canada. Paleoclimatic implications. *Geology*, **4**, 502–504.

——1985. Aminostratigraphy of Baffin Island shell-bearing deposits. *In*: ANDREWS, J. T. (ed.) *Quaternary Environments: Eastern Canadian Arctic, Baffin Bay and Western Greenland*. Allen and Unwin, Boston, 394–427.

MOTT, R. J., GRANT, D. R., STEA, R. & OCHIETTIE, S. 1986. Late glacial climatic oscillation in Atlantic Canada equivalent to the Allerod/Younger Dryas event. *Nature*, **123**, 247–250.

OSTERMAN, L. E. 1984. Benthic foraminiferal zonation of a glacial/interglacial transition from Frobisher Bay, Baffin Island, Northwest Territories, Canada. *In*: *Benthos '83, 2nd International Symposium on Benthic Foraminifera, Pau*, 471–476.

—— & NELSON, A. R. 1989. Latest Quaternary and Holocene paleoceanography of the eastern Baffin Island continental shelf, Canada: benthic foraminiferal evidence. *Canadian Journal of Earth Sciences*, **26**, 2236–2248.

——, L. E., MILLER, G. H. & STRAVERS, J. A. 1985. Late and mid-Foxe Glaciation of southern Baffin Island. *In*: ANDREWS, J. T. (ed.) *Quaternary Environments: Eastern Canadian Arctic, Baffin Bay, and Western Greenland*. Allen and Unwin, Boston, 520–545.

QUINLAN, G. 1985. A numerical model of postglacial relative sea level change near Baffin Island. *In*: ANDREWS, J. T. (ed.) *Quaternary Environments: Eastern Canadian Arctic, Baffin Bay, and Western Greenland*. Allen and Unwin, Boston, 560–584.

RODRIGUES, C. G. & VILKS, G. 1995. The impact of glacial lake runoff on the Goldthwait and Champlain seas: the relationship between glacial lake Agassiz runoff and the Younger Dryas. *Quaternary Science Reviews*, **14**, 923–944.

SCOTT, D. B., MUDIE, P. J., VILKS, G. & YOUNGER, D. C. 1984. Latest Pleistocene–Holocene paleoceanographic trends on the continental margin of Eastern Canada: foraminifera, dinoflagellate and pollen evidence. *Marine Micropaleonology*, **9**, 181–218.

SHORT, S. K., ANDREWS, J. T. & MODE, W. N. 1989. Modern and late Quaternary pollen spectra of Fiord sediments, eastern Baffin Island, Arctic Canada. *Marine Micropaleonology*, **15**, 181–202.

SLOTA, P. J., JULL, A. J. T., LINICK, T. W. & TOOLIN, L. J. 1987. Preparation of small samples for ^{14}C accelerator targets by catalytic reduction of CO. *Radiocarbon*, **29**, 303–306.

STRAVERS, J. A., MILLER, G. H. & KAUFMAN, D. S. 1992. Late glacial ice margins and deglacial chronology for Hudson Strait, Eastern Canadian Arctic. *Canadian Journal of Earth Sciences*, **29**, 1000–1017.

STUIVER, M. & BRAZIUNAS, T. F. 1993. Modeling atmospheric ^{14}C influences and ^{14}C ages of marine samples to 10,000 BC. *Radiocarbon*, **35**, 137–190.

—— & REIMER, P. J. 1986. A computer program for radiocarbon age calibration. *Radiocarbon*, **28**, 1022–1030.

—— & ——1993. Extended ^{14}C data base and revised CALIB 3.0 ^{14}C age calibration program. *Radiocarbon*, **35**, 215–230.

SYVITSKI, J. P. M. & BLAKENEY, C. (eds) 1983. *Sedimentology of Arctic Fjords Experiment: HU82–031*. Canadian Data Report on Hydrography and Ocean Sciences, **12**.

—— & PRAEG, D. B. 1987. *Sedimentology of Arctic Fjords Experiment: Data Report 3*. Canadian Report on Hydrography and Ocean Sciences, **54**.

——, FARROW, G. E., ATKINSON, R. J. A., MOORE, P. G. & ANDREWS, J. T. 1989. Baffin Island fjord macrobenthos: bottom communities and environmental significance. *Arctic*, **42**, 232–247.

——, LeBLANC, K. W. G. & CRANSTON, R. E. 1990. The flux and preservation of organic carbon in Baffin Island fjords. *In*: DOWDESWELL, J. A. & SCOURSE, J. D. (eds) *Glacimarine Environments: Processes and Sediments*. Geological Society, London, Special Publications, **53**, 177–200.

——, SCAHFER, C. T., ASPREY, K. W., HEIN, F., HODGE, G. D. & GILBERT, R. 1985. *Sedimentology of Arctic Fjords Experiment: 85–062 Expedition*. Geological Survey of Canada Open File Report **1234**.

TELLER, J. T. 1987. Proglacial lakes and the southern margin of the Laurentide Ice Sheet. *In*: RUDDIMAN, W. F. & WRIGHT, H. E. J. (eds) *North America and Adjacent Oceans During the Last Deglaciation*. Geological Society of America, Boulder, 39–70.

VILKS, G., MACLEAN, B., DEONARINE, B., CURRIE, C. G. & MORAN, K. 1989. Late Quaternary paleoceanography and sedimentary environments in Hudson Strait. *Geographie Physique et Quaternaire*, **43**, 161–176.

WALKLEY, A. 1947. A critical examination of a rapid method for determining organic carbon in soils—effects of variation in digestion conditions of inorganic soil constituents. *Soil Science*, **63**, 251–264.

WILLIAMS, K. M. 1990. Late Quaternary Paleoceanography of the western Baffin Bay region: evidence from fossil diatoms. *Canadian Journal of Earth Sciences*, **27**, 1487–1494.

WINTERS, G. V., SYVITSKI, J. P. M. & MAILLET, L. 1985. *Distribution and Dynamics of Suspended Particulate Matter in Baffin Island Fjords*. Geological Survey of Canada Open File Report, **1223**, 73–77.

Shelf erosion and glacial ice proximity in the Labrador Sea during and after Heinrich events (H-3 or 4 to H-0) as shown by foraminifera

ANNE E. JENNINGS[1], KATHY A. TEDESCO[2],
JOHN T. ANDREWS[1] & MATTHEW E. KIRBY[1]

[1] INSTAAR and Department of Geological Sciences, University of Colorado, Boulder, CO 80309–0450, USA

[2] Department of Geology, Duke University, Durham, NC 27708–0227, USA

Abstract: Collapses of the marine-based Laurentide Ice Sheet during the last glaciation are documented by large, abrupt influxes of detrital carbonate into the northwest Labrador Sea, known as detrital carbonate or Heinrich events. The extent of grounded ice on the continental shelf is poorly constrained for these events, but has been assumed to be at the shelf edge. Possible grounding line positions of ice streams in Hudson Strait and Cumberland Sound over the last c. 34 ka are delimited using the abundance of shelf-dwelling benthic foraminifera, sediment colour and calcite to dolomite ratios in two Labrador Sea cores (87033–009 LCF and 75–009-IV-55 PC). Heinrich events 1 and 2 contain no evidence of glacial erosion of the continental shelf, suggesting that the Hudson Strait ice stream may have grounded on the Hudson Strait sill or on the inner shelf rather than at the shelf edge during these events. Dark grey, dolomite-rich sediments with abundant shelf-dwelling foraminifera document an advance of Cumberland Sound ice onto the shelf after H-3 or H-4 (c. 34 ka), but before H-2 (c. 21 ka). Cumberland Sound ice re-advanced to a position at or near the shelf edge at c. 11.1 ka, during the Younger Dryas chron. This advance is nearly synchronous with an advance of Labradorean ice on the southeastern Baffin Shelf and with a detrital carbonate event in Sunneshine Fjord, to the north, suggesting climatic forcing of separate ice dispersal centres during the Younger Dryas.

Large marine-based ice sheets are inherently unstable and prone to catastrophic collapses or surges. The collapse of a large ice sheet, such as the West Antarctic Ice Sheet (WAIS), would affect global sea level, ocean circulation patterns and climate (Bindschadler 1991). During the last glaciation large portions of the northern hemisphere ice sheets were marine-based (e.g. Vorren & Kristoffersen 1986; Andrews et al. 1993). The Heinrich events document the unstable behaviour of the Laurentide Ice Sheet during the last glaciation (Heinrich 1988; Broecker et al. 1991; Andrews & Tedesco 1992; Bond et al. 1992; MacAyeal 1993) and comparisons with ice-core records have shown that they were pivotal events in global climate change (Bond et al. 1993). The geological record of the Heinrich events in the northwest Labrador Sea, close to the source of these events, provides information on glacial ice extent that is critical to understanding the dynamics of the collapses and may enable us to understand and predict the behaviour of the WAIS.

The extent of glacial ice during the Heinrich events is not known. It has been suggested that the delivery of such large quantities of ice-rafted debris to the main circulation of the North Atlantic documented by the Heinrich events requires advances or surges of the Hudson Strait ice stream across the southeastern Baffin Shelf to the shelf break (Fig. 1a; Andrews et al. 1993, 1994b). However, the composition of the Heinrich events in the northwest Labrador Sea is inconsistent with glacial erosion of the bedrock underlying the shelf seaward from the Hudson Strait. The events comprise 10–60 cm thick light brown layers containing up to 60% Palaeozoic carbonate bedrock, mainly calcite. These events in the northwest Labrador Sea have been called detrital carbonate (DC) events (Andrews & Tedesco 1992). They indicate glacial erosion of Palaeozoic carbonate bedrock within Hudson Strait, c. 200 km upflow from the shelf break (Andrews et al. 1993; Fig. 1b). The bedrock underlying the southeastern Baffin Shelf seaward from Hudson Strait is semi-consolidated Tertiary mudstone dominated by smectite (Fig. 1b; Jennings 1993). Glacial erosion products from the Tertiary mudstone have not yet been documented within any of the Heinrich events.

In this paper we use proxy evidence in deep-sea cores of glacial erosion of the continental shelf to document changes in the ice extent on the continental shelf before, during and after H-1 (14.5 ka), H-2 (20 ka) and H-3 (27 ka) or H-4

From Andrews, J. T., Austin, W. E. N., Bergsten, H. & Jennings, A. E. (eds), 1996, *Late Quaternary Palaeoceanography of the North Atlantic Margins*, Geological Society Special Publication No. 111, pp. 29–49.

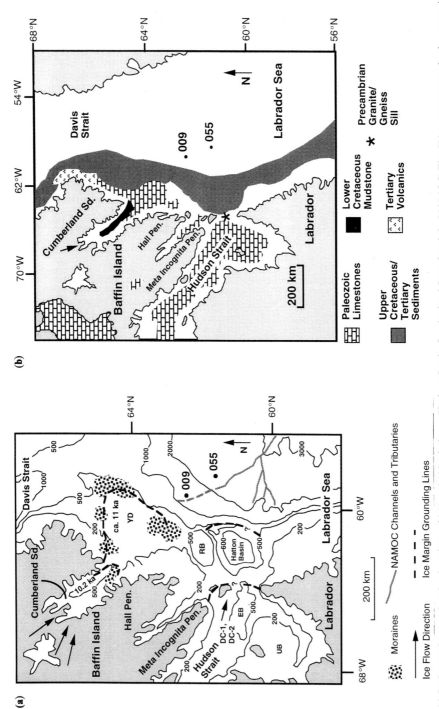

Fig. 1. (a) Bathymetric map showing locations of 055 and 009 relative to Hudson Strait, Cumberland Sound and the NAMOC. The 500 m contour marks the approximate position of the shelf edge. EB, Eastern Basin; UB, Ungava Bay; RB, Resolution Basin. The coarse stippled pattern marks the locations of moraine-like accumulations mapped by Praeg *et al.* (1986). Thick, broken lines demarcate possible grounding line positions of the Hudson Strait ice stream for both DC-1 and DC-2 and the grounding line positions inferred for the Cumberland Sound ice stream during the Younger Dryas, YD. The 10.2 ka grounding line in Cumberland Sound is from Jennings (1993). Bold arrows indicate inferred ice-flow directions. (b) Bedrock map showing the distribution of the key submarine bedrock units. The asterisk indicates the location of the Hudson Strait sill.

(34 ka) (Bond *et al.* 1993). DC-1 and DC-2 are firmly correlated with the H-1 and H-2 events (Andrews & Tedesco 1992), but DC-3 has a radiocarbon date that links it with either H-3 or H-4. An underlying assumption of this paper is that during advances of grounded glacial ice to the shelf edge, the shelf sediments and underlying bedrock are eroded by the ice and released onto the continental slope (e.g. Hesse 1992; Laberg & Vorren 1993; Hillaire-Marcel *et al.* 1994). This approach of documenting and dating the products of the glacial erosion of shelf sediments and bedrock that are redeposited in deeper water beyond the limits of glacial erosion also provides a means of obtaining longer temporal records of glacial activity than are available from the shelf.

We evaluate the extent of grounded ice emanating from two large drainage routes of the Laurentide Ice Sheet, Hudson Strait and Cumberland Sound by looking for products of glacial erosion of the shelf in two northwest Labrador Sea cores: HU75-009-IV-055 PC (hereafter 055) and 87033-009 LCF (hereafter 009) (Fig. 1). Both these cores document Heinrich events. On the basis of the detrital carbonate composition (calcite or dolomite), ^{14}C dating, sediment colour and benthic foraminiferal data on these cores we find strong evidence for advance of a Cumberland Sound ice stream to the outer shelf after H-3 or H-4 and during the Younger Dryas chron (10–11 ^{14}C ka), but our data do not confirm or deny that the Hudson Strait ice stream advanced to the shelf edge during Heinrich events 1 and 2.

Environmental and stratigraphic setting

Bathymetry

Hudson Strait and Cumberland Sound are deep, elongate marine embayments connected to the broad platform of the southeastern Baffin Shelf (Fig. 1a). Both originated as structural grabens and were subsequently modified by glacial erosion (MacLean *et al.* 1986a, b; Jennings 1993). Hudson Strait has water depths in excess of 200 m along its length, although the deep Eastern Basin west of the sill reaches depths in excess of 900 m (MacLean *et al.* 1986b). The sill separating Hudson Strait from the southeastern Baffin Shelf is between 400 and 450 m deep. On the shelf seaward from Hudson Strait the 550 m isobath marks a bathymetric passage to the shelf break (Fig. 1a). The inner part of this relatively deep shelf region is $\geqslant 600$ m deep and is known as the Hatton

Basin. Cumberland Sound reaches water depths in excess of 1200 m although its main basin is between 800 and 900 m deep. The shelf off Cumberland Sound has low relief and is $\leqslant 350$ m deep in general, shallower than the shelf off Hudson Strait (Fig. 1a; Praeg *et al.* 1986).

Bedrock geology

The bedrock distribution and composition in Hudson Strait, Cumberland Sound and the southeastern Baffin Shelf is useful for studies of sediment provenance (Fig. 1b). Hudson Strait and Ungava Bay are underlain by Palaeozoic carbonate bedrock, mainly limestone (MacLean *et al.* 1986b). The fact that the Heinrich events in Labrador Sea cores are predominantly calcite suggests glacial erosion of the limestone bedrock in Hudson Strait and/or Ungava Bay. Both dolomite and calcite rise during the DC events, but calcite is generally three to five times more abundant than dolomite during the DC events, as is shown by the calcite to dolomite ratios in the cores (Fig. 2; Andrews & Tedesco 1992). The dominance of calcite in DC events 1, 2 and 3 implies the removal of unconsolidated sediments and renewed glacial erosion of the Palaeozoic carbonate bedrock in Hudson Strait with each event.

Palaeozoic carbonate bedrock underlies the outer part of Cumberland Sound and the adjacent inner shelf, whereas black, semi-consolidated Cretaceous mudstone occurs in the deep basin within the sound (Fig. 1b; MacLean *et al.* 1986a). Carbonate analysis of glacial sediments in Cumberland Sound shows up to 9% carbonate, with dolomite dominating over calcite (Jennings 1989, 1993). These data suggest that the carbonate bedrock within the sound is a combination of limestone and dolostone. Glacially derived sediments in Cumberland Sound are also distinguished by their black colour and high kaolinite content, which were inherited from erosion of the black, lower Cretaceous bedrock (Jennings 1993).

The bedrock geology on the shelf seaward of Cumberland Sound is complex (MacLean *et al.* 1982). In a large part it is underlain by Tertiary mudstone mineralogically distinct from the Palaeozoic and Cretaceous rocks (MacLean 1985; Jennings 1993). For example, X-ray diffraction analysis of the Tertiary mudstone offshore from Cumberland Sound shows that it is dominated by smectite in the clay fraction, whereas the Cretaceous mudstone is dominated by kaolinite (Jennings 1993). In the

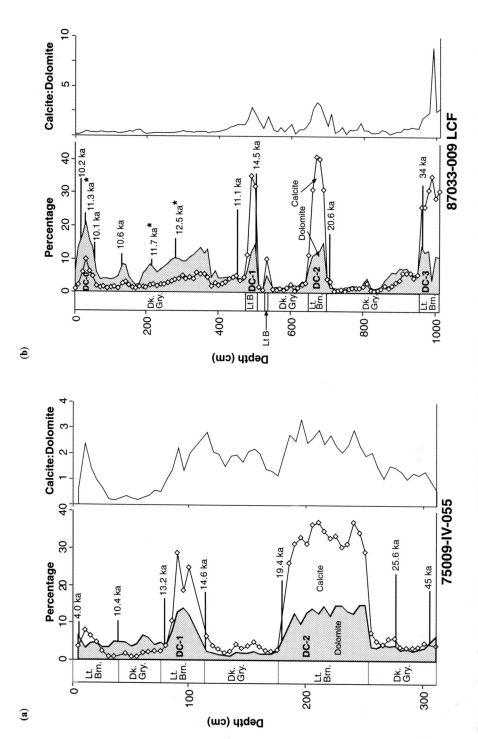

Fig. 2. Downcore logs of calcite and dolomite in cores 75009-IV-055 (**a**) and 87033-009 (**b**). Bar on the axis indicates sediment colour, with light brown units corresponding to calcite-dominated DC events. The high dolomite intervals occur within dark grey sediment. Marine reservoir corrected radiocarbon dates are indicated by black lines. Asterisks mark dates that are out of stratigraphic order and are considered to be reworked.

Hatton Basin the Tertiary bedrock underlies Baffin Shelf Drift in an angular unconformity (B. MacLean, pers. comm. 1995).

Core sites and stratigraphy

Core 055 from 2400 m water depth (61°30.3′ N and 58°38.6′ W) lies seaward of Hudson Strait in a position to receive the products of glacial erosion of the southeastern Baffin Shelf. The core was taken from a possible northern tributary of the North Atlantic Mid-Ocean Channel (NAMOC) (Hesse *et al.* 1987). The light brown DC layers in this core (Andrews & Tedesco 1992) correspond to parallel-laminated sand and parallel-laminated mud with ice-rafted debris which have been interpreted primarily as turbidites and iceberg-rafted sediments (Fig. 2a; Hesse *et al.* 1987).

Core 009 is from the continental slope seaward of Cumberland Sound at 1447 m water depth (62°30.99′ N and 59°26.82′ W). Although it is from a site to the north of the mouth of Hudson Strait, it contains light brown DC layers as well as dark grey to black intervals with subsidiary dolomite-rich detrital carbonate peaks (Fig. 2b). The lithofacies analysis by Aksu & Mudie (1985) of several cores from the outer shelf and slope near core 009 also showed light brown DC events deposited by turbidity currents and iceberg rafting and a distinct black lithofacies with abundant smectite and kaolinite clay and 20–30% detrital carbonate. In core 009, the uppermost dark grey, dolomite-rich event which occurred in the Younger Dryas chron has been termed DC-0 (Andrews *et al.* 1994a). From evidence presented in this paper we argue that the dark grey dolomite events in core 009 are associated with ice streams emanating from Cumberland Sound.

Shelf stratigraphy

Unlike the continental slope and deep-sea cores from the Labrador Sea, which have been shown to contain up to four DC events (Andrews *et al.* 1993), most marine sediment cores from the southeastern Baffin Shelf terminate within or after a calcite-dominated, detrital carbonate event of Younger Dryas age, termed DC-0 (Andrews *et al.* 1996). On the shelf outside Hudson Strait DC-0 probably records an advance of northward flowing Labrador/Ungava ice across Hudson Strait (Josenhans *et al.* 1986; Andrews *et al.* 1990; Miller & Kaufman 1990; Andrews *et al.* 1995). Sediment cores from

Resolution Basin on the inner shelf show disconformities that may be associated with glacial erosion during H-1 and H-2 (e.g. Andrews *et al.* 1990, 1991, 1994b). However, we have no core further seaward on the shelf to provide evidence pertaining to the extent of the Hudson Strait ice stream on the shelf during the Heinrich events.

On the basis of seismic surveys, Baffin Shelf Drift has been mapped as the surficial deposit on the outer shelf, seaward from Hudson Strait, confirming that an ice sheet has extended to the outer shelf in the past. The timing of deposition of the Baffin Shelf Drift is unknown and few cores have sampled this acoustic unit to define its lithological characteristics (Praeg *et al.* 1986). Much of the Baffin Shelf Drift could have been deposited during H-1 or during a much earlier event such as H-4. On the inner shelf, underlying Hatton Basin and on top of and in the lee of the Hudson Strait sill, there are multiple till sequences that attest to the complex glacial history of the Hudson Strait region (e.g. Praeg *et al.* 1986; Piper *et al.* 1990).

Our knowledge of the Pleistocene history of the Cumberland Sound ice stream is hampered by the lack of cores that extend beyond the limits of the last ice advance. Previous work has shown that ice advanced out of Cumberland Sound at least onto the inner shelf during the late Foxe (= late Wisconsinan) Glaciation (Jennings 1993). Within Cumberland Sound the entire surficial sediment section has been sampled. All that is preserved above the Cretaceous and older bedrock is till, glacial marine and post-glacial sediments from the last deglaciation (Jennings 1993). The radiocarbon dates on cores within the sound indicate that an outlet glacier was retreating from the sound by 10.2 ka. Mapping of the Baffin Shelf Drift by Praeg *et al.* (1986) shows thick moraine-like accumulations on the outer shelf near the shelf break (Fig. 1a). The glacial events responsible for these moraine-like accumulations are undated, but from regional correlations Praeg *et al.* (1986) argued that these sediments were deposited sometime between the early Foxe (= early Wisconsin) and early late Foxe Glaciation.

Materials and methods

The weight percentage of calcite and dolomite were determined gasometrically using a Chittick apparatus (Dreimanis 1962). Air-dried sediment was disaggregated through a 2000 μm screen. Representative samples of the <2000 μm material were milled to <74 μm using a mortar and

Table 1. *Radiocarbon dates*

Depth in core (cm)	Laboratory number	Material dated	Reported age	Reservoir corrected age	Reference
87033-009 LCF					
9–11	AA-7136	Mixed species benthic foraminifera	10 630 ± 380	10 180 ± 380	Kaufman & Williams (1992)
20–23	AA-8777	*Elphidium excavatum*	11 790 ± 275	11 340 ± 275	Kaufman & Williams (1992)
45–47	AA-5032	*Neogloboquadrina pachyderma*	10 530 ± 95	10 080 ± 95	Kaufman & Williams (1992)
120–122	AA-6000	*Neogloboquadrina pachyderma*	11 100 ± 85	10 650 ± 85	Kaufman & Williams (1992)
210–212	AA-6852	*Neogloboquadrina pachyderma*	12 110 ± 185	11 660 ± 185	Kaufman & Williams (1992)
280–282	AA-6853	*Neogloboquadrina pachyderma*	12 975 ± 355	12 525 ± 355	Kaufman & Williams (1992)
450–452	AA-15659	*Elphidium excavatum*	11 555 ± 130	11 105 ± 130	This study
500–501	AA-9364	*Neogloboquadrina pachyderma*	14 980 ± 90	14 530 ± 90	This study
500–501	AA-8034	*Neogloboquadrina pachyderma*	14 850 ± 205	14 400 ± 205	Kaufman & Williams (1992)
710–712	AA-13230	*Neogloboquadrina pachyderma*	21 070 ± 675	33 560 ± 675	Andrews *et al.* (1994)
75009-IV-055 PC					
4–5	AA-5998	*Neogloboquadrina pachyderma*	4 440 ± 70	3 990 ± 70	Kaufman & Williams (1992)
35–37	AA-6850	*Neogloboquadrina pachyderma*	10 850 ± 185	10 400 ± 185	Kaufman & Williams (1992)
80–82	AA-6851	*Neogloboquadrina pachyderma*	13 635 ± 190	13 185 ± 190	Kaufman & Williams (1992)
115–117	AA-5999	*Neogloboquadrina pachyderma*	15 010 ± 105	14 560 ± 105	Kaufman & Williams (1992)
179–183	AA-4700	*Neogloboquadrina pachyderma*	19 855 ± 210	19 405 ± 210	Kaufman & Williams (1992)
250–252	AA-3338	*Neogloboquadrina pachyderma*	21 508 ± 240	21 058 ± 240	Tedesco (1993)
275–277	AA-7137	*Neogloboquadrina pachyderma*	26 015 ± 1320	25 565 ± 1320	Kaufman & Williams (1992)
305–307	AA-4706	*Neogloboquadrina pachyderma*	45 500 ± 55	45 050 ± 55	Kaufman & Williams (1992)

pestle. Dolomite and calcite are differentiated in this method by their different reaction rates with the acid.

We elaborate on the earlier presented radiocarbon chronology of core 009 by adding accelerator mass spectrometry (AMS) dates after DC-3, before DC-2, after DC-1 and within DC-0 (Table 1). To obtain the most reliable chronology, these new radiocarbon dates were obtained from abundance peaks in benthic or planktic foraminifera and where possible were determined on samples of single species (Table 1). The AMS dates are given in Table 1 as reported by the University of Arizona TAMS facility and with an assumed marine reservoir correction of 450 years.

Samples for foraminiferal analysis were weighed wet and washed with distilled water on a 63 μm screen. Benthic and planktic foraminifera were picked and identified to species level from the > 63 μm fraction. Splits of at least 300 benthic and 300 planktic foraminifera were made where numbers allowed and were identified using a binocular microscope (Table 2). The foraminiferal data are expressed as benthic and planktic foraminifera per gram of dry sediment (Table 2). To obtain the dry sediment weights, a small sample from each foraminiferal sample was weighed both before and after air drying. This change in weight provided the conversion from total wet sample weight to total dry sample weight. Because some of the samples were prepared before this study was initiated, the total dry weights for these were obtained by weighing the >63 μm fraction and converting it to total dry weight using the percentage sand reported from grain size data at the same sample depth (Tedesco 1993).

Results

Detrital carbonate: proxy for glacial erosion

Core 55 contains DC-1 and DC-2, which Andrews & Tedesco (1992) correlated with Heinrich events 1 and 2 in the North Atlantic (Fig. 2a). These sediments are light brown and dominated by calcite. They stand out distinctly from the surrounding dark grey sediments (Table 1). Sediments in the lower 392 cm of the core are difficult to interpret. They may be in-place hemipelagic sediments with an ice-rafted debris component (Hesse et al. 1987) or they may represent flow-in during coring.

Core 009 contains three calcite-rich, light brown DC events. The date of 34 ka on a mixture of benthic species and *Neogloboquadrina*

pachyderma on the declining upper limb of DC-3 lies in age between H-3 and H-4 in the North Atlantic. Because of the uncertainty in the correlation between DC-3 and H-3 or -4, we continue to use the DC numbering system in the discussion and figures rather than switching to the numbering system of the Heinrich events. The calcite-rich events in both cores were considered by Andrews & Tedesco (1992) and Bond et al. (1992) to have originated from glacial erosion of Palaeozoic carbonate bedrock in Hudson Strait.

The carbonate record of 009 differs from that of 055. Following DC-3 and DC-1 the record contains dark grey to black, dolomite-rich intervals, which suggest a different sediment source than the main DC events. DC-2 is not followed by a dolomite-rich interval. The largest dolomite peak, near the core top, was termed DC-0 by Andrews et al. (1993). Radiocarbon dates on either side of this event suggest that it occurred at c. 10 ka (Fig. 2). However, a date on *Elphidium excavatum* forma *clavata* within the peak gave a much older age of 11.3 ka (Kaufman & Williams 1992). This species is considered to be a shelf dweller that is typically abundant in ice proximal glacial–marine environments (e.g. Nagy 1965; Osterman 1984; Vilks et al. 1989; MacLean et al. 1992; Jennings 1993). Thus we suggest that the foraminifera were transported from the shelf and redeposited onto the slope along with the dolomite at c. 10 ka.

In addition, we obtained a date of 11.1 ka on *E. excavatum* at 450 m in 009 (Table 1). The repercussions of this date are: (1) that two of the previously obtained dates on planktic foraminifera are out of stratigraphic order and are thus too old; (2) that the dolomite-rich upper 4.5 m of the core was deposited between c. 11 and 10 ka; and (3) core 009 contains reworked shelf sediments that are similar in colour and composition to glacial sediments in Cumberland Sound.

Planktic foraminifera: implications for environments and reliability of ^{14}C ages

The dominant planktic foraminifera in both cores is *N. pachyderma* sinistral. It constitutes >90% of the planktic foraminiferal fauna in most of the samples. The downcore abundance of planktic foraminifera in core 009 is shown in Fig. 3. The abundance of planktic foraminifera in 055 was previously evaluated by Tedesco (1993).

One of the defining characteristics of Heinrich layers is low planktic foraminiferal concentrations dominated by *Neogloboquadrina pachyderma* sinistral (Broecker et al. 1992). The

Table 2. *87033-009 Foraminifera*

Depth (cm):	1	10	21.5	41	61	91	121	133	142	161	181	199	221	231	251	281	301	321	351
Split:	0.50	0.50	0.19	0.50	0.50	0.50	0.25	0.50	0.50	0.50	0.50	0.50	0.50	0.50	0.50	0.50	0.50	0.50	0.50
Astrononion gallowayi	0	0	0	0	0	0	0	0	0	0	0	1	1	0	3	0	16	0	0
Bolivina pseudopunctata	0	0	0	0	0	0	0	0	0	0	0	0	0	0	0	0	0	0	0
Buccella spp.	0	0	0	0	0	1	0	0	0	0	0	0	1	0	0	0	0	1	0
Bulimina spp.	0	0	0	0	0	0	0	0	0	0	0	0	0	0	0	0	0	0	0
Buliminella elegantissima	0	1	5	0	0	1	1	0	1	0	0	0	0	0	0	0	0	0	0
Cassidulina reniforme	0	0	1	7	0	0	0	0	0	0	0	8	26	0	0	63	263	9	14
Cassidulina teretis	0	0	0	12	1	0	0	0	0	0	0	5	5	4	0	46	76	19	13
Cibicides spp.	0	0	1	1	0	0	0	0	0	0	0	2	0	3	1	0	0	1	0
Cyclogyra involvens	0	0	0	0	0	0	0	0	0	0	0	0	0	0	0	0	0	0	0
Dentalina spp.	0	0	0	0	0	0	0	0	0	0	0	0	0	0	0	0	0	0	0
Discorbis?	0	0	0	0	0	0	0	0	0	0	0	0	0	0	0	0	0	0	0
Elphidium exc clavata	10	86	146	67	3	0	8	0	2	4	3	36	19	3	15	18	30	37	41
E. excavatum exc	1	16	21	13	0	0	0	0	0	0	0	3	0	0	2	0	0	9	2
Eoeponidella pulchella	0	0	0	0	0	0	0	0	0	0	0	0	0	0	0	0	0	0	0
Epistominella exigua	0	0	0	0	0	0	0	0	0	0	0	0	0	0	0	0	0	0	0
Eponides tumidulus	0	0	0	0	0	0	0	0	0	0	0	0	0	0	0	0	0	0	0
Eponides weddelensis	0	0	0	0	0	0	0	0	0	0	0	0	0	0	0	0	0	0	0
Fissurina spp.	0	1	0	0	0	0	0	0	0	0	0	0	0	0	1	0	0	0	0
Fursenkoina fusiformis	0	0	0	0	0	0	0	0	0	0	0	3	0	0	0	0	5	0	0
Glabratella sp.	0	0	0	0	0	0	0	0	0	0	0	0	0	0	0	0	0	0	0
Globobullimina	0	0	0	0	0	0	0	0	0	0	0	0	0	0	0	0	0	0	0
Haynesina nana	0	0	0	0	0	0	0	0	0	0	0	1	0	0	0	0	0	0	0
Hoeglundina elegans	0	0	0	0	0	0	0	0	0	0	0	0	0	0	0	0	0	0	0
Islandiella spp.	0	0	0	9	0	0	0	0	0	0	0	0	5	3	6	5	5	2	1

Table 2. *Continued*

Depth (cm):	1	10	21.5	41	61	91	121	133	142	161	181	199	221	231	251	281	301	321	351
Split:	0.50	0.50	0.19	0.50	0.50	0.50	0.25	0.50	0.50	0.50	0.50	0.50	0.50	0.50	0.50	0.50	0.50	0.50	0.50
Lagena spp.	0	0	0	0	0	0	0	0	0	0	0	0	0	0	1	0	0	0	0
Melonis zandaamae	0	0	2	0	0	0	0	0	0	1	0	3	6	6	1	2	6	1	4
Nonion grateloupi	2	18	24	3	3	0	0	0	0	13	1	11	9	1	9	11	8	2	0
Nonionella auricula	0	0	0	0	0	0	0	0	0	0	0	0	0	0	0	0	0	0	0
Nonionella iridea	0	0	0	0	0	0	0	0	0	0	0	0	0	0	0	0	0	0	0
Nonionella turgida	0	16	39	3	0	2	0	0	0	0	0	0	2	0	0	0	0	0	1
Nonionellina labradorica	0	28	8	10	19	0	0	0	0	0	0	2	0	0	0	0	9	0	4
Nuttallides umbonifera	0	0	0	0	0	0	0	0	0	0	0	0	0	0	0	0	0	0	0
Nuttallides umbonifera	0	0	0	0	0	0	0	0	0	0	0	0	0	0	0	0	0	0	0
Oridorsalis umbonatus	0	0	0	0	0	0	0	0	0	0	0	0	0	0	0	0	0	0	0
Parafissurina spp.	0	0	0	0	0	0	0	0	0	0	0	8	8	2	0	5	0	0	1
Pullenia bulloides	0	0	0	0	0	0	0	0	0	0	0	0	0	0	0	0	0	0	0
Pullenia subcarinata	0	0	0	0	0	0	0	0	0	0	0	0	0	0	0	0	0	0	0
Quinqueloculina spp	0	0	0	0	0	0	0	0	0	0	0	0	0	0	0	0	0	0	0
Stainforthia concava	1	0	0	2	0	0	0	0	0	0	0	0	0	0	1	0	0	0	0
Stetsonia arctica	0	0	0	0	0	0	0	0	0	0	0	0	0	0	0	0	2	0	0
Tosaia hanzawai	0	0	0	0	0	0	0	0	0	0	0	0	0	0	0	0	2	0	0
Triloculina spp	0	0	0	0	0	0	0	0	0	0	0	0	0	0	0	0	0	0	0
Unidentified/other	1	0	0	0	0	0	0	0	0	0	0	3	0	0	1	0	6	0	0
No. of benthics picked	15	166	247	125	28	4	9	0	3	18	4	87	81	22	42	150	429	80	81
Total benthics	30	332	1317.3	250	56	8	36	0	6	36	8	174	162	44	84	300	858	160	162
Benthics/g sediment	2.96	16.7	84.49	28.7	5.19	1.07	1.56	0	0.87	3.78	1.39	5.05	9.26	2.37	6.06	18.2	66.1	18.4	15.5
Total shelf benthics	22	260	938.6	200	44	4	32	0	4	8	6	90	50	16	54	46	122	98	96
Shelf benthics/g	2.17	13.1	60.20	23.0	4.08	0.53	1.39	0	0.58	0.84	1.04	2.61	2.85	0.86	3.89	2.79	9.39	11.3	9.23
Planktonics/g	3.84	4.18	6.157	7.48	0.18	0	15.2	34.6	48.9	0	1.92	5.89	18.1	7.24	1.87	15.6	22.3	35.5	47.1

Table 2. *Continued*

Depth (cm):	371	381	411	431	441	451	461	471	491	501	513	523	535	551	571	601	633	641	651
Split:	0.50	0.50	0.50	0.50	0.38	0.50	0.50	0.50	0.50	0.50	0.50	0.50	0.50	0.06	0.50	0.50	0.50	1.00	1.00
Astrononion gallowayi	2	0	0	2	3	0	0	0	0	0	0	0	12	1	1	0	23	39	10
Bolivina pseudopunctata	3	0	1	9	1	0	4	6	0	0	0	0	0	7	0	0	0	0	0
Buccella spp.	0	0	0	2	0	0	0	0	0	0	0	0	1	0	0	1	0	0	0
Bulimina spp.	0	0	0	0	0	0	0	0	0	0	0	0	0	0	0	0	0	0	0
Buliminella elegantissima	62	8	32	55	11	0	6	83	0	0	0	0	0	56	0	0	1	5	0
Cassidulina reniforme	190	23	13	84	62	7	6	1	2	2	0	0	66	45	0	0	19	221	8
Cassidulina teretis	17	14	13	53	41	21	65	0	1	1	0	0	8	14	0	5	9	13	74
Cibicides spp.	0	0	0	2	8	0	1	0	1	0	0	0	0	0	0	0	0	4	3
Cyclogyra involvens	0	0	0	0	0	0	0	0	0	1	0	0	0	0	1	0	0	0	0
Dentalina spp.	0	1	0	0	1	0	0	0	0	0	0	0	0	3	0	0	0	0	1
Discorbis?	0	0	0	0	0	0	0	0	0	0	0	0	0	0	0	0	0	0	0
Elphidium exc clavata	53	27	42	103	186	200	179	10	1	0	0	0	2	27	1	0	0	0	1
E. excavatum exc	0	0	1	2	3	11	9	0	0	0	0	0	0	4	0	0	0	10	0
Eoeponidella pulchella	0	0	0	0	0	0	0	0	0	0	0	0	3	0	0	0	0	0	0
Epistominella exigua	0	0	0	0	0	0	0	0	0	0	0	0	0	1	0	0	0	4	0
Eponides tumidulus	0	0	0	0	0	0	0	0	0	0	0	0	0	0	0	0	0	0	0
Eponides wedelensis	0	0	0	0	1	0	0	0	1	0	0	0	2	0	0	0	0	0	0
Fissurina spp.	1	0	0	2	0	2	1	0	0	1	0	0	0	1	0	0	0	2	0
Fursenkoina fusiformis	24	2	2	3	14	6	1	2	0	0	0	0	0	17	0	0	0	24	1
Glabratella sp.	0	0	0	0	0	0	0	0	0	0	0	0	0	0	0	0	0	2	0
Globobullimina	0	0	0	0	2	0	0	0	0	0	0	0	0	0	0	0	0	2	0
Haynesina nana	2	0	3	7	2	0	0	0	0	0	0	0	0	2	0	0	0	0	0
Hoeglundina elegans	0	0	0	0	0	0	0	0	5	0	0	0	1	0	0	0	0	0	0
Islandiella spp.	2	3	1	1	0	0	0	0	0	0	0	0	4	1	0	0	3	0	0

Table 2. *Continued*

Depth (cm):	371	381	411	431	441	451	461	471	491	501	513	523	535	551	571	601	633	641	651
Split:	0.50	0.50	0.50	0.50	0.38	0.50	0.50	0.50	0.50	0.50	0.50	0.50	0.50	0.06	0.50	0.50	0.50	1.00	1.00
Lagena spp.	0	1	3	0	1	0	0	0	0	0	0	0	0	0	0	0	0	0	0
Melonis zandaamae	4	3	1	5	5	0	1	1	0	2	0	1	14	9	8	1	6	8	14
Nonion grateloupi	14	3	9	17	8	11	13	1	0	0	0	0	0	0	0	0	0	0	0
Nonionella auricula	2	0	2	4	3	0	0	0	0	0	0	0	1	0	0	0	0	0	0
Nonionella iridea	0	0	0	0	0	0	0	0	0	0	0	0	1	0	0	0	0	0	0
Nonionella turgida	0	3	0	9	30	11	11	3	0	0	0	0	1	13	0	0	0	0	0
Nonionellina labradorica	2	2	0	14	6	7	10	48	0	0	0	0	1	6	0	0	0	0	1
Nuttallides umbonifera	0	0	0	0	1	0	0	0	0	0	0	0	0	1	0	0	0	0	5
Nuttallides umbonifera	0	0	0	0	0	0	0	0	0	0	0	0	0	0	0	0	0	2	1
Oridorsalis umbonatus	0	0	0	0	0	0	0	0	2	1	0	0	0	0	0	0	1	1	1
Parafissurina spp.	1	0	0	0	1	0	0	0	0	0	0	0	0	0	0	0	0	3	1
Pullenia bulloides	0	0	3	3	0	1	0	0	0	0	0	0	5	1	0	0	1	16	0
Pullenia subcarinata	0	0	0	0	8	0	0	0	0	0	0	0	0	0	0	0	0	0	0
Quinqueloculina spp	0	0	0	0	0	0	0	0	0	1	0	0	4	0	0	0	0	0	0
Stainforthia concava	0	0	0	7	0	0	0	0	0	0	0	0	0	4	0	0	2	0	0
Stetsonia arctica	6	0	7	6	6	1	0	3	0	0	0	0	6	34	0	0	4	40	0
Tosaia hanzawai	0	0	0	0	0	0	0	0	0	0	0	0	1	1	0	0	0	0	0
Triloculina spp	1	0	0	0	0	0	0	0	0	0	0	0	1	0	0	0	0	0	0
Unidentified/other	4	2	5	0	1	1	0	3	1	9	0	1	7	21	10	7	0	1	10
No. of benthics picked	390	92	138	390	406	279	306	161	13	9	0	1	141	270	10	7	69	4	10
Total benthics	780	184	276	780	1082.6	558	612	322	26	18	0	2	282	4320	20	14	138	399	131
Benthics/g sediment	77.5	13.7	30.4	55.0	75.71	51.8	59.7	38.2	1.87	1.18	0	0.25	25.2	416.5	2.40	2.208	53.6	49.5	9.79
Total shelf benthics	118	64	88	248	533.3	436	398	116	2	0	0	0	40	624	2	2	52	41	12
Shelf benthics/g	11.7	4.78	9.70	17.5	37.29	40.5	38.8	13.7	0.14	0	0	0	3.57	60.17	0.24	0.315	20.2	5.08	0.89
Planktonics/g	105.3		15.6	23.4	40.42		25.7	5.58	113.4	388.2		1.24	16.00	144.0	144.0	2090.4	67.1	67.1	872.9

Planktics/g

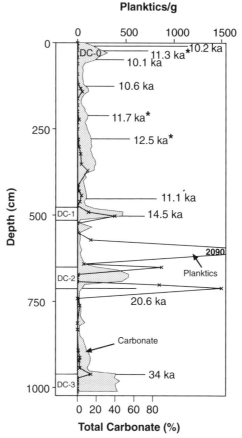

Fig. 3. Planktic foraminifera per gram of total dry sediment plotted against total carbonate in core 87033–009. Note that the colour bar of Fig. 2 is replaced with a bar delimiting the light brown, calcite-dominated DC events. Radiocarbon dated levels are indicated with horizontal black lines. Asterisks mark dates that are out of stratigraphic order and are considered to be reworked.

over-all planktic abundances in core 009 were low except on the rising and falling limbs of the DC events (Fig. 3; Table 2). In this core, the centre of each DC event (except for DC-0) is barren of planktic foraminifera and peaks in planktic abundance coincide with the onset and/or end of the DC events (Fig. 3). This pattern is best illustrated in DC-2. In DC-1 the increase in total carbonate has associated with it a peak in planktic foraminifera per gram, but the upper, falling limb of the total carbonate peak does not show a peak in planktic foraminifera. DC-0 shows no associated peak in planktic foraminiferal abundance.

Heinrich events are thought to be short duration events, probably lasting for between 250 and 1250 years (e.g. Dowdeswell *et al.* 1995). The DC events must represent intervals of

increased sedimentation rate at the core sites. Thus the peaks in planktic foraminifera per gram of dry sediment that coincide with the onset and end of the DC events must be true abundance peaks because presumably they were occurring during intervals of increased sedimentation rates associated with the detrital carbonate input. Clay-sized carbonate occurs throughout the DC events, supporting other evidence that most of the carbonate is detrital and not from foraminiferal tests (Kirby 1995).

At present we can only speculate on the origin of the planktic foraminifera peaks. They may result from better calcium carbonate preservation around DC events due to the buffering effect of detrital carbonate, or they may represent increased productivity associated with upwelling around icebergs (cf. Sancetta 1992). A benefit of

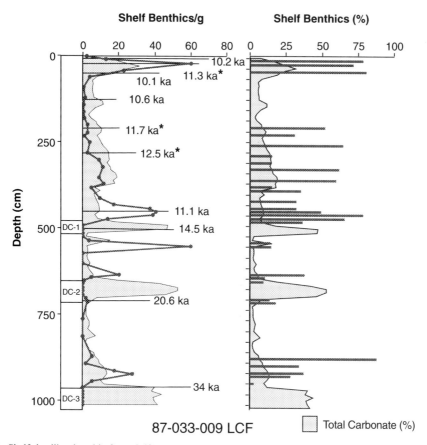

Shelf Benthics/g   **Shelf Benthics (%)**

87-033-009 LCF   □ Total Carbonate (%)

Fig. 4. Shelf-dwelling benthic foraminifera per gram of total dry sediment (left) and the percentage of shelf-dwelling benthic foraminifera (in samples containing at least 74 benthic foraminifera) plotted against total carbonate (right) in core 87033–009. The colour bar of Fig. 2 is replaced with a bar delimiting the light brown, calcite-dominated DC events. Radiocarbon dated levels are indicated with horizontal black lines. Asterisks mark dates that are out of stratigraphic order and are considered to be reworked.

the planktic foraminiferal abundance peaks is that they provide ample biogenic carbonate for reliable radiocarbon dates bounding the DC events. We consider the radiocarbon dates on planktic foraminiferal abundance peaks to be the most reliable dates in the core (Fig. 3; Table 1).

The dates of 12.5 and 11.7 ka above DC-1 are out of stratigraphic order and must be from reworked material (Fig. 3; Table 1). The dates were obtained on planktic foraminifera but they are not from planktic peaks (Fig. 3). We had considered these dates to be reliable in previous publications involving this core (Andrews & Tedesco 1992; Andrews et al. 1993, 1994a,b), but with the new date of 11.1 ka on E. excavatum forma clavata directly above DC-1, these two dates are shown to be unreliable (Figs 3 and 4; Table 1). We now suggest that these dates

represent displaced hemipelagic sediments. The date on planktic foraminifera of 10.6 ka above the dates of 12.5 and 11.7 ka is probably reliable. It is on the declining upper limb of a small planktic foraminiferal peak associated with a small detrital carbonate peak and a distinctive, diatom-rich layer (Fig. 3). It matches a date in the 009 trigger weight core (TWC) that was also obtained for N. pachyderma in the diatom layer (Kaufman & Williams 1992).

The radiocarbon date on a mixture of benthic and planktic foraminifera of 34 ka on DC-3 precedes a peak in shelf-dwelling foraminifera; among the 154 N. pachyderma submitted for dating were 30 benthic specimens, of which 14 were shelf dwellers. As a result, we know that there is a small proportion of reworked material in the date which would make it slightly older the glacial–marine sediments.

Cumberland Sound ice stream

The radiocarbon-dated, light brown, calcite-dominated DC events from Hudson Strait in core 009 provide a stratigraphic framework for investigating the activity of ice streams emanating from Cumberland Sound. The subsidiary dolomite peaks and peaks in shelf-dwelling benthic foraminifera per gram of dry sediment are associated with dark grey or black sediments in this core. These intervals are interpreted to record two advances of ice from Cumberland Sound to a position on the outer shelf or at the shelf edge (Fig. 1a). The older advance occurred between DC-3 and DC-2, but the stratigraphy in the core suggests it was probably closer in timing to DC-3. The later advance occurred during the Younger Dryas chron. It is well constrained by radiocarbon dates in the core and by the chronology of glacial events in Cumberland Sound (Jennings 1993). We suggest that the ice advanced soon after *c.* 11 ka. Two radiocarbon dates on *Elphidium excavatum*, which we assume were living in the glacial–marine evironment in front of the Cumberland Sound ice stream, suggest that there were ice-proximal glacial–marine conditions on the shelf *c.* 11 ka. The ice stream advanced over these sediments and delivered them to the slope, where we record them in core 009 (Fig. 1a). The moraine-like accumulations of Baffin Shelf Drift mapped on the shelf outside of Cumberland Sound by Praeg *et al.* (1986) may have been deposited by these ice advances, but these features have not been dated (Fig. 1a). We use these features to constrain the inferred Younger Dryas grounding line position on Fig. 1a.

An alternative possibility for delivering shelf foraminifera to the slope is an enhanced ocean current regime. For example, Hald *et al.* (1993) reported large percentages of *Elphidium excavatum* on the Barents Sea slope associated with the onset of the North Atlantic Drift in the early Holocene. We do not favour such a scenario on the southeastern Baffin Shelf because the peaks of shelf reworking in core 009 occur well before the onset of the modern current regime. The Baffin Current, which presently travels southwards along the shelf and winnows the seafloor, is thought to have been established *c.* 6 ka (Praeg *et al.* 1986; Williams *et al.* 1995) and the Western Boundary Undercurrent was not established until *c.* 10 ka (Hillaire-Marcel *et al.* 1994).

The observations that the upper 4.5 m of 009

appear to have been derived from Cumberland Sound and were deposited between *c.* 11 and 10 ka indicates high rates of sediment delivery from a glacier emanating from Cumberland Sound. The dolomite and shelf-dwelling benthic foraminiferal data suggest that the influence of the ice was greatest after DC-1, *c.* 11.1 ka (450 cm). The consistent dates of 10.6 ka on the diatom layer in both the TWC and the piston core (LCF) (120–122 cm) of core 009 suggest that hemipelagic sedimentation with little direct influence of glacial ice prevailed at that time. The uppermost dolomite-rich total carbonate peak, previously termed DC-0 (20–40 cm), is probably a sediment gravity flow deposit of glacially derived sediment. It is not directly linked with glacial ice on the shelf. DC-0 was deposited at *c.* 10 ka. Our knowledge of the history of the Cumberland Sound ice stream suggests that ice had retreated from the shelf into Cumberland Sound *c.* 10.2 ka (Jennings 1993).

Neither of the ice advances from Cumberland Sound onto the shelf documented in core 009 occurred during the last glacial maximum. The best represented ice advance, and potentially the most extensive advance of the last 34 ka, occurred during the Younger Dryas chron. The timing of the Cumberland Sound advance of *c.* 11.1–10.2 ka correlates with DC-0 (= H-0) on the southeastern Baffin Shelf (Andrews *et al.* 1995) and near Cape Dyer on the northeastern tip of Cumberland Peninsula in Sunneshine Fjord (Andrews *et al.* 1996). Cumberland Sound is a likely source in addition to Hudson Strait for the detrital carbonate peak associated with the Younger Dryas chron in the North Atlantic (Bond & Lotti 1995). The correspondence of these events on the southeastern Baffin shelf suggests synchronous ice advances from widely separated ice dispersal centres located over Foxe Basin and Labrador. This apparent synchonoeity suggests that climate played a significant part in the ice advances.

Conclusions

(1) Cumberland Sound ice advanced to the outer shelf during the Younger Dryas chron. It advanced to its maximum position by *c.* 11.1 ka and had retreated back into Cumberland Sound by 10.2 ka. The Younger Dryas advance was potentially the most extensive advance out of Cumberland Sound for the last 34 ka. It correlates regionally with Younger Dryas events in Sunneshine Fjord, to DC-0 in Resolution

Basin and to H-0 in the North Atlantic, suggesting that it advanced in response to climatic forcing.

(2) An earlier undated advance of Cumberland Sound ice onto the shelf occurred after 34 ka, between DC-2 and DC-3, but there is no evidence for a Cumberland Sound advance during the Last Glacial Maximum.

(3) The original DC-0 in core 009 is interpreted as a sediment gravity flow deposit of glacially derived sediments from Cumberland Sound. This sediment gravity flow occurred after the ice stream had retreated into Cumberland Sound.

(4) The lack of evidence for shelf erosion in the DC events in 055 and 009 highlights the uncertainty of a Hudson Strait ice stream grounded at the shelf edge during DC-2 and DC-1.

We express our deepest thanks to B. MacLean of GSC, Atlantic for allowing us to use the cores and for helping us to develop a long-term knowledge of this area. Helpful reviews were provided by B. MacLean, D. Anderson, F. Hall and W. Manley. Discussions with B. MacLean and M. Hald were very helpful and are much appreciated. This research was supported by grants NSF/OPP-9224251 and NSF/OPP-9321135.

References

AKSU, A. E. & MUDIE, P. J. 1985. Late Quaternary stratigraphy and palaeoecology of northwest Labrador Sea. *Marine Micropalaeontology*, **9**, 537–557.

ANDREWS, J. T. 1994. Wisconsinan late-glacial environmental change on the southeast Baffin shelf, southeast Baffin Island and northern Labrador. *Journal of Quaternary Science*, **9**, 179–183.

—— & TEDESCO, K. 1992. Detrital carbonate-rich sediments, northwestern Labrador Sea: implications for ice-sheet dynamics and iceberg rafting (Heinrich) events in the North Atlantic. *Geology*, **20**, 1087–1090.

——, OSTERMAN, L. E., JENNINGS, A. E., SYVITSKI, J. P. M., MILLER, G. H. & WEINER, N. 1996. Abrupt changes in marine conditions, Sunneshine Fiord, eastern Baffin Island, N.W.T. (ca.. 66° N) during the last deglacial transition: Links to the Younger Dryas ice-rafting and cold-event, and Heinrich H-0. *This volume.*

——, BOND, G., JENNINGS, A. E., KERWIN, M., KIRBY, M., MACLEAN, B., MANLEY, W. & MILLER, G. H. 1995. A Heinrich like event, H-0 (DC-0): source(s) for detrital carbonate in the North Atlantic during the Younger Dryas chron. *Paleoceanography*, **10**, 943–952.

——, ERLENKEUSER, H., EVANS, L. W., BRIGGS, W. M. & JULL, A. J. T. 1991. Meltwater and

deglaciation, SE Baffin Shelf (NE margin Laurentide Ice Sheet) between 13.5 and 7 ka: from O and C stable isotopic data. *Paleoceanography*, **5**, 621–637.

——, ——, TEDESCO, K., AKSU, A. E. & JULL, A. J. T. 1994a. Late Quaternary (Stage 2 and 3) meltwater and Heinrich events, northwest Labrador Sea. *Quaternary Research*, **41**, 26–34.

——, EVANS, L. W., WILLIAMS, K. M., BRIGGS, W. M., JULL, A. J. T., ERLENKEUSER, H. & HARDY, I. 1990. Cryosphere/ocean interactions at the margin of the Laurentide Ice Sheet during the Younger Dryas Chron: SE Baffin Shelf, Northwest Territories. *Paleoceanography*, **5**, 921–935.

——, SHILTS, W. W. & MILLER, G. H. 1983. Multiple deglaciations of the Hudson Bay Lowlands, Canada, since deposition of the Missinaibi (Last-Interglacial?) Formation. *Quaternary Research*, **19**, 18–37.

——, TEDESCO, K., BRIGGS, W. M. & EVANS, L. W. 1994b. Sediments, sedimentation rates, and environments, southeast Baffin shelf and northwest Labrador Sea, 8–26 ka. *Canadian Journal of Earth Sciences*, **31**, 90–103.

——, —— & JENNINGS, A. E. 1993. Heinrich events: chronology and processes, east-central Larentide Ice Sheet and NW Labrador Sea. *In*: PELTIER, W. R. (ed.) *Ice in the Climate System*. NATO ASI Series, **I12**, Springer Verlag, Berlin, Heidelberg, 167–186.

BILODEAU, G., DE VERNAL, A. & HILLAIRE-MARCEL, C. 1994. Benthic foraminiferal assemblages in Labrador Sea sediments: relations with deep-water mass changes since deglaciation. *Canadian Journal of Earth Sciences*, **31**, 128–138.

BINDSCHADLER, R. A. 1991. *West Antarctic Ice Sheet Initiative*. Vol. 1. *Science and Implementation Plan*. NASA Conference Publication, **3115**.

BOND, G., BROECKER, W., JOHNSEN, S., MCMANUS, J., LABEYRIE, L., JOUZEL, J. & BONAMI, G. 1993. Correlations between climate records from North Atlantic sediments and Greenland ice. *Nature*, **365**, 143–147.

——, HEINRICH, H. & 12 others 1992. Evidence for massive discharges of icebergs into the North Atlantic Ocean during the last glacial period. *Nature*, **360**, 245–249.

—— & LOTTI, R. 1995. Iceberg discharges into the North Atlantic on millennial time scales during the last glaciation. *Science*, **267**, 1005–1010.

BROECKER, W., BOND, G., KLAS, M., CLARK, E. & MCMANUS, J. 1992. Origin of the northern Atlantic's Heinrich events. *Climate Dynamics*, **6**, 265–273.

DOWDESWELL, J. A., MASLIN, M. A., ANDREWS, J. T. & MCCAVE, I. N. 1995. Iceberg production, debris rafting, and the extent and thickness of Heinrich layers (H-1, H-2) in the North Atlantic sediments. *Geology*, **23**, 301–304s.

DREIMANIS, A. 1962. Quantitative gasometric determination of calcite and dolomite by using Chittick apparatus. *Journal of Sedimentary Petrology*, **32**, 520–529.

EVANS, L. W. 1990. *Late Quaternary stratigraphy of the Hatton and Resolution Basins, Southeast Baffin Island Shelf, N.W.T., Canada.* MSc Thesis, University of Colorado, Boulder.

HALD, M., STEINSUND, P. I., DOKKEN, T., KORSUN, S., POLYAK, L. & ASPELI, R. 1993. Recent and Later Quaternary distribution of *Elphidium excavatum* f. *clavata* in Arctic Seas. *Cushman Foundation Special Publication,* **32**.

HEINRICH, H. 1988. Origin and consequences of cyclic ice rafting in the northeast Atlantic Ocean during the past 130,000 years. *Quaternary Research,* **29**, 142–152.

HESSE, R. 1992. Continental slope sedimentation adjacent to an ice margin. I. Seismic facies of Labrador slope. *Geo-Marine Letters,* **12**, 189–199.

——, CHOUGH, S. K. & RAKOFSKY, A. 1987. Northwest Atlantic Mid-Ocean Channel of the Labrador Sea. V. Sedimentology of a giant deep-sea channel. *Canadian Journal of Earth Sciences,* **24**, 1595–1624.

HILLAIRE-MARCEL, C., DE VERNAL, A., BILODEAU, G. & WU, G. 1994. Isotope stratigraphy, sedimentation rates, deep circulation, and carbonate events in the Labrador Sea during the last 200 ka. *Canadian Journal of Earth Sciences,* **31**, 63–89.

JENNINGS, A. E. 1989. *Late Quaternary history of Cumberland Sound, Baffin Island, Arctic Canada.* PhD Thesis, University of Colorado, Boulder.

——1993. The Quaternary history of Cumberland Sound, southeastern Baffin Island: the marine evidence. *Géographie physique et Quaternaire,* **47**, 21–42.

JOSENHANS, H. W., ZEVENHUIZEN, J. & KLASSEN, R. A. 1986. The Quaternary geology of the Labrador shelf. *Canadian Journal of Earth Sciences,* **23**, 1190–1213.

KAUFMAN, D. S. & WILLIAMS, K. M. (compilers) 1992. *Radiocarbon Date List VII: Baffin Island, N.W.T., Canada.* INSTAAR Occasional Paper, **48**, Institute of Arctic and Alpine Research, University of Colorado, Boulder.

——, MILLER, G. H., STRAVERS, J. A. & ANDREWS, J. T. 1993. An abrupt early Holocene (9.9–9.6 kyr BP) ice stream advance at the mouth of Hudson Strait, Arctic Canada. *Geology,* **21**, 1063–1066.

KIRBY, M. E. 1995. Clay-size carbonate in the Northwest North Atlantic, Labrador Sea: an indicator for Laurentide Ice Sheet dynamics and ice margin position. *In: 25th Arctic Workshop, Centre d'Études Nordiques, Université Laval, Québec, Canada, 16–18 March 1995,* 95.

LABERG, J. S. & VORREN, T. O. 1993. A late Pleistocene submarine slide on the Bear Island Trough Mouth Fan. *Geo-Marine Letters,* **13**, 227–234.

MACAYEAL, D. R. 1993. Binge/purge oscillations of the Laurentide Ice Sheet as a cause of the North Atlantic's Heinrich events. *Palaeoceanography,* **8**, 775–784.

MACLEAN, B. 1985. Geology of the Baffin Island shelf.

In: ANDREWS, J. T. (ed.) *Quaternary Environments: Eastern Canadian Arctic, Baffin Bay and Western Greenland.* Allen & Unwin, Boston, 154–178.

——, SRIVASTAVA, S. P. & HAWORTH, R. T. 1982. Bedrock structures off Cumberland Sound, Baffin Island Shelf: core sample and geophysical data. *In*: EMBRY, A. F. & BALKWILL, H. R. (eds) *Arctic Geology and Geophysics.* Canadian Society of Petroleum Geologists, Memoir, **8**, 279–295.

——, VILKS, G. & DEONARINE, B. 1992. Depositional environments and history of late Quaternary sediments in Hudson Strait and Ungava Bay: further evidence from seismic and biostratigraphic data. *Géographie physique et Quaternaire,* **46**, 311–329.

——, WILLIAMS, G. L., JENNINGS, A. E. & BLAKENEY, C. 1986*a*. Bedrock and surficial geology of Cumberland Sound, N.W.T. *Current Research, Part B.* Geological Survey of Canada, Paper, **86-1B**, 605–615.

——, ——, SANFORD, B. V., KLASSEN, R. A., BLAKENEY, C. & JENNINGS, A. E. 1986*b*. A reconnaissance of the bedrock and surficial geology of Hudson Strait, N.W.T. *Current Research, Part B.* Geological Survey of Canada, Paper, **86-1B**, 617–635.

MILLER, G. H. & KAUFMAN, D. S. 1990. Rapid fluctuations of the Laurentide Ice Sheet at the mouth of Hudson Strait: new evidence for ocean/ice sheet interactions as a control on the Younger Dryas. *Paleoceanography,* **9**, 907–919.

NAGY, J. 1965. Foraminifera in some bottom samples from shallow waters in Vestspitsbergen. *Norsk Polarinstitut Arbok,* **1963**, 109–125.

OSTERMAN, L. E. 1984. Benthic foraminiferal zonations of a glacial/interglacial transition from Frobisher Bay, Baffin Island, Northwest Territories, Canada. *In: Benthos'83; 2nd International Symposium on Benthic Foraminifera, Pau, April 1983,* 471–476.

PIPER, D. J. W., MUDIE, P. J., FADER, G. B., JOSENHANS, H. W., MACLEAN, B. & VILKS, G. 1990. Quaternary Geology. *In*: KEEN, M. J. & WILLIAMS, G. L. (eds) *Geology of the Continental Margin of Eastern Canada.* Geological Society of America, The Geology of North America, **I-1**, 475–607.

PRAEG, D. B., MACLEAN, B., HARDY, I. A. & MUDIE, P. J. 1986. *Quaternary Geology of the Southeast Baffin Island Continental Shelf, N.W.T.* Geological Society of Canada, Paper, **85-14**.

RASMUSSEN, T. L., VAN WEERING, TJ. C. E. & LABEYRIE, L. 1995. Paleoceanography of the Faeroe-Shetland Channel: correlation to continental records. *In: QRA Annual Discussion Meeting 1995. The Lateglacial Paleoceanography of the North Atlantic Margins, the Royal Society of Edinburgh & the Grant Institute, University of Edinburgh, 5–7 January 1995.*

SANCETTA, C. 1992. Primary production in the glacial North Atlantic and North Pacific oceans. *Nature,* **360**, 249–251.

SCHAFER, C. T. & COLE, F. E. 1982. Living benthic foraminifera distributions on the continental slope and rise east of Newfoundland, Canada. *Geological Society of America Bulletin*, **93**, 207–217.

SCOTT, D. B. & VILKS, G. 1991. Benthonic foraminifera in the surface sediments of the deep-sea Arctic Ocean. *Journal of Foraminiferal Research*, **21**, 20–38.

STRAVERS, J. A., MILLER, G. H. & KAUFMAN, D. S. 1992. Late glacial ice margins and deglacial chronology for southeastern Baffin Island and Hudson Strait, eastern Canadian Arctic. *Canadian Journal of Earth Sciences*, **29**, 1000–1017.

TEDESCO, K. A. 1993. *Late Quaternary palaeoceanography of the northwest Labrador Sea*. MSc Thesis, University of Colorado, Boulder.

THOMAS, F. C., MEDIOLI, F. S. & SCOTT, D. B. 1990. Holocene and latest Wisconsinan benthic foraminiferal assemblages and palaeocirculation history, lower Scotian slope and rise. *Journal of Foraminiferal Research*, **20**, 212–245.

VILKS, G., MACLEAN, B., DEONARINE, B., CURRIE, C. G. & MORAN, K. 1989. Late Quaternary paleoceanography and sedimentary environments in Hudson Strait. *Géographie physique et Quaternaire*, **43**, 161–178.

VORREN, T. O. & KRISTOFFERSEN, Y. 1986. Late Quaternary glaciation in the south western Barents Sea. *Boreas*, **15**, 51–59.

WILLIAMS, K. M., SHORT, S. K., ANDREWS, J. T., JENNINGS, A. E., MODE, W. N. & SYVITSKI, J. P. M. 1995. The Eastern Canadian Arctic at *c*. 6 ka: a time of transition. *Géographie physique et Quaternaire*, **49**, 13–27.

Palaeoceanographic information derived from acoustic surveys of glaciated continental margins: examples from eastern Canada

JAMES P. M. SYVITSKI[1], C. F. MICHAEL LEWIS & DAVID J. W. PIPER

Geological Survey of Canada-Atlantic, PO Box 1006, Dartmouth, Canada B2Y 4A2
[1] *Present address: Institute of Arctic and Alpine Research,*
University of Colorado at Boulder, Boulder, CO 80309–0026, USA

Abstract: Much palaeoceanographic information can be gleaned from seismic, sidescan and bathymetric data on glaciated continental shelves. High-resolution seismic reflection surveys of regional ice terminus features define palaeo-ice margins, datable using interfingering ice-proximal glacimarine deposits. Isopach maps show differences in regional accumulation rates of sediments during deglaciation phases and help locate positions of former glacifluvial discharge outlets. Maps of ice-distal glacimarine muds suggest that surface currents carrying buoyant plumes of glacial flour may extend >100 km from an ice margin. Transport and melt of icebergs controlled by circulation of deeper outer shelf and slope currents and episodic storms can result in a glacial influence >1000 km from the ice margin, but most iceberg-rafted sedimentation occurs within a few hundred kilometres of calving. The direction of these palaeo-mid-depth currents may be obtained from statistical analysis of relict iceberg scour patterns and from sediment dispersal patterns. The geometry of glacimarine deposits commonly suggests that there was water column stratification with associated weak near-seafloor currents. Comparison of the shape of glacimarine and post-glacial sediment packages shows that in many places the tidal current intensity has increased through the Holocene, reflecting sea-level change on the shelf.

Understanding how oceans operated in the past is the science of palaeoceanography. Most palaeoceanographic studies involve the interpretation of proxy environmental indicators from cores of the ocean floor, from which information on ocean climate and water masses may be extracted. Proxy indicators include a variety of microfossil groups and chemical indicators. In this paper, we point out how important palaeoceanographic information can be obtained from acoustic surveys, principally high-resolution seismic reflection profiling, but also sidescan and swath bathymetry mapping. Such acoustic data can provide important spatial and regional data lacking from studies of cores, particularly on the location of ice margins, the flux of sediment from the land to the ocean, changes in current patterns on shelves and fluctuations in sea level. Similar techniques can be applied to large glaciated lakes.

Methods

Geophysical data reported in this paper were acquired mostly over the last five years off eastern Canada and in the Canadian Great Lakes (Fig. 1), although arguments and summary figures include information collected by the Geological Survey of Canada over two decades. Details of geophysical techniques are provided in cited original sources: we present a brief summary in the following.

Seismic data were collected by very high vertical resolution (± 0.15 m) Chirp Sonar (± 0.25 m), Hunted Deep-tow and IKB-Seistec boomers, or single-channel, high-resolution (± 3 m) 10 and 40 in^3 sleeve guns. The Huntec Deep-tow signal is propagated below the influence of waves and other surface noise and is motion-compensated. The surface-towed Seistec system can operate in water depths of less than 1 m thus aiding the correlation of terrestrial and marine stratigraphies; it is a line-in-cone hydrophone system that reduces noise and the secondary returns from side echoes. The acoustic data were largely collected digitally, with post-processing techniques used to reduce noise, augment reflections from geological structures and to allow three-dimensional presentation of data.

Most of the iceberg scour marks discussed here were imaged using the Bio sidescan sonar with a composite swath width up to 1.5 km (Todd *et al.* 1988). Sidescan surveys used to augment other seismic reflection targets included 100/500 kHz Klein^{TM} 595 towfish. At the frequencies (50–500 kHz) and ranges (100–1000 m) commonly used for reconnaissance mapping of

From Andrews, J. T., Austin, W. E. N., Bergsten, H. & Jennings, A. E. (eds), 1996, *Late Quaternary Palaeoceanography of the North Atlantic Margins*, Geological Society Special Publication No. 111, pp. 51–76.

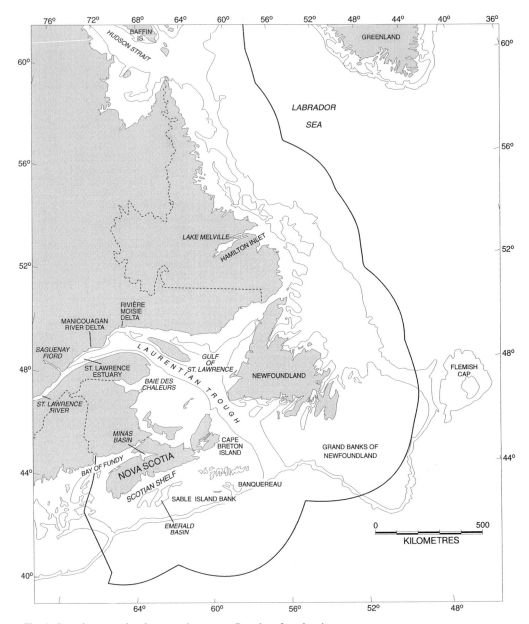

Fig. 1. Location map showing areas in eastern Canada referred to in text.

ice–seafloor interaction data, the sonars are capable of imaging textural contrasts (e.g. boulders and gravel versus sand; or broken consolidated clay blocks versus smooth mud surfaces) and distinct elevation changes relative to the seafloor (e.g. troughs and depressions or berms and ridges with relief of a few metres or less and horizontal dimensions of a few tens to a hundred metres). Analyses of scour dimensions

and azimuths are described in detail in Todd *et al.* (1988).

Swath survey data were collected using a Simrad EM100 multibeam sounder operated at 95 kHz. Bottom coverage along a swath is 1.7 times the water depth across track, using 32 narrow (2.5°) beams. The line spacings used to achieve 100% coverage, given the shelf water depths, were 50–100 m.

Ice margins

Extent of former ice sheets

Ice-contact sediments on glaciated continental shelves provide direct evidence of the extent of a former ice sheet (Andrews *et al.* 1991). Mapped from acoustic records, they are characterized by moderate to strong tone (backscatter), poor to absent stratification (lacking coherent reflections), and by upper and lower bounding surfaces that may be complex and irregular, with total relief typially < 100 m (Syvitski 1991; 1993) (Fig. 2). Two ice-contact facies, ice-deposited and ice-loaded, record the presence of grounded glacial ice. The 'ice-loaded' facies has basin-fill geometry and may consist of glacial, proglacial and post-glacial sediments, that together have been sculpted and loaded by an advancing ice sheet or ice stream (Fig. 2A). The 'ice-deposited' facies tends to have a constructional geometry and is composed of glacigenic deposits, including till, eskers, drumlins, moraines or grounding line sediments (Fig. 2B). Although it is not always possible to differentiate between ice-loaded and ice-deposited facies based on acoustic or lithological evidence (Syvitski 1991), both provide evidence for the former presence of an ice sheet.

The ice-loaded facies may contain microfossils that were deposited in proglacial sediment, in contrast with the ice-deposited facies where contemporary microfossils are normally absent: both facies may contain reworked fossils. Radiocarbon ages of ice-contact sediments are difficult to interpret because reworked microfossils and organic carbon result in ages that are 'too old'. A more reliable method is to date proximal glacimarine sediments identified on acoustic records that interfinger with ice-contact sediments deposited at the terminus of a former ice sheet (e.g. Gipp & Piper 1990; Gipp 1994) or, in more coastal settings, associated glacimarine sediments exposed on land due to isostatic uplift (Stravers & Syvitski 1989; Hein *et al.* 1993). Age determination on the more deeply buried (older) proglacial sediments constrains the time when the former ice sheet arrived, whereas the younger glacimarine sediments provide evidence of the onset of ice margin retreat.

Seismic profiles define the limit of ice-contact deposits and thus the former limit of grounded ice (Fig. 2B). On the Baffin Shelf, for example, Laurentide ice reached the shelf slope break >50 000 years ago, but during the latest Laurentide ice advance (12–14 ka) was limited to fjords and shelf-crossing troughs (Andrews *et al.* 1991). Further to the south, the Hudson Strait ice stream advanced to the shelf–slope break, retreating at about 14.5 ka (Andrews *et al.* 1991; B. MacLean pers. comm. 1995). On the Labrador Shelf, Late Wisconsinan ice reached the shelf break only within the cross-shelf troughs, and was completely contained within the inner shelf of the Grand Banks (Josenhans & Fader 1989). Within the Gulf of St Lawrence, Late Wisconsinan ice was confined to a terminal position 600 km inland from the shelf–slope break (*c.* 14.5 ka) (Dyke & Prest 1987; Syvitski & Praeg 1989). Off Nova Scotia, grounded ice reached the shelf break at about 18 ka. Off southern Newfoundland, Late Wisconsin ice reached the shelf break, where seismic records show that ice-contact sediments on the upper continental slope pass downslope into more acoustically transparent debris flow deposits (Bonifay & Piper 1988; also see Stewart and Stoker 1991; Fig. 3).

The abrupt onset of slope valleys and canyons seaward of the shelf break may also relate to the maximum ice extent and discharge points of subglacial meltwater (Piper 1988). However, it is generally not possible to identify which particular ice advance was responsible for the various canyons as slope readjustment would continue long after an ice sheet retreated and the sea level recovered (Ross *et al.* 1994; Mulder & Moran 1995).

Dynamics of former ice-sheet margins

Ice sheets with marine termini mostly ablate through iceberg calving or by meltwater discharged directly into the ocean (Syvitski 1989). The type of sediment deposits fronting the marine margin of an ice sheet depends on glaciological, oceanographic and geological parameters (Syvitski 1994). Three modern end-member settings are recognized: (1) the polar ice-shelf settings of Antarctica, where diamicton is released directly from meltout at the grounding line (Alley 1991; Domack *et al.* 1994); (2) the sub-polar fjords of East Greenland, where iceberg melt controls the release of sediment to the seafloor (Andrews *et al.* 1994; Dowdeswell *et al.* 1994; Syvitski *et al.* 1996); and (3) the temperate tidewater glaciers of southeast Alaska, where the discharge of meltwater near the grounding line results in extremely high sedimentation rates (Powell 1990). Ice-proximal deposits accumulate under the direct influence of processes restricted to the ice margin. They typically accumulate within a few kilometres of the margin, but the extent depends on the size and dynamics of the ice margin. As such, they

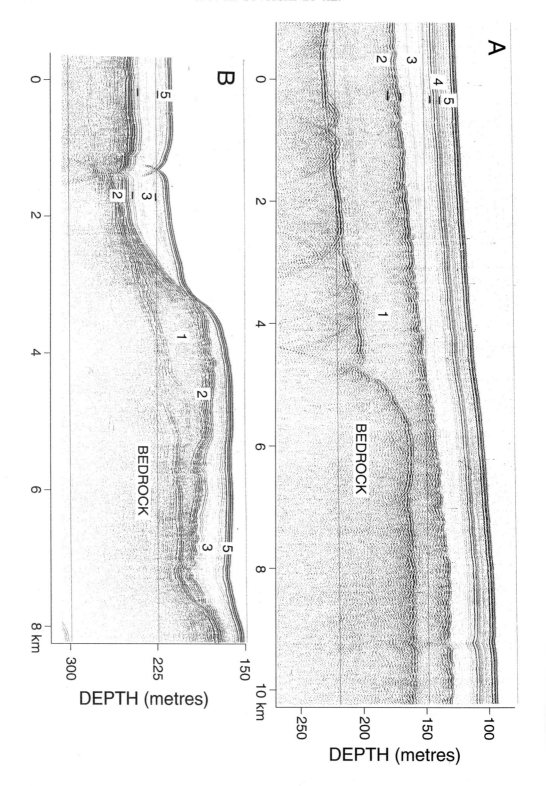

may provide important information on the relative importance of glacial meltwater compared with iceberg calving at the margin and evidence for the stability of the ice margin.

Ice-proximal glacimarine sediments at ice margins dominated by melting typically consist of layered gravelly sands and muds. On seismic records (Syvitski & Praeg 1989), these sediments are characterized by strong, closely spaced reflections and two ice-proximal glacimarine facies have been distinguished. An 'ice-retreat' facies forms by the deposition of glacimarine sediment close to an ice margin undergoing rapid retreat without opportunity to build large ice-contact fans (Fig. 4). The mapped acoustic unit is generally conformable with the underlying sediment or bedrock (Fig. 4C and 4D). A 'stable-margin' facies forms as a wedge-shaped deposit that reflects the recognized exponential decrease in the rates of sedimentation with distance from an equilibrium ice margin (Andrews & Syvitski 1994). The stable-margin facies generally shows acoustic evidence of slumps and ponded sequences (i.e. turbidites), supporting the notion of high rates of ice-marginal sediment accumulation over a relatively long period of time (see unit 2b on Fig. 4B).

Isopach maps produced from seismic profiles can readily differentiate between these ice-proximal facies and provide an insight into the discharge dynamics at former ice margins. The discontinuous distribution of ice-proximal sediments in the northwestern Gulf of St Lawrence, for example, imply large distances between ice-front discharge outlets or episodes of rapid retreat of the ice front (Syvitski & Praeg 1989). At the head of the Laurentian Trough (Fig. 4A) is one of the world's largest ice-proximal moraines, having been fed by the enormous Laurentian ice stream during the Late Wisconsinan (Syvitski & Praeg 1989): over 600 km^3 of ice-proximal sediment were deposited between 12.5 and 13.5 ka. The moraine reached a maximum thickness of 250 m and resulted in an area-averaged accumulation rate of 12 cm/year. This may be compared with the ice-proximal deposits flooring the nearby northwestern Gulf of St Lawrence, where slower ice flow into a diverging glacier margin produced an area-averaged accumulation rate of just 0.2 cm/year

between 12 and 14 ka (Syvitski 1993; Hein et al. 1993) (Fig. 5).

The coarsest ice-proximal sediments are generally grounding line fan deposits (Powell 1990) providing good evidence as to where major meltwater outlets once discharged at the margin of a former ice sheet (Syvitski 1989). During their growth, slope failure of the grounding line fans can generate numerous turbidity currents that may travel tens of kilometres from the ice margin (Hein et al. 1993).

Relict tunnel valleys, interpreted from digital bathymetric data collected on the Scotian Shelf (Fig. 6), provide direct evidence of the direction of subglacial meltwater discharge (Loncarevic et al. 1992) that may relate to the position of palaeo-ice divides (Stea et al. 1992). Valleys on the inner to mid-shelf with an irregular thalweg or anastomosing pattern are interpreted as Late Wisconsinan subglacial tunnel valleys (Barnes & Piper 1978; Loncarevic et al. 1992), reflecting basal melting of ice and perhaps the catastrophic release of meltwater. Buried valleys beneath Sable Island Bank (Boyd et al. 1988) and Banquereau (Amos & Knoll 1987) are interpreted to have a similar origin, but are older. The chaotic fill (irregular acoustic stratification) in the younger tunnel valleys may represent final ice-contact deposition, followed by rapid ice retreat and post-glacial mud deposition (Loncarevic et al. 1992).

Iceberg–seafloor interactions

At times of rapid sea-level rise and at colder high-latitude ice margins, the ice margin may be dominated by iceberg calving. Ice-proximal deposits may accumulate slowly, or even be unrecognizable at times of rapid retreat. Nevertheless, acoustic data provides important information about the source and dispersal pathways of icebergs. Much of our information comes from studies of the contemporary effects of icebergs.

Sidescan sonar is the instrumentation which inaugurated (c. 1970) the recognition and study of the effects of ice–seafloor interaction (Fig. 7). The marine research community soon reported findings of drift ice markings on the seafloor: Pelletier (1971) and Pelletier & Shearer (1972)

Fig. 2. High-resolution seismic reflection profiles of common ice-contact acoustic facies. (A) Ice-loaded glacimarine sediments (unit 1) underlying a complete deglacial stratigraphic sequence (units 2–5) of Late Wisconsinan sediments deposited within the Lower St Lawrence estuary (see Syvitski & Praeg 1989). (B) Wedge-shaped terminal moraine (unit 1) (10–40 m thick, 1–4 km wide, >120 km long) marks the most seaward extent of the Late Wisconsinan ice sheet south of Sept-Iles Quebec, in the northwestern corner of the Gulf of St Lawrence. The moraine overlies bedrock and is capped with glacimarine (units 2 and 3) and post-glacial (unit 5) sediments (see Hein et al. 1993).

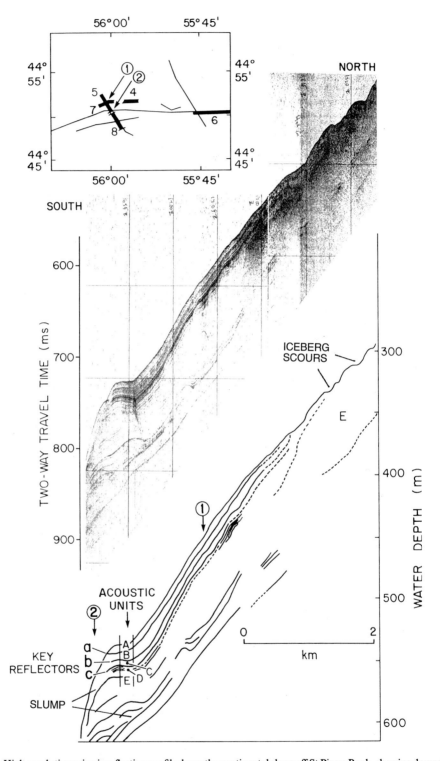

Fig. 3. High-resolution seismic reflection profile down the continental slope off St Pierre Bank, showing downslope changes in the character of unit E (ice-contact sediments interpreted as till) (after Bonifay & Piper 1988).

from the Canadian Beaufort Sea, and Reimnitz *et al.* (1972) from the Alaskan Beaufort Sea. Berkson & Clay (1973) interpreted the action of former icebergs in Lake Superior on the basis of intersecting and parallel grooves on the lake bed imaged in sidescan sonar records. Belderson *et al.* (1973) and Belderson & Wilson (1973) recognized palaeo-iceberg keel marks from sidescan sonar data collected in the eastern North Atlantic Ocean in depths down to 500 m west of the British Isles and off southern Norway.

The palaeoceanographic significance of iceberg furrows was quickly recognized. Iceberg furrows in the western North Atlantic Ocean, off northern Newfoundland, had an overall north–south trend, which was attributed to the southerly drift of the Labrador Current (Harris & Jollymore 1974; Harris 1975). A similar finding off southern Newfoundland, where modern iceberg incursions are rare, led King (1976) to recognize a relict Late Pleistocene population of iceberg furrows with significance for the history of deglaciation and sea-level change. Lewis *et al.* (1980) demonstrated the widespread occurrence of iceberg scour marks on the west Greenland and eastern Canadian continental shelves and noted their general conformity with the West Greenland, Baffin and Labrador Currents. Lien (1983*a*; 1983*b*) identified on the Norwegian shelf and slope ploughmarks left by drifting icebergs which had originated from former calving margins of northern European glaciers. Lien demonstrated the dependence of the iceberg scour distribution on water depth, sediment type and regional topography, and recognized the orientation of the relict iceberg furrows as indicators of former ocean current directions.

Once the characteristic morphology of ice-scoured seafloor was established, it became feasible to investigate the subsurface for episodes of ice-keel interaction. Stoker & Long (1984) used high-resolution seismic reflection profiles to identify and map a buried ice-scoured surface in the central North Sea dated to 17–18 ka. Similarly, Gipp (1993; 1994) inferred a regime of palaeo-iceberg scouring within the sediments of the Scotian shelf. Geological mapping of the eastern Canadian shelf further advanced knowledge of the iceberg scour distribution showing, for example, that a relict population of scours continued down the upper slope to water depths of about 650 m off Flemish Cap (Monahan & MacNab 1975), about 700 m off Labrador (Josenhans *et al.* 1986) and 750 m or more off southeast Baffin Island (Praeg *et al.* 1986; 1987).

It is remarkable that all of the foregoing interpretations of ice-scoured seafloor morphology were presented without ambiguity. This is attributed to the fact that because long linear ridge and trough features were so clearly imaged in regions of present and former glaciations or sea-ice concentrations, no other interpretation was viable. The clear imaging of features formed by ice keels is owing, in part, to the suitability of the scale of mapping provided by the generally available sidescan sonars. The swath width and resolving power of the sonars are well matched to the common widths (<10–100 m) and depths (up to a few metres) of sea ice and iceberg furrows on the seafloor.

The continental shelf of the northwest North Atlantic Ocean in Baffin Bay and Labrador Sea is presently transited by icebergs from the Greenland ice sheet (Fig. 8). The water equivalent of the output of icebergs today from Greenland (approximately 310 km^3 year^{-1}; Reeh 1989) is about the same as the annual discharge of the St Lawrence River to the North Atlantic, both important contributions of freshwater which influence the present water mass structures of the northwest Atlantic. In some years, more than 2000 icebergs survive the transit from Baffin Bay and pass south of latitude 48° N to the Grand Banks of Newfoundland, according to counts by the International Ice Patrol. These areas, with their occurrences of modern iceberg scour, have yielded information which confirms the previous interpretations of drift ice scouring and provides new insights into the processes of iceberg–seafloor interaction (Woodworth-Lynas *et al.* 1985; Hodgson *et al.* 1988; Lewis *et al.* 1988; Lewis and Woodworth-Lynas 1990).

A distinction can be made between iceberg scours in areas dominated by rotary tidal currents (curved furrows) and those in areas dominated by unidirectional oceanic currents (straighter, parallel furrows) (Todd *et al.* 1988). A population of mixed scour orientations may also be characteristic of shelves dominated by variable storm-driven currents. It is also clear that scours run up and down the bottom slopes because most icebergs on more southern shelves are able to tilt easily and adjust their draft, as they scour, to changes of several metres in the seafloor topography beneath them (Woodworth-Lynas *et al.* 1985; Hodgson *et al.* 1988). Seafloor pits up to 10 m deep are formed by icebergs, in addition to the more common furrow, some by tidal pumping and wallowing after being driven hard aground, and others by splitting and rolling energetically into the bottom (Hodgson *et al.* 1988; Parrott *et al.* 1990; Lever *et al.* 1991; Barrie *et al.* 1992). Iceberg splitting and rolling result from rapid

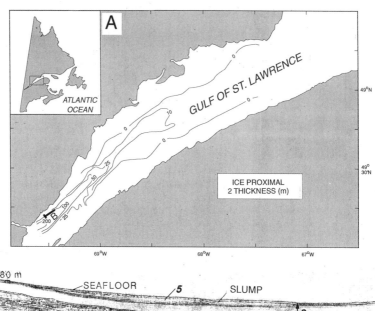

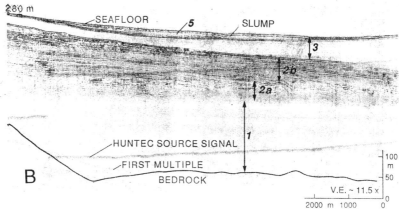

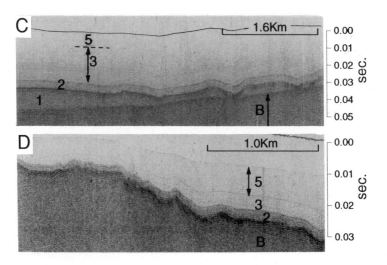

melting and deterioration, thus the occurrence of seafloor iceberg pits may imply an oceanographic environment of wind waves (no sea ice), warm surface conditions and high summer insolation.

The iceberg drift system off western Greenland and eastern Canada compares well with the cumulated evidence of individual satellite-tracked iceberg trajectories (Fig. 8). These data also revealed that large icebergs spend from 8 to 88% of their one to three year life spans aground in various sites along the continental shelf. The distribution of confirmed iceberg groundings (Fig. 8) occurs throughout the Greenland–eastern Canada iceberg drift system, showing that iceberg scour is probable wherever bathymetry and icebergs with similar draft co-occur.

The overall record of iceberg scour based on acoustic and seismic surveys off eastern Canada and western Greenland is summarized in Fig. 9. The drafts of modern 'open ocean' icebergs rarely exceed 200 m based on measurements of >500 large icebergs by the oil and gas industry between 1970 and 1990. Thus measurements of scours in these water depths reflect the modern iceberg regime. Scour widths, reflecting the dimensions of iceberg keels, are similar throughout this depth range (see width histograms for <100 and 100–200 m depths). The maximum scour depths appear to be 0.5–1 m deeper for the scours in 100–200 m water depth, possibly due to the greater momentum of larger icebergs if the strength of seafloor sediment is similar throughout. The relict scours, in water depths >200 m show greater maximum widths, possibly reflecting the action of larger icebergs from Late Pleistocene calving margins of the Laurentide and Greenland ice sheets. The rose diagrams of scour trend (Fig. 9) are consistent with the trajectories and drift system of modern icebergs. Exceptions occur at the mouth of Hudson Strait where iceberg scour trends follow tidal currents which are exceptionally strong, and on Grand Bank where the ocean currents are weak and the scour trends are formed by icebergs influenced by tidal and storm-driven currents.

Palaeohydrology

Marine paraglacial deposits result from the very high rates of sediment flux during early post-glacial times as a result of sparse vegetation and large amounts of unconsolidated glacial detritus in river basins. This peak sediment discharge in the early post-glacial period decreased to much lower values in the mid to late Holocene (Forbes 1984; Forbes & Taylor 1987; Syvitski et al. 1987; Forbes & Syvitski 1995). The initial peak supply is typically associated with rapidly ablating terrestrial ice sheets, commonly well inland from the shoreline, and enhanced sediment supply may continue for a few thousand years. Sea-level fluctuations also play a part in the development of marine paraglacial deposits, when downcutting into earlier, deltaic deposits may further augment sediment delivery to the sea.

Paraglacial deposits have been explicitly identified in coastal and marine settings using seismic profiling techniques (Syvitski & Praeg 1989). They are generally characterized by strong and dense acoustic stratification and a ponded bedding style, although the unit may distally be conformable over glacimarine muds and laterally grade into post-glacial muds (Fig. 10). Marine paraglacial deposits commonly contain unstratified lobes representing syn-depositional mass flows, as well as buried channels and shear planes related to submarine slides (Fig. 10).

Many modern deltaic environments of Canada are underlain with paraglacial sediments. Along the north shore of the Gulf of St Lawrence, for example, these wedge-shaped deposits extend 50–100 km offshore from initial thicknesses of up to 100 m. The Manicouagan Delta, whose waters flow into the Lower St Lawrence Estuary, has over 85 km^3 of paraglacial material deposited over a 2000 year interval (8.5–10.5 ka) This can be compared with the post-glacial (<8.5 ka) sedimentary cover volume of 10 km^3 (Fig. 10). The areally-averaged sedimentation rates have changed from a high of 3.1 cm/year during the early Holocene paraglacial phase to 0.09 cm/year for the mid to late Holocene post-glacial period.

Fig. 4. Ice-proximal glacimarine sediments as imaged on seismic records. (A) Isopach map of ice-proximal glacimarine sediments within the 5100 km^2 area of the Lower St Lawrence Estuary. The exponential decrease in thickness highlights the position of the Saint-Narcisse Moraine near the mouth of Saguenay fiord (c. 12.5–13.5 ka, Praeg et al. 1992). (B) High-resolution seismic profile (see arrow on A for location of profile) showing both 'retreat' (unit 2A) and 'morainal' (unit 2B) ice-proximal facies (after Syvitski & Praeg 1989). (C) and (D) Two very high resolution examples of the ice-proximal 'retreat' facies, showing conformable nature of sediment deposition (unit 2) over bedrock or ice-contact (unit 1) deposits. In all three seismic examples, unit 2 sediments are overlain by ice-distal (unit 3) and post-glacial (unit 5) sediments.

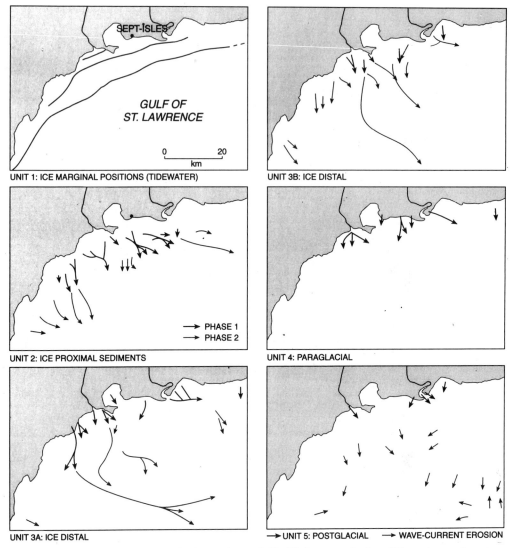

Fig. 5. Generalized transport patterns in the northwest Gulf of St Lawrence for Late Wisconsinan sediments, based on high to very high resolution seismic reflection records (Hein *et al.* 1993). Heavy lines for unit 1 mark the position of ice sheet stillstands between 12 and 14 ka. Thin arrows for unit 2 mark ice-proximal discharge outlets associated with the most seaward terminal moraine (*c.* 14 ka); thicker arrows for a later depositional phases associated with more landward moraines (*c.* 12 ka). Thick arrows for units 3A, 3B (*c.* 9–14 ka) and 4 (*c.* 6.4–9 ka) show the pathways of major sediment input; thin arrows show generalized surface circulation across the open shelf. Thick arrows of unit 5 show major fluvial inputs of post-glacial sediment (<6 ka); thin arrows show direction of wave and current erosion on the continental shelf (<9 ka) which have produced prominent lags on the seafloor.

To estimate the palaeo-discharge during the paraglacial phase, Q_p, the following formula can be used

$$Q_p = \left(\frac{Z_p}{Z_{pg}}\right)^{\frac{1}{b}} Q_{pg}$$

where

$$\frac{Z_p}{Z_{pg}} = \frac{Q_{S_p}}{Q_{S_{pg}}}$$

and Q_{pg} is the mean annual discharge of a river during the post-glacial period, Z_p/Z_{pg} is the

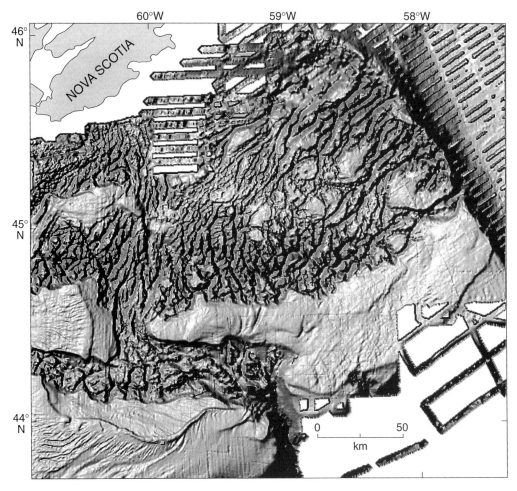

Fig. 6. Shadowgram of detailed (400 × 400 m grid) bathymetry collected between Sable Island and Cape Breton, Nova Scotia. The illumination direction is from the northwest at an elevation of 45°. In this presentation, the continuity of deeply incised valleys can be traced across the survey area. After Loncarevic *et al.* (1992).

ratio of the regionally averaged sedimentation rates between the two sedimentation periods, and provides a good approximation of the ratio of sediment delivery, Q_s, for these two periods. The power coefficient b is from the normal rating curves for rivers where $Q_s = aQ^b$ and a and b are empirical rating coefficients. Typically, values of b range from 2 to 2.5.

Thus for the Manicouagan River, the para-glacial discharge is estimated to have exceeded the post-glacial discharge conditions by a factor of 4.1–5.9 times the modern values. A similar calculation for the Riviere Moisie flowing into the northwest Gulf of St Lawrence suggests river

discharges during the paraglacial phase (10–8 ka) were on average 5.1–7.5 times the post-glacial discharge levels (<8 ka) (Syvitski 1993).

A meltwater sediment load can also be estimated from seismic data by determining the meltwater sediment volume times the regional bulk density divided by the total time of deposition. In a regional sense, the meltwater volume is the volume of ice-proximal and ice-distal glacimarine sediments and paraglacial sediments (i.e. units 2, 3 and 4 on Figs 2, 4 and 10). The areally averaged bulk density and depositional time must be determined from core data. For example, the regional Late Quaternary

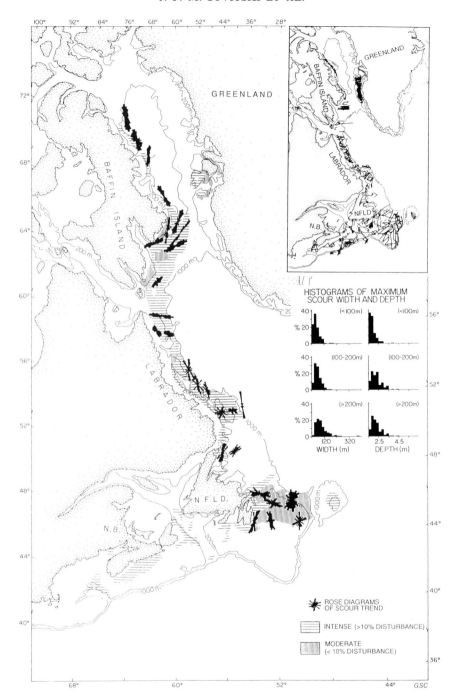

Fig. 9. Distribution of iceberg scours, eastern Canada. Rose diagrams of scour trend and histograms summarizing maximum scour depths and widths in 2 km long sample areas are shown for the continental margin from northern Baffin Island to the northern Grand Banks of Newfoundland for water depths of <100, 100–200 m and >200 m. Abstracted from ice scour databases prepared by d'Apollonia & Lewis (1981), Todd (1984), King & Gillespie (1986), Harris & Jollymore (1974), King (1976), Lewis *et al.* (1977; 1980), Brett & Zarudski (1979), Gustajtis (1979), Barrie (1980), Fader & King (1981) and Lewis & Barrie (1981). Survey lines analysed for ice scour are shown in the inset map. From Lewis and Woodworth-Lynas (1990).

Interpretation of currents from acoustic data

Introduction

Currents acting on continental shelves have many origins, being influenced by the global thermohaline circulation, tidal circulation, wind stress and freshwater discharge. Some acoustic features, such as current scours, record extreme current events, whereas others, such as iceberg scours and fine sediment distribution, may record more 'average' conditions.

Iceberg scour

Iceberg scours near ice margins are generally either rescoured or buried by younger sediments and are only rarely preserved in such a way as to be imaged by sidescan sonar—for example, on morainal ridges (King 1976) or on the continental slope. Where there is sufficient seismic data, it is possible to use seismic data to derive the statistically preferred orientation of buried iceberg scours (Gipp 1993). In this manner, Gipp (1994) was able to demonstrate that icebergs in Emerald Basin, Scotian Shelf, at 15–18 ka, moved in a clockwise circulation pattern (Gipp 1994).

Thickness variations in ice-distal sediments

Current directions can also be inferred from thickness variations in ice-distal sediments. Sedimentary layers deposited as a drape, conformable to the bottom topography, are considered to reflect sedimentation beneath a surface current (Syvitski 1989). The presence of strong bottom currents is also ruled out, for such currents would produce different depositional acoustic facies (onlap, offlap, ponded, wedging, complex). During the deposition of glacimarine sediments distal to the margin of an ice sheet, a very distinctive acoustic unit (unit 3 on Figs 1 and 3) is produced: highly transparent, commonly with few internal reflectors and very conformable to bottom topography. Ice-distal glacimarine deposits of the eastern Canadian margin are typically muddy with a variable amount of ice-rafted debris, deposited principally from meltwater plumes emanating from rapidly ablating ice margins at times of high sea level (Syvitski 1991).

By examining isopach maps of ice-distal deposits, determined from the interpretation of very high resolution seismic records, the sediment transport pathways from known ice-sheet termini can be approximated (Fig. 5).

Hein *et al.* (1993) used this technique to determine the pathways of meltwater plumes emanating from the Late Wisconsinan ice sheet over a 5000 year period (*c.* 9–14 ka) in the northwest Gulf of St Lawrence. Surface circulation in the Gulf during the Late Pleistocene was as a clockwise gyre, changing to be more coast-perpendicular in the early Holocene as a consequence of greater glacifluvial discharge (Hein *et al.* 1993). In the mid to late Holocene, the modern anticlockwise gyre was developed (Fig. 5, Hein *et al.* 1993).

Tidal currents and tidal ranges

Tidal ranges along the eastern margin of Canada have radically changed from the early Holocene period to present day conditions. For example, the Minas Basin, Bay of Fundy, is today the site of the world's largest tides, but had a much smaller tidal range in the early Holocene. It contains a 8 m thick cover of post-glacial sediments over glacimarine sediments (Amos & Long 1980). These post-glacial sediments define an upward coarsening sequence deposited in association with an increasing tidal amplitude, following a period (pre-6300 years BP) of non-tidal conditions (Amos & Long 1980). Over the last 6300 years, the mean sea level has been rising at a rate of 15 cm per century: the tidal range has been increasing at 15 cm per century (Amos 1978). This increase in tidal range and accelerated erosive power has contributed to an order of magnitude increase in annual sediment supply to the basin (Amos & Long 1980).

In recent years, the 'turn-on' effect of these mid-Holocene tidal currents has been observed on seismic records collected from a variety of coastal basins along the eastern Canadian margin: Baie des Chaleurs (Syvitski 1992), northwest Gulf of St Lawrence (Syvitski & Praeg 1989), Hamilton Inlet (Syvitski *et al.* 1993) and Hudson Strait (MacLean *et al.* 1992). However, the association with sea-level fluctuations is much more complex.

Baie des Chaleurs is a large estuary in the Gulf of St Lawrence, 180 km long and 38 km wide. Tidal currents apparently 'turned on' during the middle Holocene, at a time when modern sea levels became established and after a protracted (2000 years) period of rising water levels (Syvitski 1992). In the outer part of the bay, a large tidal channel developed concomitant with the deposition of post-glacial sediments (at 5950 ± 60 years BP according to Rodrigues *et al.* 1993) (Fig. 11B). Surrounding the tidal

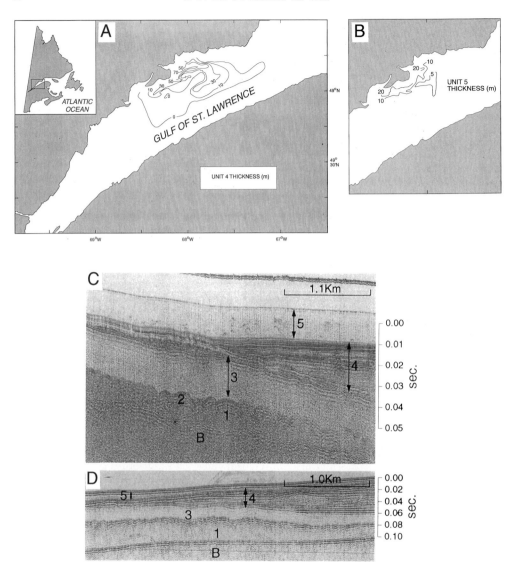

Fig. 10. Paraglacial deposits as imaged on very high resolution seismic records (unit 4) that also highlight other glacigenic units: (1) ice-contact, (2) ice-proximal, (3) ice-distal sediment and (5) post-glacial sediment. (A) Isopach map of 85 km³ of paraglacial sediments, deposited between 8.5 and 10.5 ka BP offshore of the Manicouagan river delta, along the northern margin of the deep (330 m) Lower St Lawrence Estuary. This is compared with (B), an isopach map of 10 km³ postglacial (<8.5 ka BP) deltaic sediments for the same region. (C) A Huntec profile of a thick and ponded paraglacial–deltaic unit 4 (water depth ∼250 m). (D) Further offshore (water depth ∼300 m), the paraglacial unit 4 can be seen to thin seaward (to left) (40 in³ airgun profile).

channel, acoustically transparent post-glacial sediment, comprised of well-bioturbated mud, was deposited under relatively constant sedimentation rates (Rodrigues *et al.* 1993).

In the northwest Gulf of St Lawrence, tidal currents also appear to have turned on sometime in the mid-Holocene (Syvitski & Praeg 1989; their fig. 7B), but the exact timing of the event

remains unknown; according to Rodrigues *et al.* (1993) it occurred at some time since 8000 years BP. Hein *et al.* (1993) suggest that the modern oceanographic conditions in the northwest Gulf appear to have been set up by 6700 years BP, when the sea level was about 30 m higher than present. Like the Bay of Fundy, tidal strength appears to have increased

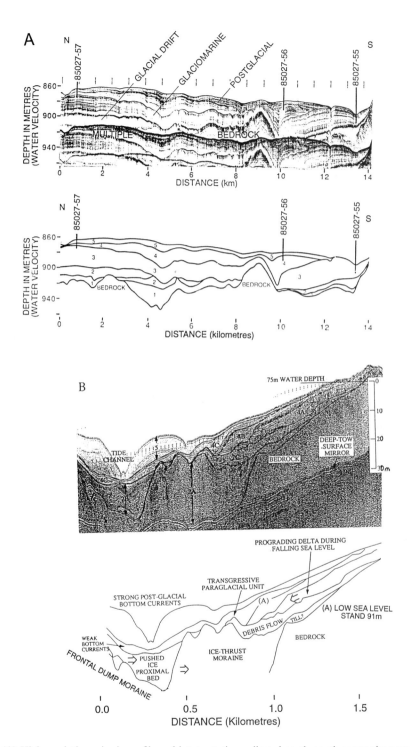

Fig. 11. (A) High-resolution seismic profile and interpretation collected north–south across the western part of the eastern basin in Hudson Strait illustrating seismic units and relationship with core localities. Interpretation also includes data obtained from lower resolution airgun system. Note the current influence (tidal indicator) on post-glacial unit five. (B) Example of the complex nature of sediment deposition throughout the Late Wisconsinan in outer Baie des Chaleurs. High-resolution sicsmic profile and interpretations demonstrate the change in bottom boundary layer conditions with the onset of post-glacial (unit 5) sediment deposition.

thoughout the Late Holocene, but concomitant with continued sea-level fall to about 2800 years BP (Hein *et al.* 1993). Presently the Gulf region experiences microtidal conditions (tidal range approximately 1.5 m).

The Hamilton Inlet system—Groswater Bay, the Narrows, Lake Melville and Goose Bay—is the largest of the Labrador coastal inlets and one of eastern Canada's largest estuaries. It extends 250 km inland from the coastline, can reach 35 km in width, and has a maximum water depth just over 200 m. Because of the isostatic adjustment of the Labrador coast since deglaciation, the Lake Melville basin has become progressively more isolated from the open ocean. Relative sea level fell rapidly (about 150 mm/year) from the marine

limits of 110 m (at 7.5 ka) in the eastern part of the lake and from 150 m at 6.5 ka in the western part of the lake (Vilks & Mudie 1983). The rate of sea-level fall was substantively slower over the last 5–6 ka (to between 3 and 6 mm/year: Vilks & Mudie 1983). Faunal zone A of Vilks *et al.* (1987) is associated with seismic unit 13.2 of Syvitski *et al.* (1993), a unit associated with evidence of strong tidal currents, including the development of tidal levees. This tidally influenced, post-glacial sediment package began formation some time between 5 and 6 ka, when the sea-level fall began to slow.

Hudson Strait is a large passageway to the interior of the Canadian land mass, and to the interior of the Laurentide ice sheet during the

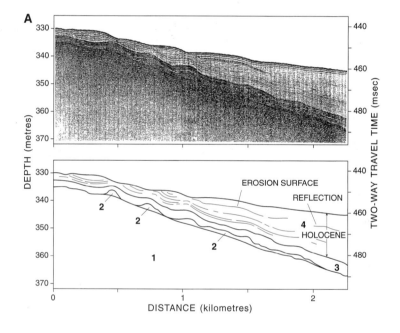

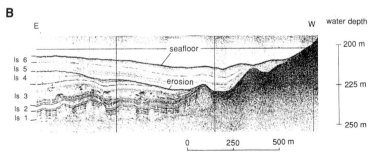

Fig. 12. Erosional surface at margin of deep-water bay corresponding to reflector (4) within the basin. Northeast Newfoundland (figure courtesy of J. Shaw, Atlantic Geoscience Centre). (B) Widespread erosion surface interpreted as resulting from storm-driven currents, Emerald Basin, Scotian Shelf (from Gipp 1994: figure reprinted with permission of the National Research Council of Canada).

Wisconsinan. It is many hundreds of kilometres long, >90 km wide and reaches water depths of 900 m. The modern tidal range in Hudson Strait is in excess of 8 m. Some time around 6300 years BP, strong tidal currents developed in association with the active deposition of post-glacial sediments, even in the deepest parts of the strait (unit 5 on Fig. 11A: MacLean *et al.* 1992). On seismic records the base of post-glacial sediments show a striking truncation of older units (Fig. 11A). The post-glacial sediments derive their sediment source from the scouring of shallower reaches of Hudson Strait. Hudson Strait has been undergoing emergence since glaciation, but the rate of emergence slowed drastically since about 6300 years BP (Gray *et al.* 1993).

Over the entire eastern seaboard of Canada, a distance of several thousand kilometres, acoustic evidence of tidal current interaction with the seafloor (Fig. 11) therefore appears to be associated with sediments that post-date 6500 years BP. This observational fact is interesting as it is associated with areas experiencing very different post-glacial sea-level fluctuations: rapidly rising water levels, rapidly falling seas, to areas somewhere in between. At about 6300 years BP ocean water levels (eustatic) approached modern levels, as the last of the Laurentide ice melted and a cooling phase began in many parts of the eastern Canadian arctic (Williams *et al.* 1995). Is this coincidental, or does the establishment of modern coastline near 6300 years BP result in the development of an established amphidromic nodal point off the Labrador margin? Or is it just coincidental that the natural period of oscillation of these coastal areas came into phase with the ocean tides?

Waves and storm-induced currents

On open continental shelves, in contrast with estuaries, it may be difficult to determine whether widespread erosion surfaces are the result of increases in tide-generated or storm-generated currents. Both cases can be distinguished from erosion by glacial re-advance by the concentration of scour around obstacles. In areas where the sea level is known to have fallen throughout the post-glacial period, basin margin sediments become progressively reworked (Barrie & Piper 1982; Piper *et al.* 1983). Shaw (pers. comm.) has shown that such reworking unconformities may extend in the basin and can then be onlapped by younger sediment, suggesting fluctuations through time in the intensity of reworking (Fig. 12A).

On the Scotian Shelf, there is a widespread erosion surface in the proglacial Emerald Silt which terminates a phase of conformable drape deposition at about 14 ka (Gipp 1994, Fig. 12B). This erosion phase probably correlates with the collapse of a late ice divide south of Cape Breton (Stea *et al.* 1992), which allowed advection of shelf water during storms from Emerald Basin into the Laurentian Channel.

Kontopoulos & Piper (1982) showed that fine sands and silts are resuspended and advected from bank areas during storms and are deposited at the margins of muddy shelf basins. On the Scotian Shelf, seismic correlation with cores from which detailed grain size data are available suggests that reflectors in basinal muds correlate with periods of enhanced storm resuspension and advection of silt (Piper & Fehr 1991). In Fig. 13, an apparent mid-Holocene increase in storminess is marked by a widespread sediment reflector.

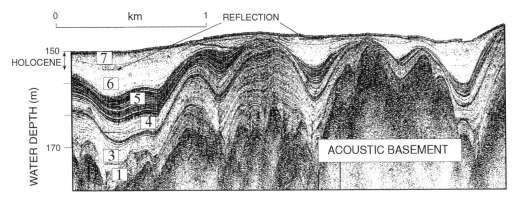

Fig. 13. Strong reflection (between units 6 and 7) corresponding to mid-Holocene increase in storminess, inner Scotian Shelf (figure courtesy of R. Stea, Nova Scotia Department of Natural Resources).

A

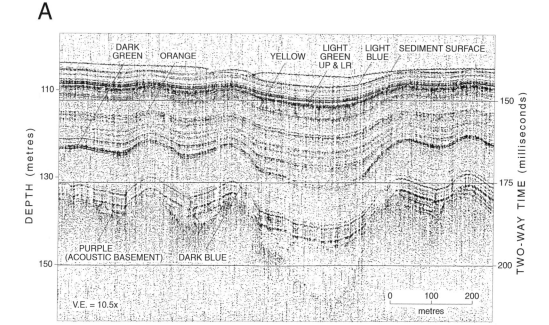

B

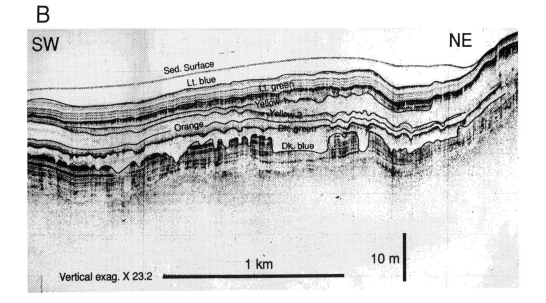

Fig. 14. High-resolution seismic reflection profiles from northern Lake Huron showing colour-named reflectors. (B) At this location the Upper and Lower Light Green reflectors are not resolved and appear as one, labelled Lt. Green. From Moore *et al.* (1994).

Sea- and lake-level fluctuations

Many of the effects of currents described here are strongly influenced by changing sea level. In coastal areas, palaeo-shorelines can be recognized from geological data in outcrop or cores. The elevation of changing sea levels further offshore on glaciated continental shelves can in places be determined from acoustic data. On shallow shelves, proglacial deltaic deposits have characteristic clinoforms, the top of which approximate to sea level. Such palaeo-deltas are common on the continental shelf south of the ice terminus corresponding to Sable Island (McLaren 1988). Marine transgression results in the planation of older deposits and local deposition in depressions (Forbes *et al.* 1991), thus allowing a distinction from ice erosion and seafloor erosion by waves and currents. Both conventional and swath bathymetry show a marked distinction in topographic roughness between areas of inner shelf crossed by the Holocene transgression and those areas below the maximum lowstand of sea level (Loncarevic *et al.* 1994). In places, small progradational deltas can be recognized at this lowstand (Stea *et al.* 1994).

Similar techniques can be used to determine variations in water levels in large lakes. However, in the relatively tranquil lacustrine environment, where water levels may fluctuate rapidly, variations in seismic reflections may also be used to infer water-level changes. This method is illustrated from Lake Huron glacilacustrine sediments. Lake Huron is part of the Laurentian Great Lakes and once in the pathway of late glacial meltwater drainage from the southern margin of the Laurentide ice sheet to the North Atlantic Ocean. At times, during the retreat of ice, all runoff from middle North America—from the catchment formed by the Cordillera to the west, the Laurentide ice sheet to the north, and the continental drainage divide to the south (Gulf of Mexico)—passed through the Huron Basin (Lewis & Anderson 1989). In high-resolution boomer surveys, a series of strong reflections was found to truncate underlying reflections on the margins of the basin, thereby defining a series of seismostratigraphic sequences (Fig. 14: Moore *et al.* 1994).

The downcore variation in bulk density, grain size and acoustic impedance were measured in a 5.5 m sediment core (Fig. 15) at the location of a seismic profile from the northern Lake Huron Basin (Fig. 14B). The three positive excursions in impedance at depths of about 20, 350 and 500 cm are sufficiently strong to produce reflections in boomer profiles and these depths

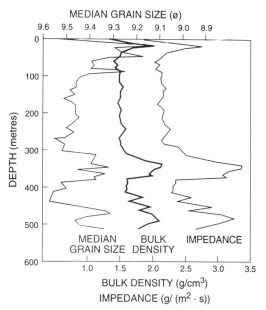

Fig. 15. Physical properties of sediments in northwestern Lake Huron, showing downcore measurements of acoustic impedance, bulk density and median grain size. From Moore *et al.* (1994).

correlate uniquely with the upper 3 subbottom reflectors in the seismic record—the Light Blue, Upper and Lower Light Green reflectors. A synthetic seismogram, formed by convolving the acoustic input signal with the measured downcore record of acoustic impedances, confirms these three reflections (Moore *et al.* 1994). The largest impedance contrast, at 350 cm, correlates with the strongest reflector, as expected. Each of the reflectors correlates in turn with a coarser zone in the clay-rich sediment, expressed as a 0.15–0.3 phi excursion in the median grain size curve (Fig. 15). On the basis of other evidence, the zones of coarser sediment are attributed to reductions in water depth; thus the seismic reflections denote lowstands in the lake level history and the finer grained sequences between reflections are the deposits of lake highstands. In this case, the fluctuations in lake level amounted to a few tens of metres (Lewis *et al.* in press).

The seismic reflections, through their correspondence with the coarser sediment zones, also relate to the attributes of fossils in the lake sediment. The $\delta^{18}O$ record of ostracode shells, indicating changes in the isotopic composition of lake water, varies sympathetically with the seismic reflection record (Fig. 16) (Rea *et al.* 1994). Figure 16 shows that each of the sediment zones producing a strong seismic reflection is

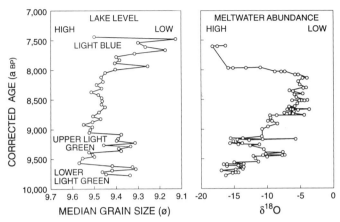

Fig. 16. The ¹⁸O record (PDB) of ostracode shells and median grain size variations versus the AMS ¹⁴C age scale for the same core as Fig. 15 in northwestern Lake Huron (from Rea *et al.* (1994). Shown is the coeval relationship of colour-named seismic reflections with increased sediment size, corresponding to lower lake levels, and lighter $\delta^{18}O$ isotopic composition of shells, corresponding to meltwater dominance.

also a zone of extremely light $\delta^{18}O$, signifying dominance of the lake by meltwater inflow. Thus the early Holocene seismic reflections indicate episodes of low lake level with high meltwater input and the intervals between reflections relate to highstands when the lake water was dominated by precipitation runoff (heavy $\delta^{18}O$).

A recently proposed scenario (Lewis *et al.* in press) suggests that the highstands in the

Huron Basin were periods of massive inflow from the southern sector of Lake Agassiz, which received precipitation runoff from much of the mid-North American continent east of the Cordillera. Conversely, the lowstands represent episodes of local meltwater inflow when the Agassiz discharge was diverted from the Great Lakes and St Lawrence River. These connections for the early Holocene of the

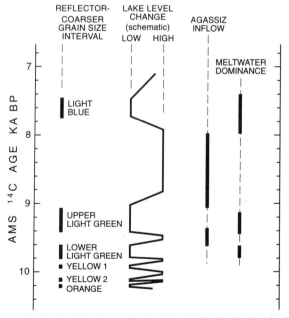

Fig. 17. Schematic history of seismic reflections and palaeolimnological variations in the Huron Basin.

Huron Basin are summarized in Fig. 17, showing the one to one relationship of seismic reflections with changes in lake level and water composition, and diversions of continental runoff to the oceans.

Conclusions

Acoustic imaging of the seafloor and subsurface Quaternary sediments, when assembled in regional map form, provides information about the geometry and thickness gradients of sediment bodies, the configurations of key erosion surfaces and other erosional features, and the physical nature of sediments. These data, combined with the attributes of sediment cores and concepts of earth processes, provide an expanded capability for more comprehensive reconstruction and synthesis of palaeoceanographic systems. The potential for expanded reconstructions has been alluded to in our use of seismic mapping data for interpreting the dynamics of ice sheets, their extent in the marine environment, and inferences about current directions, hydrology and sediment loads from former marine ice sheet margins. The reconstruction of former areas of drift ice transport and interaction with continental shelves has been greatly enhanced and has become routinely achieveable since the advent of sidescan sonar. Seismic stratigraphy and sediment attributes determined from cores have together yielded new insights about the nature of runoff from continental ice margins and its influence on hydrology and sedimentation in downstream basins. Similarly, changes in tidal current and storm wave conditions are being revealed through the combined study of sediment body configuration and grain texture. It is clear that acoustic imaging and mapping of the seafloor is a discipline that contributes to palaeoceanograpy well beyond its usual basic role of siting cores for sediment and palaeoecological analysis.

This manuscript forms a Geological Survey of Canada contribution. We thank our colleagues who have generously contributed data and who have worked in the field with us. We kindly thank L. Phillips and G. Domack for sharing their insights in their review of this manuscript.

References

ALLEY, R. B. 1991. Sedimentary processes may cause fluctuations of tidewater glaciers. *Annals of Glaciology*, **15**, 119–124.

AMOS, C. L. 1978. The post glacial evolution of the Minas Basin, Nova Scotia: a sedimentological interpretation. *Journal of Sedimentary Petrology*, **48**, 965–982.

—— & KNOLL, R. 1987. The Quaternary sediments of Banquerau, Scotian Shelf. *Geological Society of America, Bulletin*, **99**, 244–260.

—— & LONG, B. F. N. 1980. The sedimentary character of the Minas Basin, Bay of Fundy. *In*: MCMANN, S. B. (ed.) *Coastline of Canada*. Geological Survey of Canada, Paper, **80-10**, 153–180.

ANDREWS, J. T. & SYVITSKI, J. P. M. 1994. Sediment fluxes along high-latitude glaciated continental margins: Northeast Canada and Eastern Greenland. *In*: *Material Fluxes on the Surface of the Earth*. Studies in Geophysics, National Academy Press, Washington, 99–115.

——, JENNINGS, A. E., MACLEAN, B., MUDIE, P. J., PRAEG, D., VILKS, G. & HEIN, F. J. 1991. The surficial geology of the Canadian eastern Arctic and Polar continental shelves. *Continental Shelf Research*, **11**, 791–819.

——, MILLIMAN, J. D., JENNINGS, A. E., RYNES, N. & DWYER, J. 1994. Sediment thicknesses and Holocene glacial marine sedimentation rates in three east Greenland fjords (ca. 68° N). *Journal of Geology*, **102**, 669–683.

BARNES, N. E. & PIPER, D. J. W. 1978. Late Quaternary geological history of Mahone Bay, Nova Scotia. *Canadian Journal of Earth Sciences*, **15**, 586–593.

BARRIE, C. Q. & PIPER, D. J. W. 1982. *Late Quaternary Marine Geology of Makkovik Bay, Labrador*. Geological Survey of Canada, Paper, **81-17**.

BARRIE, J. V. 1980. Iceberg–seabed interaction (Northern Labrador Sea). *In*: *Proceedings of the Conference on Use of Icebergs: Scientific and Practical Feasibility, Cambridge, 1–3 April 1980*. *Annals of Glaciology*, **1**, 71–76.

——, LEWIS, C. F. M., PARROTT, D. R. & COLLINS, W. T. 1992. Submersible observations of an iceberg pit and scour on the Grand Banks of Newfoundland. *Geo-Marine Letters*, **12**, 1–6.

BELDERSON, R. H. & WILSON, J. B. 1973. Iceberg plough marks in the vicinity of the Norwegian Trough. *Norsk Geologisk Tidsskrift*, **53**, 323–328.

——, KENYON, N. H. & WILSON, J. B. 1973. Iceberg plough marks in the northeast Atlantic. *Palaeogeography, Palaeoclimatology, Palaeoecology*, **13**, 215–224.

BERKSON, J. M. & CLAY, C. S. 1973. Microphysiography and possible iceberg grooves on the floor of western Lake Superior. *Geological Society of America Bulletin*, **84**, 1315–1328.

BONIFAY, D. & PIPER, D. J. W. 1988. Late Wisconsinan ice margin on the upper continental slope off St. Pierre Bank, Eastern Canada. *Canadian Journal of Earth Sciences*, **25**, 853–865.

BOYD, R., SCOTT, D. B. & DOUMA, M. 1988. Glacial tunnel valleys and the Quaternary history of the Scotian Shelf. *Nature*, **333**, 61–64.

BRETT, C.P. & ZARUDSKI, E. F. K. 1979. *Project Westmar: a Shallow Marine Geophysical Survey on the West Greenland Continental Shelf.* Gronlands Geologiske Undersogelse Report, **87**, 27.

D'APOLLONIA, S. J. & LEWIS, C. F. M. 1980. *Iceberg Scour Data Maps for the Grand Banks of Newfoundland Between 46° and 48° N.* Geological Survey of Canada Open File Report, **819**, 13.

DOMACK, E. W., FOSS, D. J. P., SYUITSKI, J. P. & MCCLENNEN, C. E. 1994. Transport of suspended particulate matter in an Antartic fjord. *Marine Geology*, **121**, 161–170.

DOWDESWELL, J. A., WHITTINGTON, R. J. & MARIENFIELD, P. 1994. The origin of massive diamicton facies by iceberg rafting and scouring, Scoresby Sund, East Greenland. *Sedimentology*, **41**, 21–35.

DYKE, A. S. & PREST, V. K. 1987. Wisconsinan and Holocene history of the Laurentide Ice Sheet. *In*: FULTON, R. & ANDREWS, J. T. (eds) *The Laurentide Ice Sheet. Géographie Physique et Quaternaire*, **41**, 237–264.

EL-TAHAN, M., EL-TAHAN, H., COURAGE, D. & MITTEN, R. 1985. *Documentation of Iceberg Groundings.* Environmental Studies Revolving Funds Report, **07**, 162.

FADER, G. B. & KING, L. H. 1981. A reconnaissance of the surficial geology of the Grand Banks of Newfoundland. *In: Current Research, Part A.* Geological Survey of Canada Paper **81-1A**, 45–56.

FORBES, D. L. 1984. *Coastal Geomorphology and Sediments of Newfoundland.* Geological Survey of Canada, Paper, **84-1B**, 11–24.

—— & SYVITSKI, J. P. M. 1995. Paraglacial coasts. *In*: CARTER, R. W. G. & WOODROFFE, C. D. (ed.) *Coastal Evolution: Late Quaternary Shoreline Morphodynamics.* Cambridge University Press, Cambridge, 373–424.

—— & TAYLOR, R. B. 1987. Coarse-grained beach sedimentation under paraglacial conditions, Canadian Atlantic coast. *In*: FITZGERALD, D. M. & ROSEN, P. S. (eds) *Glaciated Coast.* Academic Press, San Diego, 51–86.

——, BOYD, R. & SHAW, J. 1991. Late Quaternary sedimentation and sea level changes on the inner Scotian Shelf. *Continental Shelf Research*, **11**, 1155–1179.

GIPP, M. R. 1993. The orientation of buried iceberg scours and other phenomena. *Marine Geology*, **114**, 263–272.

——1994. Late Wisconsinan deglacation of Emerald Basin, Scotian Shelf. *Canadian Journal of Earth Sciences*, **31**, 554–566.

—— & PIPER, D. J. W. 1990. Chronology of Late Wisconsinan glaciation, Emerald Basin, Scotian Shelf. *Canadian Journal of Earth Sciences*, **26**, 333–335.

GOSSON, C. M. C. 1985. Canada glaciers. *In: The National Atlas of Canada*, 5th edn (map 1:7 500 000). Geographical Services Division, Surveys and Mapping Branch, Energy, Mines and Resources, Canada.

GRAY, J., LAURIOL, B., BRUNEAU, D. & RICARD, J. 1993. Postglacial emergence of Ungava Peninsula, and its relationship to glacial history. *Canadian Journal of Earth Sciences*, **30**, 1676–1696.

GUSTAJTIS, K. S. 1979. *Iceberg Scouring on the Labrador Shelf, Saglek Bank.* Memorial University of Newfoundland, Centre for Cold Ocean Resources Engineering (C-CORE), Technical Report, Publication, **79-13**, 43.

HARRIS, I. M. 1975. Iceberg marks on the Labrador Shelf. *In*: PELLETIER, B. R. (ed.) *Offshore Geology of Eastern Canada.* Vol. 2. Geological Survey of Canada, Paper 74-30, 97–101.

—— & JOLLYMORE, P. G. 1974. Iceberg furrow marks on the continental shelf northeast of Belle Isle, Newfoundland. *Canadian Journal of Earth Sciences*, **11**, 43–52.

HEIN, F. J., SYVITSKI, J. P. M., DREDGE, L. A. & LONG, B. F. 1993. Quaternary sedimentation and marine placers along the North Shore, Gulf of St. Lawrence. *Canadian Journal of Earth Sciences*, **30**, 553–574.

HODGSON, G. J., LEVER, J. H., WOODWORTH-LYNAS, C. M. T. & LEWIS, C. F. M. (eds) 1988. *The Dynamics of Iceberg Grounding and Scouring (DIGS) Experiment and Repetitive Mapping of the Eastern Canadian Continental Shelf.* Environmental Studies Research Funds, Report, **094**, 316.

JOSENHANS, H. W. & FADER, G. B. J. 1989. A comparison of models of glacial sedimentation along the eastern Canadian margin. *Marine Geology*, **85**, 273–300.

——, ZEVENHUIZEN, J. & KLASSEN, R. A. 1986. The Quaternary geology of the Labrador Shelf. *Canadian Journal of Earth Sciences*, **23**, 1190–1213.

KING, E. L. & GILLESPIE, R. T. 1986. Regional iceberg scour distribution and variability on the eastern Canadian continental shelf. *In*: LEWIS, C. F. M., PARROTT, D. R., SIMPKIN, P. G. & BUCKLEY, J. (eds) *Ice Scour and Seabed Engineering.* Environmental Revolving Funds Report, **049**, 172–181.

KING, L. H. 1976. Relict iceberg furrows on the Laurentian Channel and western Grand Banks. *Canadian Journal of Earth Sciences*, **13**, 1082–1092.

KONTOPOULOS, N. & PIPER, D. J. W. 1982. Storm-graded sand at 200 m water depth, Scotian Shelf, eastern Canada. *Geo-Marine Letters*, **2**, 77–81.

LEVER, J. H., BASS, D. W., LEWIS, C. F. M., KLEIN, K., DIEMAND, C. E. & DYKE, M. 1991. Iceberg/seabed interaction events observed during the DIGS experiment. *Journal of Offshore Mechanics and Arctic Engineering*, **113**, 74–87.

LEWIS, C. F. M. & ANDERSON, T. W. 1989. Oscillations of levels and cool phases of the Laurentian Great Lakes caused by inflows from the glacial lakes Agassiz and Barlow-Ojib. *Journal of Paleolimnology*, **2**, 99–146.

—— & BARRIE, J. V. 1981. Geological evidence of iceberg groundings and related seafloor processes in the Hibernia Discovery area of Grand Bank, Newfoundland. *In: Proceedings of the Symposium* on *Production and Transportation Systems for the Hibernia Discovery.* Newfoundland Petroleum Directorate, Government of Newfoundland & Labrador, St. John's, 825–846.

——— & WOODWORTH-LYNAS, C. M. T. 1990. Ice scour. *In*: KEEN, M. J. & WILLIAMS, G. L. (eds) *Geology of the Continental Margin of Eastern Canada.* Geology of Canada, **2**. Geological Survey of Canada (also Geological Society of America, Geology of North America, **I-1**), 785–793.

———, BLASCO, S. M., BORNHOLD, B. D., HUNTER, J. A. M., JUDGE, A. S., KERR, J. W., McLAREN, P. G. & PELLETIER, B. R. 1977. Marine geological and geophysical activities in Lancaster Sound and adjacent fiords. *In: Report of Activities, Part A, Geological Survey of Canada, Paper,* **77-1A**, 495–506.

———, MACLEAN, B. & FALCONER, R. K. H. 1980. Iceberg scour abundance in Labrador Sea and Baffin Bay, a reconnaissance of regional variability. 1980. *In*: EDEN, W. J. (ed.) *Proceedings, First Canadian Conference on Marine Geotechnical Engineering.* The Canadian Geotechnical Society, 79–94.

———, MOORE, T. C., JR., REA, D. K., DETTMAN, D. L., SMITH, A. M. & MAYER, L. A. Lakes of the Huron basin: their record of runoff from the Laurentide Ice Sheet. *Quaternary Science Reviews*, in press.

———, PARROTT, D. R., D'APOLLONIA, S. J., GASKILL, H. S. & BARRIE, J. V. 1988. Methods of estimating rates of iceberg scouring for the Grand banks of Newfoundland. *In*: SACKINGER, W. M. & JEFFRIES, M. O. (eds) *Port and Ocean Engineering Under Arctic Conditions.* Vol. III. University of Alaska, Fairbanks, 229–254.

LIEN, R. L. 1983a. *Ployemerker etter isfjell pa norsk kontinentalsokkel (Iceberg scouring on the Norwegian continental shelf).* Institutt for Kontinentalsokkelundersokelser Pubikasjon, **109**, 147.

———1983b. Iceberg scouring on the Norwegian continental shelf. *In: Proceedings, Fifteenth Annual Offshore Technology Conference. 2–5 May 1983, Houston, TX, USA,* Vol. 2, 41–48.

LONCAREVIC, B. D., COURTNEY, R. C., FADER, G. B. J., GILES, P. S., PIPER, D. J. W., COSTELLO, G., HUGHES CLARKE, J. E. & STEA, R. R. 1994. Sonography of a glaciated continental shelf. *Geology*, **22**, 747–750.

———, PIPER, D. J. W. & FADER, G. B. 1992. Applications of high-quality bathymetry to geological interpretation of the Scotian Shelf. *Geoscience Canada*, **19**, 5–12.

MACLEAN, B., VILKS, G. & DEONARINE, B. 1992. Depositional environments and history of Late Quaternary sediments in Hudson Strait and Ungava Bay: further evidence from seismic and biostratigraphic data. *Geographie physique et Quaternaire*, **42**, 311–329.

MCLAREN, S. A. 1988. *Quaternary Stratigraphy and Sedimentation of the Sable Island Sand Body, Sable Island Bank, Outer Scotian Shelf.* Dalhousie University Centre for Marine Geology, Technical Report, **11**,.

MARKHAM, W. E. 1980. *Ice Atlas, Eastern Canadian Seaboard.* Environment Canada, Atmospheric Environment Service, Toronto.

———1981. *Ice Atlas, Canadian Arctic Waterways.* Environment Canada, Atmospheric Environment Service, Toronto.

MONAHAN, D. & MACNAB, R. F. 1975. Flemish Cap, Flemish Pass, and the northeastern Grand Banks of Newfoundland morphology. *In*: PELLETIER, B. R. (ed.) *Offshore Geology of Eastern Canada.* Vol. 2. Geological Survey of Canada, Paper, **74-30**, 207–216.

MOORE, T. C. JR., REA, D. K., MAYER, L. A., LEWIS, C. F. M. & DOBSON, D. M. 1994. Seismic stratigraphy of Lake Huron-Georgian Bay and post-glacial lake level history. *Canadian Journal of Earth Sciences*, **31**, 1606–1617.

MULDER, T. & MORAN, K. 1995. Relationship among submarine instabilities, sea level variations, and the presence of an ice sheet on the continental shelf: an example from the Verrill Canyon Area, Scotian Shelf. *Paleoceanography*, **10**, 137–154.

PARROTT, D. R., LEWIS, C. F. M., BANKE, E., FADER, G. B. J. & SONNICHSEN, G. V. 1990. Seabed disturbance by a recent (1989) iceberg grounding on the Grand Banks of Newfoundland. *In: Current Research, Part B.* Geological Survey of Canada, Paper, **90-1B**, 43–48.

PELLETIER, B. R. 1971. Side scan sonar surveys and ice scouring in the Beaufort Sea. *In: Proceedings of the Canadian Ice Seminar on Icebergs.* Canadian Forces Base Halifax, Halifax, 48–49.

——— & SHEARER, J. M. 1972. Sea bottom scouring in the Beaufort Sea of the Arctic Ocean. *In: Proceedings of the 24th International Geological Congress, Section 8.* Montreal, Quebec, 251–265.

PIPER, D. J. W. 1988. Glaciomarine sediments on the continental slope off eastern Canada. *Geoscience Canada*, **15**, 23–28.

——— & FEHR, S. D. 1991. Radiocarbon chronology of the late Quaternary sections on the inner and middle Scotian Shelf, south of Nova Scotia. *In: Current Research, Part E.* Geological Survey of Canada, Paper, **91-1E**, 321–325.

———, LETSON, J. R. J., DE IURE, A. M. & BARRIE, C. Q. 1983. Sediment accumulation in low-sedimentation, wave-dominated, glaciated inlets. *Sedimentary Geology*, **36**, 195–215.

———, MUDIE, P. J., FADER, G. B., JOSENHANS, H. W., MACLEAN, B. & VILKS, G. 1990. Quaternary Geology. *In*: KEEN, M. J. & WILLIAMS, G. L. (eds) *Geology of the Continental Margin of Eastern Canada.* Geology of Canada. **2**, 477–607.

POWELL, R. D. 1990. Glacimarine processes at grounding-line fans and their growth to ice-contact deltas. *In*: DOWDESWELL, J. A. & SCORSE, J. D. (eds) *Glacimarine Environments: Processes and Sediments.* Geological Society, London, Special Publications, **53**, 53–73.

PRAEG, D. B., D'ANGLEJAN, B. & SYVITSKI, J. P. M. 1992. Seismostratigraphy of the middle St. Lawrence Estuary: a Late Quaternary glacial marine to estuarine depositional/erosional record. *Géographie physique et Quaternaire*, **46**, 133–150.

——, MacLEAN, B. HARDY, I. A. & MUDIE, P. J. 1986. *Quaternary Geology of the Southeast Baffin Island Continental Shelf, N.W.T.* Geological Survey of Canada, Paper, **85-14**, 59–62.

——, MacLEAN, B., PIPER, D. J. W. & SHOR, A. N. 1987. Study of iceberg scours across the continental shelf and slope off southeast Baffin Island using the SEAMARC I midrange sidescan sonar. *In: Current Research, Part A.* Geological Survey of Canada, Paper, **87-1A**, 847–857.

REA, D. K., MOORE, T. C., JR., LEWIS, C. F. M., MAYER, L. A., DETTMAN, D. L., SMITH, A. M. & DOBSON, D. M. 1994. Stratigraphy and paleolimnologic record of lower Holocene sediments in northern Lake Huron and Georgian Bay. *Canadian Journal of Earth Sciences*, **31**, 1586–1605.

REEH, N. 1989. Dynamics and climatic history of the Greenland Ice Sheet. *In:* FULTON, R. J. (ed.) *Quaternary Geology of Canada and Greenland. Geology of Canada*, 1 (also Geological Society of America, The Geology of North America, **K-1**), 795–822.

REIMNITZ, E., BARNES, P. W., FORGATSCH, T. & RODEICK, C. 1972. Influence of grounding ice on the arctic shelf of Alaska. *Marine Geology*, **13**, 323–324.

ROBE, R. Q. 1980. Iceberg drift and deterioration. *In:* COLBECK, S. C. (ed.) *Dynamics of Snow and Ice Masses.* Academic Press, Toronto, 211- 259.

——1982. *Iceberg Drift Near Greenland—1980 to 1982.* United States Coast Guard Research and Development Center, Groton, Connecticut, Report, **CG-D-36-82**.

RODRIGUES, C. G., CEMAN, J. A. & VILKS, G. 1993. Late Quaternary paleoceanography of deep and intermediate water masses off Gaspé Peninsula, Gulf of St. Lawrence: foraminiferal evidence. *Canadian Journal of Earth Sciences*, **30**, 1390–1403.

ROSS, W. C., HALLIWELL, B. A., MAY, J. E., WATTS, D. E. & SYVITSKI, J. P. M. 1994. Slope readjustment: a new model for the development of submarine fans and aprons. *Geology*, **22**, 511–514.

STEA, R. R., BOYD, R., FADER, G. B. J., COURTNEY, R. C., SCOTT, D. B. & PECORE, S. S. 1994. Morphology and seismic stratigraphy of the inner continental shelf of Nova Scotia, Canada: evidence for a −65 m lowstand between 11 650 and 11 250 C[14] yr B.P. *Marine Geology*, **117**, 135–154.

——, FADER, G. B. J. & BOYD, R. 1992. *Quaternary Seismic Stratigraphy of the Inner Shelf Region, Eastern Shore, Nova Scotia.* Gelogical Survey of Canada, Paper, **92-1D**, 179–188.

STEWART, F. S. & STOKER, M. S. 1991. Problems associated with seismic facies analysis of diamicton-dominated, shelf glacigenic sequences. *Geo-Marine Letters*, **10**, 151–156.

STOKER, M. S. & LONG, D. 1984. A relict-scoured erosion surface in the central North Sea. *Marine Geology*, **61**, 85–93.

STRAVERS, J. A. & SYVITSKI, J. P. M. 1991. Early Holocene land–sea correlations and deglacial evolution of the Cambridge Fiord basin, northern Baffin Island. *Quaternary Research*, **35**, 72–90.

SYVITSKI, J. P. M. 1989. On the deposition of sediment within glacier-influenced fjords: oceanographic controls. *Marine Geology*, **85**, 301–330.

——1991. Towards an understanding of sediment deposition on glaciated continental shelves. *Continental Shelf Research*, **11**, 897–937.

——1992. Marine geology of Baie Des Chaleurs. *Geographie et Quaternaire*, **46**, 331–348.

——1993. Glaciomarine environments in Canada: an overview. *Canadian Journal of Earth Sciences*, **30**, 354–371.

——1994. Glacial sedimentation processes. *Terra Antartica*, **1**, 251–253.

—— & PRAEG, D. B. 1989. Quaternary sedimentation in the St. Lawrence and adjoining areas, Eastern Canada: an overview based on high-resolution seismo-stratigraphy. *Géographie physique et Quaternaire*, **43**, 291–310.

——, ANDREWS, J. T. & DOWDESWELL, J. A. Sediment deposition in an iceberg-dominated glacimarine environment, East Greenland: basin fill implications. *Global & Planetary Change*, in press.

——, BURRELL, D. C. & SKEI, J. M. 1987. *Fjords: Processes and Products.* Springer Verlag, New York.

——, HINDS, S. J. & BURNS, J. A. 1993. *Marine Geology of Lake Melville (Labrador).* Geological Survey of Canada Open File, Report, **2759**, 34 sheets.

TODD, B. J. 1984. *Iceberg scouring on Saglek Bank, northern Labrador Shelf.* MSc Thesis, Dalhousie University, Halifax.

——, LEWIS, C. F. M. & RYALL, P. J. C. 1988. Comparison of trends of iceberg scour marks with iceberg trajectories and evidence of paleocurrent trends on Saglek Bank, northern Labrador Shelf. *Canadian Journal of Earth Sciences*, **25**, 1374–1383.

VILKS, G. & MUDIE, P. J. 1983. Evidence for postglacial paleoceanographic and paleoclimatic changes in Lake Melville, Labrador, Canada. *Arctic & Alpine Research*, **15**, 307–320.

——, DEONARINE, B. & WINTERS, G. 1987. *Late Quaternary Marine Geology of Lake Melville, Labrador.* Geological Survey of Canada, Paper, **87-22**.

WILLIAMS, K. M., SHORT, S. K., ANDREWS, J. T., JENNINGS, A. E., MODE, W. N. & SYVITSKI, J. P. M. 1995. The Eastern Canadian Arctic at 6 KA: a time of transition. *Geographie physique et Quaternaire*, **49**, 13–27.

WOODWORTH-LYNAS, C. M. T., JOSENHANS, H. W., BARRIE, J. V., LEWIS, C. F. M. & PARROTT, D. R. 1991. The physical processes of seabed disturbance during iceberg grounding and scouring. *Continental Shelf Research*, **11**, 939–961.

——, C. M. T., SIMMS, A. & RENDELL, C. M. 1985. Iceberg grounding and scouring on the Labrador continental shelf. *Cold Regions Science and Technology*, **10**, 163–186.

Deglaciation of the inner Scotian Shelf, Nova Scotia: correlation of terrestrial and marine glacial events

R. R. STEA[1], R. BOYD[2], O. COSTELLO[3], G. B. J. FADER[4] & D. B. SCOTT[5]

[1] *Nova Scotia Department of Natural Resources, PO Box 698, Halifax, Nova Scotia, Canada B3J 2T9*
[2] *University of Newcastle, NSW 2308, Australia*
[3] *Geologisch-Paläontologisches Institut, Universität Kiel, Olshausenstrasse 40 D-2300, Kiel, Germany*
[4] *Geological Survey of Canada (Atlantic), Dartmouth, Nova Scotia, Canada B2Y 4A2*
[5] *Department of Earth Sciences, Dalhousie University, Halifax, Nova Scotia, Canada B3H 3J5*

Abstract: The inner continental shelf off Nova Scotia is an important region for correlating glacial events across the terrestrial–marine transition. The inner Scotian Shelf can be subdivided into five coast-parallel terrain zones which record glaciation and the rise and fall of relative sea levels during the late glacial period. During the initial deglaciation phase (*c.* 17–15 ka) ice was drawn out of the Gulf of Maine, isolating an ice mass over Nova Scotia which later became an active centre of outflow (Scotian Ice Divide). The Scotian Shelf End-Moraine Complex (SSEMC) formed at the margin of this glacier. Landward of the end moraine complex is a series of linear depositional basins termed the Basin Zone, containing a complete sedimentary record of events after deposition of the SSEMC. The lowest depositional sequences (sequences 1 and 2) in these basins are interpreted to be ice-proximal sediment, deposited by overflow and interflow meltwater plumes emanating from the retreating ice margin. From 13–12 ka, the sea level dropped rapidly due to glacial isostatic recovery. Ice receded out of marine areas, depositing the glacial–marine sequence 3 in the Basin Zone. A lowstand shoreline (*c.* 11.6 ka) at −65 m is marked by the landward transition from morainal topography to a shoreface ramp, terrace and wave-cut platform. Enhanced current erosion during the lowstand was recorded in the inner Scotian Shelf basins by erosional truncation of sequence 3. After this erosional event the sea level rose rapidly, concomitant with climatic warming, as indicated by foraminifera within the Basin Zone and increases in spruce pollen in cores from Nova Scotia lakes. In the Basin Zone a seismic sequence characterized by indistinct, low-amplitude reflections (sequence 4) was deposited. Increased storminess and current sediment delivery with increased sea ice and icebergs during the Younger Dryas climatic cooling (*c.* 11–10.0 ka) produced sequence 5 in the Basin Zone. Sequence 5 is correlative with a distinctive mineralic layer in lakes and periglacial and glacial sediments that overlie peat in land sections. The terrestrial and marine sections record a transition from organic-rich to inorganic sedimentation events initiated *c.* 10.8 ka. Climatic cooling and snowfield/glacier build-up on land, with increased meltwater runoff and storm-induced sedimentation in the marine realm, were the principal causes of these sedimentation events.

Palaeoclimatic research over the last two decades has focused on atmospheric, oceanic and cryospheric interactions. Problems arose from attempts to correlate the geological records on land with those from the ocean (cf. Cooke 1973). The Quaternary stratigraphic record on land is fragmentary (Grant 1989); land sections record relatively recent glacial advances and retreats in the Quaternary. Erosion, sporadic deposition and exposure, and a lack of suitable dating methods make the evidence of pre-Wisconsinan or Weichselian glaciations less resolvable (Clark *et al.* 1993). Deep ocean sediment, faunal and isotopic records provide a continuous Quaternary climatic sequence, but only give indirect clues to ice sheet activity. The continental shelf of Nova Scotia is an interface between the deep ocean and the land and provides the opportunity for regional land–sea correlation. Because glacial and non-glacial sediments are preserved in eastern Canada across the land–sea boundary to the edge of the continental shelf (King & Fader 1986; Piper *et al.* 1990), they can be directly correlated to develop a chronological framework of glacial events.

Today, most continent-wide interpretations of the Late Wisconsinan Laurentide glaciation

From Andrews, J. T., Austin, W. E. N., Bergsten, H. & Jennings, A. E. (eds), 1996, *Late Quaternary Palaeoceanography of the North Atlantic Margins*, Geological Society Special Publication No. 111, pp. 77–101.

show a relatively simple, monolithic ice sheet centred in Hudson's Bay and extending to the shelf edge off Nova Scotia (Flint 1971; Denton & Hughes 1981; Budd & Smith 1987). This is termed the 'maximum' model and is believed to represent the equilibrium condition. The contrasting 'minimum' model proposes local ice centres with thinner ice that extended only slightly off the coast of Nova Scotia, and with some highland areas bare of ice (nunataks) (Dyke & Prest 1987). These two extreme models are not in accord with recent mapping of glacial landforms and deposits in New Brunswick and Nova Scotia (Wightman 1980; Rampton *et al.* 1984; Rappol 1989; Foisy & Prichonnet 1991; Stea *et al.* 1986; 1989). The model that has evolved out of these field studies is a time transgressive model, with large, local ice-caps and divides evolving into smaller ones.

Late Wisconsinan ice covered all the highland areas and extended to the continental shelf edge (Mosher *et al.* 1989; Gipp & Piper 1989). This regional 'complex' model is essentially a compromise between the earlier models and it represents the current state of the debate.

This paper is part of a series of articles dealing with glaciation and relative sea-level change on the inner shelf of Nova Scotia and correlation of land and sea events. In the first paper, Stea *et al.* (1994) described a lowstand shoreline and correlated relative sea-level changes on land and sea. This paper will focus on the Basin Zone, a depositional basin on the Scotian Shelf with a nearly complete record of events from 15 ka to the present. The record obtained in this basin will be compared with local and regional glacial chronologies in both the marine and terrestrial environments.

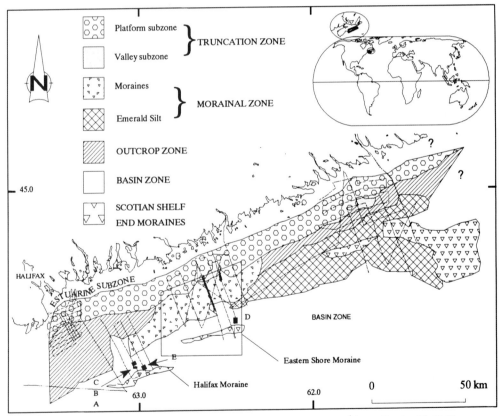

Fig. 1. Location of study area and mapped terrain zones and subzones on the inner Scotian Shelf. These zones are defined as areas of unique bottom morphology (landforms) and seismic stratigraphy. The zones are a consequence of bedrock type and structure, glacial erosional and depositional processes and sea-level rise and fall. Sites A, B, C, D and E are the locations of stratigraphic type sections. Piston core 91018-53 was collected at section E. Tracklines are shown as broken lines. Locations of seismic type sections in the Basin Zone (thickened lines) and digital grid model area (block). Modified from Stea (1995).

Physiographic setting of the marine study region

Cok (1970), King (1970) and Drapeau & King (1972) divided the Scotian Shelf into three physiographic zones: an inner zone (inner shelf) characterized by rough topography; a middle zone (central shelf) consisting of broad shore-parallel depressions; and an outer zone (outer shelf) consisting of wide, flat banks. Seismic methods have advanced considerably since the 1970s, enabling further detailed physiographic subdivisions.

The basins and banks of the outer shelf have been studied extensively (King & Fader 1986; Amos & Knoll 1987; Gipp & Piper 1989; Amos & Miller 1990; Boyd et al. 1988; McLaren 1988; King 1994; Gipp 1994). The inner shelf has been mapped and subdivided into five coast-parallel zones (Fig. 1). Kelley et al. (1989) mapped a similar progression of shore-parallel zones off the coast of Maine. These are (seaward to landward): (1) the Scotian Shelf End–Moraine Complex (King et al. 1972); (2) the Basin Zone

(this study); (3) the Outcrop Zone (Forbes et al. 1991); (4) the Morainal Zone (Stea et al. 1993); and (5) the Truncation Zone (Forbes et al. 1991; Stea et al. 1993; 1994).

The Scotian Shelf End–Moraine Complex (SSEMC) is a series of large ridges 30–40 km offshore, which are parallel to the present day Nova Scotian coastline (King et al. 1972; Fig. 1). One of these morainal ridges (the Eastern Shore Moraine), with a linear form and asymmetrical profile, is clearly resolved on a digital grid model of the bathymetry off Sheet Harbour (Fig. 2). The Basin Zone is a series of closed, sediment-infilled troughs or basins north of the SSEMC moraines in water depths greater than 145 m. These troughs are filled with glacial marine and marine sediments, seismically indicated by conformably bedded acoustic units with high amplitude, coherent reflections (Table 1; Emerald Silt) and transparent, ponded facies (Table 1; LaHave Clay). The Outcrop Zone was defined by Forbes et al. (1991) as a broad area of bedrock outcrop largely devoid of surficial sediment. The Morainal Zone was defined as a region of

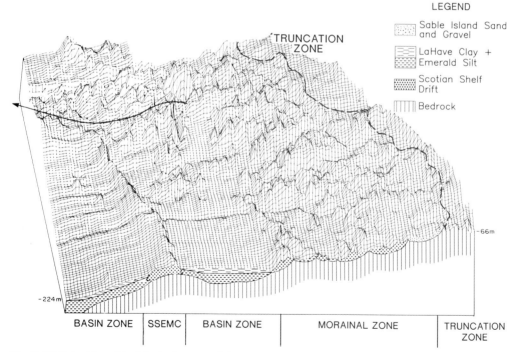

LEGEND

Sable Island Sand and Gravel

LaHave Clay + Emerald Silt

Scotian Shelf Drift

Bedrock

TRUNCATION ZONE

−66 m

−224 m

| BASIN ZONE | SSEMC | BASIN ZONE | MORAINAL ZONE | TRUNCATION ZONE |

Fig. 2. Digital grid model of the bathymetry of the inner Scotian Shelf in the Sheet Harbour transect area (for location, see Fig. 1). Bathymetry was digitized from 12 kHz seismic records of the Canadian Hydrographic Service. The tracklines were 0.93 km apart and depth measurements were taken every five minutes along lines. Note the continuity of the Scotian Shelf End–Moraine Complex (SSEMC). The view is toward the southwest from the northeastern end of the Eastern Shore Moraine.

Table 1. *Quaternary formations and seismic facies defined by King & Fader (1986) and their properties*

Formation	Facies	Lithic properties	Seismic character
Sable Island Sand and Gravel		Fine to coarse, well-sorted sand grading to subrounded to rounded gravels	Highly reflective sea bed, closely spaced, continuous reflections
Sambro Sand		Silty sand grading to gravelly sand	Similar to above
LaHave Clay	LaHave Clay	Greyish brown, soft, silty clay grading to clayey silt, confined mainly to basins and depressions in the shelf	Generally transparent without reflections, some weak, continuous, coherent reflections at the base of the section
Emerald Silt	Facies C	Not well sampled	Discontinuous, coherent reflections and incoherent zones
Emerald Silt	Facies B	Dark greyish brown, poorly sorted, clayey and sandy silt, some gravel, poorly developed rhythmic banding	Medium to low amplitude, continuous, coherent reflections; ponded depositional style
Emerald Silt	Facies A	Greyish brown, poorly sorted, clayey and sandy silt, some gravel, well developed rhythmic banding	High amplitude, continuous, coherent reflections conformable to substrate irregularities
Scotian Shelf Drift		Sandy clay, matrix-supported, diamicton	Incoherent reflections, sometimes with scattered, point source reflections

subparallel ridges landward of the Basin Zone (Stea *et al.* 1993; 1994). The Truncation Zone is marked by the change to muted topography and sand deposition in water depths of approximately 80 m (Stea *et al.* 1993; 1994) (Fig. 2).

Methods

Seismic data for the study were collected during Cruise 91018 (CSS Dawson; Fader *et al.* 1991) on the eastern inner Scotian Shelf (Fig. 1). The Huntec deep-tow boomer system was used to generate analogue seismic data with vertical resolution of less than 1 m (cf. Hutchins *et al.* 1976). Operating frequencies ranged from 500 Hz to 2 kHz with a power output of 4–6 kV. Two recorders were used, an internal transducer mounted underneath the towed sound source and an external array. The system is towed at 10–75 m water depth to minimize the effects of surface swell and wave noise. Seismic reflection data with less resolution but more penetration were obtained using a 40 in³ Haliburton sleeve gun system operating at 5–500 Hz. Bathymetric information was obtained using data produced by a hull-mounted 3.5 kHz acoustic profiler, from Canadian Hydrographic Service charts, and from the depth of the first multiple below the seabed in the Huntec records (Sylwester

1983). Seafloor topography and reflectivity were obtained using sidescan sonar designed at the Bedford Institute of Oceanography, operating at 70 kHz with a range of 1 km, and Klein dual frequency sidescan sonar systems at 100 and 500 kHz with a range of 100–400 m.

Additional data were obtained from the seismic records of a previous CSS *Dawson* cruise in 1987 (Forbes *et al.* 1991). The Nova Scotia Research Foundation Corporation deep-tow seismic system was deployed on this cruise and included a nine-element streamer and a 30-tip sparker source operating at 200 j. Echograms collected by the Canadian Hydrographic Service (14.25 kHz) were also used in the mapping of the offshore. A region from Sheet Harbour to Halifax was surveyed at a track spacing of 0.93 km (King *et al.* 1972).

Stratigraphic analysis is based on the method of Vail *et al.* (1977), termed seismic sequence analysis. This analysis is based on the recognition of unconformity-bound packages of strata. Boundaries between seismic sequences are recognized on seismic profiles by terminations of reflections. The boundaries are either erosional, lapout (hiatal) or conformable. Within each sequence, seismic 'facies' can be defined (Mitchum *et al.* 1977; Belknap & Shipp 1991). The facies are based on the continuity, amplitude and frequency of reflections. These acoustic

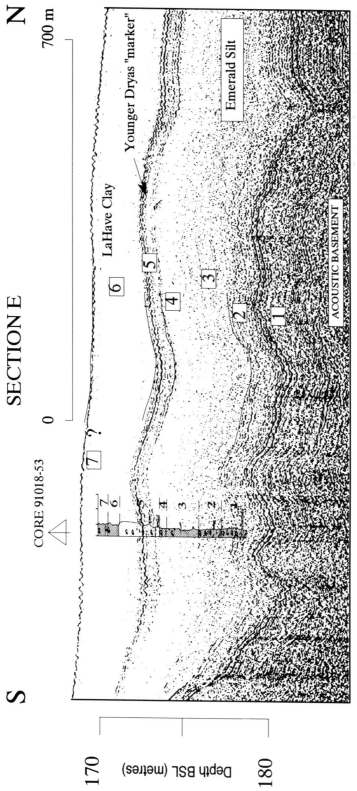

Fig. 3. Huntec seismic profile at location of core 91018-53 (E; Fig. 1). Core placement within the seismic section is based on matching high-amplitude reflections with coarse sediment beds in core 91018-53 and age dating core sediments. Note seismic marker horizon separating the Emerald Silt and LaHave Clay.

properties are an indication of the lithic properties of the strata. Seismic sequence and facies analysis allows interpretation of the depositional history of the region, including sea-level changes and changes in depositional styles during ice advance and retreat. King & Fader (1986) used seismic and lithofacies analysis to differentiate acoustic units on the Scotian Shelf. Boyd *et al.* (1988) were the first to utilize the sequence analysis approach on the Scotian Shelf in stratigraphic analyses of Sable Island Bank. Gipp (1989) defined seismic sequences within the Emerald Basin.

Sediment samples were collected with a modified benthos piston corer with a penetration capability of 20 m and a diameter of 7.3 cm. The Halifax sub-basin was piston cored at a location 2.5 km north of the Halifax Moraine (Figs 1 and 3). The core was taken 46 km south of the present coastline in 168 m water depth (Fig. 1). A distinctive, high-amplitude seismic horizon just below the LaHave Clay and above the Emerald Silt was targeted because of suspicions that it could relate to the Younger Dryas climatic event (Fig. 3; G. Fader, pers. comm. 1992). The core penetrated 9.36 m of sediment and 8.20 m of core was retained. Piston core 91018-53 was split, photographed, described and subsampled for grain size and biostratigraphic analysis. The 72 samples from this core were qualitatively analysed by D. Scott (pers. comm. 1992) and Costello (1994) for foraminiferal content. The senior author has re-interpreted some of Costello's original biofacies and includes additional data on marine pelecypod fauna. Radiocarbon dates were obtained from intact shell valves or valve fragments, and samples of total foraminifers.

Marine mollusc shell fragments and foraminifera were radiocarbon dated using accelerator mass spectrometry (AMS) and regular beta disintegration methods. Foraminifera were handpicked from sieved (<64 mm) separates for age dating. All ages were calculated with respect to the Libby half-life of 5570 years and reported with the value of one standard deviation error resulting from the random nature of the disintegration process. The reported dates are all adjusted for ^{13}C fractionation calculated relative to the PDB-1 international standard. They are not adjusted for the oceanic reservoir effect because the local variability of the effect is poorly understood. The shallow, isostatically enclosed basins of the Scotian Shelf prevented wholesale mixing of oceanic water (Piper *et al.* 1990). The 'younging', effect of mollusc burrowing may tend to mitigate or cancel out the 'aging' reservoir effect.

Results

Seismic stratigraphy of the Basin Zone

The lowest unit in the Basin Zone (Scotian Shelf Drift; Table 1) is characterized by incoherent backscatter, high reflectivity, high surface relief and local point source diffractions (Fig. 4). Over most of the Basin Zone, acoustic basement (internal reflections cannot be detected within this unit) occurs beneath a strong reflection with irregular relief marked by numerous side-echoes which extend 20–50 ms down-record. This acoustic basement is interpreted as Meguma Group bedrock (King & Fader 1986). Six stratified seismic sequences (1–6) with a total thickness from 12 to 14 m overlie acoustically incoherent units, the Scotian Shelf Drift (Table 1) and acoustic basement (bedrock) (A; Figs 1 and 4).

Sequence 1 is characterized by moderately continuous to discontinuous reflections of low to medium amplitude with local point source diffractions (boulders) (A; Fig. 4). At a reference section north of the Eastern Shore Moraine (D; Fig. 1), the lowest sequence (Fig. 5) has a draped geometry and consists of hummocky, coherent reflections of low continuity and low to moderate amplitude. Sequence 1 is generally thickest on the north side of the Eastern Shore and Halifax moraines (Fig. 1), thinning markedly in a northward direction to the Morainal Zone which marks the northern boundary of the Basin Zone.

Sequence 2 exhibits reflections of moderate to high continuity and amplitude. It has variable thicknesses, thickening on the northern and southern boundaries of the Basin Zone. Sequences 1 and 2 have a discordant relationship at the basin margin in section A (Fig. 4), but appear conformable in section D (Fig. 5). The reflection configurations of sequences 1 and 2 are similar to those described for the Emerald Silt facies 'A' by King & Fader (1986) (Table 1). Gipp (1989: 116) reported steep, erosional features on the Emerald Silt surface marked by hyperbolae and depressions, and interpreted these as buried pockmarks and iceberg furrows. These features are rare or absent in the Basin Zone of the inner shelf.

An erosional sequence boundary (A; Figs 4 and 5) separates sequences 2 and 3. This sequence boundary is best developed where it merges with an erosional surface that truncates sequences 1 and 2 on the northern side of the Eastern Shore Moraine (Fig. 5). This boundary in the rest of the basin is formed by downlap of sequence 3. In section A (Fig. 4) the acoustic impedance boundary represented by the unconformity is

C

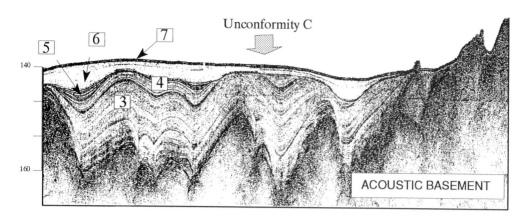

Unconformity C

ACOUSTIC BASEMENT

B

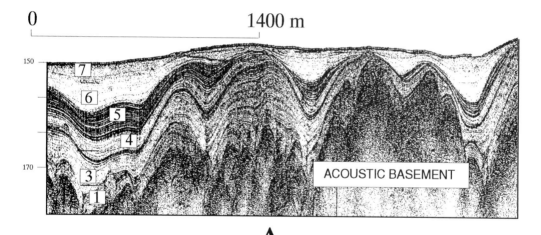

0   1400 m

ACOUSTIC BASEMENT

A

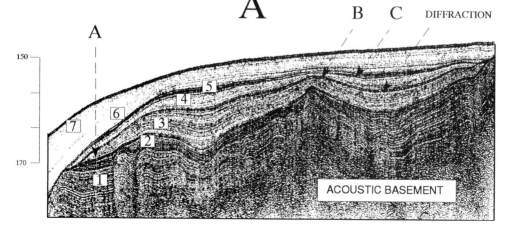

ACOUSTIC BASEMENT

N

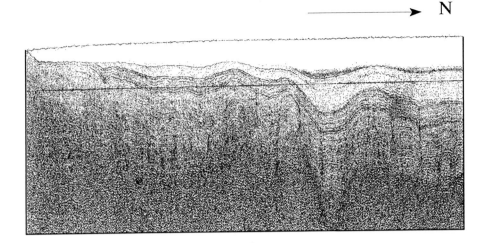

INTERPRETATION

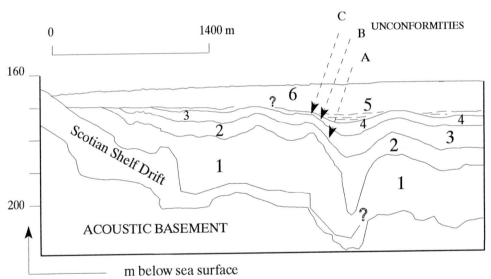

Fig. 5. Huntec seismic profile and interpretation of a reference section (D; Fig. 1) near Sheet Harbour. Seismic sequences (1–6) and erosional sequence boundaries (A–C) are shown. Depths are in metres below the sea surface.

indicated by a 'double' reflection, which may indicate an abrupt grain size change or the presence of gas (Belknap & Shipp 1991; Bacchus 1993).

Sequences 3 and 4 are characterized by reflections of low to moderate amplitude and continuity, and high reflection frequency. They are ponded in broad hollows within the underlying

Fig. 4. (Overleaf) Three reference sections for the Basin Zone near Halifax. Sequences are indicated by numbers (1–7) and erosional sequence boundaries by letters (A–C) (locations of segments A, B and C on Fig. 1). The arrow at the top of segment C marks a prominent unconformity near the top of sequence 4, probably formed during deposition of sequence 5.

acoustic strata. sequence 3 is thickest close to the moraines, whereas sequence 4 is thickest in the middle of the Basin Zone. Sequence 3 differs from sequence 4 with a higher percentage of point source diffractions (boulders) and slightly higher amplitude reflections. They are separated by an erosional sequence boundary (B; Figs 4 and 5). Sequences 3 and 4 are equivalent to Emerald Silt facies 'B' (Table 1). The rhythmic reflections evident in sequences 2, 3 and 4 may result from acoustic impedance contrasts between sand and silt layers and massive muds.

The boundary between sequences 4 and 5 is an unconformity (erosional truncation). This hiatal boundary can be traced to a well-developed planar erosional surface exposing sequences 3 and 4 near the landward basin margin (arrow, Fig. 4). At the type section (B, Fig. 4), sequence 5 consists of extremely high amplitude reflections (Emerald Silt Facies A) with a conformable or draped depositional style. Section D (Fig. 5), 50 km northeast, has a contrasting onlap-fill morphology.

Sequence 6 has reflections of low amplitude and continuity that onlap sequence 5 at the sequence boundary (C; Fig. 4) and is the seismostatigraphic equivalent to the LaHave Clay Formation of King & Fader (1986; Table 1). It is thickest in the northern end of the Basin Zone concomitant with the thinnest regions of Emerald Silt (sequences 1–4). A sequence boundary (6–7) is recognizable in sparker records B and C (Fig. 4), but is not seen in the Huntec records. Sequence 7 is marked by reflections of slightly higher amplitude than sequence 6.

Lithofacies of the Basin Zone. The core lithostratigraphy is described in Fig. 6.

Biofacies of the Basin Zone

Biofacies A. In core 91018-53, seven major biofacies were defined (Fig. 7). At the base of the core (800–620 cm) the dominant benthic foraminiferal species are *Elphidium excavatum* f. *clavatum* and *Cassidulina reniforme* (Fig. 7). Planktonic species are rare to absent. The

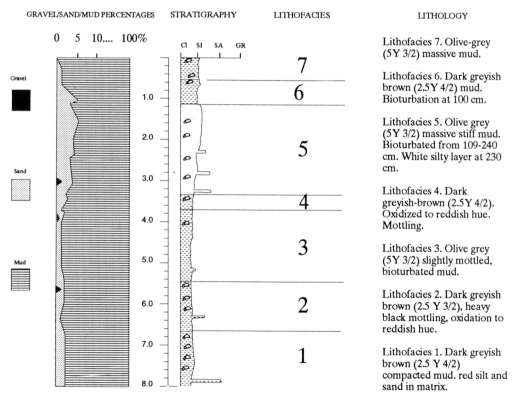

Fig. 6. Lithology, lithofacies and gravel/sand/mud percentages in core 91018-53. Dashed patterns refer to predominately clay–silt strata. Dotted pattern refers to sandy mud horizon (lithofacies 5).

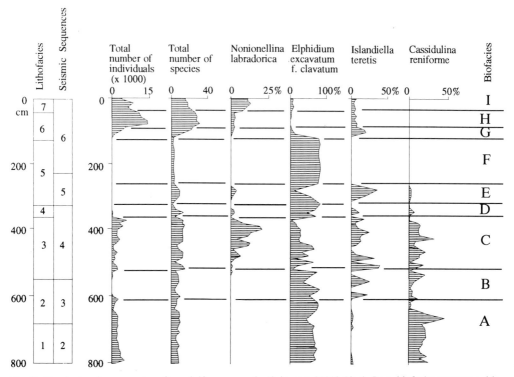

Fig. 7. Graph showing percentage foraminifera versus depth in core 91018-53. A–I are biofacies represented by foraminiferal assemblages (modified after Costello 1994).

preponderance of these species is indicative of a temperate ice margin (Scott *et al.* 1984). The total counts average about 2000 individuals/ 10 cm³. A single pelecypod valve (*Nucula* sp.) from the base of the core (750 cm) was dated at $13\,050 \pm 140$ [14]C years BP. The age at the base of the core is interpolated at 13.5 ^{14}C years BP. The core does not penetrate to the base of seismic sequence 2, but the basal age of sequence 2 is interpolated to be 14 ka (Fig. 8).

Biofacies B. Biofacies B from 620 to 520 cm depth, is characterized by a marked drop in total foraminiferal abundances to 103–500/10 cm³, similar but higher than abundances in biofacies E–F (described later). There is an influx of detrital material including reworked organics and reddish clastic grains between 500 and 600 cm. *Elphidium excavatum* f. *clavatum* remains the dominant species, but *Islandiella teretis* begins to appear in significant numbers. Between 570 and 530 cm the foraminiferal counts decrease to less than 300/ 10 cm³. Shell dates (*Yoldia thraciaeformis*) of $12\,020 \pm 90$ (590 cm) and $12\,230 \pm 70$ [14]C years BP were obtained from biofacies B. The interpolated age for the base of this interval is $12\,200$ [14]C years BP (Fig. 8).

Biofacies C. From 520 to 370 cm counts of total foraminifera increase to average about 2000/ 10 cm³. The fauna evolves into an assemblage similar to the present day benthic foraminiferal assemblage of the outer Labrador Current (34.5‰ salinity; 2–4°C; Scott *et al.* 1984) with the return of abundant *Nonionellina labradorica* and *Islandiella teretis*; however, *Elphidium excavatum* f. *clavatum* and *Cassidulina reniforme* are still the dominant species. The faunal assemblage of biofacies C persists to about 390 cm where *Cassidulina reniforme* decreases. *Nonionellina labradorica* peaks and then decreases markedly towards the top of biofacies C and total foraminiferal counts increase up-core until a marked drop at the top of biofacies C. An age of $12\,420 \pm 80$ [14]C years BP was obtained from bulk foraminifera. This date is approximately 1000 a older than the predicted age from the mollusc age–depth curve (Fig. 8). 'Old carbon' contamination may account for this discrepancy because foraminiferal samples cannot be etched and pretreated. Nielsen *et al.* (in press) found that total foraminiferal dates were systematically older than mollusc ages, which they interpret as a result of reworking (see Jennings *et al.* this volume). In biofacies C reworking appears to be

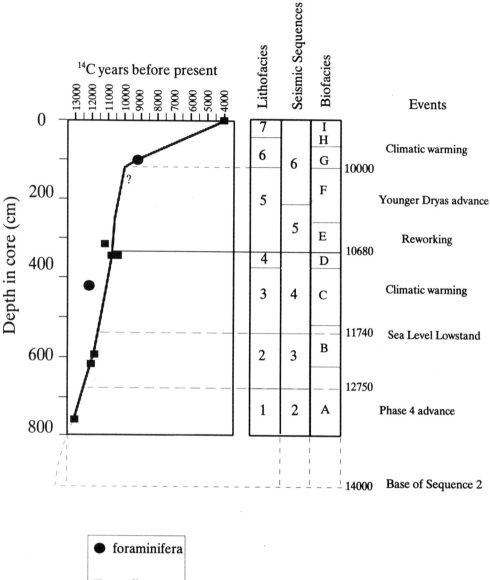

Fig. 8. Summary diagram of core 91018-53 showing correlation among foraminiferal assemblages, lithofacies and seismic sequences. Included are the interpolated ages of the boundaries between lithofacies, biofacies (foraminiferal assemblages) and seismic sequences (modified after Costello 1994 and Stea 1995).

minimal based on the abundance of 'new' species. Nielsen *et al.* (in press) also noted that the foram–mollusc age discrepancy decreases with decreasing sedimentation rates, from as high as 5000 to 600 years with sedimentation rates similar to core 91018-53 (1 m/ka). The interpolated age for the base of biofacies C is 11 650 ^{14}C years BP.

Biofacies D. Betweeen 370 and 340 cm the total foraminiferal count decreases from 600/10 to 300/10 cm[3]. *Elphidium excavatum* f. *clavatum* returns as the dominant species, but without a concomitant *C. reniforme* increase. Biofacies D was duplicate-dated to assess sampling variability and ages of 10 740 ± 90 and 10 870 ± 70 ^{14}C years BP were obtained from shell fragments (*Y. thraciaeformis*) at 345 cm. The age at the base of this interval is interpolated as 10 900 ^{14}C years BP (Fig. 8).

Biofacies E and F. Abruptly, at 340 cm, the total foraminiferal count drops markedly to less than 200/10 cm³, concomitant with the influx of sandy sediment (Figs 6 and 7). The faunal assemblage changes to one dominated by *E. excavatum* f. *clavatum* and several other species, including *N. labradorica, I. teretis* and *C. reniforme* (biofacies E). The variability in species percentages is not significant, however, because of low count totals (Patterson & Fishbein 1989). In this core interval there is an increase in reddish brown organic fragments (possibly algae, twigs and one spruce needle) and pyritized organic fragments. The base of biofacies E corresponds to the base of sandy lithofacies 5 (Figs 6 and 7). A shell sample (*Y. thraciaeformis*) at 287 cm produced an age of 11 340 ± 70 ^{14}C years BP. This shell is probably reworked from older deposits as erosion of previous deposits is clearly evident on the seismic records (Fig. 4). Biofacies E is largely a reworked assemblage. From 260 to 125 cm (biofacies F) total foraminiferal amounts remain low (17–132/10 cm³), but *E. excavatum* f. *clavatum* becomes the dominant species. Diatoms are common within biofacies E and F occurring in pulses of abundance. Diatoms have been reported in association with sea or pack ice (Kennett 1982). The interpolated age from the age–depth curve for the base of biofacies E (lithofacies 5) is 10 680 ^{14}C years BP (Fig. 8).

Biofacies G, H and I. From 104 cm to the top of the core there is a highly diverse assemblage of calcareous foraminifera (planktonic and benthic), with 4000–14 000 individuals per 10 cm³ (biofacies G–I; Fig. 7). The dominant species are *Bulimina marginata, N. labradorica, C. laevigata* and *Bolivina subaenariensis*. These biofacies are consistent with Holocene slope–shelf faunas of the Scotian Shelf described by Scott *et al.* (1984; 1989). A radiocarbon date of 9220 ± 90 ^{14}C years BP was obtained from total foraminifera at 98–100 cm depth (Fig. 8). A shell fragment (*Clinocardium* sp.) from 24 cm depth was dated at 3970 ± 60 ^{14}C years BP. The interpolated age at the base of biofacies G, based on an age-depth curve, is 9500 ^{14}C years BP (Fig. 8).

Correlations between core sections and seismic sections

The discrepancy of 1.16 m between the apparent penetration (clay on the outer core barrel) and actual core recovery is due to: (1) sediment being forced away form the core barrel by the force of core penetration and core acceleration (bypassing; Buckley *et al.* 1994); (2) sediment compaction; and (3) incorrect scope length. Apparently, the piston did not start moving at the correct time (D. J. W. Piper, pers. comm. 1994).

Assuming hypotheses 1 and or 3 to be correct, the core can be plotted on the seismic column displaced under the sea surface by 1.16 m. The horizontal position of the core in relation to the seismic section is shown on Fig. 3, but there may be up to 100 m of horizontal uncertainty (Fehr 1991). The trigger weight core did not deploy with core 91018-53, hence valuable information about the surface metre of sediment was lost.

The core and seismic stratigraphy may be best matched by correlating a unique event horizon in the core with a recognizable event in the seismic record. The uppermost sandy horizon within lithofacies 5 at 2.3 m can be matched neatly with the top of sequence 5 (Emerald Silt facies A) consisting of high amplitude reflecting horizons. If this match is made then the core is displaced under the sea surface by 1.2–1.8 m. This is close to agreement with the discrepancy between penetration and recovery.

Using the previously defined core placement within the acoustic section, and the core sediment properties, the core seismic sequences, facies, lithofacies and biofacies can be correlated. These correlations are illustrated in Fig. 8.

Interpretation of depositional processes

Sequence boundaries, as defined, have no genetic connotations but are purely descriptive (Mitchum *et al.* 1977). In models developed by Vail *et al.* (1977) sequence boundaries are considered to result from varying eustasy, tectonics and sediment supply producing changes in relative sea level (RSL). The basins in the inner shelf were always below sea level, hence the sequence boundaries must have formed from marine or glacial erosion and submarine onlap. The RSL fall may have indirectly played a part in some regions of the inner shelf basins. As the RSL falls, storm wave reworking is an increasingly important erosional agent. The RSL fall may have been sporadic rather than continuous, responding to advances of ice, forebulge migration and meltwater loading (Bloom 1963; Belknap *et al.* 1987; Stea *et al.* 1994). Resuspension by turbidity and currents generated by tidal and storm waves are probably the main mechanisms generating lapout boundaries and ponded geometries (Barrie & Piper 1982).

Erosional truncation surfaces can be produced by currents, density flows and by direct glacial erosion. Wedge-shaped sediment geometries are indicative of tidal currents (Piper *et al.* 1983; Syvitski *et al.* this volume).

Sequences 1 and 2

Sequences 1 and 2 are thickest at the southern end of the basins nearest the moraines (Figs 4 and 5). Although not directly sampled, it is assumed that they have common lithic characteristics with Emerald Silt facies A and C in the deeper basins south of the Scotian Shelf End–Moraine Complex (Table 1). Emerald Silt facies A and C are characterized by draped geometries. Reflections traceable for tens of kilometres are unique to facies A. Two conflicting interpretations have been proposed to explain the properties of these acoustic units: (1) rapid deposition beneath a debris-laden ice shelf by suspension settling (King & Fader 1986; Belknap & Shipp 1991; Bacchus 1993) and (2) suspension settling from overflow plumes away from a stationary ice front (Oldale *et al.* 1990). It is generally agreed that a draped geometry results from rapid suspension fallout and high sedimentation rates (Barrie & Piper 1982; Syvitski 1991; Belknap & Shipp 1991). Hypotheses 1 and 2 both produce draped geometries if the sedimentation rate is rapid enough. Facies C, without bedding, has rarely been sampled and is interpreted either as a grounding line proximal deposit or a till (King & Fader 1986). Rhythmic bedding can be produced by episodic deposition resulting from periodic changes in sediment delivery, by tidal action and seasonal (varve-like) variation in sediment supply (Phillips *et al.* 1991). The continuity of glaciomarine sediments can be explained by both models.

Powell (1984), Oldale *et al.* (1990), Anderson *et al.* (1991) and Syvitski (1991) argued that ice shelves cannot form in temperate zones. Belknap & Shipp (1991) countered some of the arguments based on ice dynamics by suggesting that the Gulf of Maine ice shelf was fed by fast-moving ice streams and buttressed by numerous pinning points. Gipp (1989) suggested a short-lived ice shelf in the Emerald Basin.

The most likely pinning points of a hypothetical ice shelf on the Scotian Shelf would be the outer banks. King & Fader (1986: 55) proposed that the SSEMC was formed underneath the ice shelf, at a sub-shelf pinning point, whereas till tongues and interfingering glaciomarine sediments formed simultaneously on the north and south sides of the moraines. The author did not observe till tongues on the landward (inner shelf basin) side of the SSEMC. On the landward side of the SSEMC, seismic records show a diachronous onlap relationship between the moraines and Emerald Silt facies A. If the ice shelf was pinned on the outer banks and Emerald Silt formed simultaneously with the SSEMC, then the sediment thicknesses should be approximately equal in basins north and south of the SSEMC, or perhaps thicker on the northern (glacier-proximal) inner shelf basins. However, sequence 1 thins sequentially to the north or landward of the SSEMC between a series of smaller moraines until it pinches out entirely (Stea 1995). These data suggest that at least the inner shelf basins were not covered by an ice shelf. The lack of iceberg scours in basin sediments of the inner shelf can be related to water depths. Iceberg furrowing seems to be restricted to the top surface of the SSEMC in the study area, in water depths less than 170 m.

Sequence 1 and 2 strata were deposited during sequential retreat and re-advances of the ice margin, represented by 'lift-off' moraines in the Basin Zone and DeGeer moraines in the Morainal Zone.

Sequences 3 and 4

Sequences 3 and 4 are correlative with biofacies B–D (Figs 7 and 8). Dominance of *Elphidium* within biofacies B suggests lowered salinities in an ice marginal setting (Osterman 1984; Scott *et al.* 1984). Biofacies C–D exhibit an increasing up-section trend to a cold water, higher salinity benthic fauna characteristic of the outer Labrador Current today (Scott *et al.* 1984). The lower part of the Holocene LaHave Clay (biofacies H) has a similar fauna (Fig. 7). On the Newfoundland shelf, foraminiferal assemblages associated with the upper part of Emerald Silt facies B are similar to the lowest parts of the LaHave Clay (Scott *et al.* 1984).

The onlap depositional style of sequences 3 and 4 has been interpreted as a result of resedimentation by currents and wave action (Barrie & Piper 1982; Piper *et al.* 1983; Gipp 1989; Belknap & Shipp 1991) or from reduced rates of deposition (Vorren *et al.* 1990). Asymmetrical thickness distibutions in the Basin Zone suggest wedging by tidal currents (Gipp 1989). Higher percentages of point source diffractions (boulder or boulder dumps), higher amplitude reflections and increased sediment thicknesses towards the former ice margin (northward; Fig. 4) suggest that sequence 3 was deposited closer to a glacial terminus than sequence 4. The frequency of point source diffractions implies that iceberg rafting played an important part in the deposition of this unit (Belknap & Shipp 1991; Bacchus 1993). The increased flux of sediment and erosion at the sequence boundary (B; Figs 4 and 5) may be due to: (1) falling sea levels and the increased influence of storm waves with suspension and transport of material from shallower areas to the Basin Zone; and (2) glacier re-advance, RSL rise and increased sedimentation and current erosional activity due to the proximity of a grounding line.

A sequence boundary may be formed by subglacial erosion, in the case of truncation, or by proglacial erosion and by slump-driven turbidity currents adjacent to a grounding line. Renewed crustal depression by advancing ice can form basin-wide sequence boundaries by changing the accommodation space available for sediment fill. Hypothesis 1 is favoured because the sea level had dropped to its lowest point *c.* 11.6 ka (Stea *et al.* 1994). Hypothesis 2 is less likely because at the time of formation of the sequence 3/4 boundary (11.7 ka), ice had retreated to the land areas of Nova Scotia (Gipp 1989; Stea & Mott 1989). Sequence 4, characterized by low amplitude reflections, was deposited during a quiescent phase when much of the outer banks were exposed, suppressing wave activity in the inner shelf basins.

Sequence 5

Sequence 5 is composed of conformably bedded, Emerald Silt facies 'A' , marked by an influx of coarser material and a drop in total foraminiferal abundance. The hypotheses put forward to explain the boundary between sequences 3 and 4 are also tenable for sequence 5. Hypothesis 1 (falling RSL) is unlikely because at the time of sequence 5 deposition (10.8 ka) sea levels had already dropped to their lowest levels (11.6 ka) and were rising (Stea *et al.* 1994). A glaciomarine environment (hypothesis 2) may be indicated by the *Elphidium*-dominated foraminiferal assemblage (Fig. 7), but the absence of *C. reniforme* is enigmatic as the two forms are normally found together in these Pleistocene glaciomarine environments (Scott & Medioli 1980; Vilks 1981; Seidenkrantz 1993). Diatom fluxes within

sequence 5 may point to an increased cover of winter sea ice and inorganic nutrient fluxes with decreased zooplankton grazing (Kennett 1982; Sancetta 1989). A core in deeper water from the Emerald Basin (83-012-01P; 20 km southeast of the study area) has a richer benthic fauna across a thinner correlative interval, which suggests a lower distal sedimentation rate (Scott *et al.* 1989; Costello 1994). The ice source probably was not a calving margin because point source diffractions (boulders) are lacking.

Sequence 5 thickens towards the south, away from the extensive Younger Dryas marine ice margin proposed by King (1994) and the less extensive terrestrial margins postulated by Stea & Mott (1989). Erosional surfaces synchronous with sequence 5 (Fig. 4) did not form by ice advances because lake sediment records indicate that adjacent land areas were cleared of ice by 12 ka and Younger Dryas glaciers were restricted to northern Nova Scotia (Stea & Mott 1989).

We interpret this event horizon as a response to increased sedimentation and erosion. The increased sediment flux and current activity can be explained by: (1) rising sea levels over the outer banks creating enhanced wave erosion on the inner shelf as the outer banks became submerged and no longer inhibited the propagation of open sea waves; (2) increased frequency of storms and precipitation concomitant with ice build-up on land (Stea & Mott 1989); (3) debris-laden sea ice and increased sediment supply from the devegetated coastline which was about 20 km seaward of present (Stea *et al.* 1994); and (4) permanent and semi-permanent snowpacks and small glaciers, terminating in shallow water northeast of the study area, providing plumes of low-salinity, sediment-laden water. The intensity of the sedimentation response during the Younger Dryas climatic event is unparalleled during late glacial and Holocene times when glaciers were removed from the Basin Zone. Stea *et al.* (1992*b*) presented a preliminary interpretation of pre-Holocene marine events on the inner shelf after initial seismostratigraphic interpretation. Although details have changed, the basic six phase evolutionary model is still valid (Fig. 9).

Fig. 9. Six-phase model of proposed deglaciation and sea level events on the Eastern Shore of Nova Scotia (modified after Stea *et al.* 1992*b*). (1) Scotian Shelf end moraines form at the ramp-margin of a grounded glacier. (2) Retreat to 'proto' moraine. Proglacial deposition of sequence 1. (3) Retreat, then a re-advance or surge *c.* 13 ka forming 'symmetrical' moraines and sequence 2 in the Basin Zone (Stea 1995). (4) Retreat and shoaling of the glacier; increased wave activity, turbulence, and dropping sea levels entrain sediments. Sequence 3 deposited in the Basin Zone. (5) Lowstand nadir. Erosion at the lowstand nadir produces a shoreline (Truncation Zone–Transition Subzone) and sequence boundary 3–4 in the Basin Zone. Subsequent sea-level rise and climatic warming. Sequence 4 deposited in the Basin Zone. (6) Climatic cooling, and increased storminess, sea ice and icebergs increase sedimentation rates during the Younger Dryas. Sequence 5 is deposited in the Basin Zone.

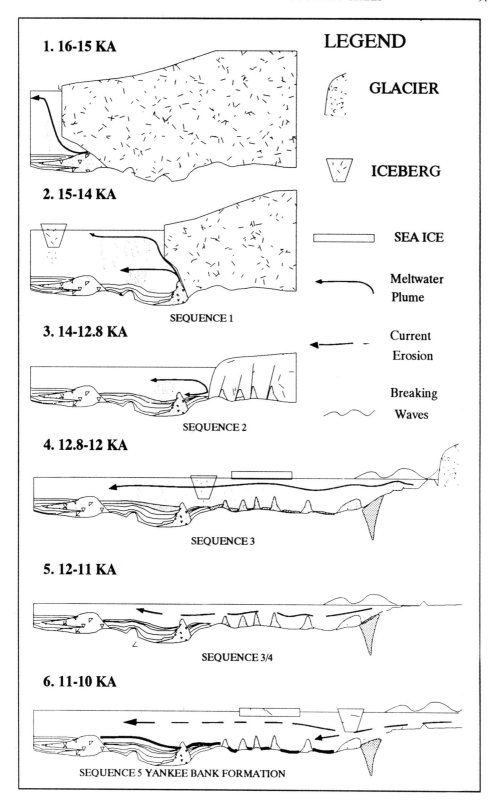

The erosional boundary between sequences 6 and 7 may indicate a period of increased current activity (storminess) during the Holocene. The age of this event could not be determined because of the poor quality of the upper part of the seismic record at the core section (Fig. 4).

Lithostratigraphic designations

The inner shelf basins reveal a sequence of glaciomarine and marine deposits that are broadly similar to the post-glacial depositional sequences described in many of the glaciated shelves of the northern hemisphere (Syvitski 1991). These sections were deposited during ice retreat and (at least in the inner shelf) are strongly diachronous at the base or ice proximal parts (Emerald Silt facies A), becoming broadly synchronous in the ice distal facies (Emerald Silt facies B). The correspondence of seismic sequences over a broad area implies an analogous deglaciation history.

King & Fader (1986) set up a lithostratigraphic framework for glaciomarine deposits in the Scotian Shelf. The Emerald Silt Formation was defined by King & Fader (1986) as gravelly mud and mud overlying the Scotian Shelf Drift and underlying the LaHave Clay (Table 1). The Emerald Silt encompasses sequences 1–4 and facies A, B and C. The uppermost sequences of the Basin Zone (6, 7; Fig. 4) are correlative with

the LaHave Clay Formation (King & Fader 1986; 1988; Table 1). They represent Holocene marine deposition. The interpolated basal date of 9.2 ka (Fig. 8) agrees well with the basal date of the LaHave Clay (9.4 ka) obtained in the northern Emerald Basin by King & Fader (1988). Sequence 5, dated between 10.7 and 9.2 ka, separates the Emerald Silt and the LaHave Clay (Fig. 8). Sequence 5 can be traced to an unconformity at the top of the Emerald Silt Formation, in the northeastern Emerald Basin, dated between 10.0 and 10.5 ka (King & Fader 1988). This sequence (inner shelf), characterized by Emerald Silt facies A with high amplitude reflections, is a marker horizon on the inner shelf, is regionally mappable, has unique seismic, lithic and biological characteristics, and should be conferred with formation status to augment King & Fader's (1986) useful classification. We propose the name Yankee Bank Formation (the nearest geographical name to the type section) to apply to sequence 5–Lithofacies 5–Biofacies E–F, bounded on the bottom by the Emerald Silt Formation and on the top by the LaHave Clay Formation (Table 2).

Local and regional correlations

The Yankee Bank Formation can be traced in basins across the continental shelf of Nova Scotia and possibly the Gulf of St Lawrence and Newfoundland. Marsters (1988) described a core (77-15) off Mahone Bay (see also Piper *et al.* 1986) with an oscillation in foraminiferal assemblages from an ice-marginal fauna (*Elphidium-Cassidulina*) (5.4–3.7 m) to a zone with low foraminiferal counts (2.5–3 m) and then a post-glacial assemblage (0–2 m) characterized by increasing numbers of *I. teretis*. Marsters (1988) interpreted the 'barren zone' as a period of rapid deposition. The similarity in biostratigaphy and depth suggests that the 'barren zone' is correlative with the Yankee Bank Formation. The seismic record of this core site does not resolve any distinct horizon, but is of poor quality (Piper *et al.* 1986). In the Emerald Basin a correlative horizon has been noted, but its significance was not discussed (Moran *et al.* 1989; Buckley *et al.* 1994). At a similar core level, Scott *et al.* (1989) reported a short interval of increased sediment flux and a return to an ice marginal fauna, but failed to recognize this as the equivalent of the Younger Dryas. Scott *et al.* (1989) and Keigwin & Jones (1995) argued that oxygen isotope data from these cores did not indicate a meltwater spike before or during the

Table 2. *Correlation of seismic sequences, Quaternary formations, and genetic interpretations for the study region*

Sequence	Formation	Interpretation
6	LaHave Clay	Holocene marine clay
5	Yankee Bank Formation	'Paraglacial' deposit
4	Emerald Silt Formation	Glacial marine deposit—distal
3		
2		Glacial marine deposit—proximal
1		
	Scotian Shelf Drift	Till
	Acoustic basement	Bedrock–Meguma Group metasediments

Younger Dryas expected from flood trigger theories (cf. Broecker & Denton 1990), but a short positive excursion in $^{18}O/^{16}O$ ratios dated c. 11 ka, however, indicates a climatic cooling. Examination of recent cores from the Emerald Basin has revealed a correlative horizon between the Emerald Silt and LaHave Clay (P. Mandell pers. comm. 1995; Hall this volume). The boundary between sequences 4 and 5 in the southwest Emerald Basin is a single strong reflection that Piper & Fehr (1991) attributed to the Younger Dryas climatic event. On Banquereau, Amos & Miller (1990) interpreted a conformably bedded sand unit dated at 11 ka as a proglacial unit based on the presence of an ice-marginal foraminiferal fauna.

Figure 10 is a summary correlation diagram of formations, seismic sequences and seismic facies within the inner and outer Scotian Shelf and Gulf of Maine basins. Each region displays a general progression from Scotian Shelf Drift (massive glaciomarine) to Emerald Silt facies A and facies B (proximal to distal glaciomarine) (cf. Syvitski 1991). The distal glaciomarine unit of Bacchus (1993) is a weakly stratified, ponded unit, similar to the uppermost seismic sequence 4 of the Emerald Silt, which varies from acoustically transparent to weakly stratified. It may be correlative with the lower portion of the LaHave Clay or the uppermost Emerald Silt Formation

(Fig. 10). Separating the transitional and distal glaciomarine facies in the Gulf of Maine is a strong double reflection which has been termed the Truxton Event (G. Fader pers. comm. 1992). In some areas of the Gulf of Maine this horizon is represented by a series of high-amplitude reflections. Cores through this unit revealed a distinctive, laminated, red–brown, gravelly to sandy mud (Bacchus 1993: 172). The Truxton Event in the Gulf of Maine was estimated to be between 14.4 and 12.5 ka based on amino acid racemization dating, but the method has a 2000 year uncertainty (Bacchus 1993). Possible correlative horizons in the inner shelf study area are the sequence 3/4 boundary and the Yankee Bank Formation (Fig. 10).

Loring & Nota (1973) reported a reddish, gravelly sand unit at the base of Holocene mud in the Gulf of St Lawrence, which they interpreted as till from a local ice advance. They obtained shell ^{14}C ages between 10 and 11 ka and correlated the distinctive reddish horizon with the European Younger Dryas event. Syvitski (1991) defined a coarse, well-stratified 'paraglacial' unit at the same stratigraphic interval as that described by Loring & Nota. He interpreted this distinct reflection horizon as a result of increased sedimentation due to widespread melting and a sea-level lowstand.

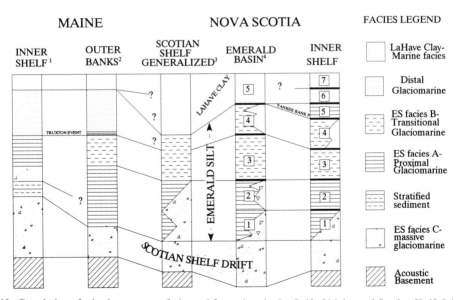

Fig. 10. Correlation of seismic sequences, facies and formations in the Gulf of Maine and Scotian Shelf. Seismic sequences numbered 1–7. Sequence boundaries are shown as bold lines. Maine inner shelf stratigraphy from Belknap & Shipp (1991). Maine outer shelf stratigraphy from Bacchus (1993). Generalized Scotian Shelf stratigraphy from King & Fader (1986). Emerald Basin seismic stratigraphy from Gipp (1989) and Piper & Fehr (1991).

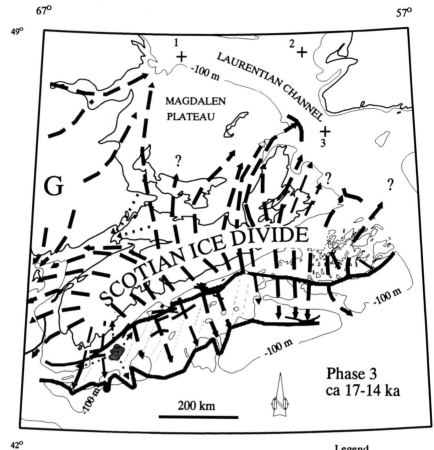

Phase 3
ca 17-14 ka

200 km

Phase 4
ca 12.7 ka

200 km

Legend

Ice flow line .... – ➔

Ice flow line (later).......... · · · ▸

Ice margin....................... ——

Ice shelf............................ ⟨∕∕⟩

Ice rise............................

End moraines................

G Gaspereau Ice
Centre/Divide

Conolly *et al.* (1967) described two 'brick red till' units in cores in the Gulf of St Lawrence below Holocene mud (Fig. 11). They correlated these 'tills' with reddish ice-rafted layers in cores from the adjacent continental slope dated between 12 and 15 ka. Bond & Lotti (1995) reported an age date of 13.3 ka above the 'brick red till' unit in core V17-203 (2, Fig. 11). These reddish coarse units probably represent iceberg tills or proximal glacial marine deposition from phase 3 and 4 ice advances into the Laurentian Channel through troughs in the Magdalen Plateau, which is underlain by Carboniferous continental red beds (Fig. 11). Josenhans *et al.* (1991) describe 'till-tongues' that emanate from the Cape Breton Channel and pinch out into Emerald Silt in the Laurentian Channel, marking the former ice marginal position of a localized ice stream (Fig. 11). Diamicton from this till-tongue was found to have a Cape Breton provenance (Stea 1991). The ice stream can be traced to the Scotian Ice Divide over mainland Nova Scotia, which flowed northward across highland areas and then was funnelled into the submarine channels that dissect the Magdalen Plateau (Stea *et al.* 1989). The SSEMC was deposited between 17 and 14 ka during the development of the Scotian Ice Divide (Gipp 1989; Stea *et al.* 1992a; 1992b; Fig. 11). Correlation of the SSEMC and terrestrial ice flow events was based on till lithology, grain size and provenance for both terrestrial and marine units (Stea *et al.* 1992b; Stea 1995).

Bond & Lotti (1995) correlated the red brick 'till' unit with Heinrich event 1 (*c.* 14 ka) in deep ocean cores, characterized by peaks of hematite-coated grains presumably derived from Appalachian–Carboniferous red bed sources. Based on correlations established in this paper, Heinrich events can be tied to local ice development in eastern Canada rather than surges of Laurentide ice (MacAyeal 1993).

The Morainal Zone (Figs 1 and 2) and proglacial sequence 2 (Emerald Silt facies A) are interpreteted as marginal deposits of a short-lived re-advance from local ice centres in northern Nova Scotia (ice flow phase 4; Fig. 11) (Stea *et al.* 1992b). The correlation is based on land–sea till lithology and the orientation of moraines within the Morainal Zone (Stea 1995). Sequence 2 is interpreted as a proglacial deposit from phase 4 ice and is dated between 12.7 and 14.0 ka. Raised marine deposits along the Bay of Fundy at the phase 4 ice margin are dated from 14.5 to 12.6 ka (Stea *et al.* 1987). Glacial re-advances at *c.* 13 ka have been proposed in Newfoundland, New Brunswick and Maine (Borns & Hughes 1977; Brookes 1977; Proudfoot *et al.* 1988; Nicks 1988). These advances may be correlative with the Port Huron advance of the midcontinent, as Borns & Hughes (1977) first suggested.

Correlation of marine and terrestrial deglaciation records

Seismic sequences within the sedimentary infill of the Basin Zone record deglaciation and sea-level change. The sedimentary record from core 91018-53 in the Halifax subzone spans the time from 13 to 2 ka. On land, lake core records span the same length of time (Mott *et al.* 1986; Ogden 1987; Jetté & Mott 1989) and can be used for correlation.

Most lake cores in Nova Scotia show successions of pollen zones and lithostratigraphy that indicate climatic fluctuations (Livingstone & Livingstone 1958; Mott *et al.* 1986; Ogden 1987; Jetté & Mott 1989; Mayle *et al.* 1993). Glacio-fluvial sand and glaciolacustrine, rhythmically laminated mud can be found at the base of most lakes in Nova Scotia. Over most of mainland Nova Scotia, these deposits are succeeded by black or brown organic mud accumulation (gyttja), which has been radiocarbon dated between 13 and 12 ka (Jetté & Mott 1989; Mott 1994). Most pollen successions in lake gyttja during this time record a change from tundra to spruce forests, indicating climatic amelioration (Ogden 1987; Jetté & Mott 1989; Mott 1994). Around 10.8 ka an abrupt and pronounced climatic deterioration occurred that strongly affected the landscape and its vegetation cover. Lake cores reveal a sedimentological 'oscillation' that marks the Younger Dryas chronozone

Fig. 11. Evolution (advance and retreat) of ice divides and domes over Maritime Canada during the Late Wisconsinan (17–10 ka). (A) Advance and retreat of phase 3 ice (Scotian Ice Divide). A short-lived ice shelf pinned on the outer banks may have formed during initial deglaciation from a larger ice mass (Escuminac Ice Center) centred on the Magdalen Plateaux (Phase 2). An ice rise was postulated by Gipp (1989) in southern Nova Scotia. The landward ice margin is marked by the Scotian Shelf End–Moraine Complex. Cores from Loring & Nota (1973; 1) and Conolly *et al.* (1967; 2–3) marked by crosses. (B) Ice flow phase 4. Ice flow data from: Chalmers 1895; Prest & Grant 1969; Rampton *et al.* 1984; Pronk *et al.* 1989; Rappol 1989; Stea *et al.* 1992a; Stea 1995).

(11 000–10 000 years BP). This oscillation is defined by a distinct mineralic layer that separates gyttja near the base of the cores (Mott *et al.* 1986) from gyttja that constitutes the rest of the cores. This mineralic layer is bracketed by radiocarbon dates ranging from 11 000 to 10 200 years BP with a mean of approximately 10.8 ka (Mott & Stea 1994). Changes in pollen assemblages in these lakes imply a warmer–cold–warmer climatic cycle. In southern Nova Scotia, the mineralic layer formed by solifluction of the adjacent devegetated slopes and runoff from ephemeral or permanent snowpacks during the reversion to cold climatic conditions (Stea & Mott 1992; Mott & Stea 1994). The remaining record in the lake cores indicates an initial rapid warming and climate fluctuations during the Holocene (Ogden 1987; Jetté & Mott 1989).

In northern mainland Nova Scotia, stratigraphic sections reveal diamictons, clay and sand overlying peat deposits that pre-date the mineralic layer in lake chronologies (Fig. 12). Radiocarbon ages from wood and peat at the top of the peat layer and from the top of the lower gyttja layer cluster around 10.8 ka (Fig. 13). Stea

& Mott (1989) interpret these findings as indications of renewed glacierization in this region *c.* 10.8 ka.

Offshore seismic sequences and events can be correlated with the onshore lake stratigraphy. We correlate the Yankee Bank Formation with the Younger Dryas mineralic layer in the lakes and glacigenic sediments that overlie peat in land sections. In both terrestrial and marine records a zone of increased inorganic sedimentation is bracketed by organic-rich sediments with biota indicative of a warming trend. The inorganic sedimentation events were initiated at around 10.8 ka and represent climatic cooling and snowfield or glacier build-up on land and increased sedimentation in the marine realm. The initiation dates on land and in the ocean are synchronous (Figs 8 and 13). The 400 year lag time of oceanic ^{14}C equilibration (Mangerud 1972) is widely used and may not be applicable here as partial isolation from the open ocean may have increased the mixing time within these nearshore basins. Circulation changes in the ocean at that time may have also affected reservoir ages (Broecker & Denton 1990).

Fig. 12. Intensely deformed and compacted peat beds overlain by diamicton interpreted as till at Collins Pond, Nova Scotia (Stea & Mott 1989; Stea & Mott 1992; Mott & Stea 1994). This is the type section for glacigenic deposits of the Younger Dryas chronozone in Nova Scotia.

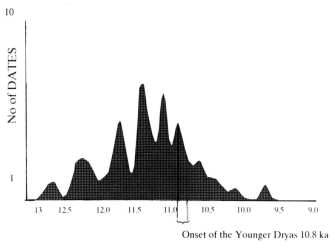

Fig. 13. Uncalibrated histogram of ^{14}C dates from 55 peat and wood samples collected from the top and bottom of buried late glacial organic horizons found throughout Nova Scotia. Onset of the Younger Dryas *c.* 10.8 ka is indicated by the rapid increase in intensity of dates. The ^{14}C histogram program from Stolk *et al.* (1994).

Discussion

Debate on the causes of climate change during the last termination has focused on the relative importance of external climatic forcing (e.g. astronomical) versus internal glaciodynamic and oceanic feedback mechanisms within large ice sheets (Crowley & North 1991). The case for climatic forcing can be strengthened if advances from autonomous, smaller scale glaciers are synchronous and matched by cooling records in their periglacial environments.

Seismic sequences and facies in the inner shelf basins of Nova Scotia record the changing depositional regimes associated with advances, stillstands and retreats from Appalachian-centred glaciers rather than the Laurentide ice sheet, as so commonly depicted in publications (cf. Denton & Hughes 1981). Glaciomarine sedimentation events in offshore basins exhibit a millennial-scale periodicity that matches climatic oscillations documented in terrestrial records. Figure 14 compares the chronology of Appalachian glacier advances documented in this study with the southern sector of the Laurentide ice sheet, Agassiz flood events and deep-sea Heinrich events. The early deglaciation record of Appalachian ice on the Scotian Shelf is not well constrained, but appears to be in phase with advancing Laurentide ice (Fayette Stade). Formation of the Scotian Ice

Divide (Fig. 14), however, appears out of phase with Laurentide ice, occurring during an interstadial in the continental chronology. This divide resulted from drawdown into the isostatically depressed Bay of Fundy and was later stabilized by isostatic uplift along the Atlantic margin (Prest & Grant 1969; Stea 1995). Ice streams confined to submarine channels that cut the Magdalen Plateau produced iceberg discharges that may have contributed to deep sea Heinrich layer 1. This layer features a peak in red bed derived material (Bond & Lotti 1995). Bond & Lotti (1995) suggest that during Heinrich events 1 and 2, Icelandic and Laurentide (Appalachian?) ice sheets discharged icebergs synchronously. Late glacial re-advances *c.* 12.7 ka (Robinsons Head–Phase 4–Sequence 2; *c.* 12.7) can be correlated with mid-continent advances (Fig. 14) and northwest Atlantic counterparts (Elverhøi *et al.* 1995). Keigwin & Jones (1995) document a local cooling event in Scotian Slope cores (*c.* 13 ka). The Younger Dryas event has been correlated across the Atlantic (Mott *et al.* 1986; Broecker & Denton 1990). Iceberg discharges and increased snowfall as storm tracks shifted over the region, may have accentuated local cooling during the Younger Dryas, which was also driven by external forcing tuned to the millennial Dansgaard–Oeschger cycles.

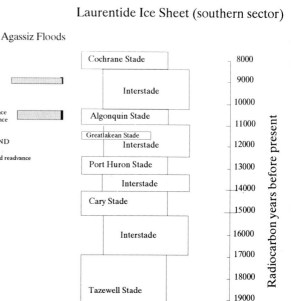

Fig. 14. Correlation of glacial advances and retreats from the mid-continent (Laurentide ice sheet), including meltwater fluxes from Lake Agassiz, with the glacial and 'para' glacial record of the Appalachian ice complex. Also shown is the chronology of deep sea Heinrich events. Laurentide record modified from Mayewski *et al.* (1981).

References

AMOS, C. L. & KNOLL, R. G. 1987. The Quaternary sediments of Banquereau, Scotian Shelf. *Geological Society of America Bulletin*, **99**, 244–260.
—— & MILLER, A. A. L. 1990. The Quaternary stratigraphy of southwest Sable Island Bank, eastern Canada. *Geological Society of America Bulletin*, **102**.
ANDERSON, J. B., KENNEDY, D. S., SMITH, M. J. & DOMACK, E. W. 1991. Sedimentary facies associated with Antarctica's floating ice masses. *In*: ANDERSON, J. B. & ASHLEY, G. M. (eds) *Glacial Marine Sedimentation; Paleoclimatic Significance*. Geological Society of America, Special Paper, **261**, 1–25.
BACCHUS, T. S. 1993. *Late Quaternary stratigraphy and evolution of the eastern Gulf of Maine*. PhD Thesis, University of Maine, Orono.
BARRIE, Q. C. & PIPER, D. J. W. 1982. *Late Quaternary Marine Geology of Makkovic Bay, Labrador*. Geological Survey of Canada, Paper, **81–17**.
BELKNAP, D. F. & SHIPP, R. C. 1991. Seismic stratigraphy of glacial marine units, Maine inner shelf. *In*: ANDERSON, J. B. & ASHLEY, G. M. (eds) *Glacial Marine Sedimentation: Paleoclimatic Significance*. Geological Society of America, Special Paper, **261**, 137–157.

——, ANDERSEN, B. G. & 10 others 1987. Late Quaternary sea-level changes in Maine. *In*: NUMMEDAL, D., PILKEY, O. H. JR & HOWARD, J. D. (eds) *Sea-level Fluctuations and Coastal Evolution*. SEPM, Special Publication, **41**, 71–85.
BLOOM, A. L. 1963. Late Pleistocene fluctuation of sea-level and post-glacial crustal rebound in coastal Maine. *American Journal of Science*, **261**, 862–879.
BOND, G. C. & LOTTI, R. 1995. Iceberg discharges into the North Atlantic on millenial time scales during the last glaciation. *Science*, **267**, 1005–1010.
BORNS, H. W. JR & HUGHES, T. J. 1977. The implications of the Pineo Ridge readvance in Maine. *Géographie physique et Quaternaire*, **31**, 203–206.
BOYD, R., SCOTT, D. B. & DOUMA, M. 1988. Glacial tunnel valleys and Quaternary history of the outer Scotian Shelf. *Nature*, **333**, 61–64.
BROECKER, W. A. & DENTON, G. H. 1990. What drives glacial cycles? *Scientific American*, Jan, 49–56.
BROOKES, I. A. 1977. Radiocarbon age of Robinson's Head moraine, west Newfoundland, and its significance for postglacial sea-level changes. *Canadian Journal of Earth Sciences*, **14**, 2121–2126.
BUCKLEY, D. E., MACKINNON, W. G., CRANSTON, R. E. & CHRISTIAN, H. 1994. Problems with piston core sampling: mechanical and geochemical diagnosis. *Marine Geology*, **117**, 95–106.

BUDD, W. F. & SMITH, I. N. 1987. Conditions for growth and retreat of the Laurentide Ice Sheet. *Géographie physique et Quaternaire*, **41**, 279–290.

CHALMERS, R. 1895. Report on the surface geology of eastern New Brunswick, northwestern Nova Scotia and a portion of Prince Edward Island. *Geological Survey of Canada, Annual Report 1894*, Vol. 1, No. 7, Part M.

CLARK, P. U., CLAGUE, J. J. & 14 others 1993. Intitiation and development of the Laurentide and Cordilleran ice sheets following the last glaciation. *Quaternary Science Reviews*, **12**, 79–114.

COK, A. E. 1970. *Morphology and surficial sediments of the eastern half of the Nova Scotia Shelf*. PhD Dissertation, Dalhousie University, Halifax.

CONOLLY, J. R., NEEDHAM, H. D. & HEEZEN, B. C. 1967. Late Pleistocene and Holocene sedimentation in the Laurentian Channel. *Journal of Geology*, **75**, 131–147.

COOKE, H. B. S. 1973. Pleistocene chronology: long or short? *Quaternary Research*, **3**, 206–220.

COSTELLO, O. P. 1994. *Paleooceanographic reconstruction of the inner Scotian Shelf during the Younger Dryas: a benthic foraminiferal study*. BSc (Hons) Thesis, Dalhousie University, Halifax.

CROWLEY, T. J. & NORTH, G. R. 1991. *Paleoclimatology*. Oxford University Press, New York.

DENTON, G. H. & HUGHES, T. J. 1981. *The Last Great Ice Sheets*. Wiley, Toronto.

DRAPEAU, G. & KING, L. H. 1972. *Surficial Geology of the Yarmouth–Browns Bank Map Area*. Geological Survey of Canada, Marine Science Paper, **72-24**.

DYKE, A. S. & PREST, V. K. 1987. Late Wisconsinan and Holocene history of the Laurentide Ice Sheet. *In*: FULTON, R. J. & ANDREWS, J. T. (eds) *The Laurentide Ice Sheet*. *Géographie physique et Quaternaire*, **41**, 237–264.

ELVERHØI, A., ANDERSEN, E. & 8 others 1995. The growth and decay of Late Weichselian ice sheet in Western Svalbard and adjacent areas based on provenance studies of the marine record *In*: *Quaternary Research Association, Royal Society of Edinburgh, Annual Discussion Meeting 1995, Abstracts Volume*.

FADER, G. B. J., MILLER, R., STEA, R. R. & PECORE, S. 1991. *Cruise Report 91018: HMCS Dawson, Operations on the Inner Scotian Shelf*. Geological Survey of Canada, Open File, **2633**.

FLINT, R. F. 1971. *Glacial and Quaternary Geology*. Wiley, Toronto.

FOISY, M. & PRICHONNET, G. 1991. Reconstruction of glacial events in southeastern New Brunswick. *Canadian Journal of Earth Sciences*, **28**, 1594–1612.

FORBES, D. L., BOYD, R. & SHAW, J. 1991. Late Quaternary sedimentation and sea-level changes on the inner Scotian Shelf. *Quaternary Shelf Research*, **11**, 1155–1179.

GIPP, M. R. 1989. *Late Wisconsinan deglaciation of Emerald Basin*. MSc Thesis, Memorial University, St Johns, Newfoundland.

——1994. Late Wisconsinan deglaciation of Emerald Basin, Scotian Shelf. *Canadian Journal of Earth Sciences*, **31**, 554–566.

—— & PIPER, D. J. W. 1989 Chronology of Late Wisconsinan glaciation, Emerald Basin, Scotian Shelf. *Canadian Journal of Earth Sciences*, **26**, 333–335.

GRANT, D. R. 1989. Quaternary geology of the Atlantic Appalachian region of Canada. *In*: FULTON. R. H. (ed.) *Quaternary Geology of Canada and Adjacent Greenland*. Geological Survey of Canada, Geology of Canada, **1** (also Geological Society of America, The Geology of North America, **K-1**), 393–440.

HUTCHINS, R. W., McKEOWN, D. & King, L. H. 1976. A deep tow high resolution seismic system for continental shelf mapping. *Geoscience Canada*, **3** 95–100.

JETTÉ, H. & MOTT, R. J. 1989. Palynostratigraphie du tardiglaciaire et de l'Holocéne de la région du lac Chance Harbour, Nouvelle-Ecosse. *Géographie physique et Quaternaire*, **43**, 27–38.

JOSENHANS, H., JOHNSTON, L., JARRETT, K., SMITH, D. & ZEVENHUISEN, J. 1991. Surficial geological investigations in the Gulf of St. Lawrence. *Cruise Report: Hudson 90-028*.

KEIGWIN, L. D. & JONES, G. A. 1995. The marine record of deglaciation from the continental margin off Nova Scotia. *Paleooceanography*, **10**, 973–985.

KELLEY, J. T., BELKNAP, D. F. & SHIPP, R. C. 1989. Sedimentary framework of the southern Maine inner continental shelf: Influence of glaciation and sea-level change. *Marine Geology*, **90**, 139–147.

KENNETT, J. P. 1982. *Marine Geology*. Prentice-Hall, Englewood Cliffs.

KING, L. H. 1970. *Surficial Geology of the Halifax–Sable Island Map Area*. Marine Science Branch, Geological Survey of Canada, Paper, **1**.

——1994. Proposed Younger Dryas glaciation of the eastern Scotian Shelf. *Canadian Journal of Earth Sciences*, **31**, 401–417.

—— & FADER, G. B. 1986. Wisconsinan glaciation of the Continental Shelf of Southeast Atlantic Canada. *Geological Survey of Canada, Bulletin*, **363**.

—— & ——1988. *A Comparison Between the Late Wisconsinan History of Southwest and Northeast Emerald Basins*. Geological Survey of Canada, Open File, Report **2060**.

——, MACLEAN, B. & DRAPEAU, G. 1972. The Scotian Shelf submarine end-moraine complex. *In*: *Proceedings of International Geological Congress, 24th Session, Section 8; Marine Geology and Geophysics*, 237–249.

LIVINGSTONE, D. A. & LIVINGSTONE, B. G. R. 1958. Late-glacial and postglacial vegetation from Gillis Lake in Richmond County, Cape Breton Island, Nova Scotia. *American Journal of Science*, **256**, 341–359.

LORING, D. H. & NOTA, D. J. G. 1973. Morphology and sediments of the Gulf of St. Lawrence. *Fisheries Research Board of Canada, Bulletin*, **182**.

MACAYEAL, D. R. 1993. Binge/purge oscillations of the Laurentide ice sheet as a cause of the North Atlantic's Heinrich Events. *Paleoceanography*, **8**, 775–784.

MAYLE, F. E., LEVESQUE, A. J. & CWYNAR, L. C. 1993. Alnus as an indicator taxon of the Younger Dryas cooling in Eastern North America. *Quaternary Science Reviews*, **12**, 295–305.

MANGERUD, J. 1972. Radiocarbon dating of marine shells, including a discussion of apparent ages of Recent shells from Norway. *Boreas*, **1** 143–172.

MARSTERS, S. 1988. *Latest Pleistocene–Holocene paleoceanographic trends on the inner shelf of the south shore of Nova Scotia: benthic foraminiferal evidence*. BSc (Hons) Thesis, Dalhousie University, Halifax.

MCLAREN, S. A. 1988. *Quaternary Stratigraphy of the Sable Island Sand Body*. Dalhousie University Centre for Marine Geology, Technical Report, **11**.

MAYEWSKI, P., DENTON, G. H. & HUGHES, T. J. 1981. Late Wisconsinan ice sheets in North America. *In*: DENTON, G. H. & HUGHES, T. J. (eds) *The Last Great Ice Sheets*. Wiley, Toronto, 67–178.

MITCHUM, R. M. JR, VAIL, P. R. & THOMPSON, S. 1977. Seismic stratigraphy and global changes of sea-level; part 2, the depositional sequence as a basic unit for stratigraphic analysis. *In*: *Seismic Stratigraphy: Applications for Hydrocarbon Exploration*. American Association of Petroleum Geologists, Memoir, **26**, 53–62.

MORAN, K., PIPER, D. J. W., MAYER, L., COURTNEY, R., DRISCOLL, A. H. & Hall, F. R. 1989. Scientific results of long coring on the eastern Canadian continental margin. *In*: *Proceedings 21st Annual Offshore Technology Conference, Houston, TX*, **5963**, 65–71.

MOSHER, D. C., PIPER, D. J. W., VILKS, G. V., AKSU, A. E. & FADER, G. B. 1989. Evidence for Wisconsinan glaciations in the Verrill Canyon area, Scotian Slope. *Quaternary Research*, **31**, 27–40.

MOTT, R. J., 1994. Wisconsinan late-glacial environmental change in Nova Scotia: a regional synthesis. *Journal of Quaternary Science*, **9**, 155–160.

—— & STEA, R. R. 1994. Late-glacial (Alleröd/Younger Dryas) buried organic deposits, Nova Scotia, Canada. *Quaternary Science Reviews*, **12**, 645–657.

——, GRANT, D. R. G., STEA, R. R. & OCCHIETTI, S. 1986. Late-glacial climatic oscillation in Atlantic Canada equivalent to the Alleröd-Younger Dryas event. *Nature*, **323**, 247–250.

NICKS, L., 1988. *A study of the glacial stratigraphy and sedimentation of the Sheldon Point Moraine, Saint John, New Brunswick*. MSc Thesis, Dalhousie University, Halifax.

NIELSEN, S. H., CONRADSEN, K., HEINEMEIER, J., KNUDSEN, K. L., NIELSEN, H. L., RUD, N. & SVEINBJÖRNSDÓTTIR, Á. E. Radiocarbon dating of shells and foraminifera from the Skagen core, Denmark: evidence of reworking. *In*: *15th International Radiocarbon Conference*, in press.

OGDEN, J. G. III, 1987. Vegetational and climatic history of Nova Scotia. I. Radiocarbon-dated pollen profiles from Halifax, Nova Scotia. *Canadian Journal of Botany*, **65**, 1482–1490.

OLDALE, R. N., WILLIAMS, R. S. JR & COLMAN, S. M. 1990. Evidence against a Late Wisconsinan ice shelf in the Gulf of Maine. *Quaternary Science Reviews*, **9**, 1–13.

OSTERMAN, L. E. 1984. Late Quaternary foraminifera of Baffin Island continental shelf cores. *In*: *Geological Society of America, 94th Annual Meeting, Abstracts with Programs*, **16**(6), 618.

PATTERSON, R. T. & FISHBEIN, E. 1989. Re-examination of the statistical methods used to determine the number of point counts needed for micropaleontological quantitative research. *Journal of Paleontology*, **63**, 245–248.

PHILLIPS, A. C., SMITH, N. D. & POWELL, R. D. 1991. Laminated sediments in prodeltaic deposits, Glacier Bay, Alaska. *In*: ANDERSON, J. B. & ASHLEY, G. M. (eds) *Glacial Marine Sedimentation: Paleoclimatic Significance*. Geological Society of America Special Paper, **261**, 51–60.

PIPER, D. J. W. & FEHR, S. D. 1991. Radiocarbon chronology of Late Quaternary sections on the inner and middle Scotian Shelf, south of Nova Scotia. *In*: *Current Research, Part E*. Geological Survey of Canada, Paper, **91-1E**, 321–325.

——, LETSON, J. R. J., DEIURE, A. M. & BARRIE, C. Q. 1983. Sediment accumulation in low sedimentation, wave dominated, glaciated inlets. *Sedimentary Geology*, **36**, 195–215.

——, MUDIE, P. J., FADER, G. B., JOSENHANS, H. W., MACLEAN, B. & VILKS, G. 1990. Quaternary Geology. *In*: KEEN, M. J. & WILLIAMS, G. L. (eds) *Geology of the Continental Margin of Eastern Canada*. Geological Survey of Canada, Geology of Canada, **2**, 475–607.

——, ——, LETSON, J. R. J., BARNES, N. E. & IULIUCCI, R. J. 1986. *The Marine Geology of the Inner Scotian Shelf Off the South Shore, Nova Scotia*. Geological Survey of Canada, Paper, **85-19**.

POWELL, R. D. 1984. Glacimarine processes and inductive lithofacies modelling of ice shelf and tidewater glacier sediments based on Quaternary examples. *Marine Geology*, **57**, 1–52.

PREST, V. K. & Grant, D. R. 1969. *Retreat of the Last Ice Sheet from the Maritime Provinces—Gulf of St. Lawrence Region*. Geological Survey of Canada, Paper, **69-33**.

PRONK, A. G., BOBROWSKY, P. T. & PARKHILL, M. A., 1989. An interpretation of the late Quaternary glacial flow indicators in the Baie des Chaleurs region, northern New Brunswick. *Géographie physique et Quaternaire*, **43**, 179–190.

PROUDFOOT, D. N., GRANT, D. R & BATTERSON, M. J. 1988. Quaternary Geology of Western Newfoundland. *Geological Association of Canada, Annual Meeting, St. Johns, Newfoundland. Field Trip Guidebook*.

RAMPTON, V. N., GAUTHIER, R. C., THIBAULT, J. & SEAMAN, A. A. 1984. *Quaternary Geology of New Brunswick*. Geological Survey of Canada, Memoir, **416**.

RAPPOL, M. 1989. Glacial history of northwestern New Brunswick. *Géographie physique et Quaternaire*, **43**, 191–206.

SANCETTA, C. 1989. Processes controlling the accumulation of diatoms in sediments: a model derived from British Columbian fjords. *Paleoceanography*, **4**, 235–251.

SCOTT, D. B. & MEDIOLI, F. S. 1980. Post-glacial emergence curves in the Maritimes determined from marine sediment in raised basins. *In*: *Proceedings, Canadian Coastal Conference, 1980*, 428–446.

——, BAKI, V. & YOUNGER, C. D. 1989. Late Pleistocene–Holocene paleoceanographic changes on the eastern Canadian margin: stable isotopic evidence. *Palaeogeography, Palaeoclimatology, Palaeoecology*, **74**, 279–295.

——, MUDIE, P. J., VILKS, G. & YOUNGER, D. C. 1984. Latest Pleistocene–Holocene paleoceanographic trends on the continental margin of Eastern Canada: foraminiferal, dinoflagellate and pollen evidence. *Marine Micropaleontology*, **9**, 181–218.

SEIDENKRANTZ, M. S. 1993. Benthic foraminiferal and stable isotope evidence for a 'Younger Dryas-style' cold spell at the Saalian–Eemian transition, Denmark. *Palaeogeography, Palaeoclimatology, Palaeoecology*, **102**, 103–120.

STEA, R. R., 1991. *Clastic Dispersal in the Laurentian Channel off Cape Breton Island and Mainland Nova Scotia: Test of a Glacial Dispersal Model*. Dalhousie University Centre for Marine Geology, Technical Report, **13**.

——1995. *Late Quaternary Glaciations and Sea-level Change Along the Atlantic Coast of Nova Scotia*. PhD Dissertation, Dalhousie University, Halifax.

—— & MOTT, R. J. 1989. Deglaciation environments and evidence for glaciers of Younger Dryas age in Nova Scotia, Canada. *Boreas*, **18**, 169–187.

—— & ——1992. Sedimentation response to climate change in Maritime Canada during the Younger Dryas Chronozone. *In*: *Wolfville '92, Geological Association of Canada – Mineralogical Association of Canada Joint Annual Meeting, Abstracts Volume*, A66.

——, BOYD, R., FADER, G. B. J., COURTNEY, R. C., SCOTT, D. B. & PECORE, S. S. 1994. Morphology and seismic stratigraphy of the inner continental shelf off Nova Scotia, Canada: evidence for a −65 m lowstand between 11 650 and 11 250 ^{14}C yr B.P. *Marine Geology*, **117**, 135–154.

——, CONLEY, H., & BROWN, Y. (compilers) 1992a. *Surficial Geology of the Province of Nova Scotia; Nova Scotia Department of Natural Resources, Map 92-1, Scale 1:500 000*.

——, FADER, G. B. J., & BOYD, R. 1992b. Quaternary seismic stratigraphy of the inner shelf region, Eastern Shore, Nova Scotia. *In*: *Current Research, Part D*. Geological Survey of Canada, Paper, **92-1D**, 179–187.

——, FINCK, P. W. & WIGHTMAN, D. M. 1986. *Quaternary Geology and Till Geochemistry of the Western Part of Cumberland County, Nova Scotia (sheet 9)*. Geological Survey of Canada, Paper, **85-17**.

——, PECORE, S. & FADER, G. B. J. 1993. *Quaternary Stratigraphy and Placer Gold Potential of the Inner Scotian Shelf*. Nova Scotia Department of Natural Resources, Mines and Energy Branches, Paper, **93-2**.

——, SCOTT, D. B. & 9 others 1987. Quaternary glaciations, geomorphology and sea-level changes: Bay of Fundy Region. *In*: *NATO Advanced Course on Sea-level Correlations and Applications, Halifax, Nova Scotia, Field Trip Guidebook*.

——, TURNER, R. G., FINCK, P. W. & GRAVES, R. M. 1989. Glacial dispersal in Nova Scotia: a zonal concept. *In*: DILABIO, R. N. W. & COKER, W. B. (eds) *Drift Prospecting*. Geological Survey of Canada, Paper, **89-20**, 155–169.

STOLK, A. D., TÖRNQVIST, T. E., HEKHUIS, K. P. V., BERENDSEN, H. J. A. & VAN DER PLICHT, J. 1994. Calibration of ^{14}C histograms: a comparison of methods. *Radiocarbon*, **36**, 1–10.

SYLWESTER, R. L. 1983. Single-channel, high resolution, seismic reflection profiling: a review of the fundamentals and instrumentation. *In*: GEYER, R. A. (ed.) *CRC Handbook of Geophysical Exploration at Sea*. CRC Press, Boca Raton, 77–124.

SYVITSKI, J. P. M. 1991. Towards an understanding of sediment deposition on glaciated continental shelves. *Continental Shelf Research*, **11**, 897–937.

VAIL, P. R., MITCHUM, R. M. & 6 others 1977. Seismic stratigraphy and global changes in sea level. *In*: PAYTON, C. E. (ed.) *Seismic Stratigraphy – Applications to Hydrocarbon Exploration*. Association of Petroleum Geologists, Memoir, **26**.

VILKS, G. 1981. Late glacial-postglacial foraminiferal boundary in sediments of Eastern Canada, Denmark and Norway. *Geoscience Canada*, **8**, 48–55.

VORREN, T. O., LEBESBYE, E. & LARSEN, K. B. 1990. Geometry and genesis of the glacigenic sediments in the southern Barents Sea. *In*: DOWDESWELL, J. A. & SCOURSE, J. D. (eds) *Glaciomarine Environments: Processes and Sediments*. Geological Society of London, Special Publications, **53**, 269–288.

WIGHTMAN, D. M. 1980. *Late Pleistocene glaciofluvial and glaciomarine sediments on the north side of the Minas Basin, Nova Scotia*. PhD Thesis, Dalhousie University, Halifax.

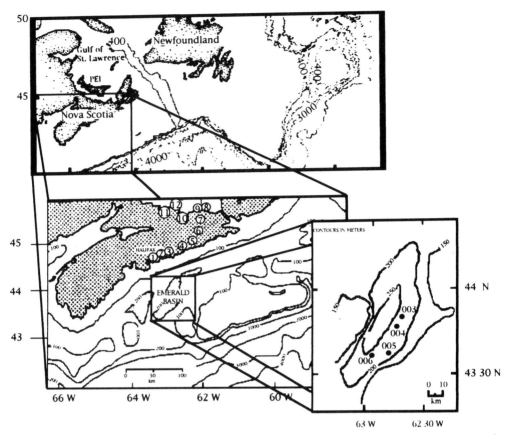

Fig. 1. Location of the Emerald Basin cores, Nova Scotian outcrop samples, and the Gulf of St Lawrence sample used in this study.

The objectives of this research were to: (1) determine if rock magnetic analyses of the Emerald Basin sediments show distinct changes that could be used to provide a stratigraphy within individual cores; (2) determine if rock magnetic data can be used to correlate between cores from different parts of the basin; (3) place these data within a time stratigraphic frame-work; and (4) determine the provenance of these sediments; in particular, if red beds derived from the Gulf of St Lawrence were entering the basin at any time.

The rock magnetic signature of the red beds should differ significantly by a strong signal indicative of 'hematite' (i.e. canted-antiferro-magnetic minerals). However, the red beds are not be the sole source of hematite from the mainland as chemical weathering, such as during soil formation, and the natural hematite content of other rock types are additional sources. How-ever, the non-red bed sources have a significant contribution from 'magnetite' (i.e. ferrimagnetic

minerals) which will dominate their rock magnetic signals (e.g. Hall & King, 1989; Bloemendal *et al.* 1992), whereas the red beds are dominated by the hematite signal (Pan & Symons 1993).

Methods

Four cores from the central portion of the Emerald Basin (Fig. 1 Table 1; CSS *Hudson*; 10 cm inner diameter) were used in this study. Huntec seismic records suggest that till tongues were not present at any of the study sites. Discrete samples were extracted from the cores by inserting a square stainless-steel chimney into the split core face. The sample was extruded from the chimney using a plastic piston pushed through the top. The bottom 2–5 mm of material were removed from each sample. The sample was then placed inside a 5 cm^3 plastic cube. Orientation was maintained with respect to the

Table 1. *The Latitude, longitude, and water depths of cores used in this study*

Core	Latitude (N)	Longitude (W)	Water depth (m)
H87003-003	43°52.90′	62°46.97′	232
H87003-004	43°53.10′	62°47.70′	235
H88010-005	43°53.04′	62°47.94′	240
H87003-006	43°37.56′	63°04.99′	247

downcore (+Z) direction. Discrete samples were collected at 5 cm intervals for cores 003, 004 and 006. Samples from core 005 were collected at within ±1 cm of the depths that were used for pore water chemistry (Fitzgerald *et al.* 1989;

Buckley 1991) at about 20 cm intervals. Till units, observed at the base of some of the cores, were not sampled.

Eleven samples (Fig. 1; Table 2) of outcrops along the Nova Scotian mainland and one borehole sample from the Gulf of St Lawrence were collected and subjected to the same rock magnetic measurements as the core samples. Three of these samples (8, 11 and 12) are red beds and sample 12 is the borehole sample. Two of the outcrop samples (2, magnetite dominated, and 11, hematite dominated) were crushed, mixed in various proportions and subjected to the same rock magnetic analyses to determine how the mixing of particles of varying composition could affect the rock magnetic signature (e.g. Bloemendal *et al.* 1992).

Table 2. *Outcrop rocks used in this study. The formation names and ages are from Bujak* et al. *(1980)*

Sample site	Formation	Rock type	Age
1	Goldenville	Schist	Cambrian
2	Goldenville	Schist	Cambrian
3	Unknown	Intrusive rocks	Carboniferous
4	Goldenville	Schist	Cambrian
5	Halifax	Slate	Cambrian/Ordovician
6	Horton Group	Shale	Carboniferous
7	Windsor Group	Gypsum	Carboniferous
8	Fisset Brook, Greenville River, Rapid Brook, and Nutby	Sandstone (red bed)	Carboniferous
9	Jeffers and Warwick	Siltstone	Proterozoic
10	Canso Group	Sandstone	Carboniferous
11	Pictou	Sandstone/shale (red bed)	Carboniferous
12	Pictou (?)	Sandstone (red bed)	Carboniferous

Table 3. *Interpretation of rock-magnetic parameters used here and the units for data reported here. Note that these parameters are used as indicators of magnetic mineral variability only and may not reflect changes in other particulate fluxes*

Parameter	Interpretation	Relative values		SI units (volume corrected values)
		High*	Low	
K (susceptibility)	Concentration	High	Low	10^{-5} SI
$IRM_{1.2T}$	Concentration	High	Low	10^{-3} A/m
K_{ARM}	Concentration (also affected by grain size)	High	Low	10^{-5} SI
K_{ARM}/K	Grain size	Fine	Coarse	Unitless
$SIRM/K$	Grain size	Fine	Coarse	10^2 A/m
HIRM	Hematite concentration†	High	Low	10^{-3} A/m
$S_{-0.1T}$	Coercivity‡	High	Low	Unitless
$S_{-0.3T}$	Magnetite§/hematite concentration ratio	Higher magnetite	Higher hematite	Unitless

* For example, if the susceptibility values are high, the magnetic mineral concentration is considered high.
† Canted antiferromagnetic minerals.
‡ This parameter is not a direct measure of coercivity. We use this as a way of indicating how the actual coercivity values should change downcore.
§ Ferrimagnetic minerals.

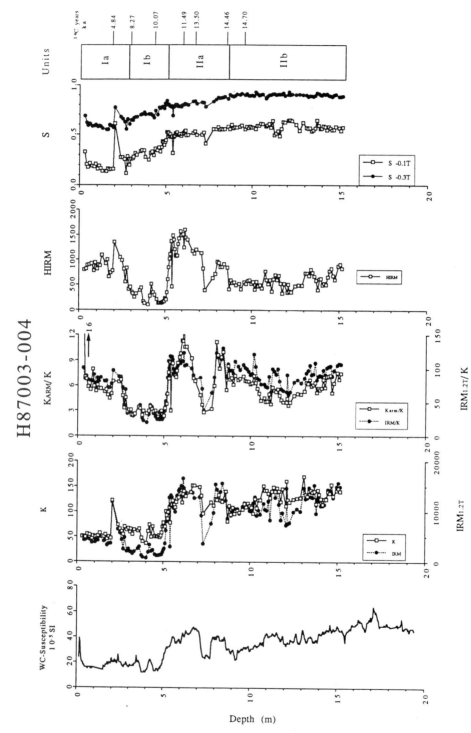

Fig. 2. Rock magnetic variability of core 004 with the unit and subunit boundaries. The units for the data shown here are given in Table 3.

During the sampling trip we did not acquire samples from all rock types on Nova Scotia, in particular those from the interior portion of the peninsula and Prince Edward Island. However, we feel that we did acquire a representative sampling of the various magnetic mineralogies that could be deposited into the Emerald Basin. In particular, we were looking for evidence of sediment originating from the Gulf of St Lawrence region, i.e. red beds (Pan & Symons 1993).

Interpretations of the rock magnetic data used in this study are given in Table 3. Additional discussions of these techniques can be found in numerous papers, in particular, Hall & King (1989) and King & Channel (1991). The rock magnetic analyses performed in this study included magnetic susceptibility measurements [whole core (before core splitting: 12.5 cm diameter sensor loop) and discrete sample] using the Bartington Instruments system set on the cgs scale and converted to SI units by multiplying these data by 4π.

Anhysteretic remanent magnetizations (ARMs) were then applied (99 mT AC magnetic field with a biasing 0.1 mT DC magnetic field) and

coverted to anhysteretic susceptibility (K_{ARM}) by dividing the ARM by 79.6 A/m; the intensity of the DC field (0.1 mT = 79.6 A/m). The ARMs were applied at the University of Rhode Island using the DTECH PARM system and measured using a 2G cryogenic magnetometer.

Isothermal remanent magnetizations (IRMs) were then applied at 1.2 T ($IRM_{1.2T}$), and two reversed fields ($IRM_{-0.1T}$ and $IRM_{-0.3T}$). The IRM data were used to calculate HIRM [$(IRM_{1.2T} + IRM_{-0.3T})/2$] and the S ratio [$-IRM_{(-0.1 \text{ and } -0.3T)}/IRM_{1.2T}$]. The IRMs were applied using a ASC Impulse Magnetizer and measured using the Molspin magnetometer at the University of Delaware. After the completeion of these analyses, we discovered an error in the standard we used with the spinner magnetometer which only affects the IRM measurements. This error was corrected by multiplying the IRM values by 2.57.

Age control was provided by six ^{14}C dates acquired on core 004 (Fehr 1989; Piper & Fehr 1991). These dates were marine-reservoir corrected using 410 years. Lithological boundary ages were determined after the downcore plots

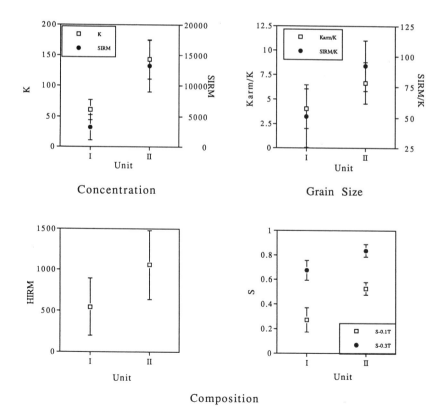

Concentration

Grain Size

Composition

Fig. 3. Statistical comparisons of the rock magnetic data from the two major units defined in this text. The data from all cores are included in this figure. The error bars represent one standard deviation from the mean.

of these dates were fitted to a downcore-linear curve, a third-order polynomial and a cubic spline.

Unit and subunit boundaries were defined by visually significant changes and statistcal comparisons of the rock magnetic parameters downcore. Apparent changes in individual rock magnetic parameters must occur at the same depths within individual cores for a boundary to be assigned. Reed (1994) used the lithofacies names described by King & Fader (1988; i.e. Emerald Silt, Lahave Clay) for defined units. However, because the units we describe do not include seismic analyses as a basis for determining boundaries, in this text, we refer to them as rock magnetic units I (topmost), II, etc.

Results

All of the data (IRM values are uncorrected) we collected are given in Reed (1994). However, because all of the cores have similar rock magnetic variability downcore, we show selected data only (core 004; Fig. 2).

The top of core 004 has significantly higher values of K_{ARM}/K (16) than the remainder of the core. Similar values occur at the top of core 006, but are absent from cores 003 and 005. This result probably indicates that the core barrels did not sample the sediment–water interface, particularly within cores 003 and 005. These relatively high values of K_{ARM}/K probably reflect of the deposition of fine-grained magnetite that is not seen deeper in the core that is probably bacterial in origin.

From these analyses we defined two major units and four subunits (Fig. 2). For core 004, we define the unit I/unit II boundary to be at about 5 m, with subunit boundaries at about 2.8 (Ia/Ib) and 9 (IIa/IIb) m. The results shown in Fig. 3 suggest that, overall, unit I has lower concentration values (K and SIRM), coarser magnetic mineral grain size values (K_{ARM}/K and SIRM/K), lower hematite concentration (HIRM) and higher coercivity values with lower magnetite/hematite ratios ($S_{-0.1T}$ and $S_{-0.3T}$, respectively).

The results in Fig. 4 show that with respect to subunit Ia, subunit Ib has lower K_{ARM}/K and

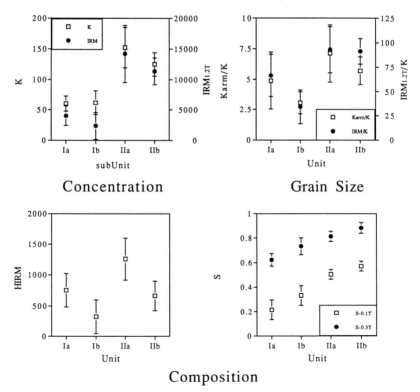

Fig. 4. Statistical comparisons of the rock magnetic data from the four subunits defined in this text. The data from all cores are included in this figure. The error bars represent one standarad deviation from the mean.

H88010-005

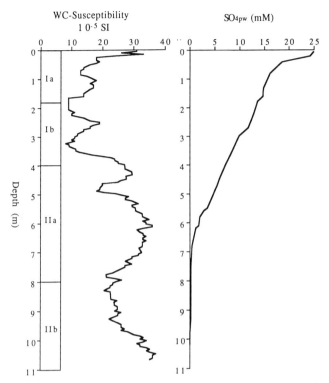

Fig. 5. Comparisons of the whole core (WC) magnetic susceptibility and pore water (PW) sulphate data (Fitzgerald *et al.* 1989) for core 005.

HIRM, and higher $S_{-0.1T, 0.3T}$ values. K and $S_{-0.3T}$ values do not change accross the boundary (Fig. 2). With respect to subunit IIa, subunit IIb has lower K_{ARM}/K and HIRM values, whereas the K values increase across the IIa/IIb boundary (Fig. 2). The S values are similar for both subunits. From the subunit IIa/b boundary to the top of the core, the S- parameters steadily decrease in value upcore, whereas HIRM fluctuates between subunits. These results suggest that although the hematite concentration fluctuates across boundaries, the proportion of hematite with respect to magnetite generally increases upcore. This pattern can result from either (1) chemical alteration of magnetite in the sediments, or (and) (2) changing proportions of source rocks to the site that favours increased hematite deposition upcore.

Gipp (1989) suggested that the magnetic susceptibility records of unit I could indicate reduction diagenesis (i.e. the alteration of magnetic iron oxides into non-magnetic iron sulphides; Karlin & Levi 1983; Leslie *et al.* 1990). However, the comparison of the whole core magnetic susceptibility data with the results of pore water sulphate analyses of core 005 (Fitzgerald *et al.* 1989; Buckley 1991; Fig. 5) suggests that reduction diagenesis was not an important process affecting these sediments; in fact, the sulphate values remain relatively high into unit II. Therefore we concluded that changes in rock magnetic parameters probably resulted from changes in sedimentological properties that are reflected in assigned units.

Figure 6 shows the HIRM data between cores. Based on the criteria described earlier, the same units and subunits can be seen in all the cores, with the exception of core 006 which does not have a signal suggestive of subunit IIb. The depths of all boundaries for all the cores are given in Table 4. The comparison of data from core 005 with the other cores indicates that the top of subunit Ia was not sampled. Although the HIRM values between 0.25 and 4 m are similar in value to subunit Ib for the other cores, we place to Ia/Ib boundary at about 1.8 m. The comparison of pore water chemistry samples from core 005 with other cores from the

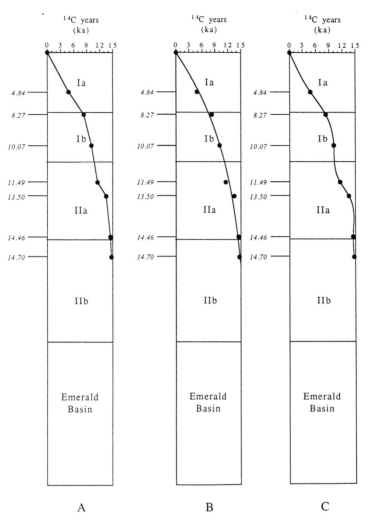

Fig. 8. Age–depth models for core 004 with the unit and subunit boundaries. (A) Linear connection between data points. (B) Third-order polynomial. (C) cCbic spline. The materials used in these analyses can be found in Piper & Fehr (1991).

before mixing with material from site 11, perhaps some residue from the mortar and pestle. Nonetheless, with respect to the $S_{-0.3T}$ values, these data suggest that the proportion of the red bed sediments must be at least 80% of the total sediment for its presence to be detected with the methods used here. This result is consistent with those of Bloemendal *et al.* (1992) using synthetic magnetic mineral sample mixtures.

Discussion

The ages of unit boundaries determined in these analyses are consistent with those of seen in other portions of the Scotian Shelf (Stea *et al.* 1994; this volume) and models of ice-sheet decay for eastern North America (Teller 1986). In particular, the subunit and unit boundaries occur at the ends of short period glacial readvances (Table 5). Teller (1986) suggested that by 14 ka, ice should have retreated sufficiently to open an outlet to the Atlantic Ocean through the Gulf of St Lawrence for large volumes of glacial meltwater, especially for large plumes that emanated from Glacial Lake Agassiz. Moreover, palaeoceanographic models of the Scotian Shelf suggest that by 12 ka, perhaps as early as 14 ka, a proto-Scotian Shelf current should have developed on the shelf (Piper 1991b).

Table 5. *Proposed ages of rock magnetic unit boundaries. Included are the ages of seismic boundaries defined by King & Fader (1988)*

Seismic: rock magnetic unit	Age (ka)		Deglacial event Teller (1986)
	King & Fader	This study	
Subunit Ia/Ib	Not defined	8.0	Marquette re-advance
Lahave Clay/Emerald Silt: unit I/II	10.5–10	11.2–10.2	Younger Dryas
Emerald Silt B/A: subunit IIa/IIb	15.5–15	14.5	Port Huron Stade
Emerald Silt/Scotian Shelf Drift	18–17.5	Not defined	Glacial maximum

The sea-level curve for the Scotian Shelf suggests that by the time of the Younger Dryas, sea level was at about −85 m below present mean sea level (Amos & Miller 1990; Piper 1991a). A more recent sea-level curve developed for the inner portion of the Scotian Shelf for the past 15 ka (Stea *et al.* 1994) shows a Younger Dryas lowering of sea level to about −65 m below the present mean sea level. These sea-level models suggest that during the Younger Dryas, the Emerald Basin remained submerged (water depths of cores studied >200 m bsl). We might expect that this combination of glacial retreat, sea level and circulation on the shelf should have delivered red sediments from the Gulf of St Lawrence onto the shelf and into the Emerald Basin.

The rock magnetic data that we present here suggest either that (1) none of the red sediments, common in and around the Gulf of St Lawrence, are in the Emerald Basin or (2) if they are present, the concentrations are too low to detect using these rock magnetic techniques. Although the latter possibility can occur, we consider it unlikely. Instead, these red sediments probably bypassed the central shelf and were confined to

the Laurentian Channel system, which acted as a conduit for red sediments entering the North Atlantic (Hall 1990).

The position of the ice sheet and its movement on the Nova Scotian mainland would have precluded the red sediment from reaching the shelf (Stea *et al.* this volume). In addition, King (1994) suggests that during the Younger Dryas, the extent of glacial ice on the Scotian Shelf north of Emerald Basin was sufficient to prevent any sediment from the Gulf of St Lawrence reaching the Emerald Basin. Thus the sediment source would have been confined to the southeast side of the Nova Scotian peninsula. Further, the data presented in Fig. 9 here suggest that the source of younger sediments has affinities towards more northeasterly portions of Nova Scotia, although more evidence is required to conclude this change.

Conclusions

The results of these analyses suggest that: (1) rock magnetic data provide an excellent means of developing a lithostratigraphy within

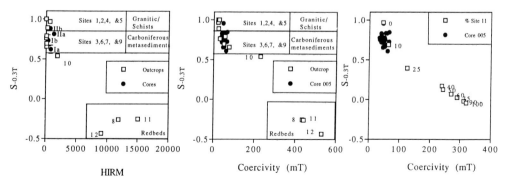

Fig. 9. Comparisons of the rock magnetic data from the piston cores with the outcrop and Gulf of St Lawrence data. The value labels of (A) and (B) are of the site numbers. (C) and (D) are the comparisons of the core data with the samples mixed from sites 2 and 11. The value labels are given with respect to the percentage of site 11 material in individual samples.

sediments of the Emerald Basin; (2) reduction diagenesis was probably not an important process affecting the rock magnetic signal observed in these cores; (3) apparent rock magnetic unit and subunit boundaries can be connected to changes in deglacial patterns along eastern North America (Teller 1986); and (4) the post-glacial sediments deposited into the Emerald Basin probably originated from the front (southeastern) portion of the Nova Scotian mainland as red bed derived materials from the northwestern part of the peninsula probably bypassed the shelf during glacial meltwater events. The combination of these data with continuing micropalaeontological, physical properties and seismic analyses will allow us to develop a better understanding of the post-glacial environmental changes associated with the Scotian Shelf region.

We thank the captain and crew of the CSS *Hudson* for their excellent work in retrieving these cores, and the scientists and staff of the Bedford Institute of Oceanography, especially, K. Moran and D. Piper. We also thank J. W. King for allowing us to use the palaeomagnetics facility at the University of Rhode Island. Comments provided by A. Jennings, R. Stea, and J. Rosenbaum were beneficial to the completion of this paper. This research was funded by the University of Delaware Research Foundation Grant No. LTR-910117 and the National Science Foundation Grant No. OCE92–03833.

References

ALAM, M. 1987. Late Quaternary plume, nepheloid and turbidite sedimentation and effect of the Gulf Stream near the tail of the Grand Banks, Newfoundland. *Marine Geology*, **74**, 277–290.

——, PIPER, D. J. W. & COOKE, B. S. 1983. Late Quatenary stratigraphy and paleoceanography of the Grand Banks continental margin, eastern Canada. *Boreas*, **12**, 253–261.

AMOS, C. L. & MILLER, A. A. L. 1990. The Quaternary stratigraphy of southwest Sable Island, eastern Canada. *Geological Society of America Bulletin*, **102**, 915–934.

BLOEMENDAL, J., KING, J. W., HALL F. R. & DOH, S. J. 1992. Rock-magnetism of late Neogene and Pleistocene deep-sea sediments: relationship to sediment source, diagenetic processes, and sediment lithology. *Journal of Geophysical Research*, **97**, 4361–4375.

BOND, G. & LOTTI, R. 1995. Iceberg discharges into the North Atlantic on millenial timescales during the last deglaciation. *Science*, **267**, 1005–1010.

BOYLE, E. A. & KEGWEIN, L. D. 1987. North Atlantic thermohaline circulation during the past 20,000 years linked to high-latitude surface temperature. *Nature*, **330**, 35–40.

BROEKER, W. S., BOND, G., KLAS, M., BONANI, G. & WOLFLI, W. 1990. A salt oscillator in the glacial North Atlantic, 1 The concept. *Paleoceanography*, **5**, 469–477.

——, KENNETT, J. P., FLOWER, B. P., TELLER, J. T., TRUMBORE, S., BONANI G. & WOLFLI, W., 1989. The routing of meltwater from the Laurentide ice-sheet during the Younger Dryas cold episode. *Nature*, **341**, 318–321.

——, PETEET D. M. & RIND, D. 1986. Does the ocean–atmosphere system have more than one stable mode of operation? *Nature*, **315**, 21–26.

BUCKLEY, D. E. 1991. Deposition and diagenetic alteration of sediment in Emerald Basin, the Scotian Shelf. *Continental Shelf Research*, **11**, 1099–1122.

BUJAK, J. P. & DONOHOE, H. V. JR. 1980. *Geological Highway Map of Nova Scotia*. Atlantic Geoscience Society, Special Publication, **1**.

FEHR, S., 1991. *A geoacoustical model for the upper sediments of Emerald Basin*, Master's Thesis, Dalhousie University.

FITZGERALD, R. A., WINTERS, G. V., BUCKLEY, D. E. & LEBLANC, K. W. G. 1989. *Geochemical Data From Analyses of Sediments and Pore Water Obtained From Piston Corers and Box Cores Taken From Bedford Basin, Lahave Basin, Emerald Basin, and the Slope of the Southern Scotian Shelf, Hudson Cruise 88–010*. Geological Survey of Canada, Open File, Report, **47**, 110.

GIPP, M., 1989. *Late Wisconsin deglaciation of Emerald Basin, Scotian Shelf*. Master's Thesis, Memorial University of Newfoundland.

HALL, F. R. 1990. *The rock-magnetic sugnature of high-latitude northern-hemispheric deep-sea sediments and their relationships to Quaternary glacial cycling*. Doctoral Dissertation, University of Rhode Island.

—— & KING, J. W. 1989. Rock-magnetic stratigraphy of Site 645 (Baffin Bay) from ODP Leg 105. In: SRIVASTIVA, S. P., ARTHUR, M. A., CLEMENT, B. et al. (eds) *Proceedings of the ODP, Scientific Results*, **105**, 843–859.

KARLIN, R. & LEVI, S. 1983. Diagenesis of magnetic minersals in Recent haemipelagic sediments. *Nature*, **303**, 327–330.

KEIGWIN, L. D., JONES, G. A. & LEHMAN, S. J. 1991. Deglacial meltwater discharge, North Atlantic deep circulation, and abrupt climate change. *Journal of Geophysical Research*, **96**, 16 811–16 826.

KING, J. W. & CHANNEL, J. E. T. 1991. Sedimentary magnetism, environmental magnetism, and magnetostratigraphy. *Reviews of Geophysics, Supplement*, 358–370.

——, BANERJEE, S. K., MARVIN, J. & OZDEMIR, O. 1982. A comparison of different magnetic methods for determining the relative grain size of magnetite in natural materials: some results from lake sediments. *Earth and Planetary Science Letters*, **59**, 404–491.

KING, L. H. 1994. Proposed Younger Dryas glaciation of the eastern Scotian Shelf. *Canadian Journal of Earth Science*, **31**, 401–417.

—— & FADER, G. B. J. 1986. Wisconsinan glaciation of the Atlantic continental shelf of southeast Canada. *Geological Survey of Canada Bulletin*, **363**.

—— & —— 1988. *Wisconsinan Ice on the Scotian Shelf*. Geological Survey of Canada, Open File, **1972**.

—— & —— 1989. *A Comparison Between the Late Wisconsinan History of Southwest and Northeast Emerald Basin*. Geological Survey of Canada, Open File, **2060**.

——, ROKOENGEN, K., FADER, G. B. J. & GUNLEIKSRUD, T. 1991. Till-tongue stratigraphy. *Geological Society of America Bulletin*, **103**, 637–659.

LESLIE, B. W., LUND, S. P. & HAMMOND, D. E. 1990. Rock-magnetic evidence for the dissolution and authigenic growth of magnetic minerals within anoxic marine sediments of the California continental borderland. *Journal of Gephyisical Research*, **95**, 4437–4452.

MOTT, R. J., GRANT, D. R., STEA, R. & OCHIETTIE, S. 1986. Late glacial climatic oscillation in Atlantic Canada equivalent to the Allerod/Younger Dryas event. *Nature*, **123**, 247–250.

PAN, H. & SYMONS, D. T. A. 1993. The Pictou redbeds Pennsylvanian pole: could Phanerozoic rocks in the interior United States be remagnetized? *Journal of Geophysical Research*, **98**, 6227–6235.

PIPER, D. J. W, 1991*a*. Seabed geology of the Canadian eastern continental shelf. *Continental Shelf Research*, **11**, 1013–1035.

——1991*b*. *Surficial Geology and Physical Properties 7: Paleoceanography and Paleoglaciology*. East Coast Basin Atlas Series: Scotian Shelf. Atlantic Geoscience Centre, Canadian Geological Survey.

—— & FEHR, S. D. 1991. Radiocarbon chronology of late Quaternary sections on the inner and middle Scotian Shelf, south of Nova Scotia. *Current Research, Part E*. Geological Survey of Canada, Paper, **91-1E**, 321–325.

——, MUDIE, P. J., FADER, G. B., JOSENHANS, H. W., MACLEAN, B. & VILKS, G. Quaternary geology. *In*: KEEN, M. J. & WILLIAMS, G. L. (eds) *Geology of the Continental Margin of Eastern Canada*. Geological Society of America, The Geology of North America, **I-1**, 475–607.

REED, S. J. 1994. *A paleo- and rock-magnetic study of Late Quaternary fine-grained sediments in the Emerald Basin*. Master's Thesis, University of Delaware.

ROOTH, C. G. H. 1990. *Meltwater Younger Dryas upheld. Nature*, **343**, 702.

STEA, R. R., BOYD, R., FADER, G. B. J., COURTNEY, R. C., SCOTT, D. B. & PECORE, S. S. 1994. Morphology and seismic stratigraphy of the inner continental shelf off Nova Scotia, Canada: evidence for a −65 m lowstand between 11,650 and 11,250 C^{14} yr B.P. *Marine Geology*, **117**, 135–154

TELLER, J. T. 1986. Proglacial lakes and the southern margin of the Laurentide ice sheet. *In*: RUDDIMAN, W. & WRIGHT, H. E. (eds.) *North America and Adjacent Oceans during the Last Deglaciation*. Geological Society of America, The Geology of North America, **K-3**, 39–70.

THOMPSON, R. & OLDFIELD, F. 1986. *Environmental Magnetism*. Allen & Unwin, Boston.

Deep-sea ostracode shell chemistry (Mg:Ca ratios) and Late Quaternary Arctic Ocean history

THOMAS M. CRONIN[1], GARY S. DWYER[2], PAUL A. BAKER[2],
JULIO RODRIGUEZ-LAZARO[3] & WILLIAM M. BRIGGS JR[4]

[1] 955 US Geological Survey, Reston, VA 22092, USA
[2] Department of Geology, Duke University, Durham, NC 27708, USA
[3] University Pais Vasco, Bilbao, Spain
[4] INSTAAR, University of Colorado, Boulder, CO 80309, USA

Abstract: The magnesium:calcium (Mg:Ca) and strontium:calcium (Sr:Ca) ratios were investigated in shells of the benthic ostracode genus *Krithe* obtained from 64 core-tops from water depths of 73 to 4411 m in the Arctic Ocean and Nordic seas to determine the potential of ostracode shell chemistry for palaeoceanographic study. Shells from the Polar Surface Water (−1 to −1.5°C) had Mg:Ca molar ratios of about 0.006–0.008; shells from Arctic Intermediate Water (+0.3 to +2.0°C) ranged from 0.09 to 0.013. Shells from the abyssal plain and ridges of the Nansen, Amundsen and Makarov basins and the Norwegian and Greenland seas had a wide scatter of Mg:Ca ratios ranging from 0.007 to 0.012 that may signify post-mortem chemical alteration of the shells from Arctic deep-sea environments below about 1000 m water depth. There is a positive correlation ($r^2 = 0.59$) between Mg:Ca ratios and bottom-water temperature in *Krithe* shells from Arctic and Nordic seas from water depths <900 m. Late Quaternary *Krithe* Mg:Ca ratios were analysed downcore using material from the Gakkel Ridge (water depths 3047 and 3899 m), the Lomonosov Ridge (water depth 1051 m) and the Amundsen Basin (water depth 4226 m) to test the core-top Mg:Ca temperature calibration. Cores from the Gakkel and Lomonosov ridges display a decrease in Mg:Ca ratios during the interval spanning the last glacial/deglacial transition and the Holocene, perhaps related to a decrease in bottom water temperatures or other changes in benthic environments.

The Arctic Ocean and adjacent Nordic seas (Greenland, Norwegian, Icelandic seas) play an important part in global climate through their effect on the formation of northern hemisphere deep-water and thermohaline circulation (Aagaard *et al.* 1985) and the influence of sea ice cover on albedo, surface ecosystems and productivity (Clark 1990; Untersteiner 1990). Early studies of cores from the Fram Strait first showed that late Quaternary oceanographic changes could be linked with climatic warming and ice sheet discharge in high latitudes (Zahn *et al.* 1985; Jones & Keigwin 1988). More recent cruises have obtained cores from the central Arctic Ocean that have demonstrated that significant changes occurred in the central Arctic during the last deglaciation and the Holocene. Most notably, variations in the stable isotopic composition of benthic and planktonic foraminifers (Stein *et al.* 1994a; 1994b) and oscillations in deep-sea benthic ostracode faunas (Cronin *et al.* 1994; 1995) imply major changes in Arctic sea ice conditions, surface productivity, temperature and salinity, and deep-water formation during deglaciation. Data on deep-sea Arctic cores have been supplemented by terrestrial-based studies of glacial history, which also suggest linkages between continental ice sheets and Arctic Ocean history (i.e. Andrews *et al.* 1993; Lehman & Forman 1992), and by detailed palaeoceanographic studies of the Nordic seas (Henrich *et al.* 1995; Sarnthein & Altenbach 1995).

Given the importance of the Arctic Ocean in global climate, there is a need for additional tools for palaeoceanographic reconstruction in high latitudes. This is partially because stable oxygen isotopic records from foraminifera from the Arctic Ocean and adjacent subpolar seas defy straightforward palaeoceanographic interpretation due to the complex effects of meltwater on surface-water salinity as well as changes in water temperatures and ice volume (Spielhagen & Erlenkeuser 1994). Moreover, there is an increasing need to provide independent methods to estimate past oceanic water temperatures in regions undergoing rapid and frequent oceanographic changes (Lehman & Keigwin 1991; Koc & Jansen 1994). As part of a larger effort to develop the use of ostracode faunal assemblages (Cronin *et al.* 1995) and shell trace element chemistry (Dwyer *et al.* 1995) in palaeoceanography, we have studied the magnesium:calcium (Mg:Ca) and strontium:calcium (Sr:Ca) ratios of the calcitic shells of the benthic deep-sea

From Andrews, J. T., Austin, W. E. N., Bergsten, H. & Jennings, A. E. (eds), 1996, *Late Quaternary Palaeoceanography of the North Atlantic Margins*, Geological Society Special Publication No. 111, pp. 117–134.

ostracode genus *Krithe* as a palaeotemperature proxy in Arctic and Nordic seas. The Mg–Ca shell chemistry of *Krithe* has been used successfully to estimate the bottom water temperature history of the deep North Atlantic Ocean (Dwyer *et al.* 1995) and the Coral Sea (Correge 1993) and this method also has potential in other oceanic environments.

Our goals in this paper are to (1) determine the range of variation in Mg : Ca ratios in *Krithe* from the major Arctic and Nordic sea water masses; (2) improve the calibration of Mg : Ca ratios to water temperature, first by obtaining ratios from shells living in water of very cold temperatures (-1.5 to $+2.5°C$) and then by comparing these ratios to those obtained on *Krithe* from relatively warm thermocline waters in the North Atlantic Ocean; and (3) examine downcore changes in Mg : Ca ratios for the last glacial period, the last deglaciation and the Holocene.

As one of the first studies of its kind, it is important to stress the preliminary nature of the results and the probability that future studies will improve our understanding of the syngenetic and post-mortem effects on the chemistry of marine ostracode shells. Nonetheless, several important patterns in spatial and temporal variation in Mg : Ca ratios have been observed in *Krithe* that suggest their potential use for estimating the history of bottom water temperature and perhaps other changes in benthic habitats.

Trace element studies of microfossil shells

There is abundant evidence that the co-precipitation of magnesium in inorganic (Morse & Mackenzie 1990; Burton & Walter 1991) and biogenic calcite (Chave 1954) precipitated from sea water is dependent on water temperature. In studies of calcareous microfossils, Delaney *et al.* (1985) did not find conclusive evidence that Mg : Ca ratios were temperature dependent in cultured and core-top planktonic foraminifers, but Izuka (1988) and Nurnberg (1995) showed a good correlation of Mg : Ca ratios to temperature in detailed studies of benthic and planktonic foraminifers, respectively, from core-tops taken from a wide range of water temperatures. Nurnberg (1995) gave a useful summary of planktonic foraminiferal Mg : Ca ratios.

Ostracodes are another microfossil group with calcitic shells with magnesium concentrations that vary taxonomically, ontogenetically and with water temperature (Cadot & Kaesler 1977).

Studies of non-marine and brackish water ostracodes (Chivas *et al.* 1986; De Deckker *et al.* 1988) confirmed Cadot & Kaesler's (1977) results on marine taxa by demonstrating a positive correlation between temperature and Mg : Ca ratios in ostracode shells. Indeed, three separate studies of Mg : Ca ratios in the predominantly deep-sea genus *Krithe* from different oceanic regions have each demonstrated a strong temperature dependence of Mg : Ca ratios (Cadot & Kaesler 1977; Correge 1993; Dwyer *et al.* 1995). Correge's specimens came from regions in the Coral Sea with a temperature range of 2–6°C, and Dwyer *et al.* (1995) used *Krithe* from the North Atlantic Ocean ranging from 2 to 14°C. In the present paper, we examine the Mg : Ca–temperature relationship in *Krithe* from Arctic and Nordic seas to obtain information from temperatures below 2.5°C.

Materials and methods

We used material from core-tops described in detail by Cronin *et al.* (1994; 1995) as a source of *Krithe* from the Arctic and Nordic seas. Much of this material came from recent cruises to the Arctic Ocean by the *Polarstern* (Futterer 1992; 1994); other material came from the *Polar Star* cruise to the Northwind Ridge and earlier cruises of the *Polarstern* and *Meteor* to the Norwegian and Greenland Seas (see Cronin *et al.* 1995). Table 1 gives the sample data and Mg : Ca ratios for a total of 164 *Krithe* that we analysed from core tops. Figure 1 shows the location of material from the 1993 *Polarstern* cruise to the Laptev Sea, which provided some of the best surface material in terms of the occurrence of *Krithe* with preserved appendages (Cronin in press).

One important conclusion emerging from the study by Dwyer *et al.* (1995) of North Atlantic core-tops was that it was extremely important to use specimens that show no signs of post-mortem downslope transportation or alteration. In fact, Dwyer *et al.* found that the intrasample variation in Mg : Ca ratios was substantially lower in downcore samples from DSDP site 607 (3400 m water depth) than in samples from core-tops from the thermocline along the ocean margins. This was considered to most likely be due to the greater possibility of bioturbation, transportation and temporal variation in bottom water temperatures at ocean margin sites compared with deep-sea sites.

Ostracode specimens in which the soft parts or appendages are preserved, especially from core

Table 1. Shell geochemical data for Krithe from the Arctic Ocean and Nordic seas

Sample	Plotted*	Region	Site†	Core	Interval (cm)	Water depth (m)	Temperature (°C)	Salinity (‰)	Species	Weight (µg)	Mg:Ca	Sr:Ca	Na:Ca	Pres‡	Phase§	Number§
1	Y	Laptev Sea	2461	2	0–1	73	−1.36	33.92	glacialis	32	0.00637	0.00371	0.00450	5	6	19
2	Y	Laptev Sea	2461	2	0–1	73	−1.36	33.92	glacialis	18	0.00654	0.00344	0.00852	5	6B	70
3	Y	Laptev Sea	2461	2	0–1	73	−1.36	33.92	glacialis	44	0.00666	0.00351	0.00540	5	6	18
4	Y	Laptev Sea	2461	2	0–1	73	−1.36	33.92	glacialis	23	0.00743	0.00381	0.00435	5	6	17
5	Y	Laptev Sea	2481	2	0–1	100	−1.22	34.94	glacialis	14	0.00672	0.00349	0.00537	3	6B	78
6	Y	Laptev Sea	2481	2	0–1	100	−1.22	34.35	glacialis	11	0.00683	0.00357	0.00592	4	6B	79
7	Y	Laptev Sea	2481	2	0–1	100	−1.22	34.35	glacialis	22	0.00757	0.00352	0.00607	4	6	56
8	Y	Laptev Sea	2478	3	0–1	101	−1.07	34.23	glacialis	24	0.00664	0.00359	0.00657	4	6	66
9	Y	Laptev Sea	2478	3	0–1	101	−1.07	34.23	glacialis	25	0.00687	0.00392	0.00555	6	6	39
10	Y	Laptev Sea	2478	3	0–1	101	−1.07	34.23	glacialis	35	0.00766	0.00362	0.00595	4	6	38
11	Y	Laptev Sea	2452	2	0–1	132	−0.98	34.28	glacialis	32	0.00903	0.00359	0.00624	5	6	51
12	Y	Laptev Sea	2451	4	0–1	144	−1.07	34.32	glacialis	15	0.00717	0.00354	0.00876	4	6B	68
13	Y	Laptev Sea	2451	4	0–1	144	−1.07	34.32	glacialis	10	0.00729	0.00362	0.00603	3	6B	67
14	Y	Barents Sea	2143		0–1	197	−1	34.81	glacialis	20	0.00775	0.00356		1	1	32a
15	Y	N. Greenland	BartLT35			200	−1	34.86	glacialis	36	0.00721	0.00339	0.00618	3	9	34
16	Y	N. Greenland	BartLT35			200	−1	34.86	glacialis	38	0.00775	0.00346	0.00635	2	9	33
17	Y	Laptev Sea	2460	3	0–1	213	1.44	34.85	glacialis	10	0.00913	0.00354	0.00520	6	6B	69
18	Y	Laptev Sea	2484	3	0–1	235	0.2	34.71	glacialis	22	0.00905	0.00359	0.00546	6	6	40
19	Y	Laptev Sea	2484	3	0–1	235	0.2	34.71	glacialis	24	0.00945	0.00367	0.00490	6	6	41
20	Y	Kara Sea	106		surface	265	1.3	34.95	glacialis	21	0.01046	0.00386		0	0	16
21	Y	Kara Sea	106		surface	265	1.31	34.95	glacialis	19	0.01115	0.00359		1	1	43a
22	Y	Kara Sea	106		surface	265	1.31	34.95	glacialis	18	0.01211	0.00361		1	1	44a
23	Y	Northwind Ridge	PL92ARB	17	0–2	402	0.5	34.85	glacialis	32	0.00944	0.00362		5	1	46b
24	Y	Northwind Ridge	PL92ARB	17	0–2	402	0.421	34.85	glacialis	17	0.01051	0.00369		4	0	12
25	Y	Northwind Ridge	PL92ARB	17	0–2	402	0.5	34.85	glacialis	27	0.01094	0.00362		7	1	46f
26	Y	Northwind Ridge	PL92ARB	17	0–2	402	0.5	34.85	glacialis	13	0.01160	0.00350		1	1	46d
27	Y	Northwind Ridge	PL92ARB	17	0–2	402	0.5	34.85	glacialis	12	0.01177	0.00356		1	1	46h
28	Y	Northwind Ridge	PL92ARB	17	0–2	402	0.5	34.85	glacialis	33	0.01192	0.00351		7	1	46e
29	Y	Northwind Ridge	PL92ARB	17	0–2	402	0.5	34.85	glacialis	14	0.01276	0.00337		1	1	46a
30	Y	Northwind Ridge	PL92ARB	17	0–2	402	0.5	34.85	glacialis	12	0.01303	0.00356		7	1	46g
31	Y	Barents Sea	2140		0–1	461	1.048	34.92	glacialis	23	0.00946	0.00361		6	1	31b
32	Y	Barents Sea	2140		0–1	461	1.048	34.92	glacialis	26	0.01054	0.00346		7	1	31a
33	Y	Laptev Sea	2459	2	0–1	517	0.68	34.87	glacialis	17	0.00965	0.00365	0.00520	5	6	16
34	Y	Laptev Sea	2476	3	0–1	524	0.51	34.87	glacialis	26	0.00968	0.00346	0.00653	5	6	65
35	Y	Laptev Sea	2476	3	0–1	524	0.51	34.87	glacialis	33	0.00992	0.00360	0.00655	5	6	64
36	Y	Yermak Plateau	2214	4	0–1	552	2.0096	34.89	glacialis	22	0.01125	0.00395		5	1	42a
37	Y	Laptev Sea	2482	3	0–1	557	0.25	34.83	glacialis	22	0.01101	0.00359	0.00935	2	6	53
38	Y	Laptev Sea	2482	3	0–1	557	0.25	34.83	glacialis	24	0.01308	0.00359	0.00959	2	6	55
39	Y	Laptev Sea	2482	3	0–1	557	0.25	34.35	glacialis	13	0.01331	0.00355	0.00865	5	6B	80
40	Y	Laptev Sea	2482	3	0–1	557	0.25	34.83	minima	5	0.01591	0.00333	0.00849	1	6	54
41	Y	Norwegian Sea	PL91ARBC	10	0–1	562	1.8	34.91	glacialis	13	0.01038	0.00304		4	1	52b

Table 1. *Continued*

Sample	Plotted*	Region	Site†	Core	Interval (cm)	Water depth (m)	Temperature (°C)	Salinity (‰)	Species	Weight (µg)	Mg:Ca	Sr:Ca	Na:Ca	Pres‡	Phase§	Number§
42		Norwegian Sea	PL91ARBC	10		562	1.8	34.91	glacialis	14	0.01104	0.00306		4	1	52a
43	Y	Barents Sea	2139			752	0.8	34.92	glacialis	25	0.01274	0.00357		1	1	33a
44	Y	Yermak Plateau	2213	4	0–1	897	−0.3445	34.9	glacialis	24	0.00911	0.00342		5	1	41a
45	Y	Barents Slope	2447	4	0–1	1024	−0.18	34.91	glacialis	25	0.01060	0.00357	0.00752	2	6	9
46	Y	Barents Slope	2447	4	0–1	1024	−0.18	34.91	glacialis	8	0.01117	0.00352	0.00741	4	6	10
47	Y	Barents Slope	2447	4	0–1	1024	−0.18	34.91	glacialis	21	0.01119	0.00331	0.00627	6	6	6
48	Y	Barents Slope	2447	4	0–1	1024	−0.18	34.91	glacialis	6	0.01307	0.00311	0.00483	5	6	7
49	Y·	Barents Slope	2447	4	0–1	1024	−0.18	34.91	glacialis	6	0.01427	0.00338	0.00579	4	6	8
50		Morris Jesup Rise	2200	4		1074	−0.2428	34.89	glacialis	23	0.01641	0.00320		2	6	37a
51		Morris Jesup Rise	2202			1083	−0.414	34.89	minima	7	0.01512	0.00347		2	0	9
52		Fram Strait	1904	1		1182	−1.012	34.92	glacialis	23	0.00843	0.00327		1	1	26a
53		Fram Strait	1904	1		1182	−1.012	34.92	glacialis	13	0.00956	0.00219		2	1	26b
54		Fram Strait	1704	3		1195	−0.833	34.92	glacialis	23	0.01107	0.00335		1	1	24a
55		Fram Strait	1704	3		1195	−0.833	34.92	glacialis	20	0.01176	0.00339		1	1	24b
56	Y	Laptev Sea	2483	2	0–1	1216	−0.4	34.88	glacialis	26	0.00942	0.00331	0.00709	3	6	63
57	Y	Nansen Basin	PI191 BC	8		1348	−0.621	34.91	glacialis	26	0.01050	0.00339		2	0	2
58	Y	Northwind Ridge	PI192BC	16		1388	−0.358	34.9	glacialis	27	0.01008	0.00288		2	0	11
59	Y	Northwind Ridge	PL92ARB	16		1388	−0.3	34.9	glacialis	20	0.01130	0.00304		2	1	45b
60		Lomonosov Ridge	2177			1388	−0.539	34.92	glacialis	9	0.01172	0.00349		4	0	4
61	Y	Northwind Ridge	PL92ARB	16		1388	−0.3	34.9	glacialis	24	0.01308	0.00297		1	1	45a
62		Norwegian Sea	PL91ARBC	11		1536	−1.142	34.91	glacialis	23	0.00915	0.00314		6	1	51b
63		Norwegian Sea	PI91ARBC	11		1536	−1	34.91	glacialis	30	0.00916	0.00314		4	0	10
64		Norwegian Sea	PL91ARBC	11		1536	−1.142	34.91	glacialis	8	0.01054	0.00330		7	1	51a
65		Lomonosov Ridge	2184			1640	−0.486	34.91	glacialis	22	0.01791	0.00267		2	1	5
66	Y	Laptev Sea	2464	2	0–1	1760	−0.75	34.92	glacialis	20	0.00912	0.00319	0.00623	5	6	20
67	Y	Laptev Sea	2464	2	0–1	1760	−0.75	34.92	glacialis	14	0.00924	0.00321	0.00588	3	6B	71
68	Y	Laptev Sea	2464	2	0–1	1760	−0.75	34.92	glacialis	25	0.00941	0.00322	0.00586	4	6	22
69	Y	Laptev Sea	2464	2	0–1	1760	−0.75	34.92	glacialis	13	0.00953	0.00328	0.00533	3	6B	72
70	Y	Laptev Sea	2464	2	0–1	1760	−0.75	34.92	glacialis	21	0.01078	0.00320	0.00635	5	6	21
71		Greenland Sea	1560	3		1824	−0.948	34.91	glacialis	21	0.01026	0.00307		7	1	25a
72		Greenland Sea	1560	3		1824	−0.948	34.91	glacialis	24	0.01370	0.00314		4	1	25b
73	Y	Laptev Sea	2468	3	0–1	1991	−0.79	34.94	glacialis	9	0.00952	0.00324	0.00446	5	6	48
74	Y	Laptev Sea	2468	3	0–1	1991	−0.79	34.93	glacialis	24	0.00959	0.00303	0.00688	3	6	24
75	Y	Laptev Sea	2468	3	0–1	1991	−0.79	34.94	glacialis	20	0.00992	0.00308	0.00642	4	6	47
76	Y	Laptev Sea	2468	3	0–1	1991	−0.79	34.93	glacialis	30	0.01057	0.00303	0.00811	3	6	23
77	Y	Laptev Sea	2468	3	0–1	1991	−0.79	34.93	glacialis	14	0.01098	0.00313	0.00637	3	6	25
78	Y	Laptev Sea	2468	3	0–1	1991	−0.79	34.93	glacialis	7	0.01160	0.00312	0.00617	1	6	26
79	Y	Laptev Sea	2468	3	0–1	1991	−0.79	34.93	glacialis	20	0.01160	0.00309	0.00688	3	6	27
80		Lomonosov Ridge	2183	6		2016	−0.5177	34.95	glacialis	20	0.01267	0.00315		6	1	36a
81	Y	Fram Strait	2215			2019	−1	34.92	glacialis	26	0.01009	0.00297		4	0	15
82	Y	Barents Slope	2446	3	0–1	2025	−0.81	34.93	glacialis	19	0.00982	0.00301	0.00521	5	6	50

Table 1. Continued

Sample	Plotted*	Region	Site†	Core	Interval (cm)	Water depth (m)	Temperature (°C)	Salinity (‰)	Species	Weight (μg)	Mg:Ca	Sr:Ca	Na:Ca	Pres‡	Phase§	Number§
83		GIN Seas/Fram Strait	1741	3		2059	−1.155	34.92	glacialis	30	0.01028	0.00312		2	1	30a
84		GIN Seas/Fram Strait	1741	3		2059	−1.155	34.92	glacialis	27	0.01165	0.00305		5	1	30b
85		GIN Seas/Fram Strait	23453	1		2061	−1.033	34.92	glacialis	20	0.00881	0.00324	0.00499	6	1	19c
86		GIN Seas/Fram Strait	23453	1		2061	−1.033	34.92	glacialis	20	0.00945	0.00319		7	1	19a
87		GIN Seas/Fram Strait	23453	1		2061	−1.033	34.92	glacialis	19	0.00980	0.00328	0.00377	6	1	19e
88		GIN Seas/Fram Strait	23453	1		2061	−1.033	34.92	glacialis	20	0.01008	0.00322		7	1	19b
89		GIN Seas/Fram Strait	23453	1		2061	−1.033	34.92	glacialis	17	0.01014	0.00310		7	1	20a
90		GIN Seas/Fram Strait	23453	1		2061	−1.033	34.92	glacialis	23	0.01062	0.00306		5	1	19f
91		GIN Seas/Fram Strait	23453	1		2061	−1.033	34.92	glacialis	17	0.01082	0.00325		4	1	20e
92		GIN Seas/Fram Strait	23453	1		2061	−1.033	34.92	glacialis	24	0.01101	0.00312		2	1	20d
93		GIN Seas/Fram Strait	23453	1		2061	−1.033	34.92	glacialis	19	0.01212	0.00274		5	1	20c
94		GIN Seas/Fram Strait	23453	1		2061	−1.033	34.92	glacialis	18	0.01323	0.00312		4	1	20b
95		GIN Seas/Fram Strait	23453	1		2061	−1.033	34.92	glacialis	21	0.01339	0.00298		1	1	20f
96		GIN Seas/Fram Strait	1873	1		2109	−1.009	34.92	glacialis	25	0.00969	0.00317		2	1	21a
97		GIN Seas/Fram Strait	1707	1		2118	−1.037	34.92	glacialis	34	0.01055	0.00321		4	1	23a
98		GIN Seas/Fram Strait	1707	1		2118	−1.037	34.92	glacialis	26	0.01182	0.00315		2	1	23b
99		GIN Seas/Fram Strait	23454	2		2162	−1.033	34.92	glacialis	31	0.00959	0.00291		6	1	27a
100		GIN Seas/Fram Strait	23454	2		2162	−1.033	34.92	glacialis	21	0.00968	0.00321		5	1	27b
101		GIN Seas/Fram Strait	23456	6		2200	−1.086	34.92	glacialis	26	0.00890	0.00316		6	1	29a
102		GIN Seas/Fram Strait	23456	6		2200	−1.086	34.92	glacialis	31	0.00968	0.00305		5	1	29b
103		GIN Seas/Fram Strait	23457	3		2259	−1.038	34.92	glacialis	27	0.00925	0.00323	0.00620	4	1	17f
104		GIN Seas/Fram Strait	23457	3		2259	−1.038	34.92	glacialis	12	0.00934	0.00313	0.00460	4	1	17d
105		GIN Seas/Fram Strait	23457	3		2259	−1.038	34.92	glacialis	28	0.00940	0.00316	0.00648	2	1	17e
106		GIN Seas/Fram Strait	23457	3		2259	−1.038	34.92	glacialis	25	0.00948	0.00311	0.00627	4	1	18e
107		GIN Seas/Fram Strait	23457	3		2259	−1.038	34.92	glacialis	29	0.00995	0.00310	0.00599	4	1	17h
108		GIN Seas/Fram Strait	23457	3		2259	−1.038	34.92	glacialis	24	0.01007	0.00318	0.00786	2	1	18b
109		GIN Seas/Fram Strait	23457	3		2259	−1.038	34.92	glacialis	28	0.01008	0.00309	0.00667	4	1	17c
110		GIN Seas/Fram Strait	23457	3		2259	−1.038	34.92	glacialis	26	0.01010	0.00319	0.00491	4	1	17j
111		GIN Seas/Fram Strait	23457	3		2259	−1.038	34.92	glacialis	18	0.01015	0.00311	0.00619	4	1	18f
112		GIN Seas/Fram Strait	23457	3		2259	−1.038	34.92	glacialis	24	0.01022	0.00310	0.00576	2	1	18d
113		GIN Seas/Fram Strait	23457	3		2259	−1.038	34.92	glacialis	25	0.01038	0.00322	0.00628	4	1	18g
114		GIN Seas/Fram Strait	23457	3		2259	−1.038	34.92	glacialis	24	0.01055	0.00316	0.00720	4	1	17b
115		GIN Seas/Fram Strait	23457	3		2259	−1.038	34.92	glacialis	26	0.01076	0.00290	0.00531	4	1	17a
116		GIN Seas/Fram Strait	23457	3		2259	−1.038	34.92	glacialis	26	0.01082	0.00302	0.00490	4	1	17g
117		GIN Seas/Fram Strait	23457	3		2259	−1.038	34.92	glacialis	26	0.01102	0.00314	0.00592	2	1	17i
118		GIN Seas/Fram Strait	23457	3		2259	−1.038	34.92	glacialis	25	0.01116	0.00310	0.00747	4	1	18c
119		GIN Seas/Fram Strait	23457	3		2259	−1.038	34.92	glacialis	22	0.01132	0.00304	0.00622	4	1	18a
120	Y	Laptev Sea	2469	3	0–1	2332	−0.81	34.94	glacialis	24	0.00791	0.00323	0.00480	5	6	49
121	Y	Laptev Sea	2469	3	0–1	2332	−0.81	34.94	glacialis	10	0.00895	0.00321	0.00482	5	6	29
122	Y	Laptev Sea	2469	3	0–1	2332	−0.81	34.94	glacialis	21	0.00912	0.00304	0.00498	5	6	28
123	Y	Laptev Sea	2469	3	0–1	2332	−0.81	34.94	glacialis	9	0.01274	0.00307	0.00525	4	6	30

Table 1. Continued

Sample	Plotted*	Region	Site†	Core	Interval (cm)	Water depth (m)	Temperature (°C)	Salinity (‰)	Species	Weight (µg)	Mg:Ca	Sr:Ca	Na:Ca	Pres‡	Phase§	Number§
124		GIN Seas/Fram Strait	23455	2		2362	-1.101	34.92	glacialis	27	0.00973	0.00326		4	1	28a
125		GIN Seas/Fram Strait	23455	2		2362	-1.101	34.92	glacialis	23	0.01083	0.00305		4	1	28b
126		Laptev Sea	2459	2	0-1	2420	-0.79	34.93	glacialis	22	0.00764	0.00319	0.00611	3	6	15
127	Y	Yermak Plateau	2212	6		2485	-0.8	34.92	glacialis	18	0.01017	0.00311		2	0	8
128	Y	Yermak Plateau	2212	6		2485	-0.8205	34.92	glacialis	16	0.01080	0.00305		1	1	40a
129	Y	Yermak Plateau	2212	6		2485	-0.8205	34.92	glacialis	12	0.01206	0.00306		1	1	40b
130		Morris Jesup Rise	NP19	14		2500	-0.768	34.92	glacialis	11	0.01637	0.00302		1	1	35a
131	Y	Laptev Sea	2456	2	0-1	2520	-0.79	34.93	glacialis	38	0.00714	0.00361	0.00603	5	6	13
132	Y	Laptev Sea	2456	2	0-1	2520	-0.79	34.93	glacialis	24	0.00940	0.00316	0.00634	3	6	12
133	Y	Laptev Sea	2456	2	0-1	2520	-0.79	34.93	glacialis	12	0.01180	0.00300	0.00618	3	6	14
134	Y	Barents Slope	2444	1	0-1	2566	-0.8	34.94	glacialis	15	0.01062	0.00316	0.00682	2	6	44
135	Y	Barents Slope	2444	1	0-1	2566	-0.8	34.94	glacialis	5	0.01997	0.00289	0.00947	2	6	45
136	Y	Laptev Sea	2472	3	0-1	2620	-0.79	34.94	glacialis	26	0.00854	0.00316	0.00578	5	6	58
137	Y	Laptev Sea	2472	3	0-1	2620	-0.79	34.94	glacialis	11	0.01021	0.00313	0.00482	5	6	59
138	Y	Laptev Sea	2472	3	0-1	2620	-0.79	34.94	glacialis	9	0.01045	0.00315	0.00604	4	6B	77
139	Y	Laptev Sea	2472	3	0-1	2620	-0.79	34.94	glacialis	10	0.01072	0.00312	0.00341	5	6	60
140		Morris Jesup Rise	NP21	3		2793	-0.539	34.93	glacialis	13	0.01009	0.00323		4	1	34a
141	Y	Barents Slope	2442	4	0-1	2915	-0.78	34.93	glacialis	9	0.00870	0.00327	0.00670	6	6	1
142		Gakkel Ridge	2206	4		2993	-0.7674	34.39	glacialis	17	0.01142	0.00317		1	1	39a
143	Y	Barents Slope	2445	3	0-1	2995	-0.77	34.94	glacialis	13	0.01003	0.00305	0.00652	2	6	3
144	Y	Barents Slope	2445	3	0-1	2995	-0.77	34.94	glacialis	7	0.01009	0.00303	0.00583	6	6	5
145	Y	Barents Slope	2445	3	0-1	2995	-0.77	34.94	glacialis	5	0.01048	0.00296	0.00570	4	6	4
146		Gakkel Ridge	2163			3047	-0.95	34.39	glacialis	11	0.01236	0.00302		2	1	1
147	Y	Laptev Sea	2471	3	0-1	3048	-0.76	34.94	glacialis	15	0.00825	0.00319	0.00487	2	6B	75
148	Y	Laptev Sea	2471	3	0-1	3048	-0.76	34.94	glacialis	14	0.00969	0.00324	0.00352	6	6	37
149	Y	Laptev Sea	2471	3	0-1	3048	-0.76	34.94	glacialis	27	0.00996	0.00309	0.00493	4	6	36
150	Y	Laptev Sea	2471	3	0-1	3048	-0.76	34.94	glacialis	26	0.01029	0.00298	0.00547	4	6	35
151	Y	Laptev Sea	2471	4	0-1	3233	-0.76	34.94	glacialis	15	0.01130	0.00298	0.00732	4	6	62
152	Y	Laptev Sea	2470	4	0-1	3233	-0.75	34.94	glacialis	19	0.00844	0.00311	0.00508	4	6	31
153	Y	Laptev Sea	2470	4	0-1	3233	-0.75	34.94	glacialis	14	0.00877	0.00306	0.00551	2	6B	73
154	Y	Laptev Sea	2470	4	0-1	3233	-0.75	34.94	glacialis	15	0.00878	0.00306	0.00358	6	6	33
155	Y	Laptev Sea	2470	4	0-1	3233	-0.75	34.94	glacialis	14	0.00896	0.00308	0.00514	3	6B	74
156	Y	Laptev Sea	2455	3	0-1	3429	-0.73	34.94	glacialis	15	0.00936	0.00309	0.00261	6	6	46
157	Y	Laptev Sea	2455	3	0-1	3429	-0.73	34.94	glacialis	11	0.01039	0.00313	0.00396	5	6	11
158		GIN Seas/Fram Strait	1736	1		3500	-1.088	34.89	glacialis	12	0.00929	0.00318		6	1	22a
159		Morris Jesup Rise	2204	3		3899	-0.7058	34.94	glacialis	17	0.01273	0.00270		2	1	38b
160		Morris Jesup Rise	2204	3		3899	-0.7058	34.94	glacialis	13	0.01369	0.00290		1	1	38a
161	Y	Barents Slope	PI191BC			24004	-0.94	34.94	glacialis	22	0.00912	0.00299		4	0	3
162		Amundsen Basin	2193			4337	-0.95	34.94	glacialis	13	0.01123	0.00284		5	0	6
163		Amundsen Basin	2175			4411	-0.94	34.94	glacialis	17	0.00939	0.00324		5	0	14
164		Northwind Ridge	PI188BC	22					glacialis	19	0.01146	0.00347		2	0	13

* Site numbers are Polarstern cruise locations.
† Plotted in figure profile Mg:Ca versus depth.
‡ Shell preservation index 1, transparent to 7, white and opaque.
§ 'Phase' and 'number' refer to original processing and laboratory codes.

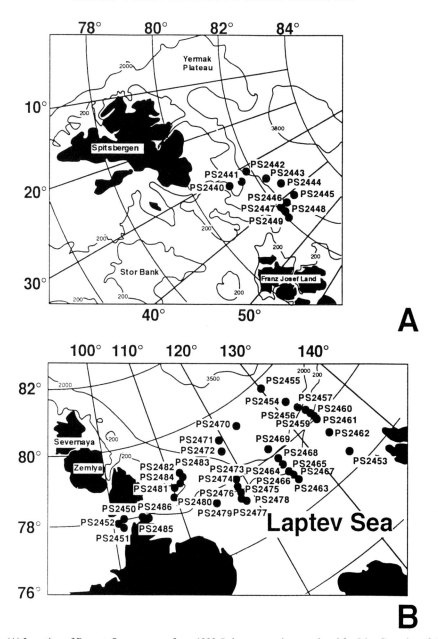

Fig. 1. (**A**) Location of Barents Sea core-tops from 1993 *Polarstern* stations analysed for Mg:Ca ratios of *Krithe*. (**B**) Location of Laptev Sea core-tops from 1993 *Polarstern* stations analyzed for Mg:Ca ratios of *Krithe*. Depth transects are those labelled in Fig. 4.

sites where the bottom water temperature was measured, are ideal for this study and generally yield the most consistent results. Such was the case for most of the 1993 *Polarstern* material from the Laptev and Barents Seas (Fig. 1). Cronin *et al.* (1995) showed the location in Norwegian and Greenland seas of other

samples from core tops of variable preservation used in the present study.

Table 2 gives the Mg:Ca ratios of 48 downcore specimens analysed from four Arctic cores. These cores were selected because they come from ridges or submarine topographic highs away from the influence of turbidite

Table 2. *Downcore geochemical data from ostracode shells*

Core	Depth (cm)	Mg:Ca	Sr:Ca	Na:Ca	Pres*	Species†	Ph 6 samp‡
Gakkel Ridge							
2206	0	0.00906	0.00313	0.00536	1	*glacialis*	81
2206	1	0.01067	0.00303	0.00574	1	*glacialis*	83
2206	1	0.01056	0.00303	0.00671	1	*glacialis*	84
2206	2	0.01217	0.00289	0.00547	1	*glacialis*	85
2206	3	0.01074	0.00301	0.00640	1	*glacialis*	86
2206	3	0.01062	0.00297	0.00453	1	*glacialis*	87
2206	4	0.01043	0.00320	0.00659	1	*glacialis*	88
2206	5	0.01235	0.00300	0.00630	3	*glacialis*	89
2206	5	0.01010	0.00313	0.00537	2	*glacialis*	90
2206	7	0.00984	0.00300	0.00589	1	*glacialis*	91
2206	7	0.01491	0.00288	0.00628	1	*glacialis*	92
2206	10	0.01098	0.00300	0.00551	1	*glacialis*	93
2206	10	0.01333	0.00294	0.00634	3	*glacialis*	94
2163	1	0.01197	0.00309	0.00724	3	*glacialis*	95
2163	1	0.01068	0.00317	0.00522	3	*glacialis*	96
2163	2	0.01065	0.00292	0.00758	1	*glacialis*	97
2163	2	0.01093	0.00298	0.00539	1	*glacialis*	98
2163	2	0.01086	0.00305	0.00658	1	*glacialis*	99
2163	3	0.00985	0.00300	0.00484	4	*glacialis*	100
2163	3	0.01150	0.00304	0.00632	5	*glacialis*	101
2163	4	0.01334	0.00308	0.00766	2	*glacialis*	102
2163	4	0.01444	0.00279	0.00673	3	*glacialis*	103
2163	4	0.01480	0.00292	0.00715	2	*glacialis*	104
2163	5	0.01261	0.00291	0.00593	1	*glacialis*	105
2163	5	0.01162	0.00311	0.00595	1	*glacialis*	106
2163	5	0.00995	0.00309	0.00679	2	*glacialis*	107
2163	7	0.01205	0.00297	0.00574	2	*glacialis*	108
2163	7	0.01228	0.00283	0.00694	2	*glacialis*	109
2163	12	0.01357	0.00301	0.00612	2	*glacialis*	110
2163	25	0.01137	0.00276	0.00530	4	*glacialis*	111
2163	26	0.01243	0.00280	0.00582	5	*glacialis*	112
Amundsen Basin							
2170	12	0.00914	0.00309	0.00421	4	*glacialis*	113
2170	11	0.00969	0.00294	0.00454	5	*glacialis*	114
2170	11	0.00918	0.00297	0.00248	6	*glacialis*	115
2170	9	0.00907	0.00285	0.00399	5	*glacialis*	116
2170	9	0.00941	0.00288	0.00322	5	*glacialis*	117
2170	9	0.00928	0.00294	0.00372	6	*glacialis*	118
2170	8	0.00893	0.00287	0.00415	5	*glacialis*	119
2170	8	0.00883	0.00299	0.00320	5	*glacialis*	120
2170	7	0.00890	0.00296	0.00286	6	*glacialis*	121
2170	7	0.00877	0.00306	0.00381	6	*glacialis*	122
2170	6	0.00925	0.00303	0.00375	6	*glacialis*	123
2170	6	0.00893	0.00292	0.00330	5	*glacialis*	124
2170	5	0.00904	0.00299	0.00362	5	*glacialis*	125
2170	5	0.00822	0.00294	0.00409	5	*glacialis*	126
2170	4	0.00846	0.00298	0.00404	5	*glacialis*	127
2170	4	0.01148	0.00268	0.00460	6	*glacialis*	128
2170	3	0.00908	0.00289	0.00545	6	*glacialis*	129
2170	2	0.00927	0.00290	0.00504	5	*glacialis*	130
2170	1	0.00901	0.00299	0.00356	4	*glacialis*	131
2170	1	0.00952	0.00301	0.00411	5	*glacialis*	132
Lomonosov Ridge							
2185	19	0.02860	0.00238	0.00544	5	*glacialis*	133
2185	19	0.02539	0.00299	0.00677	5	*min*	134
2185	18	0.01803	0.00293	0.00741	5	*glacialis*	135
2185	18	0.02353	0.00294	0.00675	5	*min*	136

Table 2. *Continued*

Core	Depth (cm)	Mg:Ca	Sr:Ca	Na:Ca	Pres*	Species†	Ph 6 samp‡
Lomonsov Ridge							
2185	17	0.02068	0.00281	0.00626	5	*glacialis*	137
2185	17	0.02146	0.00311	0.00670	5	*min*	138
2185	14	0.02218	0.00291	0.00678	5	*glacialis*	140
2185	14	0.01548	0.00332	0.02488	2	*min*	141
2185	12	0.02488	0.00317	0.00659	4	*min*	142
2185	11	0.01728	0.00311	0.00661	1	*min*	143
2185	10	0.01338	0.00330	0.01104	1	*min*	144
2185	6	0.01239	0.00310	0.00691	1	*glacialis*	145
2185	4	0.01045	0.00313	0.00789	2	*glacialis*	146
2185	4	0.01526	0.00305	0.00630	2	*min*	147

*Shell preservation index: 1, transparent to 7, opaque white.
† Original laboratory processing code number.
‡ All specimens *Krithe glacialis* or *K. minima* (= min).

sedimentation (Stein *et al.* 1994*a*). The locality data for these cores are given in Table 3.

Magnesium, strontium and calcium were measured on single ostracode valves using a SpectraSpan 7 direct current plasma (DCP) atomic emission spectrometer at Duke University Department of Geology following the cleaning and preparation procedures described in Dwyer *et al.* (1995). Trace element analyses of microfossils generally have potential for contamination (see Nurnberg 1995), thus it is useful to describe the methodology in detail. Ostracodes were brush-picked from the $\geq 150\,\mu m$ sediment fraction with deionized water and cleaned using ethanol or Clorox. We have used this cleaning method for several thousand analyses of both modern and fossil valves of more than 10 species of *Krithe* from a wide range of oceanic conditions and sediment types, including many areas of the North and South Atlantic Ocean, Chilean fjords and outcrop sections in Central America. Based on optical microscopic inspection, individual valves were then assigned a visual preservation index (VPI) ranging from 1 (transparent) to 7 (opaque white). Swanson & van der Lingen (1994) also developed a similar visual corrosion index

ranging from 0 for transparent, well-preserved shells to 6 for chalky shells that collapse on wetting. The preservation states of Atlantic and Arctic Ocean *Krithe* generally correspond to Swanson & van der Lingen's values 0 to 3 and we rarely encountered and have not analysed very poorly preserved *Krithe* corresponding to their states 4–7. Dwyer *et al.* (1995) found only a weak correlation between our ostracode VPI and Mg:Ca ratios in the Pliocene and Quaternary from the North Atlantic Ocean, leading to the conclusion that, if post-mortem alteration of the shell (dissolution and/or recrystallization) is the cause of increasingly opaque shells, this process, nonetheless, exerted little control on the Mg:Ca ratio in *Krithe* shells.

Following treatment with Clorox, each valve was sonicated in a two-step bath of deionized water and dissolved in 4–30 ml of 0.05 M nitric acid, depending on the weight of the valve. For most samples, Ca and Mg were determined simultaneously on the SpectraSpan 7 DCP spectrometer. About 15 of the specimens from the 1991 *Polarstern* cruise were analysed by atomic absorption spectrometry (AAS) with a Perkin-Elmer 5000 atomic absorption spectro-

Table 3. *Multicore data for Arctic Ocean Mg : Ca analyses of the ostracode* Krithe

Site	Region	Latitude (°N)	Longitude (°)	Water depth (m)
PS2163-1	Gakkel Ridge	86.24	59.22E	3040
PS2170-4	Amundsen Basin	87.59	60.77E	4226
PS2185-4	Lomonosov Ridge	87.63	144.05E	1051
PS2206-4	Gakkel Ridge	84.28	2.51W	2993

See Fütterer (1992) and Stein *et al.* (1994*a*) for core information; Stein *et al.* (1994*a*) for stable isotope and AMS data.

1994*b*; Cronin *et al.* 1994). We plotted temperature profiles from different regions in the Eurasian Basin against the Mg : Ca ratios. Figure 4 shows a general pattern of low Mg : Ca ratios for samples from Polar Surface Water tightly clustered near 0.007, increasing scatter with depth, and generally the highest Mg : Ca values between 300 and 1000 m in the Arctic Intermediate Layer. Below 1000 m Mg : Ca ratios are scattered, tend to decrease with greater depth, but never reach the extremely low ratios of 0.006–0.007 typical of Polar Surface Water.

To further investigate temperature versus Mg : Ca ratios, we plotted them against bottom water temperature for all Arctic and Nordic sea specimens from water depths less than 900 m (except one valve weighing 5 μg with an anomalously high Mg : Ca ratio) to eliminate any post-mortem effects that occur mainly in abyssal environments (Fig. 5). These data essentially represent the Polar Surface Water and Arctic Intermediate Water masses. The results show a positive correlation ($r^2 = 0.59$) between bottom water temperature and Mg : Ca over the temperature range −1.5 to +2.5°C. There are several possible explanations for the scatter. One factor may simply be related to the fact that the bottom water temperature varies at many sites, especially in the Polar Surface Water and Atlantic Intermediate Water, and it may be that the adult valve measured did not secrete its final adult shell at the indicated temperature. In the case of the 1991 and 1993 *Polarstern* sites, bottom water temperatures were collected on the same cruise as the core-tops and most of these core-top samples had ostracode specimens with preserved appendages. Therefore, the results from these cruises are probably the most reliable in providing a calibration of Mg : Ca with temperature. For other core-tops, temperature estimates were obtained from published sources and may not be as reliable as is needed for calibration. Varying chemical parameters at the sediment–water interface may also account for scatter to an unknown degree.

Lastly, we compared Arctic Mg : Ca ratios with those from the Atlantic Ocean from a temperature range of 2–14°C (Dwyer *et al.* 1995), also determined from analyses of *Krithe*, to see if the two data sets can be tied together to provide a single calibration graph. Figure 6 shows that the Arctic calibration Mg : Ca ratios for 0°C are only slightly higher (about <0.002)

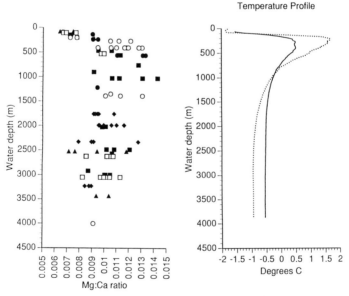

Fig. 4. Plot of water temperature profiles from different regions of the Arctic Ocean against Mg : Ca ratios in *Krithe* from depth transects in Laptev and Barents Seas and other regions. Transect 1 (closed squares), stations 2143, 2140, 2214, 2139, 2213, 2447, 2215, 2446, 2212, 2444, 2442 and 2445; transect 2 (closed circles), stations 2481, 2452, 2451, 2484, 2482 and 2483; transect 3 (closed triangles), stations 2461, 2460, 2459, 2456 and 2455; transect 4 (closed diamonds), stations 2464, 2468, 2469 and 2470; transect 5 (open squares), stations 2478, 2476, 2472 and 2471; others (open circles), Bart LT35, Kara 106, Pl91BC-08; Pl91-BC02, Pl92-ARB-16 and Pl92-ARB-17. See Table 1 and Fig. 1 for location of stations.

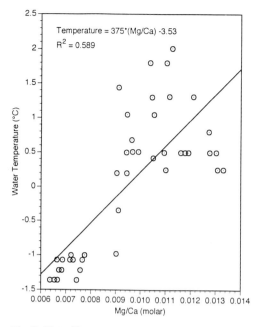

Fig. 5. Plot of bottom water temperature versus Mg : Ca ratio in *Krithe* for specimens from water depths less that 900 m.

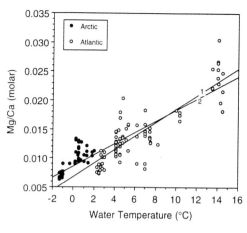

Fig. 6. Plot of Arctic Mg : Ca ratio data (filled circles) with North Atlantic Mg : Ca data on *Krithe* from Dwyer *et al.* (1995). Atlantic and Arctic data together, $R^2 = 0.757$.

than the value predicted by extrapolation of the curve of Dwyer *et al.* (1995) and that the lowest Mg : Ca ratios below 0.007 from cold Polar Surface Water are lower than all but two values from the North Atlantic data set. Thus the Arctic Mg : Ca data presented here support the hypothesis developed from Pacific (Correge 1993) and Atlantic (Dwyer *et al.* 1995) material that water temperature is a major factor in determining Mg : Ca ratios in ostracode shells.

Core-top Sr : Ca ratios

The ratio of strontium to calcium in marine biogenic calcite is a complex subject discussed in detail by Morse & Mackenzie (1991). Although our main goal was to evaluate Mg : Ca ratios, we also obtained baseline information on Sr : Ca ratios in *Krithe* that may be of use in future studies. Figure 7 shows plots of Sr : Ca ratios against water depth, temperature and salinity, respectively, from all Arctic and Nordic seas core-top samples. There is no obvious relationship between Sr : Ca ratios and temperature or salinity. However, there is a general trend of decreasing Sr : Ca ratios with increasing water

depth. The cause of this trend is not known. Laboratory experiments with inorganic calcite have demonstrated that co-precipitation of Sr into calcite is strongly controlled by precipitation rate (see Morse & Mackenzie 1991 for review). Strontium uptake into biogenic calcite, however, is a poorly understood process. Thus the possible causes for the Sr : Ca depth trend observed in Arctic *Krithe*, including variable shell growth rate, post-mortem alteration or pressure effects, are speculative until further research is conducted.

Late Quaternary Mg : Ca records

Figure 8 is a plot of downcore Mg : Ca ratios for four multicores: one from the Lomonosov Ridge (PS2185), two from the Gakkel Ridge (PS2163, PS2206) and one from the Amundsen Basin (PS2170). Each point in Fig. 8 represents the analysis of a single valve or the mean of two to three valves. Geochronology of these cores is based on AMS radiocarbon dating and isotope stratigraphy given by Stein *et al.* (1994a; 1994b). Originally it was hoped that we could compare shell geochemistry for the LGM, the last deglacial interval, and the Holocene, but *Krithe* were not preserved in all samples, so only the following general late Quaternary patterns can be observed.

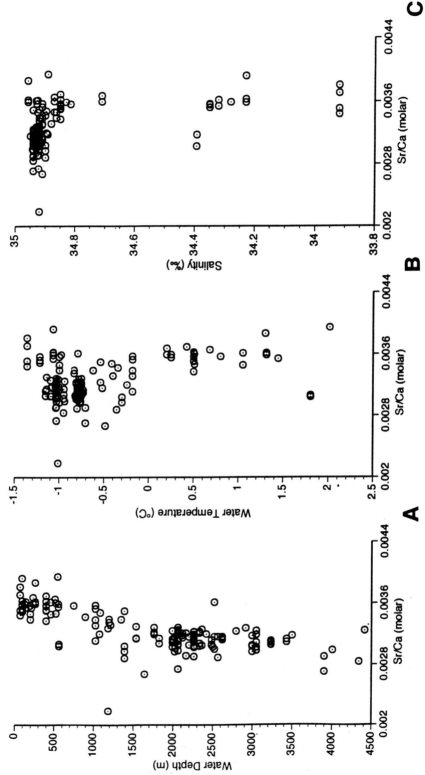

Fig. 7. Plot of Sr:Ca ratios in Arctic and Nordic seas *Krithe* against (A) water depth, (B) bottom water temperature and (C) salinity.

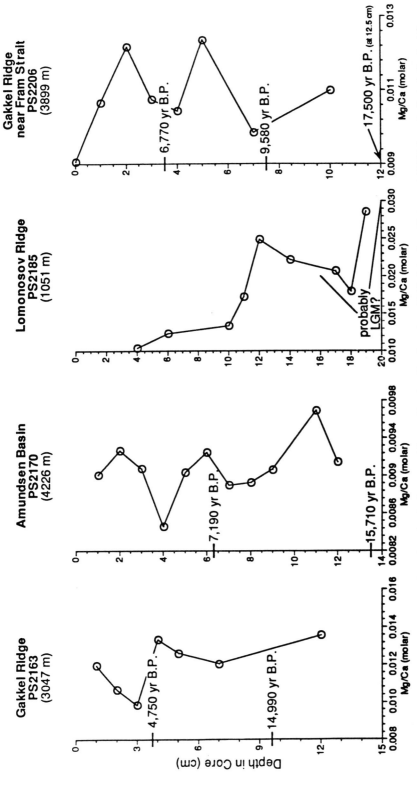

Fig. 8. Plot of Mg:Ca ratios downcore from four Arctic Ocean multicores. Depths of radiocarbon AMS dates from Stein *et al.* (1994*a*) are indicated. See text for discussion and Table 3 for core locations.

Core PS2163. There is a slight decrease in Mg:Ca ratios from about 0.0135 near 12 cm to 0.0105 in the uppermost 3 cm of this core from 3040 m on the eastern Gakkel Ridge. If these values record bottom water temperature, they suggest relatively warmer bottom water conditions at this depth during the last glacial period and the early Holocene compared with the late Holocene.

Core PS2170. This core has a relatively stable record of Mg:Ca ratios from 12 cm dated at about 14 000 years BP to 1 cm, except for a spike at 4 cm near about 5000 years BP. This record suggests fairly stable bottom water environments since the LGM in the deepest parts of the Amundsen Basin, a pattern supported by faunal assemblage data from this core (Cronin *et al.* 1995). Using the calibration of Mg:Ca to temperature dev-eloped above, bottom water temperature would have been about 0°C for much of the last 14 000 years.

Core PS2185. This core is the shallowest investigated and, although it is not dated by ^{14}C, the LGM is considered to be near the 20 to 22 cm level based on isotope stratigraphy (Stein *et al.* 1994*a*) and ostracode faunal patterns (Cronin *et al.* 1995). The high Mg:Ca values from 17 to 19 cm would, according to this age model, represent the deglacial interval or slightly earlier at a time when major faunal changes were occurring at this site and elsewhere on the Lomonosov Ridge (Cronin *et al.* 1995). The faunal data provide evidence for major changes in benthic environments in the central Arctic on the Lomonosov Ridge region that are hypothesized to reflect changes in deep-water characteristics. The Mg:Ca ratios of 0.019–0.028 are extremely high for a deep-sea environment and would yield bottom water temperatures as high as >8–10°C at the 12–19 cm level, dropping to 1°C by the late Holocene. It is likely that the Mg:Ca ratios from at least the lower portion of this core are due to diagenetic factors affecting the shell chemistry.

Core PS2206. This core comes from 2993 m on the western end of the Gakkel Ridge and shows a net decrease in Mg:Ca ratios similar to that obtained from core PS2163 from the more eastern part of the Gakkel Ridge at approximately the same depth. This good correspondence suggests that the same factors, possibly temperature, are controlling the Mg:Ca ratios in *Krithe* at both sites.

Discussion and conclusions

It is clear from our studies that quality core-tops containing living or recently dead individuals are essential for investigating the causes of trace element variability in ostracode shells. This requirement is even more acute in the Arctic Ocean where relatively slow sediment accumulation rates and bioturbation can lead to temporal averaging of the uppermost few centimetres of cores. Moreover, slow burial also lends itself to possible influence of post-mortem alteration of shell chemistry by near-surface processes such as the formation of ferromanganese crusts and oxic dissolution. In fact, Nurnberg (1995) noticed anomalously high Mg:Ca ratios in the planktic foraminifer *Neogloboquadrina pachyderma* that came from regions in the Arctic Oceans located under perennial sea ice. These areas—from 2000 to more than 4000 m—also showed a wide scatter in ostracode Mg:Ca ratios. There is also a wide scatter in the Mg:Ca ratios of deep samples from the Nordic seas where sea ice is much more variable.

Our examination of the highest quality core-top material suggests that bottom water temperature significantly affects Mg:Ca ratios in *Krithe* from the Arctic Ocean. Moreover, Mg:Ca ratios of 0.006–0.007 from the coldest water (−1.5 to −1.2°C), are near the value expected if the North Atlantic calibration graph, which ranges from 2 to 14°C (Dwyer *et al.* 1995), were extrapolated to lower temperatures.

Our downcore Mg:Ca ratios generally suggest that changes in bottom water environments occurred during the glacial–deglacial transition in the deep Arctic Ocean, which either led to changes in the primary precipitation of Mg:Ca in ostracode shells or alteration of the original shell chemistry. The observed variations in Mg:Ca at some sites (2163, 2206) are in the proper direction and of the right magnitude if temperature or some temperature-related factor caused the patterns. Higher Mg:Ca ratios from late glacial age sediments may indicate higher bottom water temperatures at some depths in the Eurasian Basin, perhaps reflecting reduced ventilation from deep-water formation due to greater sea ice cover and bottom water warming from vertical diffusion. The challenge for future workers will be to understand and decouple the primary signal in shell chemistry, reflecting factors that control the co-precipitation of magnesium during ostracode shell secretion from those secondary post-mortem effects which can alter the original composition of the shell.

We are grateful to D. Futterer, R. Stein, R. Spielhagen, D. Nürnberg, C. Vogt and H. Bauch for providing samples, to E. Klein for providing unlimited access to the Duke University DCP, and to T. Holtz Jr for technical support. This work was funded by the USGS Global Change Program, NSF Grants OPP-09400250 to P. A. Baker and G. S. Dwyer and OPP-9400255 to W. M. Briggs Jr and Spanish Ministry of Education and Science (DGICYT PR94–177) to J. Rodriguez-Lazaro. We are grateful to S. Hakkinen for helpful discussion of Arctic oceanography. We thank J. Andrews and W. Austin for inviting us to participate in the conference on the Late Glacial of the North Atlantic. We are greatful to R. L. Kaesler, J. E. Hazel and D. A. Willard for helpful reviews.

References

AAGAARD, K., SWIFT., J. H. & CARMACK, E. C. 1985. Thermohaline circulation in the Arctic Mediterranean Seas. *Journal of Geophysical Research*, **90** (C3), 4833–4846.

ANDREWS, J. T., DYKE, A. S., TEDESCO, K. & WHITE, J. W. 1993. Meltwater along the Arctic margin of the Laurentide ice sheet (8–12 ka): stable isotopic evidence and implications for past salinity anomalies. *Geology*, **21**, 881–884.

BURTON, E. A. & WALTER, L. M. 1991. The effects of P_{CO_2} and temperature on magnesium incorporation in calcite in seawater and $MgCl_2$–$CaCl_2$ solutions. *Geochemica et Cosmochemica Acta*, **55**, 777–785.

CADOT, H. M., JR & KAESLER, R. L. 1977. *Magnesium Content of Calcite in Carapaces of Benthic Marine Ostracoda.* University of Kansas Paleontological Contributions, Paper, **87**, 1–23.

CHAVE, K. E., 1954. Aspects of the biogeochemistry of magnesium 1. Calcareous marine organisms. *Journal of Geology*, **62**, 266–283.

CHIVAS, A. R., DE DECKKER, P., CALI, J. A., CHAPMAN, A., KISS, E. & SHELLEY, J. M. G. 1993. Coupled stable-isotope and trace-element measurements of lacustrine carbonates as paleoclimatic indicators. *American Geophysical Monographs*, **78**, 113–121.

——, —— & SHELLEY, J. M. G. 1983. Magnesium, strontium, and barium partitioning in non-marine ostracode shells and their use in paleoenvironmental reconstructions—a preliminary study. In: MADDOCKS, R. F. (ed.) *Applications of Ostracoda.* University of Houston Geoscience, 238–249.

——, —— & —— 1986. Magnesium content of non-marine ostracod shells: a new palaeosalinometer and palaeothermometer. *Palaeogeography, Palaeoclimatology, Palaeoecology*, **54**, 43–61.

CLARK, D. L. 1990. Arctic Ocean ice cover, geologic history and climatic significance. In: GRANTZ, A., JOHNSON, L. & SWEENEY, J. F. (eds) *The Arctic Ocean Region.* Geological Society of America, The Geology of North America, **L**, 53–62.

CORREGE, T. 1993. Preliminary results of paleo-temperature reconstruction using the magnesium to calcium ratio of deep-sea ostracode shells from the Late Quaternary of site 822, Leg 133 (Western Coral Sea). *Proc. ODP, Sci. Res.*, **133**, 175–180.

CRONIN, T. M. Distribution of deep-sea Ostracoda in the Arctic Ocean. *Berichte zur Polarforschung*, in press.

——, HOLTZ, T. R., JR, STEIN, R., SPIELHAGEN, R., FUTTERER, D. & WOLLENBERG, J. 1995. Late Quaternary paleoceanography of the Eurasian Basin, Arctic Ocean. *Paleoceanography*, **10**(2), 259–281.

——, —— & WHATLEY, R. C. 1994. Quaternary paleoceanography of the deep Arctic Ocean based on quantitative analysis of Ostracoda. *Marine Geology*, **19**, 305–332.

DELANEY, M. L., BE, A. W. H. & BOYLE, E. A. 1985. Li, Sr, Mg, Na in foraminiferal calcite shells from laboratory culture, sediment traps and sediment cores. *Geochemica et Cosmochemica Acta*, **49**, 1327–1341.

DE DECKKER, P., CHIVAS, A. R., SHELLEY, J. M. G. & TORGERSEN, T. 1988. Ostracod shell chemistry: a new paleoenvironmental indicator applied to a regressive/transgressive record from the Gulf of Carpentaria, Australia. *Palaeogeography, Palaeoclimatology, Palaeoecology*, **66**, 231–241.

DWYER, G. S., CRONIN, T. M., BAKER, P. A., RAYMO, M. E., BUZAS, J. S. & CORREGE, T. 1995. North Atlantic deep-water temperature change during late Pliocene and late Quaternary climatic cycles: new insight from ostracode shell chemistry. *Science*, **270**, 1347–1351.

FUTTERER, D. (ed.) 1992. Arctic '91: Die Expedition ARK-VIII/3 mit FS Polarstern 1991. *Berichte zur Polarforschung*, **107**.

——1994. Die expedition ARCTIC '93 der Fahrtabschnitt ARK-IX/4 mit FS Polarstern 1993. *Berichte zur Polarforschung*, **149**.

HENRICH, R., WAGNER, T., GOLDSCHMIDT, P. & MICHELS, K. 1995. Depositional regimes in the Norwegian–Greenland Sea: the last two glacial to interglacial transitions. *Geologische Rundschau*, **84**, 28–48.

IZUKA, S. K. 1988. Relationship of magnesium and other minor elements in tests of *Cassidulina subglobosa* and *C. orianulata* to physical oceanic properties. *Journal of Foraminiferal Research*, **18**, 151–157.

JONES, G. A. & KEIGWIN, L. D. 1988. Evidence from Fram Strait (78 N) for early deglaciation. *Nature*, **336**, 56–59.

KOC, N. & JANSEN, E. 1994. Response of the high-latitude Northern hemisphere to orbital climate forcing: evidence from the Nordic Seas. *Geology*, **22**, 523–526.

LEHMAN, S. J. & FORMAN, S. L. 1992. Late Weichselian glacier retreat in Kongsfjorden, West Spitzbergen, Svalbard. *Quaternary Research*, **37**, 139–154.

—— & KEIGWIN, L. D. 1991. Sudden changes in North Atlantic circulation during the last deglaciation. *Nature*, **356**, 757–762.

MORSE, J. W. & MACKENZIE, F. F. 1990. *Geochemistry of Sedimentary Carbonates*. Elsevier, Amsterdam.

NURNBERG, D. 1995. Magnesium in tests of *Neogloboquadrina pachyderma* sinistral from high northern and southern latitudes. *Journal of Foraminiferal Research*, **25**, 350–368.

SARNTHEIN, M. & ALTENBACH, A. V. 1995. Late Quaternary changes in surface water and deep water masses of Nordic seas and north-eastern North Atlantic—a review. *Geologische Rundschau*, **84**, 89–107.

SPIELHAGEN, R. & ERLENKEUSER, H. 1994. Stable oxygen and carbon isotopes in planktic foraminifers from Arctic Ocean surface sediments: reflection of the low salinity surface water layer. *Marine Geology*, **119**, 227–250.

STEIN, R., NAM, S. I., SCHUBERT, C., VOGT, C., FUTTERER, D. & HEINMEIER, J. 1994a. The last deglaciation event in the eastern Central Arctic Ocean. *Science*, **264**, 692–696.

——, SCHUBERT, C., VOGT, C. & FUTTERER, D. 1994b. Stable isotope stratigraphy, sedimentation rates, and salinity changes in the latest Pleistocene to Holocene eastern central Arctic Ocean. *Marine Geology*, **119**, 333–356.

SWANSON, K.M & VAN DER LINGEN, G. J. 1994. Podocopid ostracod dissolution- description of a new paleoenvironmental tool, with examples from the eastern Tasman Sea. *In*: VAN DER LINGEN, G. J., SWANSON, K. M. & MUIR, R. J. (eds) *Evolution of the Tasman Sea Basin. Proceedings of the Tasman Sea Conference, 27–30 November, 1992.* Balkema, Rotterdam, 245–260.

UNTERSTEINER, P. 1990. Structure and dynamics of the Arctic Ocean ice cover. *In*: GRANTZ, A., JOHNSON, L. & SWEENEY, J. F. (eds) *The Arctic Ocean Region*. Geological Societyof America, The Geology of North America, **L** 37–52.

ZAHN, R., MARKUSSEN, B. & THIEDE, J. 1985. Stable isotope data and depositional environments in the late Quaternary Arctic Ocean. *Nature*, **314**, 433–435.

Late Quaternary glacial history and short-term ice-rafted debris fluctuations along the East Greenland continental margin

RUEDIGER STEIN, SEUNG-IL NAM, HANNES GROBE & HANS HUBBERTEN

Alfred-Wegener-Institute for Polar and Marine Research, Columbusstrasse, 27568 Bremerhaven, Germany

Abstract: High-resolution stable oxygen and carbon isotope and sedimentological investigations were carried out on four west–east profiles at the East Greenland continental margin between 68° and 75° N. The sediment cores represent distinct glacial/interglacial palaeoclimatic episodes over the past 190 ka. Based on oxygen isotope stratigraphy and AMS ^{14}C dating, our data can be well correlated with the global climate record. However, there are some excursions from the global climate curve suggesting a local/regional overprint by meltwater events of the Greenland Ice Sheet, especially at the beginning of isotope stage 3 and during Termination 1. Distinct high-amplitude variations in supply of ice-rafted debris (IRD) indicate repeated advances and retreats of the Greenland Ice Sheet, causing fluctuations in the massive production and transport of icebergs into the Greenland Sea. During the last 190 ka, a number of IRD peaks appear to be correlated with cooling cycles observed in the GRIP Greenland Ice Core. Drastic events in iceberg discharge along the East Greenland continental margin recurred at very short intervals of 1000–3000 years (i.e. much more frequently than the about 10 000 years associated with Heinrich events), suggesting short-term collapses of the Greenland Ice Sheet on these time-scales. These late Weichselian Greenland Ice Sheet oscillations appear to be in phase with those in the Barents Sea area. Maximum flux rates of terrigenous (ice-rafted) material were recorded at the continental slope between about 21 and 16 ka, which may correspond to the maximum (stage 2) extension of glaciers on Greenland. The beginning of Termination I is documented by a distinct shift in the oxygen isotopes and a most prominent decrease in flux of IRD at the continental slope caused by the retreat of continental ice masses.

Sedimentary processes, terrigenous sediment supply and biogenic productivity along the East Greenland continental margin are influenced by fluctuations in the extent of the Greenland Ice Sheet, the extent of sea ice, the rate of drifting icebergs, meltwater input and/or oceanic circulation, i.e. factors which are all assumed to be controlled by climate (Figs 1 and 2). The reconstruction of this environmental history of the East Greenland margin and the correlation between terrestrial and marine records are major objectives of the ESF–PONAM (European Science Foundation–Polar North Atlantic Margins) programme (Elverhøi & Dowdeswell 1991). Terrestrial field work on eastern Greenland (e.g. Hjort 1981; Funder 1989; Möller *et al.* 1991; Funder *et al.* 1994) and numerous investigations performed on marine sediments from the Norwegian–Greenland Sea (e.g. Henrich *et al.* 1989; Gard & Backman 1990; Vogelsang 1990; Koç Karpuz & Jansen 1992; Baumann *et al.* 1993) gave important information about changes in palaeoclimate during the last glacial/interglacial cycles. Only a few palaeoenvironmental studies, however, were performed in the heavily sea ice covered East Greenland continental margin area (e.g. Marienfeld 1992; Mienert *et al.* 1992; Stein *et al.* 1993; Williams 1993; Nam *et al.* 1995). Transport by icebergs is the main mechanism supplying terrigenous material here. In particular, the occurrence of sand- and gravel-sized particles in marine sediments is assumed to be delivered by both icebergs and sea ice and is generally accepted to be a useful tool for identifying ice-rafted debris (IRD) input and reconstructing the activity of glaciers on land (e.g. Ruddiman 1977; Shackleton *et al.* 1984; Grobe 1987; Spielhagen 1991; Hebbeln *et al.* 1994; Fronval *et al.* 1995). As shown in the example of Fig. 3 the sedimentary records from the profile off Scoresby Sund (cf. Fig. 2) are characterized by high-amplitude variations in IRD, suggesting major short-term variations in glacier extension on Greenland (Nam 1996). The IRD-rich horizons, interpreted as short-lived massive discharges of icebergs, are widespread features in the late Pleistocene North Atlantic and intensely investigated and discussed in the recent publications (e.g. Andrews & Tedesco 1992; Bond *et al.* 1992; Broecker *et al.* 1992; Bond & Lotti 1995). These so-called 'Heinrich layers' or 'Heinrich events'

From Andrews, J. T., Austin, W. E. N., Bergsten, H. & Jennings, A. E. (eds), 1996, *Late Quaternary Palaeoceanography of the North Atlantic Margins*, Geological Society Special Publication No. 111, pp. 135–151.

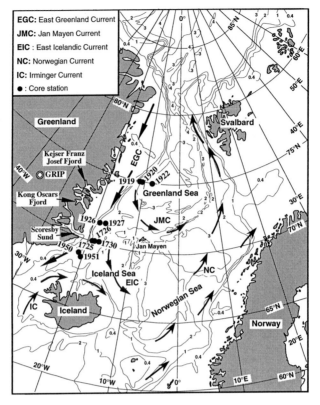

Fig. 1. Bathymetry and major surface water current patterns of the Greenland–Iceland–Norwegian Sea and core locations at the East Greenland continental margin. Bathymetry in 1000 m.

(Heinrich 1988; Broecker *et al.* 1992) occurring every 5–10 ka, are inconsistent with Milanko-vitch orbital periodicities and their origin is still under discussion (e.g. Bond *et al.* 1992).

In this paper, we concentrate on stable isotope stratigraphy and IRD and its change through

time and space. Major questions to be answered are as follows. Is it possible to link the IRD records with the Greenland Ice Sheet history and the terrestrial climate record? What is the frequency of variability of IRD input? Is it possible to link some of our IRD peaks to

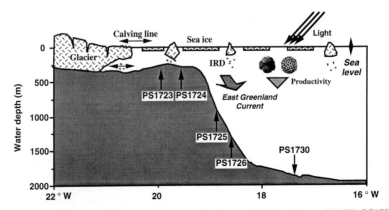

Fig. 2. Simplified scheme of the continental margin profile off Scoresby Sund (cores PS1723–PS1730), indicating the major climatic and oceanographic factors and processes controlling the sedimentation along the East Greenland continental margin.

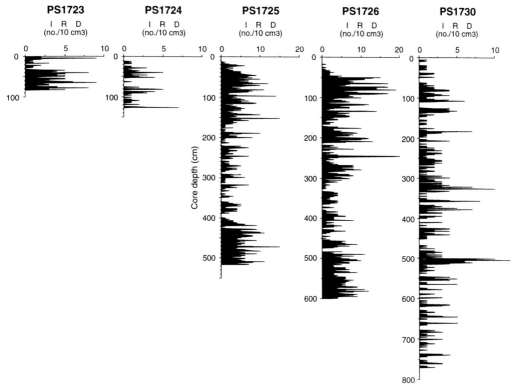

Fig. 3. Distribution of IRD (i.e. gravel fraction >2 mm, counted in X-radiographs and expressed as numbers per 10 cm³) at cores PS1723–PS1730. For location of profile, see Figs 1 and 2.

Heinrich events? Furthermore, we try to correlate our marine data with the GRIP Ice Core record.

Methods

Sediments were recovered by gravity coring (with a diameter of 12 cm) on four profiles perpendicular to the East Greenland continental margin between about 68° and 75° N during *Polarstern* expeditions ARK-V/3 and ARK-VII/3 in 1988 and 1990, respectively (Fig. 1, Table 1). The coring positions have been carefully selected based on Parasound and Hydrosweep profiling. The water depths of core sites vary between 280 and 3400 m. The age represented in the sedimentary sequences is Late Pleistocene to Holocene as based on AMS ^{14}C dating and oxygen stable isotope records.

Before opening, magnetic susceptibility was determined using a Bartington MS2 core logger (for detailed descriptions of the applied equipment and method, see Nowaczyk 1991; Fütterer 1992). After opening, all cores were described in detail. X-Radiographs were made from all cores for the determination of sedimentary structures.

Coarse-grained detritus >2 mm was counted in 1 cm intervals from the X-radiographs to evaluate the content of IRD (Grobe 1987). The IRD values were smoothed by a five-point moving average.

All cores were routinely sampled at 5–10 cm intervals; additional samples were taken at distinct changes in lithology and/or colour. About 30 cm³ subsamples were taken for coarse

Table 1. *Core number, core length, latitude and longitude and water depth of cores investigated*

Core No.	Core length (cm)	Latitute (° N)	Longitude (° W)	Water depth (m)
PS1919	373	74°59.8′	11°54.2′	1876
PS1920	750	74°59.7′	11°04.3′	2717
PS1922	493	75°00.0′	08°46.3′	3350
PS1926	319	71°29.6′	18°16.5′	1493
PS1927	491	71°29.7′	17°07.1′	1734
PS1725	516	70°06.9′	18°49.9′	879
PS1726	600	70°07.0′	18°38.9′	1174
PS1730	779	70°07.2′	17°42.1′	1617
PS1950	421	68°53.4′	20°55.7′	1480
PS1951	789	68°50.5′	20°49.2′	1481

at about 18, 21, 24, 31 and 48 ka coincide with relatively high magnetic susceptibility values. The IRD maxima at about 16, 38, 44, 52 and 58 ka, on the other hand, do not show any such increased values. This means that the former IRD peaks may contain higher amounts of basaltic material, whereas the latter IRD intervals are relatively enriched in sedimentary rock fragments. It has to be considered, however, that the whole core magnetic susceptiblity technique automatically provides a smoothed record and single IRD peaks of a few centimetres in thickness may be not reflected in the magnetic susceptibility record. A more detailed mapping and characterization of the different lithologies at the cores from all other profiles using microscopy and XRD analyses follows to distinguish between local and regional IRD events.

A comparison of the IRD signal off Scoresby Sund and the isotope record from the GRIP Summit Ice Core (Dansgaard *et al.* 1993; Fig. 9) suggests that most of the distinct IRD peaks coincide with intervals of very light isotope values, i.e. times of colder air temperatures over Greenland. In addition, at our study sites, increased iceberg discharges occur more frequenty than the Heinrich Events (cf. Bond & Lotti 1995; Fronval *et al.* 1995). The iceberg discharge in the Norwegian Sea from the Fennoscandian Ice Sheet correlates with the GRIP Greenland air temperature record in the same way as our IRD record off Greenland (Fronval *et al.* 1995). Thus our data support the model of these workers that coherent fluctuations in the Fennoscandian and Laurentide/ Greenland ice sheets occur on time-scales of a few thousand of years, i.e. distinctly shorter than the Milankovitch orbital cycles.

The last 30 000 years of East Greenland glacial history

In the well-dated cores PS1927, PS1730 and PS1951, changes in IRD discharge are presented in more detail for the last 30 000 years (Fig. 10). Major IRD pulses occur almost contemporaneously at all three cores near 29, 27–26, 23–22, 21–20, 18–17, 16 and 15–14 (radiocarbon) ka. The peaks at 27–26, 21–20, and 15–14 (radiacarbon) ka (or 31–30, 22–21 and 16–15 ka in calendar years; Fig. 9) are correlated with the Heinrich events H3, H2 and H1, respectively. Thus drastic events in iceberg discharge along the East Greenland continental margin recurred at very short intervals of 1000–3000 years, suggesting short-term collapses of the Greenland Ice

Sheet on these time-scales. Short-term fluctuations of IRD deposition on millennial time-scales, i.e. much more frequently than the about 10 000 years associated with Heinrich events, have been described by Bond & Lotti (1995) from their high-resolution studies of North Atlantic deep-sea sediments.

At all three cores, maximum fluxes of (coarse-grained) terrigenous material occur between about 21 and 16 ka BP (Fig. 10). Within this period, the maximum IRD discharges were also recorded (cf. for example, the distinct IRD pulse at deep-sea core PS1922, AMS ^{14}C dated to 18.6 ka; Fig. 4c). The Greenland Ice Sheet probably had its maximum late Weichselian extension and reached the fjord mouth and shelf areas during this period. This event coincides in age and duration with the culmination of the Flakkerhuk stade described in the Jameson Land/Scoresby Sund area (Funder 1989; Funder *et al.* 1994). Large amounts of terrigenous material deposited at the continental margin might have been derived from the inner Scoresby Sund, where all young unlithified sediments were most probably eroded by glaciers (Dowdeswell *et al.* 1991; Uenzelmann-Neben *et al* 1991; Marienfeld 1992). This late Weichselian East Greenland ice sheet oscillation appears to be in phase with that in the Barents Sea area (Hebbeln *et al.* 1994; Stein *et al.* 1994*a*).

The most prominent change from the end of the last glacial to the Holocene time (Termination 1) is characterized by a shift in the oxygen isotope records towards lighter values and by a decrease in the amount of IRD (Figs 4–7). This lowered ice rafting from Greenland near 15–14 ka is earlier than the rapid glacial retreat on Svalbard around 13–12.5 ka (e.g. Svendsen & Mangerud 1992).

The increased flux rates of terrigenous material at about 11 ka, which coincide with slightly increased abundances of IRD (Fig. 10), correspond to the Younger Dryas cooling event (e.g. Duplessy *et al.* 1981; Fairbanks 1989; Andrews *et al.* 1990; Kennett 1990). At that time, i.e. after the recession of glaciers that followed the Flakkerhuk glaciation, the East Greenland glaciers advanced again, however, without reaching the outer fjords/shelf ('Milne Land stade'; Funder 1989). These re-advanced glaciers may have caused the increase in IRD discharge near 11 ka.

Minor amounts of IRD were deposited at all core sites during the Holocene (Figs 4–7). Most of the material transported by icebergs was already discharged and deposited in the fjords, as shown for the Scoresby Sund fjord system (Marienfeld 1992; Stein *et al.* 1993).

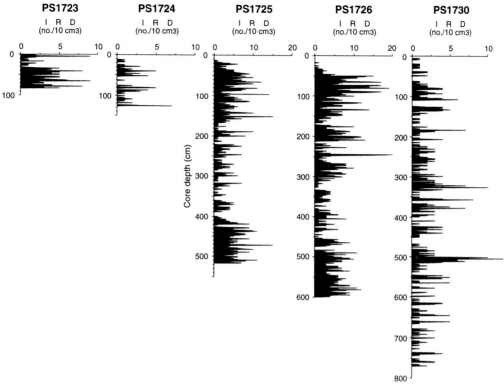

Fig. 3. Distribution of IRD (i.e. gravel fraction >2 mm, counted in X-radiographs and expressed as numbers per 10 cm^3) at cores PS1723–PS1730. For location of profile, see Figs 1 and 2.

Heinrich events? Furthermore, we try to correlate our marine data with the GRIP Ice Core record.

Methods

Sediments were recovered by gravity coring (with a diameter of 12 cm) on four profiles perpendicular to the East Greenland continental margin between about 68° and 75° N during *Polarstern* expeditions ARK-V/3 and ARK-VII/3 in 1988 and 1990, respectively (Fig. 1, Table 1). The coring positions have been carefully selected based on Parasound and Hydrosweep profiling. The water depths of core sites vary between 280 and 3400 m. The age represented in the sedimentary sequences is Late Pleistocene to Holocene as based on AMS ^{14}C dating and oxygen stable isotope records.

Before opening, magnetic susceptibility was determined using a Bartington MS2 core logger (for detailed descriptions of the applied equipment and method, see Nowaczyk 1991; Fütterer 1992). After opening, all cores were described in detail. X-Radiographs were made from all cores for the determination of sedimentary structures.

Coarse-grained detritus >2 mm was counted in 1 cm intervals from the X-radiographs to evaluate the content of IRD (Grobe 1987). The IRD values were smoothed by a five-point moving average.

All cores were routinely sampled at 5–10 cm intervals; additional samples were taken at distinct changes in lithology and/or colour. About 30 cm^3 subsamples were taken for coarse

Table 1. *Core number, core length, latitude and longitude and water depth of cores investigated*

Core No.	Core length (cm)	Latitute (°N)	Longitude (°W)	Water depth (m)
PS1919	373	74°59.8′	11°54.2′	1876
PS1920	750	74°59.7′	11°04.3′	2717
PS1922	493	75°00.0′	08°46.3′	3350
PS1926	319	71°29.6′	18°16.5′	1493
PS1927	491	71°29.7′	17°07.1′	1734
PS1725	516	70°06.9′	18°49.9′	879
PS1726	600	70°07.0′	18°38.9′	1174
PS1730	779	70°07.2′	17°42.1′	1617
PS1950	421	68°53.4′	20°55.7′	1480
PS1951	789	68°50.5′	20°49.2′	1481

Table 2. *AMS* [14]*C datings of sediment samples from selected core intervals; listed are uncorrected radiocarbon ages and reservoir-corrected (550 years) ages. AAR-1291, AAR-1292, etc. are the sample numbers at the AMS* [14]*C dating laboratory of the Institute of Physics and Astronomy, Aarhus University, Denmark*

Core	Laboratory No	Depth (cm bsf)	Age (years BP)	Reservoir corrected age (years BP)
PS1919-2	AAR-1291	7	7 820 ± 100	7 270 ± 100
	AAR-1292	13	16 620 ± 180	16 070 ± 180
	AAR-1293	51	20 050 ± 260	19 500 ± 260
	AAR-1294	100	31 500 ± 570	30 950 ± 570
PS1920-1	AAR-1295	6	5 230 ± 90	4 680 ± 90
	AAR-1296	47	17 380 ± 180	16 830 ± 180
	AAR-1297	80	12 050 ± 130	11 500 ± 130
	AAR-1298	144	24 330 ± 370	23 780 ± 370
PS1922-1	AAR-1299	156	19 180 ± 290	18 630 ± 290
PS1926-1	AAR-1301	1	540 ± 110	−10 ± 110
	AAR-1302	32	15 490 ± 210	14 940 ± 210
PS1927-2	AAR-1303	8	6 630 ± 90	6 080 ± 90
	AAR-1304	52	13 760 ± 170	13 210 ± 170
	AAR-1305	72	16 620 ± 160	16 070 ± 160
	AAR-1704	100	18 910 ± 210	18 360 ± 210
	AAR-1705	140	21 240 ± 250	20 690 ± 250
	AAR-1306	170	23 230 ± 240	22 680 ± 240
PS1726-1		40	Vedde ash	10 600
	AAR-1149	60	15 590 ± 130	15 040 ± 130
	AAR-1150	80	18 900 ± 170	18 350 ± 170
	AAR-1701	90	19 950 ± 270	19 400 ± 270
	AAR-1151	120	27 500 ± 330	26 950 ± 330
PS1730-2	AAR-1152	20	8 460 ± 10	7 910 ± 110
		35	Vedde ash	10 690
	ARR-1153	70	14 870 ± 140	14 320 ± 140
	AAR-1154	80	16 820 ± 150	16 270 ± 150
	AAR-1155	90	19 150 ± 190	18 600 ± 190
	AAR-1156	140	23 550 ± 360	23 000 ± 360
	AAR-1157	160	25 450 ± 310	24 900 ± 310
	AAR-1158	200	28 500 ± 650	27 950 ± 650
PS1950-2	AAR-1307	58	14 710 ± 140	14 160 ± 140
PS1951-1	ARR-1308	60	15 050 ± 130	14 500 ± 130
	AAR-1309	72	15 840 ± 140	15 290 ± 140
	ARR-1702	83	17 380 ± 190	16 830 ± 190
	AAR-1703	123	19 760 ± 240	19 210 ± 240
	AAR-1310	156	22 060 ± 240	21 510 ± 240

fraction analysis, stable isotopes and ^{14}C dating. Further subsamples were taken for the analysis of grain size distribution, clay mineralogy, carbonate and organic carbon content. The accompanied sedimentological data are presented and discussed in Stein *et al.* (1993), Nam (1996), Nam *et al.* (1995). Flux rates of terrigenous matter were calculated following van Andel *et al.* (1975).

Stable oxygen and carbon isotope records were determined on planktonic foraminiferal tests *N. pachyderma* sin. with 10 specimens per sample of the 125–250 μm fraction, using a Finnigan MAT 251 mass spectrometer. Two thousand specimens of *N. pachyderma* sin. per sample were selected for AMS ^{14}C dating of the uppermost intervals (Table 2). The dating was performed at the AMS [14]C Dating Laboratory of the Institute of Physics and Astronomy, Aarhus University, Denmark.

Results and discussion

Based on the lithological core description, the sediments of all cores investigated are dominantly of terrigenous origin and show distinct

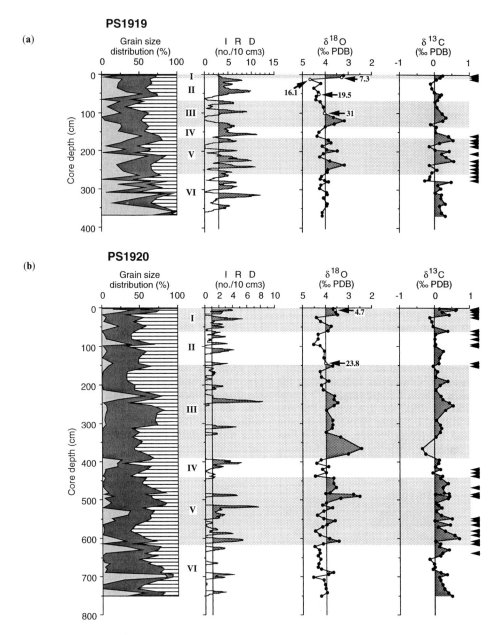

Fig. 4. Records from sediment cores (**a**) PS1919, (**b**) PS1920 and (**c**) PS1922. For all cores, grain-size distributions (sand–silt–clay), the amount of IRD i.e. gravel fraction >2mm, counted in X-radiographs, smoothed by the five-point moving average method, and expressed as numbers per 10 cm³) and stable oxygen and carbon isotope values (measured on the planktonic foraminifer *N. pachyderma* sin.) are shown. Roman numbers indicate oxygen isotope stages. Arrows in the oxygen isotope record and numbers indicate AMS ^{14}C ages (cf. Table 2). Black triangles mark samples in which the benthic foraminifer *C. wuellerstorfi* is present.

at about 18, 21, 24, 31 and 48 ka coincide with relatively high magnetic susceptibility values. The IRD maxima at about 16, 38, 44, 52 and 58 ka, on the other hand, do not show any such increased values. This means that the former IRD peaks may contain higher amounts of basaltic material, whereas the latter IRD intervals are relatively enriched in sedimentary rock fragments. It has to be considered, however, that the whole core magnetic susceptibility technique automatically provides a smoothed record and single IRD peaks of a few centimetres in thickness may be not reflected in the magnetic susceptibility record. A more detailed mapping and characterization of the different lithologies at the cores from all other profiles using microscopy and XRD analyses follows to distinguish between local and regional IRD events.

A comparison of the IRD signal off Scoresby Sund and the isotope record from the GRIP Summit Ice Core (Dansgaard *et al.* 1993; Fig. 9) suggests that most of the distinct IRD peaks coincide with intervals of very light isotope values, i.e. times of colder air temperatures over Greenland. In addition, at our study sites, increased iceberg discharges occur more frequently than the Heinrich Events (cf. Bond & Lotti 1995; Fronval *et al.* 1995). The iceberg discharge in the Norwegian Sea from the Fennoscandian Ice Sheet correlates with the GRIP Greenland air temperature record in the same way as our IRD record off Greenland (Fronval *et al.* 1995). Thus our data support the model of these workers that coherent fluctuations in the Fennoscandian and Laurentide/ Greenland ice sheets occur on time-scales of a few thousand of years, i.e. distinctly shorter than the Milankovitch orbital cycles.

The last 30 000 years of East Greenland glacial history

In the well-dated cores PS1927, PS1730 and PS1951, changes in IRD discharge are presented in more detail for the last 30 000 years (Fig. 10). Major IRD pulses occur almost contemporaneously at all three cores near 29, 27–26, 23–22, 21–20, 18–17, 16 and 15–14 (radiocarbon) ka. The peaks at 27–26, 21–20, and 15–14 (radiocarbon) ka (or 31–30, 22–21 and 16–15 ka in calendar years; Fig. 9) are correlated with the Heinrich events H3, H2 and H1, respectively. Thus drastic events in iceberg discharge along the East Greenland continental margin recurred at very short intervals of 1000–3000 years, suggesting short-term collapses of the Greenland Ice

Sheet on these time-scales. Short-term fluctuations of IRD deposition on millennial time-scales, i.e. much more frequently than the about 10 000 years associated with Heinrich events, have been described by Bond & Lotti (1995) from their high-resolution studies of North Atlantic deep-sea sediments.

At all three cores, maximum fluxes of (coarse-grained) terrigenous material occur between about 21 and 16 ka BP (Fig. 10). Within this period, the maximum IRD discharges were also recorded (cf. for example, the distinct IRD pulse at deep-sea core PS1922, AMS ^{14}C dated to 18.6 ka; Fig. 4c). The Greenland Ice Sheet probably had its maximum late Weichselian extension and reached the fjord mouth and shelf areas during this period. This event coincides in age and duration with the culmination of the Flakkerhuk stade described in the Jameson Land/Scoresby Sund area (Funder 1989; Funder *et al.* 1994). Large amounts of terrigenous material deposited at the continental margin might have been derived from the inner Scoresby Sund, where all young unlithified sediments were most probably eroded by glaciers (Dowdeswell *et al.* 1991; Uenzelmann-Neben *et al* 1991; Marienfeld 1992). This late Weichselian East Greenland ice sheet oscillation appears to be in phase with that in the Barents Sea area (Hebbeln *et al.* 1994; Stein *et al.* 1994a).

The most prominent change from the end of the last glacial to the Holocene time (Termination 1) is characterized by a shift in the oxygen isotope records towards lighter values and by a decrease in the amount of IRD (Figs 4–7). This lowered ice rafting from Greenland near 15–14 ka is earlier than the rapid glacial retreat on Svalbard around 13–12.5 ka (e.g. Svendsen & Mangerud 1992).

The increased flux rates of terrigenous material at about 11 ka, which coincide with slightly increased abundances of IRD (Fig. 10), correspond to the Younger Dryas cooling event (e.g. Duplessy *et al.* 1981; Fairbanks 1989; Andrews *et al.* 1990; Kennett 1990). At that time, i.e. after the recession of glaciers that followed the Flakkerhuk glaciation, the East Greenland glaciers advanced again, however, without reaching the outer fjords/shelf ('Milne Land stade'; Funder 1989). These re-advanced glaciers may have caused the increase in IRD discharge near 11 ka.

Minor amounts of IRD were deposited at all core sites during the Holocene (Figs 4–7). Most of the material transported by icebergs was already discharged and deposited in the fjords, as shown for the Scoresby Sund fjord system (Marienfeld 1992; Stein *et al.* 1993).

Conclusions

The results of our detailed sedimentological investigations of sediment cores from the East Greenland continental margin can be summarized as follows.

(1) The sedimentary records give important information about the East Greenland glacial history during the last 190 ka. Most of the oxygen isotope curves resemble the global isotope record, with some excursions to lighter values representing local/regional meltwater events.

(2) According to the amount of IRD, numerous major pulses of glacial activity and supply of terrigenous material by glacio-marine processes occurred during the last 190 ka. The correlation between IRD peaks and magnetic susceptibility suggests changes in the composition of IRD in time and space, reflecting iceberg discharge from different source areas. This conclusion, however, has to be proved by further microscopic and XRD analyses of the terrigenous material.

(3) A comparison of the IRD signal off Scoresby Sund and the oxygen isotope records from the GRIP Summit Ice Core suggests that most of the distinct IRD peaks coincide with times of colder air temperatures over Greenland.

(4) The events in iceberg discharge along the East Greenland continental margin recurred at very short intervals of 1000–3000 years. Rapid collapses of the Greenland Ice Sheet occur on millennial time-scales, i.e. more frequently than the 5000–10 000 years fre-quency associated with Heinrich events. Furthermore, our data support coherent fluctuations in the Fennoscandian/Barents Sea and Laurentide/Greenland ice sheets.

(5) The maximum flux of terrigenous (coarse-grained) material recorded at about 21–16 ka indicates the maximum late Weichselian extension of the East Greenland Ice Sheet. This event coincides in age and duration with the culmination of the Flakkerhuk stade described in the Jameson Land/Scoresby Sund area.

(6) The increased flux rates of terrigenous material and slightly increased abundances of IRD at about 11 ka correspond to the Younger Dryas cooling event or Milne Land stade glacial advance.

For technical assistance and discussion of data, we sincerely thank G. Meyer, H. Röben, N. Scheele and M. Seebeck. The AMS ^{14}C datings were performed by J. Heinemeier, Institute of Physics and Astronomy, Aarhus University, Denmark. The captain and the crew of R.V. *Polarstern* are gratefully acknowledged for co-operation during the expeditions ARK-V/3 and ARK-VII/3. We thank Á. Geirsdóttir and F. R. Hall for their numerous constructive comments for improvement of the manuscript. This is contribution No. 1025 of the Alfred Wegener Institute for Polar and Marine Research.

References

ANDREWS, J. T. & TEDESCO, K. 1992. Detrital carbonate-rich sediments, northwestern Labrador Sea: implications for ice-sheet dynamics and iceberg rafting (Heinrich) events in the North Atlantic. *Geology*, **20**, 1087–1090.

——, EVANS, L. W., WILLIAMS, K. M., BRIGGS, W. M., ERLENKEUSER, H., HARDY, I. & JULL, A. J. T. 1990. Cryosphere/ocean interactions at the margin of the Laurentide Ice Sheet during the Younger Dryas Chron: southeastern Baffin shelf, Northwest Territories. *Paleoceanography*, **5**, 921–935.

BARD, E., ARNOLD, M., FAIRBANKS, R., & HAMELIN, B. 1993. ^{230}Th–^{234}Cl and ^{14}C ages obtained by mass spectrometry in corals. *Radiocarbon*, **35**, 191–199.

BAUMANN, K.-H., LACKSCHEWITZ, K. S., ERLENKEUSER, H., HENRICH, R. & JÜNGER, B. 1993. Late Quaternary calcium carbonate sedimentation and terrigenous input along the East Greenland continental margin. *Marine Geology*, **114**, 13–36.

BIRGISDÓTTIR, L. 1991. Die paläo-ozeanographische Entwicklung der Islandsee in der letzten 550,000 Jahre. *Berichte SFB 313, Universität Kiel*, **34**.

BOND, G. C. & LOTTI, R. 1995. Iceberg discharges into the North Atlantic on millennial time scales during the last glaciation. *Science*, **267**, 1005–1010.

——, HEINRICH, H. & 12 others 1992. Evidence for massive discharges of icebergs into the North Atlantic ocean during the last glacial period. *Nature*, **360**, 245–249.

BROECKER, W., BOND, G., KLASS, M., CLARK, E. & McMANUS, J. 1992. Origin of the northern Atlantic's Heinrich events. *Climate Dynamics*, **6**, 265–273.

CHAPPELL, J. & SHACKLETON, N. J. 1986. Oxygen isotopes and sea level. *Nature*, **324**, 137–140.

DANSGAARD, W., JOHNSEN, S. J., & 9 others 1993. Evidence for general instability of past climate from a 250-kyr ice-core record. *Nature*, **364**, 218–220.

DOWDESWELL, J. A., VILLINGER, H., WHITTINGTON, R. J. & MARIENFELD, P. 1991. The Quaternary marine record in the Scoresby Sund fjord system, East Greenland: preliminary results and interpretation. *In:* MÖLLER P. *et al.* (eds) *The Last Interglacial–Glacial Cycle: Jameson Land and Scoresby Sund, East Greenland.* LundQua Report Series, **33**, 149–155.

DUPLESSY, J. C., DELIBRIAS, G., TURON, J. L., PUJOL, C. & DUPRAT, J. 1981. Deglacial warming of the northeastern Atlantic Ocean: correlation with the paleoclimatic evolution of the European continent. *Palaeogeography, Palaeoclimatology, Palaeoecology*, **35**, 121–144.

——, LABEYRIE, L., JUILLET-LECLERC, A., MAITRE, F., DUPRAT, J. & SARNTHEIN, M. 1991. Surface salinity recontruction of the North Atlantic Ocean during the last glacial maximum. *Oceanologica Acta*, **14**, 311–324.

ELVERHØI, A. & DOWDESWELL J. A. 1991. Polar North Atlantic Margins (PONAM). *ESF – Communications*, **25**, 16–17.

FAIRBANKS, R. G. 1989. A 17,000-year glacio-eustatic sea level record: influence of glacial melting rates on the Younger Dryas event and deep-ocean circulation. *Nature*, **342**, 637–642.

FRONVAL, T., JANSEN, E., BLOEMENDAL, J. & JOHNSEN, S. 1995. Oceanic evidence for coherent fluctuations in Fennoscandian and Laurentide ice sheets on millennium timescales. *Nature*, **374**, 443–446.

FUNDER, S. 1984. Chronology of the last interglacial/glacial cycle in Greenland: first approximation. *In*: MAHANEY W. C. (ed.) *Correlation of Quaternary chronologies*. Geo Books, Norwich, 261–279.

——1989. Quaternary geology of the ice-free areas and adjacent shelves of Greenland. *In*: FULTON, R. J. (ed.) *Quaternary Geology of Canada and Greenland*. Gelogical Survey of Canada, Geology of Canada, **1** (also Geological Society of America, The Geology of the North America, **K-1**), 743–792.

——, HJORT, C., & LANDVIK, J. Y. 1994. The last glacial cycle in East Greenland, an overview. *Boreas*, **23**, 283–293.

FÜTTERER, D. K. 1992. ARCTIC'91: the Expedition ARK-VIII/3 of RV 'Polarstern' in 1991. *Berichte zur Polarsternforschung*, **107**.

GARD, G. & BACKMAN, J. 1990. Synthesis of Arctic and subarctic coccolith biochronology and history of North Atlantic Drift Water influx during the last 500 000 years. *In*: BLEIL, U. & THIEDE, J. (eds) *Geological History of the Polar Oceans: Arctic Versus Antarctic*. Nato ASI Series C, Kluwer Academic, Dordrecht, **308**, 539–576.

GORSHKOV, S. G. 1983. *World Ocean Atlas*. Vol. 3. *Arctic Ocean*. Pergamon, Oxford.

GROBE, H. 1987. A simple method for the determination of ice-rafted debris in sediment cores. *Polarforschung*, **57**, 123–126.

HEBBELN, D., DOKKEN, T., ANDERSEN, E. S., HALD, M., & ELVERHØI, A. 1994. Moisture supply for northern ice-sheet growth during the Last Glacial Maximum. *Nature*, **370**, 357–360.

HEINRICH, H. 1988. Origin and consequences of cyclic ice rafting in the northeast Atlantic Ocean during the past 130 000 years. *Quaternary Research*, **29**, 142–152.

HEINRICH, R., KASSENS, H., VOGELSANG, E. & THIEDE, J. 1989. Sedimentary facies of glacial-interglacial cycles in the Norwegian Sea during the last 350 ka. *Marine Geology*, **86**, 283–319.

HJORT, C. 1981. A glacial chronology for the northern East Greenland. *Boreas*, **10**, 259–274.

ISRAELSON, C., FUNDER, S., & KELLY, M. 1994. The Aucellaelv stade at Aucellaelv, the first Weichselian glacier advance in scoresby Sund, East Greenland. *Boreas*, **23**, 424–431.

JONES, G. A. & KEIGWIN, L.D. 1988. Evidence from Fram Strait (78°N) for early deglaciation. *Nature*, **336**, 56–59.

JÜNGER, B. 1993. *Tiefenwassererneuerung in der Grnlandsee während der letzten 340 000 Jahre*. PhD Dissertation, Universität Kiel.

KENNETT, J. P. 1990. The Younger Dryas cooling event: an introduction. *Paleoceanography*, **5**, 891–896.

KOÇ KARPUZ, N. & JANSEN, E. 1992. A high-resolution diatom record of the last deglaciation from the SE Norwegian Sea: documentation of rapid climatic changes. *Paleoceanography*, **7**, 499–520.

LACKSCHEWITZ, K. S. 1991. Sedimentationsprozesse am aktiven mittelozeanischen Kolbeinsey Rücken, nördlich von Island. *Geomar Report*, **9**.

MANGERUD, J., LIE, S. E. FURNES, H. & KRISTIANSEN, I. L. 1984. A Younger Dryas ash bed in Western Norway, and its possible correlations with tephra in cores from the Norwegian Sea and the North Atlantic. *Quaternary Research*, **21**, 85–104.

MARIENFELD, P. 1992. Postglacial sedimentary history of Scoresby Sund, East Greenland. *Polarforschung*, **60**, 181–195.

MARTINSON, D. G., PISIAS, N. G., HAYS, J. D., IMBRIE, J., MOORE, T. C., & SHACKLETON, N. J. 1987. Age dating and the orbital theory of ice ages: development of high-resolution 0 to 300,000-year chronostratigraphy. *Quaternary Research*, **27**, 1–29.

MIENERT, J., ANDREWS, J. T. & MILLIMAN, J. D. 1992. The East Greenland continental margin (65° N) since the last deglaciation: changes in seafloor properties and ocean circulation. *Marine Geology*, **106**, 217–238.

MØLLER, P., HJORT, C., ADRIELSSON, L. & SALVIGSEN, O. 1994. Glacial history of interior Jameson Land, East Greenland. *Boreas*, **23**, 320–348.

——, HJORT C. & INGOLFSSON, O. 1991. The last interglacial/glacial cycle: preliminary report on the PONAM fieldwork in Jameson Land and Scoresby Sund, East Greenland. *Lundqua Rep*, **33**.

NAM, S.-I. 1996. *Late Quaternary glacial/interglacial changes in paleoclimate and paleoceanographic circulation along the East Greenland continental margin*. PhD Thesis, Bremen University.

——, STEIN, R., GROBE, H. & HUBBERTEN, H. 1995. Late Quaternary glacial/interglacial changes in sediment composition at the East Greenland continental margin and their paleoceanographic implications. *Marine Geology*, **122**, 243–262.

NOWACZYK, N. R. 1991. Hochauflösende Magnetostratigraphie spätquartärer Sedimente arktischer Meeresgebiete. *Berichte zur Polarforschung*, **78**.

ROBINSON, S. G., MASLIN, M. A. & MCCAVE, I. N. 1995. Magnetic susceptibility variations in late Pleistocene deep-sea sediments of the N.E. Atlantic: implications for ice-rafting and paleocirculation at the last Glacial Maximum. *Paleoceanography*, **10**, 221–250.

RUDDIMAN, W. F. 1977. North Atlantic ice-rafting: a major change at 75,000 years before the present. *Science*, **196**, 1208–1211.

SARNTHEIN, M., JANSEN, E. & 7 others 1992. δ18-O time-slice reconstruction of meltwater anomalies at Termination I in the North Atlantic between 50 and 80° N. *In*: BARD, E. & BROECKER, W. S. (eds) *The Last Deglaciation: Absolute and Radiocarbon Chronologies*. NATO ASI Seires, **12**, 183–200.

SEJRUP, H. P., SJØHOLM, J., FURNES, H., BEYER, I., EIDE, L., JANSEN, E. & MANGERUD, J. 1989. Quaternary tephrachronology on the Iceland Plateau, north of Iceland. *Journal of Quaternary Science*, **4**, 109–114.

SHACKLETON, N. J. 1987. Oxygen isotopes, ice volume and sea level. *Quaternary Science Reviews*, **6**, 183–190.

—— & OPDYKE, N. D. 1973. Oxygen isotope and paleomagnetic stratigraphy of equatorial Pacific Core V28–238: oxygen isotope temperatures and ice volume on a 105 year and 106 year scale. *Quaternary Research*, **3**, 39–55.

——, BACKMAN, J. & 7 others 1984. Oxygen isotope calibration of the onset of ice- rafting and history of glaciation in the North Atlantic region. *Nature*, **307**, 620–623.

SPIELHAGEN, R. F. 1991. Die Eisdrift in der Framstrasse während der letzten 200 000 Jahre. *GEOMAR Report*, **4**.

STEIN, R., GROBE, H., HUBBERTEN, H., MARIENFELD, P. & NAM, S. 1993. Latest Pleistocene to Holocene changes in glaciomarine sedimentation in Scoresby Sund and along the adjacent East Greenland Continental Margin: Preliminary results. *Geo-Marine Letters*, **13**, 9–16.

——, NAM, S.-I., SCHUBERT, C., VOGT, C., FÜTTERER, D. & HEINEMEIER, J. 1994a. The last deglaciation event in the eastern central Arctic Ocean. *Science*, **264**, 692–696.

——, SCHUBERT, C., VOGT, C., & FÜTTERER, D. K. 1994b. Stable isotope stratigraphy, sedimentation rates, and salinity changes in the latest Pleistocene to Holocene central Arctic Ocean. *Marine Geology*, **119**, 333–355.

STREETER, S. S., BELANGER, P. E., KELLOGG, T. B. & J. C. DUPLESSY 1982. Late Pleistocene paleo-oceanography of the Norwegian-Greenland Sea: benthic foraminiferal evidence. *Quaternary Research*, **18**, 72-90.

SVENDSEN, J. I. & MANGERUD, J. 1992. Paleoclimatic inferences from glacial fluctuations on Svalbard during the last 20,000 years. *Climate Dynamics*, **6**, 213–220.

UENZELMANN-NEBEN, G., JOKAT, W. & VANNESTE, K. 1991. Quaternary sediments in Scoresby Sund, East Greenland: their distribution as revealed by reflection seismic data. *Lundqua Report*, **33**, 139–148.

VAN ANDEL, T. H., HEATH, G. R. & MOORE, T. C. 1975. *Cenozoic History and Paleoceanography of the Central Equatorial Pacific*. Memoir of the Geological Society of America, **143**.

VOGELSANG, E. 1990. Paläo-Ozeanographie des Europäischen Nordmeeres an Hand stabiler Kohlenstoff- und Sauerstoffisotope. *Berichte SFB 313, Universität Kiel*, **23**.

WILLIAMS, K. M. 1993. Ice sheet and ocean interactions, margin of the east Greenland ice sheet (14 ka to Present): diatom evidence. *Paleoceanography*, **8**, 69–83.

Late Quaternary sedimentation along a fjord to shelf (trough) transect, East Greenland (*c.* 68° N)

J. T. ANDREWS[1], ANNE E. JENNINGS[1], T. COOPER[1],
KERSTIN M. WILLIAMS[1] & J. MIENERT[2]

[1] *INSTAAR and Department of Geological Sciences, Box 450, University of Colorado,
Boulder, CO 80309, USA*
[2] *Geomar, Kiel, Germany*

Abstract: The East Greenland continental margin between *c.* 66 and 68° N consists of a major fjord/trough system that extends from Kangerdlugssuaq Fjord, along Kangerdlugssuaq Trough to Denmark Strait. Measurements of the temperature and salinity of the water column along this transect indicates that 'warm' water (0–2°C) underlies the surface Polar Water of the East Greenland Current. A series of short (1–3 m) gravity cores along the fjord/trough transect have sufficient numbers of foraminifera that a suite of AMS ^{14}C dates has been obtained, including both basal and core-top age estimates. Rates of sediment accumulation vary through space and time; over the last 1 ka estimates vary from *c.* 3 to 0.1 m. These dates and measurements of sediment density, together with measurements of the percentages by weight of total organic carbon and biogenic silica, are used to show graphs of fluxes of the organic and inorganic sediment components over the last 1–14 ka. An analysis of the net flux of foraminifera indicates a reduction in numbers during the Younger Dryas chronozone and a general similarity with data from the Renland (East Greenland) ice core data.

The East Greenland margin south of 72° N consists of three major fjord/trough systems that provide routes for the transportation of glacial ice, meltwater and sediments to the shelf break and onto the slope (Funder & Larsen 1989; Sommerhoff *et al.* 1979; Somerhoff 1981). To the north there is the Scorsby Sund system, which is being studied as part of the PONAM project (Marienfeld 1992*b*; Stein *et al.* 1993; Nam *et al.* 1995). The middle system consists of the area that we deal with, the Kangerdlugssuaq Fjord/Trough system (Sommerhoff 1981; Larsen 1983; Mienert *et al.* 1992; Williams 1993), whereas to the south, the trough *c.* 63°30′ N was been drilled during ODP Leg 152 (Larsen *et al.* 1994). These systems provide an opportunity to examine ice sheet/ocean interactions in a critical region of the North Atlantic, near the Denmark Strait outflow.

The East Greenland coast in the vicinity of 68° N (Fig. 1) consists of two distinct regions. South of Kangerdlugssuaq Fjord the coast is heavily glacierized and outlets from the ice sheet reach tide water; few fjords are exposed. However, to the north of and including Kangerdlugssuaq Fjord, the late Quaternary ice retreat of outlets from the Inland Ice and local glacier systems have resulted in the exposure of a number of fjords. Before our work there has been virtually no research on the Quaternary history of this portion of the East Greenland continental margin. Brooks (1979) made some pertinent observations on vertical limits of glaciation in Kangerdlugssuaq Fjord and Larsen (1983) described the basic surficial and bedrock geology of this shelf. However, there were few data on the actual limits of Weischelian ice on the East Greenland shelf during the Flakkerhuk (last) glaciation and as of 1989 there was no date that constrained the location of the late glacial maximum ice margin (Funder 1989; Funder & Larsen 1989). Funder (1989) suggested that deglaciation of the shelf occurred rapidly close to 14 ka, a time when evidence for meltwater has been reported from the Nordic seas (Jones & Keigwin 1988; Koc & Jensen 1994).

Our research commenced in 1988 with a joint GeoMar/WHOI/INSTAAR cruise and other cruises were undertaken in 1990 and 1991 (Andrews *et al.* 1994; Jennings & Helgadottir 1994; Mienert *et al.* 1992; Williams 1993; Williams *et al.* 1995), and in 1993 on *CSS Hudson*.

Objectives

This paper examines the nature of the sediments and the sedimentation rates from a series of gravity cores collected in 1988 and 1991 (Fig. 1). Some of these data were presented previously (Andrews & Syvitski 1994; Mienert *et al.* 1992), but we have obtained several additional AMS [14]C

From Andrews, J. T., Austin, W. E. N., Bergsten, H. & Jennings, A. E. (eds), 1996, *Late Quaternary Palaeoceanography of the North Atlantic Margins*, Geological Society Special Publication No. 111, pp. 153–166.

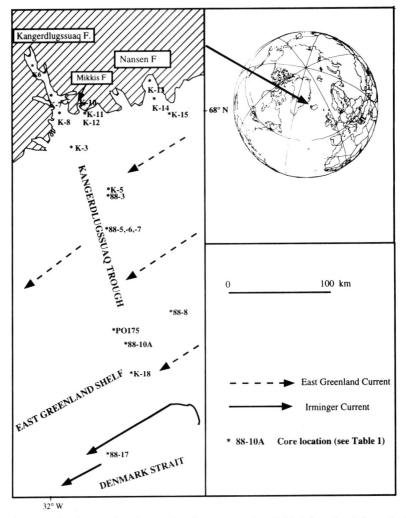

Fig. 1. Location map showing core locations and surface currents (see Table 1 for other information).

dates from some 1988 cores and present new data from the 1991 coring expedition. Our overall focus has been to describe and interpret the sediment sequences and palaeoceanographic conditions along the transect from Kangerdlugssuaq Fjord (and adjacent fjords), to the Kangerdlugssuaq Trough and into Denmark Strait (e.g. Kellogg 1984). What is particularly significant in our view is the fact that we have obtained dates from cores where we would expect there to be high rates of sediment accumulation, such as in Kan-gerdlugssuaq and Nansen fjords. In our definition of 'sediments' we will include the bulk or total sediment, plus present information on the rate of biogenic silica, foraminiferal and total organic carbon (TOC%) accumulations.

Background

Gravity sediment coring, airgun and Huntec seismic surveys, and CTD measurements were undertaken in 1991 from the Icelandic vessel *Bjarni Saedumndsson* in the area of East Greenland around 68° N, specifically on the inner shelf, within the Kangerdlussuaq Trough, and in (north to south) the Nansen, Mikis and Kangerdlugssuak fjords (Mienert *et al.* 1992; Williams 1993).

Temperatures and precipitation

The mean annual temperature is probably close to −5°C (Hastings 1960); the mean annual

precipitation (water equivalent) varies from
c. 80 cm on the outer coast to 30 cm at higher
elevations (Omuru & Reeh 1991); however, the
details of the regional climatology are poorly
known.

Modern oceanography

Killerich (1945) shows a series of hydrographic
stations (#118 to 131) heading into and from
Kangerdlugssuaq Fjord which were obtained in
1933 (Killerich, 1945, fig. 22). In 1991, conductivity, temperature, and salinity casts were
made along the Kangerdlugssuaq Trough and
into Kangerdlugssuaq, Mikis and Nansen fjords
(Jennings & Helgadottir 1994). The area is swept
by the southward flowing cold waters of the East
Greenland Current (Killerich 1945). In Septem-
ber/October 1991, however, the surface waters
showed a tongue of 3°C water extending north
and somewhat east of the axis of the trough.
This wedge of warmer surface water is also
evident on earlier compilations of oceanographic data (Killerich 1945; Dietrich 1969;
Kraus 1958). Beneath this layer, at depths
down to c. 150 m is the cold core of Polar
Water with temperatures −1°C or so and
salinities of 31.0–32‰ (Killerich 1945). Below

this at depths of c. 200 m or deeper there is a
pronounced intrusion of modified Atlantic
Water (i.e. Arctic Intermediate Water) (Killerich 1945; Stefansson 1962; Johannessen 1986;
Swift 1986; Blindheim 1990). Within Kangerdlussuaq Fjord, the Arctic Intermediate Water
has temperatures of 1–2°C and salinities of
between 34.5 and 34.8‰. Figure 2 illustrates
temperature and salinity profiles from three sites
along the trough/fjord system, namely 91-K18,
91-K5 and 91-K6.

The cold, low salinity surface water of the East
Greenland Current is capped by land-fast sea ice
and by drifting pack ice for nine months of the
year; in some years heavy pack ice is present
throughout the entire 'open water' season. Icebergs from various outlet glaciers along the East
Greenland margin drift southward and scour the
seafloor at depths of ≤200–300 m (Dowdeswell
et al. 1992; 1993; Mienert et al. 1992).

From the glaciological and palaeoceanographic viewpoint one of the key elements is
the presence along this 200–300 km transect of
relatively warm water below the cold core of
Polar Water. The precise mechanisms for this
advection is not known (Killerich 1945), but are
under investigation (Andrews et al. in prep).

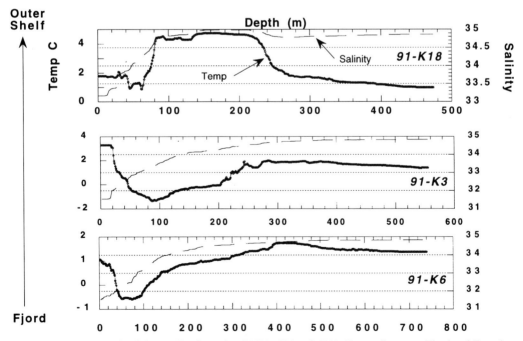

Fig. 2. Temperature and salinity profiles from sites 91-K3, -K6 and -K18, Kangerdluggsuaq Fjord and Trough
(see Table 1, Fig. 1); solid line is temperature and broken line is salinity.

Modern glaciology

The current glaciology of this region has been described by Dwyer and Nutall (Dywer 1993; Nuttall 1993) and is further discussed in papers by Reeh (1985; 1991) and Andrews *et al.* (1994). This area of East Greenland is heavily glacierized. Some, but not all, calving, ice margins are fronted by a complex or melange of sea ice/icebergs that are called 'sikussuaq' by the local Innuit. Inspection of Landsat imagery (Dywer 1993) indicates that on time-scales of 20 years the calving fronts and fronts of the sikussuaqs have undergone only relatively small changes in position.

It is estimated that the calving fluxes from Kangerdlugssuak Gletcher and Christian IV Gletscher (Nansen Fjord) are of the order of 15 km³ and *c*. 3 km³, respectively (Andrews *et al.* 1994). Given our knowledge of the height of the equilibrium line and the net mass balance as a function of elevation (Reeh 1991), we have estimated that the total meltwater runoff into the fjords is 4.4 and 1.7 km³/year for Kangerdlugssuaq and Nansen fjords, respectively. This gives iceberg/meltwater flux ratios of around 4 : 1 and 2 : 1, respectively – these compare with 2 : 1 for the Jacobshavn Gletcher in West Greenland (Echelmeyer *et al.* 1992).

Data methods

Cores were collected from basins and troughs. Huntec high-resolution acoustic profiling in 1988, 1991 and 1993 showed that the inner shelf is largely devoid of sediment, in agreement with the broad generalization portrayed by Funder & Larsen (1989). However, relatively thick sediment sequences occur within the fjords (e.g. Andrews *et al.* 1994) and from the mid- to outer shelf within Kangerdlugssuaq Trough.

AMS ^{14}C dating of small (mg) samples of foraminifera have vastly increased our ability to develop quantitative estimates of the rates of sediment accumulation in ice-proximal/ice-distal glacial marine settings. All our dates were obtained through the NSF-Arizona AMS Facility (Linick *et al.* 1986; Slota *et al.* 1987) (Table 1). Dates are reported relative to the -25% δ^{13}C standard; we have subtracted 550 a for the regional ocean reservoir effect (Hjort 1973; Tauber & Funder 1975). Ideally, samples submitted for dating should be composed of single species of planktonic or benthic foraminifera, but this was not always possible at our core sites. The known offset between radiocarbon years and sidereal or calendar years (Bard *et al.* 1990; 1993)

does affect rates of sediment accumulation based on the radiocarbon time-scale; accordingly we have calibrated our ^{14}C dates to calendar years (cal a) using the program CALIB (Stuiver & Reimer, 1986), with a -100 ± 50 reservoir correction. The calibrated years and the ± 1 sigma age range (cal BP) are shown on Table 1. Age models for presenting our results are based on a least-squares second or third polynomial fit to the depth/cal age data, and then solving for the estimated age of a particular sampled level. We concentrate on cores from fjords, from troughs on the inner shelf, and cores more distal to the East Greenland coast (Fig. 1).

Our estimates of TOC% are based on a titration procedure (Walkley 1947) that calibrates well against loss on ignition-based methods. In our work on foraminifera (e.g. Jennings & Helgadottir 1994; Williams *et al.* 1995), we screen material $\geqslant 0.63$ mm and report the results as foraminifera/g, as well the separate fractions of benthic and planktonic species. Our studies of diatoms and the biogenic silica content is also calculated on a weight percentage basis. The biogenic silica extraction procedure is based on an extraction and measurement procedure outlined previously (Mortlock & Froelich 1989), which we have validated with the LDEO Laboratory.

We are able to derive sediment fluxes for these components of the sediment column because we determined both the dry and wet sediment densities. Our procedure is to take 8 cm³ samples once the cores are split. These samples are weighed, air-dried and then reweighed to obtain the variables wet and dry volume density, and moisture content. Sediment samples are processed in the Sedimentological Laboratory, INSTAAR using wet sieving and the Sedigraph for a combined -2ϕ to 11ϕ (sand to fine clay) range. The sediment coarser than 2 mm is calculated as a percentage of the total sediment, whereas the sum of sand, silt and clay is normalized to sum to 100%.

Results

Patterns and rates of sedimentation

Basal radiocarbon dates from these 1–3 m gravity cores range in age from *c*. 1 ka cal BP to nearly 17 ka cal BP (Table 1 Fig. 3). Dates on core-tops from sites outside the fjords range between modern (91-K15) and 1.3 ka cal BP (91-K18B). There are no statistically significant reversals in the sequences, although there are instances, such as in 91-18B, where the mean calibrated dates are slightly reversed. The short gravity cores did

Table 1. *Radiocarbon dates from East Greenland. See Fig. 1 for core locations*

Core depth (cm)	Laboratory number	Date	Error	Cal date	1σ range (cal year)
91-K7 (68°15.7′ lat., 32°05.83′ long., 862 water depth)					
265	AA-10603	1310	60	935	875–1040
91-K8 (68°07.99′ lat., 31°51.71′ long., 872 water depth)					
108	AA-11871	1155	55	775	720–870
226	AA-11872	1390	55	1025	945–1100
91-K14 (68°11.49′ lat., 29°35.74′ long., 459 water depth)					
50	AA-12891	855	60	530	495–610
115	AA-10567	1440	70	1070	985–1165
170	AA-8332	1800	110	1420	1305–1550
91-K15 (68°06.02′ lat., 29°27.16′ long., 445 water depth)					
7.5	AA-11446	85	45	0	
163	AA-11447	8590	70	9350	9225–9415
91-K5 (67°24.59′ lat., 31°03.98′ long., 622 water depth)					
2.5	AA-9065	1000	60	650	575–710
69	AA-9066	5840	120	6330	6210–6485
	AA-8333	9105	140	9880	9660–9990
88-3 (67°24.59′ lat., 31°03.98′ long., 624 water depth)					
0	AA-6830	1380	65	1000	930–1100
79	AA-5990	8615	75	9365	9245–9430
	AA-4666	9375	70	10 100	10 010–10 230
88-5A (67°07.54′ lat., 30°54.26′ long., 707 water depth)					
2	AA-4338	985	50	840	570–685
7	AA-6829	3210	70	3145	3020–3250
28	AA-4529	5835	60	6320	6270–6420
74	AA-3976	8965	110	9685	9565–9842
88-10A (66°12.19′ lat., 30°39.29′ long., 496 water depth)					
7	AA-6825	3210	70	3145	3017–3252
22	AA-4530	9270	80	9995	9916–10 120
50	AA-14208	12 210	110	13 885	13 710–14 070
89	AA-14209	13 050	140	15 035	14 770–15 310
101	AA-4026	13 585	110	15 865	15 660–16 065
91-18B (65°57.77′ lat., 30°38.0′lat., 470 water depth)					
4.5	AA-12892	1680	50	1300	1255–1385
37	AA-14210	5215	75	5660	5575–5765
62	A-11874	9292	80	10 010	9935–10 145
77	AA-14211	9240	90	9975	9880–10 095
98	AA-11875	12 325	80	14 020	13 860–14 190
150	AA-8329	12 865	305	14 600	14 180–15 080
150	AA-8330	12 470	205	14 200	13 920–14 510
150	AA-8331	12 085	115	13 625	13 460–13 800
91-K11A (68°06.94′ lat., 31°25.9′ long., 244 water depth)					
15	AA-11585	1465	55	1110	1025–1190
84	AA-11584	9975	100	10 960	10 569–11 190
91-K11B (244 water depth)					
67	AA-8327	9435	50	10 040	9990–10 160
PO-175/15 (66°45.83′lat., 30°50.42′ long., 295 water depth)					
3	AA-6847	1300	55	930	865–1025
29	AA-15687	13 100	100	15 195	14 960–15 430
59	AA-15688	12 000	145	13 500	13 500–13 900
95	AA-6849	13 300	145	15 435	15 160–15 700
194	AA-7150	14 465	200	16 985	16 880–17 095
311	AA-6848	14 845	190	17 420	17 185–17 655

Water depth in metres.

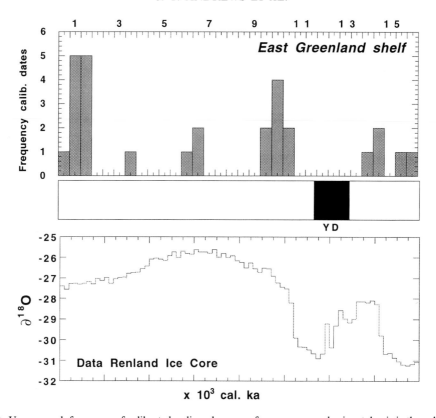

Fig. 3. Upper panel: frequency of calibrated radiocarbon ages from our cores, horizontal axis is the cal ka, showing the YD chronozone. Middle panel: location of the Younger Dryas Event. Lower panel: $\delta^{18}O$ data from the Renland Ice Cap (Johnsen *et al.* 1992) at 200 years sample resolution.

not penetrate into any basal diamictons on the floors of the trough, thus calibrated ^{14}C dates represent minimum ages for deglaciation. To look at rates of sediment accumulation as a function of time for the Denmark Strait to Kangerdlugssuaq Fjord transect, we constructed Fig. 4. This figure shows core depth on the vertical axis and distance along the transect on the horizontal axis. 'Distance' is measured from the present coastline, thus samples within Kangerdlugssuaq and Nansen fjords are shown at negative distances. All levels with AMS dates are shown on Fig. 4 and isochrons (in cal ka) are drawn through the data points.

The results (Table 1, Fig. 4) indicate that deglaciation of the mid- and outer shelf occurred before 17.4 cal ka BP. Sedimentation rates in the mid-shelf (trough) area are moderate between 15.4 and 17.4 cal ka BP at about 1 m/ka cal., but in the last 15 ka cal sedimentation rates decreased to 0.06 m/1 ka cal Unfortunately, we do not have sufficient core penetration from our inner shelf sites to determine at what depths

materials >10 and <15 ka cal BP occur. However, we do know from our Huntec seismic surveys in 1991, on sites close to the present coastline, that several tens of metres of sediment underlie sites 91-K11 and 91-K15 where dates of 9–11 ka cal BP have been obtained.

In Fig. 4 we link the sediment rate data to an inferred glacial history for this section of the East Greenland margin by plotting isochrons in core depth/distance space. This figure clearly demonstrates the tremendous difference between sedimentation rates within the fjords and those on the adjacent shelf-troughs. The 1 ka cal BP isochron rises sharply from the fjords to the innermost shelf and further seaward most core-top dates are in the 1.0 ka cal BP range (Table 1; Fig. 4). As the gravity coring operation probably resulted in the loss of some sediment close to the sediment–water interface, dates from the core-tops probably overestimate the apparent surface age. This problem was addressed in 1993 by a programme of box coring from *CSS Hudson*. Nevertheless, the pattern of Fig. 4 would not be

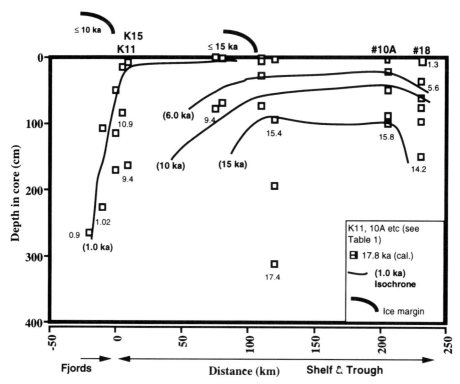

Fig. 4. Isochrons on sediment thickness as a function away from the East Greenland margin. Suggested minimum positions of ice margins are based on evaluation of the pattern of sedimentation in the cores. The isochrons are in cal ka BP.

fundamentally altered and we conclude that today relatively little sediment escapes from the fjords onto the shelves, further stressing the importance of sediment trapping within the fjords (Andrews *et al.* 1994).

The 10 ka cal BP isochron lies at depths usually <1 m for nearly 200 km seaward of the East Greenland coast (Fig. 4). Only at 91-K15 is there substantially more sediment accumulated during this period. Furthermore, in the outer basin of Mikis Fjord, dates of nearly 11 ka cal BP occur at a depth of 0.84 m (Table 1). The pattern of sedimentation on the inner, mid- and outer shelf *c*. 10 ka cal BP suggests that ice margins were located within the fjords. During the last 10 cal ka sedimentation rates averaged <0.1 m/ ka at sites on the shelf.

By inference with other ice-proximal to ice-distal sediment sequences (e.g. Andrews & Syvitski 1994), we interpret the rate of sediment accumulation as a first-order indicator of ice proximity. Because we have not been able to date any transitional glacial/glacial marine sediments, our estimates of the location of the

ice margins are based on qualititative assessments of the relationships between sedimentation rates in ice-proximal and ice-distal glacial marine locations (Andrews & Syvitski 1994). Thus the suggested ice margin positions that we show for ⩽15 and ⩽10 ka cal BP must be regarded as hypotheses that require longer cores for verification, although verification is also possible through ongoing studies of high-resolution Huntec DTS records collected in 1993 by *CSS Hudson* along and across Kangerdlugssuaq Trough. At the moment there is no conclusive data either for or against the notion that the late Weischelian ice edge was located at the shelf break and contributing sediment into Denmark Strait, although the clearest morphological evidence for morainal sedimentation on the shelf occurs close to PO-175/15 (Fig. 1).

The frequency distribution of the ^{14}C dates is intriguing, especially when considered in terms of sedimentation rates. Of particular interest is the Younger Dryas (YD) interval, which along the Eastern Canadian margin was a time of enhanced sediment production and an increase in the rate of sediment accumulation (Andrews *et al.* 1990). By contrast, in the cores that cover this interval off East Greenland, namely 88–10A, PO-175–15 and 91-K18B, the YD chronozone is not represented by a flush of sediment, indeed the rates of sediment accumulation are low across this event (Fig. 3). Although the sedimentation rates are plotted as continuous across the YD chronozone, in reality it is possible that sedimentation virtually ceased.

Stable isotope data from the Renland Ice Cap, East Greenland (Johnsen *et al.* 1992), shows a change toward lighter $\delta^{18}O$ values, coincident with this interval of low to non-deposition in these three cores. A similar phenomenon has been reported by Polyak *et al.* (1995) from cores in the southeastern Barents Sea, where pulses of sedimentation occurred on either side of an interval of non-deposition which is bracketed by dates of *c.* 12.1 and 10.4 ka BP (13.65–11.5 cal ka BP). However, along the mid- and

outer East Greenland shelf, rates of sedi-ment accumulation were clearly higher before 13 cal ka BP, but show no clear sediment pulse after the period of low or no deposition. However, rates of sediment accumulation from sites closer to the coast of East Greenland show an interval of rapid sedimentation between *c.* 9 and 10 cal ka BP (Fig. 3), but even at these sites the actual amount of sediment accumulated is relatively small.

Marienfeld's data from cores in outer Scorsby Sund (Marienfeld 1992*a*; 1992*b*) suggest that during the YD that area was covered by a permanent cover of sea ice and the resulting sediment was a thin unit of laminated mud. On a different time-scale, but invoking a similar process, Jennings & Weiner (unpublished data) noted that sediment in Nansen Fjord, dated to the Medieval Warm Period, is a diamicton, but that the subsequent cooler period of the Little Ice Age is represented by laminated muds.

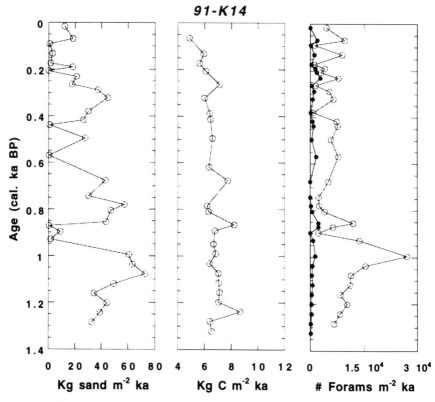

Fig. 5. Data from Nansen Fjord, core 91-K14, showing the net fluxes of coarse sand and carbon and (right-hand panel) the total number of foraminifera (closed circles) and planktonic foraminifera (black circles) against calibrated age scale.

Fluxes

Our units are either weights of sand, carbon (C) or biogenic silica (Bs) or numbers per square metre per cal ka (e.g. $kg\,m^{-2}\,ka^{-1}$). These are of course net fluxes and are influenced by a number of factors that can alter the original amount of material deposited on the seafloor, such as dissolution, winnowing and bacterial action (Syvitski *et al.* 1990). We use medium to coarse sand as a proxy for iceberg rafting and ice proximity, although there is no doubt that the flux to the seafloor of this size range can be influenced by other factors. We use numbers of foraminifera $m^{-2}\,ka^{-1}$, $kg\,C\,m^{-2}\,ka^{-1}$, and $kg\,Bs\,m^{-2}\,ka^{-1}$ as indicators of net marine productivity in surface or near-surface waters, as well as at the sediment–water interface.

Fjord site 91-K14. Our ice-proximal core, 91-K14, is from Nansen Fjord within 30 km of a major tide water outlet. Sedimentation rates are about 1.2 m cal ka^{-1} and the core extends through the last 1 ka BP (Jennings & Weiner unpublished data). We assume a constant rate of sediment

accumulation. The sand flux record shows a number of peaks and troughs (Fig. 5), varying from 72 to 0 kg m^{-2} ka^{-1}. There is a clear trend for the coarse sand flux to decrease from a peak during the Medieval Warm Period. Numbers of benthic foraminifera (m^{-2} ka^{-1}) (Fig. 5) also show a decrease throughout the last 1 ka with a major peak about 1 cal ka of 25 000 foraminifera m^{-2} ka^{-1}. Over the last 800 years, benthic foraminiferal numbers preserved in the sediments have averaged about 5000 specimens m^{-2} ka^{-1}. Planktonic foraminifera are present in all but three levels, but with numbers about one-tenth of the benthic foraminifera (e.g. Jennings & Helgadottir 1994). The net TOC flux follows a similar pattern to the foraminifera, decreasing from around 8 to 5 kg C m^{-2} ka^{-1}. Analysis of the sediments for diatoms indicated very low numbers and no biogenic silica flux has been attempted.

Mid shelf/trough. Most of the data we present comes from 88-5A (Fig. 1). The coarse sand flux retained within the sediments shows a slight increase during the last 9 cal ka BP, with a large

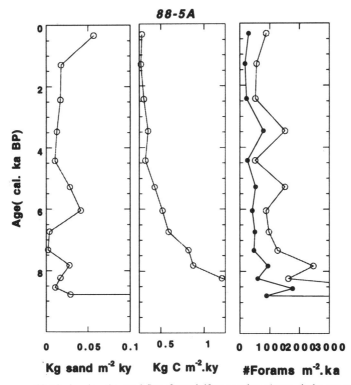

88-5A

Age(cal. ka BP)

| 0   0.05   0.1 | 0.5   1 | 0   10002000 03000 |

Kg sand m⁻² ky   Kg C m⁻².ky   #Forams m⁻².ka

Fig. 6. Data from core 88-5A showing the sand flux, foraminifera numbers (open circles are total numbers and the closed diamonds represent the number of plankton), carbon and biogenic silica flux against calibrated ages.

excursion towards the top of the core (Fig. 6), but the median flux is only 0.18 kg m^{-2} ka. The estimates for C and numbers of foraminifera both decrease, the former very smoothly. In contrast, the biogenic silica increases steadily towards the present with a median value of 4 kg m^{-2} ka. Inspection of the core shows that a substantial fraction of the Bs signal is associated with the presence of large numbers of sponge spicules.

Outer shelf/trough. The coarse sand flux in 91-18B is low with a single maximum of around 1.2 kg m^{-2} ka^{-1} near the core-top and a smaller peak near the base of the core (Fig. 7). However, for most of the last 14 cal ka BP the sand flux has been very low at $\leqslant 0.2$ kg m^{-2} ka^{-1}. The total and planktonic foraminiferal fluxes show initial high levels followed by a pronounced trough *c.* 12 cal ka BP and then a rise to relatively constant net fluxes at about 6 cal ka BP. The average number of foraminifera m^{-2} ka^{-1} is about 250, thus providing a contrast with the higher values determined from the ice-proximal setting. However, core 91-K14 (Fig. 5) covers

the last 1 cal ka, where as 91-18B extends across the last 15 cal ka BP. Based on the determination of the total organic carbon, the net carbon flux averaged 0.5 kg m^{-2} ka^{-1}; the record shows a peak early in the deglacial cycle, with a single point trough at 12.5 cal ka BP and then a slight but persistent decrease during the Holocene.

The results of the biogenic silica analyses show that it varied between 0.015 and 0.04 g cm^{-3}. When converted to a flux, the net biogenic silica flux averaged 2.8 kg m^{-2} ka^{-1}; however, early in the last deglacial cycle productivity was high and reached values as high as 7 kg m^{-2} ka^{-1}. There is a noticeable decline during the YD chronozone, which is followed by a smaller peak at *c.* 11 cal ka BP (Fig. 7). Thereafter, the net biogenic silica flux decreased steadily during the Holocene.

Conclusions and discussion

In the outer and mid-trough area our sampling strategy of samples every 5 cm gives adequate relatively high-resolution during the initial phase

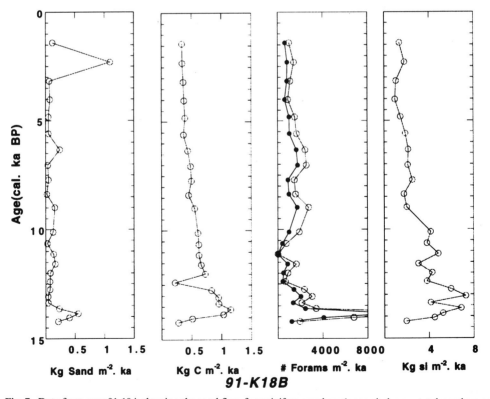

Fig. 7. Data from core 91-18A showing the sand flux, foraminifera numbers (open circles are total numbers and the closed diamonds represent the number of plankton), carbon and biogenic silica flux against calibrated ages.

of deglaciation >10 cal ka BP, but provides only moderate resolution during the Holocene. Many records show a persistent trend towards a decrease in net biological productivity throughout the Holocene (Figs 6 and 7), although when looked at in the detail of 91-K14 (Fig. 5) (Jennings & Weiner unpublished data), this statement may hide significant temporal variability.

Funder (1989) suggested that the margin of the East Greenland ice sheet may have retreated rapidly c. 14 ka BP Although our cores rarely retrieved sediment of this age, nevertheless, the isochrons of sediment age along the fjord to trough transect (Fig. 4) imply that this hypothesis may be correct. This may be one explanation for the meltwater signal noted in the Nordic Seas of a similar age (Jones & Keigwin 1988; Koc & Jansen 1994; Hald & Andrews 1995).

Two of the surprising features of our data, mentioned in part in earlier publications (Andrews & Syvitski 1994; Mienert et al. 1992) are that: (1) rates of Holocene sediment accumulation are relatively low along this

sector of the East Greenland Continental margin and (2) the operational distinction of IRD indicates that very few sand-sized materials are being transported and deposited in the troughs.

The graph of sediment age as a function of core depth and distance (Fig. 4) suggests that sedimentation virtually ceased during the YD chronozone. This may indicate that the palaeoceanographic model proposed for Scorsby Sund and its trough, applied along a larger sector of the East Greenland margin (Marienfeld 1992a; 1992b), thus the notable reduction in net fluxes in several components (Figs 4, 6 and 7) may be associated with the establishment of a quasi-permanent sea ice cover along the East Greenland shelf.

The data from 91-K18A supports our earlier ideas based on 88-10A (Williams 1993; Williams et al. 1995) of a peak in productivity during the local Allerod/Bolling interval. This event appears in all cores that extends back through the YD interval. There is a compelling parallelism in

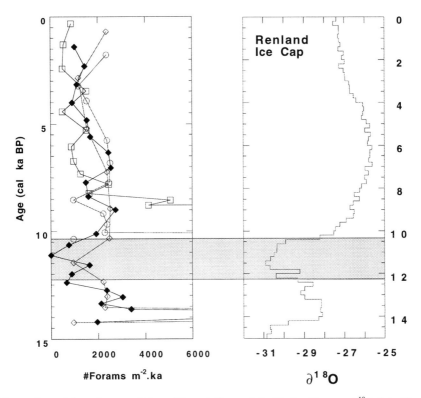

Fig. 8. Comparison of the net accumulation of foraminifera and the Renland ice core $\delta^{18}O$ data. The closed diamonds are 91-18B; open diamonds are 88-10A; open squares 88-3; and open circles 88-5A. The dotted area represents an interval when both the Renland ice core record and the East Greenland foraminiferal fluxes show coeval evidence for cooler/harsher conditions.

trends between the $\delta^{18}O$ record from Renland (Johnsen *et al.* 1992) and our records from the East Greenland margin $c.\,68°\,N$ (Fig. 8). Additional data on cores collected in 1988 are available to add to those we have discussed earlier and Fig. 8 shows plots of variations in the numbers of foraminifera for 91-18B, 88-10A, 88-5A and 88-3. Two cores extend across the YD cold interval and we plot the foraminiferal data against the $\delta^{18}O$ record from the Renland Ice Cap, East Greenland (Johnsen *et al.* 1992) over the last 15 cal ka – this record is plotted at a 200 years resolution. The foraminiferal records show high values during the interval 14–13 cal ka and then a significant decrease in numbers coincident with the YD chronozone. During the same interval of time the Renland ice core data show lighter $\delta^{18}O$ values. At site V28-14 in Denmark Strait (64°47′ N, 29°34′ W, water depth 1855 m), Kellogg (1984) documented a rapid glacial/Holocene transition between 9 and 10 ^{14}C ka BP, but new dates from this core (Bond 1994) shows that a peak in foraminiferal concentrations occurred before the YD, in keeping with our data.

Because of the slow Holocene rates of sediment accumulation, our data pick up a persistent trend for a decrease in surface and bottom productivity (Figs 6 and 7), but the sample resolution is insufficient at present to resolve decadal to century scale changes within the Holocene; however, in cores from high accumulation sites, such as Nansen Fjord (Fig. 5), detailed late Holocene climate changes are recorded (Jennings & Weiner unpublished data).

Our research has been supported by the National Science Foundation and Office of Naval Research under grant OPP-9224254 and the Lamont/Scripps/ NOAA Consortium on Climate Research, grant NA47GP0188. We thank the Danish and Greenland governments for permission to work in national waters. Our thanks to the Icelandic Marine Research Institute for their scientific and logistical support. The paper has been reviewed by S. Funder and J. Syvitski and we thank them for their advice and comments.

References

ANDREWS, J. T. & SYVITSKI, J. P. M. 1994. Sediment fluxes along high latitude continental margins (NE Canada and E. Greenland). *Sedimentary Geofluxes*, National Academy of Sciences, Washington, DC.

——, EVANS, L. W., WILLIAMS, K. M., BRIGGS, W. M., ERLENKEUSER, H., HARDY, I. & JULL, A. J. T. 1990. Cryosphere/ocean interactions at the margin of the Laurentide Ice Sheet during the Younger Dryas Chron: SE Baffin Shelf, Northwest Territories. *Paleoceanography*, 5, 921–935.

——, MILLIMAN, J. D., JENNINGS, A. E., RYNES, N. & DWYER, J. 1994. Sediment thicknesses and Holocene glacial marine sedimentation rates in three east Greenland fjords (ca. 68° N). *Journal of Geology*, 102, 669–683.

——, OLAFSSON, J. & THOR, K. Temperature and salinity measurements from the East Greenland Shelf and Fjords, ca. 68° N: Fall 1991, in press.

BARD, E., ARNOLD, M., FAIRBANKS, R. G. & HAMELIN, B. 1993. ^{230}Th–^{230}U and ^{14}C ages obtained by mass spectrometry on corals. *Radiocarbon*, 35, 191–200.

——, FAIRBANKS, R. G., HAMELIN, B. & ZINDLER, A. 1990. Calibration of the ^{14}C timescale over the past 30,000 years using mass spectrometric U–Th ages from Barbados corals. *Nature*, 345, 405–410.

BLINDHEIM, J. 1990. Arctic Intermediate Water. *Deep-Sea Research*, 37, 1–15.

BOND, G. C. 1994. Abrupt climate changes and ice rafting regimes in the North Atlantic. Progress Report. *Abrupt Climate Change Project, Newsletter*, 2, 1–2.

BROOKS, C. K. 1979. Geomorphological observations at Kangerdlugssuaq, East Greenland. *Meddeleser om Gronland, Geoscience No. 1*.

DIETRICH, G. (eds) 1969. *Atlas of the Hydrography of the Northern Atlantic Ocean Based on the Polar Front Survey of the INternational Geophysical Year, Winter and Summer 1958*. Council for the Exploration of the Sea, Hydrographic Service, Copenhagen.

DOWDESWELL, J. A., WHITTINGTON, R. J. & HODGKINS, R. 1992. The sizes, frequencies, and freeboards of East Greenland icebergs observed using ship radar and sextant. *Journal of Geophysical Research*, 97, 3515–3528.

——, VILLINGER, H., WHITTINGTON, R.-J. & MARIENFELD, P. 1993. Iceberg scouring in Scorsby Sund and on the East Greenland Continental Shelf. *Marine Geology*, 111, 37–53.

DWYER, J. L. 1993. *Monitoring characteristics of glaciation in the Kangerdlugssuaq Fjord region, East Greenland, using digital LANDSAT MSS and TM Data*. MSc Thesis, University of Colorado, Boulder.

ECHELMEYER, K., HARRISON, W. D., CLARKE, T. S. & BENSON, C. 1992. Surficial glaciology of Jakobshans Isbrae, West Greenland: part II. Ablation, accumulation and temperature. *Journal of Glaciology*, 38, 169–181.

FUNDER, S. 1989. Quaternary geology of the ice-free areas and adjacent shelves of Greenland. *In*: FULTON, R. J. (eds) *Quaternary Geology of Canada and Greenland*. Geological Survey of Canada, 743–792.

—— & LARSEN, D. 1989. Quaternary geology of the ice-free areas and adjacent shelves of Greenland. *In*: FULTON, R. J. (ed.) *Quaternary Geology of Canada and Greenland*. Geological Survey of Canada, 769–772.

HALD, M. & ANDREWS, J. T. 1995. Response of the high-latitude Northern Hemisphere to orbital climate forcing: evidence from the Nordic Seas: comment and reply. *Geology*, 23, 382–384.

HASTINGS, A. D. 1960. *Environment of Southeast Greenland*. Quatermaster Research and Engineering Command, Technical Report, **EP-140**.

HJORT, C. 1973. A sea correction for East Greenland. *Geologiska Foreningen i Stockholm Forhandlingar*, **95**, 132–134.

JENNINGS, A. E. & HELGADOTTIR, G. 1994. Foraminiferal assemblages from the fjords and shelf of Eastern Greenland. *Journal Foraminiferal Research*, **24**, 123–144.

JOHANNESSEN, O. M. 1986. Brief overview of the physical oceanography. *In*: HURDLE, B. G. (ed.) *The Nordic Seas*, Springer, New York, 103–128.

JOHNSEN, S., CLAUSEN, H. B., DANSGAARD, W., GUNDESTRUP, N. S., HANSSON, M., JOHNSSON, P., STEFFENSEN, P. & SVEINBJORNSDOTTIR, A. E. 1992. A "deep" ice core from East Greenland. *Meddelelser om Gronland, Geoscience*, **29**.

JONES, G. A., & KEIGWIN, L. D. 1988. Evidence from the Fram Strait (78 N) for early deglaciation. *Nature*, **336**, 56–59.

KELLOGG, T. B. 1984. Late-glacial/Holocene high-frequency climatic changes in deep-sea cores from the Denmark Strait. *In*: MØRNER, N. A. & KARLEN, W. (eds) *Climatic Changes on a Yearly to Millennial Basis*. Reidel, Dordrecht, 123–133.

KILLERICH, A. 1945. On the hydrography of the Greenland Sea. *Neddelelser om Gronland*, **144**.

KOC, N. & JANSEN, E. 1994. Response of the high-latitude Northern Hemisphere to orbital climate forcing: evidence from the Nordic Seas. *Geology*, **22**, 523–526.

KRAUS, W. 1958. Die hydrographischen Untersuchungen mit "Anton Dohrn" auf dem ost- westgronlandischen Schelf im September–Oktober 1955. *Berichte der Deutschen Wissenschaftlichen Kommission für Meeresforschung*, **15**, 77–104.

LARSEN, B. 1983. Geology of the Greenland–Iceland Ridge in the Denmark Strait. *In*: BOTT, M. H. P., SAXOV, S., TALWANI, P. & THIEDE, J. (eds) *Structure and Development of the Greenland–Scotland Ridge*. Plenum, London, 425–444.

LARSEN, H. C., SAUNDERS, A. D., CLIFT, P. D., BEGET, J., WEI, W., SPEZZAFERRI, S. & PARTY, O. L. S. 1994. Seven million years of glaciation in Greenland. *Science*, **264**, 952-955.

LINICK, T. W., JULL, A. J. T., TOOLIN, L. J. & DONAHUE, D. J. 1986. Operation of the NSF Arizona accelerator facility for radioistope analysis results from selective collaborative research projects. *Radiocarbon*, **28**, 522–533.

MARIENFELD, P. 1991. ^{14}C Dates of glacimarine sediments from Scorsby Sund, East Greenland. *LUNDQUA*, **33**, 165–169.

——1992a. Postglacial sedimentary history of Scorsby Sund, East Greenland. *Polarforschung*, **60**, 181–195.

——1992b. Recent sedimentary processes in Scoresby Sund, East Greenland. *Boreas*, **21**, 169–186.

MIENERT, J., ANDREWS, J. T. & MILLIMAN, J. D. 1992. The East Greenland continental margin (65° N) since the last deglaciation: changes in sea floor properties and ocean circulation. *Marine Geology*, **106**, 217–238.

MORTLOCK, R. A. & FROELICH, A. 1989. A simple method for the rapid determination of biogenic opal in pelagic marine sediments. *Deep Sea Research*, **36**, 1415–1426.

NAM, S. I., STEIN, R., GROBE, H. & HUBBERTEN, H. Late Quaternary stable isotope records and glacial/interglacial changes in sediment composition at the East Greenland continental margin. *Marine Geology*, **122**, 243–262.

NUTTALL, A. M. 1993. *Glaciological investigations in East Greenland using digital LANDSAT imagery*. MPhil Thesis, Cambridge.

OMURU, A. & REEH, N. 1991. New precipitation and accumulation maps for Greenland. *Journal Glaciology*, **37**, 140–148.

POLYAK, L., LEHMAN, S. J., GATAULLIN, V. & JULL, A. J. T. 1995. Two-step deglaciation of the southeastern Barents Sea. *Geology*, **23**, 567–571.

REEH, N. 1985. Greenland ice-sheet mass balance and sea-level change. *In*: *Glaciers, Ice Sheets, and Sea Level: Effect of a CO2 Induced Climatic Change*. United States Department of Energy, Seattle, 155–171.

——1991. Parameterization of melt rate and surface temperature on the Greenland Ice Sheet. *Polarforschung*, **59**, 113–128.

SLOTA, P. J., JULL, A. J. T., LINICK, T. W. & TOOLIN, L. J. 1987. Preparation of small samples for ^{14}C accelerator targets by catalytic reduction of CO_2. *Radiocarbon*, **29**, 303–306.

SOMMERHOFF, V. G. 1981. Geomorphologische Prozesse in der Labrador-und Irmingersee. Ein Beitrag zur submarinen Geomorphologie einer subpolaren Meeresregion. *Polarforschung*, **51**, 175–191.

——, LARSEN, B. & MICHIER, G. 1979. Zur Frage der topographischen Steuerung der ozeanischen Polarfront vor Sudgronland. *Polarforschung*, **48**, 63–69.

STEFANSSON, U. 1962. North Icelandic Waters. *Rit Fiskideildar*, III. Bind, Vol. 3.

STEIN, R., GROBE, H., HUBBERTEN, H., MARIENFELD, P. & NAM, S. 1993. Latest Pleistocene to Holocene changes in glaciomarine sedimentation in Scorsby Sund and along the adjacent East Greenland Continental Margin: Preliminary results. *Geo-Marine Letters*, **13**, 9–16.

STUIVER, M. & REIMER, P. J. 1986. A computer program for radiocarbon age calibration. *Radiocarbon*, **28**, 1022–1030.

SWIFT, J. H. 1986. The Arctic Waters. *In*: HURDLE, B. G. (eds) *The Nordic Seas*. Springer-Verlag, New York, 129–154.

SYVITSKI, J. P. M., LEBLANC, K. W. G. & CRANSTON, R. E. 1990. The flux and preservation of organic carbon in Baffin Island fjords. *In*: DOWDESWELL, J. A. & SCOURSE, J. D. (eds) *Glacimarine Environments: Processes and Sediments*. Geological Society, London, Special Publications, **53**, 177–200.

TAUBER, H. & FUNDER, S. 1975. *Carbon 14 content of recent molluscs from Scoresby Sund, central East Greenland*. The Greenland Geological Survey, Report, **75**, 95–99.

WALKLEY, A. 1947. A critical examination of a rapid method for determining organic carbon in soils. Effects of variation in digestion conditions of inorganic soil constituents. *Soil Science*, **63**, 251–264.

WILLIAMS, K. M. 1993. Ice sheet and ocean interactions, margin of the East Greenland Ice Sheet (14 ka to present): diatom evidence. *Paleoceanography*, **8**, 69–83.

——, ANDREWS, J. T., WEINER, N. & MUDIE, P. J. The Late Quaternary paleoceanography: Kangerdlugssuaq Trough, East Greenland, mid to outer Continental shelf. *Arctic and Alpine Research*, **27**, 352–363.

North Atlantic sea surface conditions during the Younger Dryas cold event

J. C. DUPLESSY, L. D. LABEYRIE & M. PATERNE

Centre des Faibles Radioactivités, Laboratoire mixte CNRS-CEA,
91198 Gif sur Yvette cedex, France

Abstract: A map has been drawn of the oxygen isotopic composition ($\delta^{18}O$) of planktonic foraminifera which deposited their shells in isotopic equilibrium with ambient surface waters during the Younger Dryas cold event. These $\delta^{18}O$ values were derived from the $\delta^{18}O$ values of *Neogloboquadrina pachyderma* (left coiling) and *Globigerina bulloides*, which lived in their respective optimum temperature ranges. This map reflects the main trends of the sea surface temperature field during the Younger Dryas, but does not exhibit any $\delta^{18}O$ anomaly associated with continental ice-sheet melting. This result rules out all the theories relating the Younger Dryas cooling to injection of continental ice-sheet meltwater with very low $\delta^{18}O$ value into the North Atlantic Ocean. This reconstruction suggests that drifting of Arctic sea ice transported by the East Greenland Current may be a possible cause for the strong cooling which occurred in the middle of the last deglaciation.

The most impressive of the deglacial climatic excursions is the Bolling/Allerod–Younger Dryas oscillation and its termination leading to warm Holocene conditions. The Younger Dryas took the deglaciated areas of Scandinavia and north-western Europe back into almost glacial conditions after these areas had enjoyed warm temperatures for about two millennia. At the Allerod–Younger Dryas transition, 11 000 radiocarbon years ago, temperatures dropped by 6–8°C in the northwestern Atlantic (Ruddiman & McIntyre 1973; 1981; Duplessy *et al.* 1981; 1992) and even more on the nearby European continent (Van der Hammen 1957; Coope 1977; Mangerud 1987).

The cooling which marked the end of the warm Allerod period developed within a few decades (Taylor *et al.* 1993) and the Younger Dryas has been often considered as a typical example of abrupt climatic change. The origin of this cold event is still largely unknown, despite the large number of scenarios for it which have been proposed. Mercer (1969), and later Ruddiman & McIntyre (1981), suggested that its onset marks a major influx of tabular icebergs from a disintegrating Arctic ice shelf. Boyle & Keigwin (1987) called on shifts in the pattern of orographic winds in response to the retreat of the ice sheets as a possible cause. Johnson & McClure (1976) remarked that the beginning of the Younger Dryas event coincides with the diversion of Laurentide meltwater from the Mississippi to the St Lawrence River. Later Rooth (1982) and Broecker *et al.* (1988) suggested that the impact of this diversion was to decrease the salinity of the northern North Atlantic, eventually to the point of turning off

deep water production in the North Atlantic and stopping the Nordic Heat Pump – that is, the advection of warm surface waters to the high latitudes. Other potential points of freshwater injection into the North Atlantic have been proposed, noticeably iceberg discharge from Hudson Bay, the discharge of the Baltic Ice Lake into the Norwegian Sea or the waning of the Barents Sea ice sheet into the Arctic Ocean (Berger 1990). Because the study of the inception of the Younger Dryas event offers an opportunity to analyse the positive feedbacks which amplify a minor perturbation applied to a climate system, it is important to determine the causes of this event if it is not a simple manifestation of the stochastic behaviour of the climate system.

In this paper, we reconstruct the mean conditions prevailing at the surface of the North Atlantic Ocean during the Younger Dryas by mapping the oxygen isotopic composition of planktonic foraminifera which lived in their respective optimum temperature ranges. We then use this reconstruction to describe the circulation of the North Atlantic Ocean and test the various mechanisms which have been proposed as causes of this abrupt cooling.

Strategy

Ideally, a reconstruction of conditions prevailing at the sea surface should rest on both a sea surface temperature (SST) and a sea surface salinity (SSS) map, as has been shown for the last glacial maximum (CLIMAP 1981; Duplessy *et al.* 1991). The SST estimates are derived from

From Andrews, J. T., Austin, W. E. N., Bergsten, H. & Jennings, A. E. (eds), 1996, *Late Quaternary Palaeoceanography of the North Atlantic Margins*, Geological Society Special Publication No. 111, pp. 167–175.

Table 1. *Location of North Atlantic cores providing a record of the Younger Dryas*

Core	Latitude	Longitude	Equilibrium value with summer SST calculated from		August SST	References
			Pachy δ^{18}	Bullo δ^{18}		
V 27-60	72.11	8.35	3.47		<6	1
M 23-259	72.02	9.16	3.30			2
K-11	71.47	1.36	3.14		<6	3
M 17-732	71.37	4.13	3.19			2
HM 71-14	69.50	−18.05	3.35			4
HM 71-12	68.26	13.52	3.42			4
M 23-074	67.05	2.55				2
M 23-071	66.40	4.54	3.10			2
V 28-14	64.47	−29.34	2.92		6.9	5, 6
HM 52-43	63.31	0.44	3.08		6	7
UB 31-33	63.38	1.46	2.30			2
HU 75-41	62.39	−53.53	3.38		<6	8
NO 77-14	62.27	−20.25	2.86			1
NA 81-04	62.14	−2.20	2.76			1
V 23-42	62.11	−27.56			7	9
SU 90-24	62.04	−37.02	2.93			1
M 16-396	61.52	−11.15	2.79			2
SU 90-32	61.47	−22.26	2.51			1
TROLL 3.1	60.47	3.43	2.45			10
CH 73-110	59.30	−8.56	2.59			1
HU 75-37	59.09	48.24	2.95			1
HU 84-030-004	58.13	−48.56	3.25			11
HU 90-013-013	58.13	−48.23	3.00			12
SU 90-16	58.13	−45.10	2.99			1
BOFS 17K	58.00	−16.30		2.16	9.9	13
CH 77-03	57.56	−29.06	2.69			1
V 23-23	56.05	−44.33	2.69			14
NA 87-22	55.30	−14.42		2.08	10	15
M 17049	55.16	−26.44	2.68			2
CH 73-139C	54.38	−16.21		2.29	10	16
V 30-105	54.31	−36.30	2.63			6
KN 51-PG 13	54.28	−15.18	2.47			6
V 23-81	54.02	−16.08	2.31		8.7	17, 6
HU 84-030-003	53.20	−45.16	2.58			12
V 27-116	52.50	−30.20	2.75		8	18, 19
HU 91-045-094	50.12	−45.41	2.81			12
K 708-1	50.00	−23.45			12.4	9
ODP 609	49.53	−24.14		1.82		20, 21
CH 72-101	47.38	−8.29	2.15		6.7	16
CH 72-104	45.56	−8.47	2.26		6.7	16
V 30-97	44.06	−32.30			10.2	9
SU 90-11	44.04	−40.01		1.54		1
CHN 82-20	43.30	−29.52		1.35		22
SU 90-08	43.03	−30.03		1.27	10.8	1
CH 69-09	41.45	−47.21		1.28		1
NO 82-13	40.33	−10.27		1.56		1
SU 81-18	37.46	−10.11		1.43	14	15
NO 78-07	34.20	−7.01		1.22		1

The $\delta^{18}O$ value of planktonic foraminifera has been calculated either from the $\delta^{18}O$ value of *N. pachyderma* (left coiling) when SST was lower than 10°C or from the $\delta^{18}O$ value of *G. bulloides* for SST higher than 8°C (see text). Only SST estimates derived from high sedimentation rate cores (with minimal bioturbation effect) are reported.

References are: 1, this work; 2, Kiel measurements reported in Sarnthein *et al.* (1995); 3, Duplessy *et al.* 1975; 4, Bergen measurements reported in Sarnthein *et al.* (1995); 5, Kellogg *et al.* 1978; 6, Bard *et al.* 1994; 7, Veum *et al.* 1992; 8, Fillon & Duplessy 1980; 9, Ruddiman & McIntyre 1984; 10, Lehman *et al.* 1991; 11, Scott *et al.* 1989; 12, Hillaire Marcel *et al.* 1994; 13, Cambridge measurements reported in Sarnthein *et al.* (1995); 14, Mix & Fairbanks 1985; 15, Duplessy *et al.* 1992; 16, Duplessy *et al.* 1981; 17, Jansen & Veum 1990; 18, Ruddiman & McIntyre 1981; 19, Imbrie *et al.* 1989; 20, Bond *et al.* 1992; 21, Bond *et al.* 1993; 22, Keigwin & Lehman 1994.

foraminiferal counts to which are applied a transfer function (Imbrie & Kipp 1971). The SSS estimates are derived from the $\delta^{18}O$ value of planktonic foraminifera and SST estimates, both linked through the palaeotemperature equation (Duplessy *et al.* 1991).

This approach is not easily feasible for the Younger Dryas because of the short duration of this cold event, which was preceded and followed by major warm episodes. As in most locations of the North Atlantic, sediment accumulates at a rate of only a few centimetres per thousand years, the continual mixing of recently deposited sediment has disturbed the original micropalaeontological and isotopic signals and introduced warm foraminiferal shells into the cold Younger Dryas original fauna. Bioturbation acts thus as a low-pass filter by reducing the signal amplitude, so that the SST estimates for the Younger Dryas are significantly too warm in most sediment cores (Bard *et al.* 1987; 1994).

We therefore took account of SST estimates only in those cores which have a high sedimentation rate and where the impact of bioturbation is minimized (Table 1). The SST and SSS estimates can then be generated for the whole deglaciation following the method of Duplessy *et al.* (1992; 1993). Examples are given in Fig. 1. These records show that the summer SSS has been low during all the cold events of the last deglaciation, in particular the Younger Dryas.

However, the small number of cores with a sufficiently high sedimentation rate prevents us from generating meaningful maps of SST and SSS for the whole North Atlantic.

The impact of bioturbation is less severe for the $\delta^{18}O$ value of the cold foraminiferal species *Neogloboquadrina pachyderma* (left coiling), because this species was absent in the middle latitudes and less abundant in the higher latitudes of the North Atlantic during both the Bolling/Allerod and the Preboreal warm episodes (Fig. 2). Therefore, the $\delta^{18}O$ value of *N. pachyderma* (left coiling) shells deposited during the Younger Dryas has been almost fully preserved in the sedimentary record, even in cores of which the sedimentation rate is only a few cm/ka. At lower latitudes, in warmer waters, the abundance of *N. pachyderma* (left coiling) decreases and we have analysed Globigerina *bulloides*, which becomes one of the dominant species.

The $\delta^{18}O$ values of *N. pachyderma* (left coiling) and *Globigerina bulloides* record faithfully both summer SST and sea water $\delta^{18}O$ (a proxy for salinity) only within the optimum temperature range of these species (i.e. less than 10°C for *N. pachyderma* (left coiling) and in the range 8–22°C for *Globigerina bulloides*). We therefore used the SST estimates obtained in the high sedimentation rate cores as a guide to select the foraminiferal species of which the $\delta^{18}O$ value was taken into account to estimate Younger Dryas conditions (Table 1).

CH 72104 (46° 54' N - 8° 05' W - 4400m)

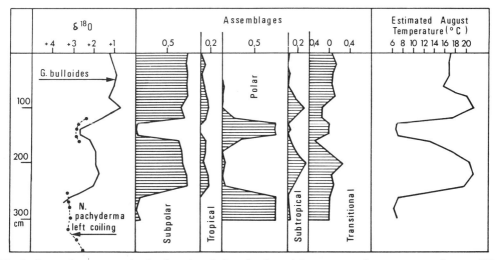

Fig. 1. Oxygen isotope record, microfaunal analysis and estimated August sea surface temperature for core CH 72–104 from the Bay of Biscay (Duplessy *et al.* 1981).

　　　　　　　　　　　　　J. C. DUPLESSY *ET AL.*

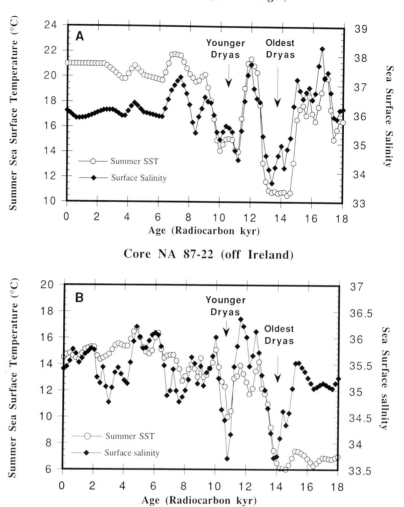

Fig. 2. Sea surface temperature and salinity estimates for cores NA 87–22 and SU 81-18. All values have been interpolated every 200 years (details of the calculations are given in Duplessy *et al.* 1992).

Finally, as within their optimum temperature range the isotopic temperature determined from the isotopic composition of foraminiferal shells is summer SST minus 1°C for *G. bulloides* and summer SST minus 2.5°C for *N. pachyderma* (left coiling), we corrected for this offset and calculated the δ^{18}O value of planktonic foraminiferal shells in isotopic equilibrium with summer conditions by subtracting 0.60‰ from the measured δ^{18}O value of *N. pachyderma* (left coiling) and 0.24‰ from the measured δ^{18}O value of *G. bulloides*. The results are reported in Table 1 and plotted in Figs 3 and 4.

Results and discussion

The planktonic foraminiferal δ^{18}O values are linked to the summer SST by the palaeotemperature equation

$$t = 16.9 - 4.38(\delta - \delta_{w}) + 0.10(\delta - \delta_{w})^2$$

where t is the summer SST, δ the δ^{18}O value of the planktonic foraminiferal shell in isotopic equilibrium with ambient water and δ_{w} the δ^{18}O value of the sea water. Low foraminiferal δ^{18}O values thus reflect either high temperatures or

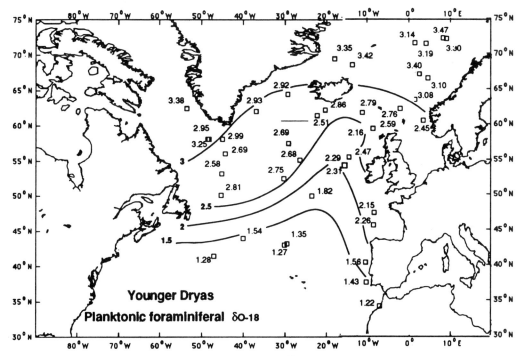

Fig. 3. Reconstruction of the oxygen isotopic composition ($\delta^{18}O$) of planktonic foraminifera which deposited their shells in isotopic equilibrium with ambient surface water during the Younger Dryas cold event.

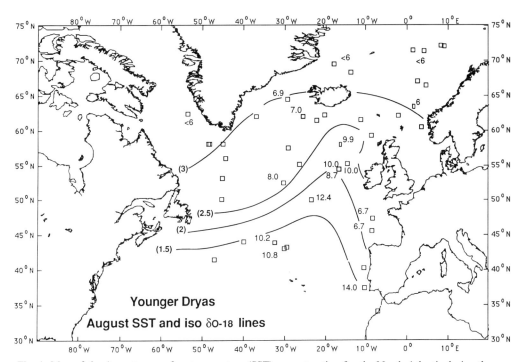

Fig. 4. Map of the August sea surface temperature (SST) reconstruction for the North Atlantic during the Younger Dryas event. Only cores with high sedimentation rates providing reliable SST estimates are taken into account. The iso-$\delta^{18}O$ lines from Fig. 3 are plotted for comparison. Note the broad agreement between the SST and $\delta^{18}O$ patterns.

low sea water $\delta^{18}O$ values (i.e. low salinity). Conversely, high foraminiferal $\delta^{18}O$ values reflect either low temperatures or high sea water $\delta^{18}O$ value (i.e. high salinity). However, the range of temperature and sea water $\delta^{18}O$ variations is very different. From the tropics to polar areas, the temperature decreases by about $20°C$, resulting in a $\delta^{18}O$ increase of 5‰, whereas the sea water $\delta^{18}O$ decreases only by about 1‰, so the temperature signal should be dominant in a map such as Fig. 3. Major changes associated with continental ice-sheet melting or meltwater injection should be superimposed on this pattern and appear distinctly in the melting area because of the extremely low $\delta^{18}O$ value of polar continental ice (-30 to -40‰ versus that of the mean ocean water). For instance, meltwater has been clearly recorded, with an amplitude close to 1‰, in the oxygen isotopic record of the massive iceberg discharges of the last glaciation, the so-called Heinrich events (Bond *et al.* 1992; 1993).

The map (Fig. 3) shows a progressive increase in the foraminiferal $\delta^{18}O$ values towards the north, indicating that the temperature signal (Fig. 4) is dominant in the reconstructed pattern of $\delta^{18}O$ variation. A large $\delta^{18}O$ gradient is observed in the polar front area previously recognised by Ruddiman & McIntyre (1973; 1981). However, our data show that temperate waters extended beyond $55°N$ in the central northeastern Atlantic, whereas cold, fresh waters were present in the Bay of Biscay. In the western Atlantic, the $\delta^{18}O$ values indicate the presence of cold water extending south of $50°N$.

One of the most surprising result of Fig. 3 is the absence of any evidence of major continental ice meltwater injection during the Younger Dryas. The westernmost cores do not exhibit lower $\delta^{18}O$ values reflecting strong meltwater flux from the St Lawrence, whereas the easternmost cores in the Norwegian Sea do not reflect any significant injection of meltwater from either the Baltic Lake or the Barents ice shelf; the latter disintegrated two to three millennia earlier (Jones & Keigwin 1988; Sarnthein *et al.* 1992, 1995). In addition, no meltwater pulse was observed in the $\delta^{18}O$ records of any North Atlantic core at the Allerod/ Younger Dryas transition.

The isotopic map (Fig. 3) shows the Younger Dryas as a period of weak, but still significant, warm North Atlantic drift toward the Norwegian Sea opposed to a strong East Greenland Current bringing large amounts of cold water and sea ice to the western North Atlantic. This reconstruction is supported by the presence in summer of an ice-free corridor off Norway, which was recognized by the presence of Arctic

diatoms (Koç *et al.* 1993). The occurrence of a strong East Greenland Current is in agreement with the volcanic ash contours from Ruddiman & Glover (1975). The marine ash layer 1, which was produced by ice-rafted ashes, has been correlated with the continental Vedde Ash in Norway (Mangerud *et al.* 1984) and the Skogar tephra in Iceland (Norddahl & Haflidason 1992). These ashes were emitted during a vigorous phreatic eruption of the Katla volcano, about $10\,600 \pm 60$ radiocarbon years ago (Mangerud *et al.* 1984). The abundance of ice-rafted ashes allows us to reconstruct the dispersal route of outflowing Arctic icebergs (Ruddiman & Glover 1975), demonstrates the presence of sea ice in the mid-latitudes of the North Atlantic Ocean, and illustrates the great strength of the East Greenland Current during the Younger Dryas event.

Although some sediment from the western Atlantic contains detrital carbonate originating from Canada, North Atlantic sediments from the Younger Dryas are basically free of ice-rafted debris (Ruddiman & McIntyre 1981). Moreover, the foraminiferal species *N. pachyderma* (left coiling) exhibits generally a maximum of abundance (Ruddiman & McIntyre 1981; Bard *et al.* 1987; Keigwin & Lehman 1994), indicating that the productivity did not drop to low values as is observed during the Heinrich events. These results, as well as the absence of the isotopic signature characteristic of huge iceberg melting, demonstrates that the Younger Dryas is not due to a massive iceberg discharge released from one of the disintegrating ice sheets, in agreement with the minimal melting of continental ice-sheets reconstructed by Fairbanks (1989). The Younger Dryas can therefore not be considered as an Heinrich event and results from a mechanism which is not related to the behaviour and disintegration of continental ice sheets. The absence of major freshwater anomalies is sup-ported by previous observations showing that the oceanic circulation in the North Atlantic was not significantly different from the modern day (Jansen 1985; Jansen & Veum 1990; Veum et al., 1992; Labeyrie *et al.* 1992; Sarnthein *et al.* 1995).

The only possibility of conciliating the demonstrated presence of drifting ice over the North Atlantic Ocean (Ruddiman & Glover 1975; Ruddiman & McIntyre 1981) and the absence of an isotopic anomaly in the planktonic foraminiferal record is to assume that the drifting ice resulted from sea ice originating from the Arctic Ocean and brought to the North Atlantic by a strong East Greenland Current. Icebergs released by continental, marine-based ice sheets have a very low $\delta^{18}O$ value, reflecting the very low temperature at which the snow forming the ice formed. By contrast, sea ice, which results from sea water freezing, has approximately the same $\delta^{18}O$ value as ocean water, because the isotopic fractionation associated with water freezing is close to zero (Craig & Gordon 1965). As a result, the formation and melting of sea ice leave no imprint on the surface sea water $\delta^{18}O$, whereas the salinity experiences major variations (Duplessy 1970). Drifting sea ice produced in the Arctic Ocean, transported by the East Greenland Current and melting in the North Atlantic polar front would therefore produce no significant surface water $\delta^{18}O$ variations. However, the underlying sediment would receive the Katla ashes carried by the drifting ice when this later melted.

How could the Arctic Ocean suddenly have produced a much larger amount of sea ice than it did during the Allerod warm period? Two major factors may have played a significant part. Firstly, the Chukchi and Siberian seas exhibit today a large continental shelf at a water depth close to 50 m and produce a significant amount of sea ice. Shelves were exundated during the last glaciation and at the beginning of the deglaciation. Recent AMS dating of peat layers in cores from the shelf region of the Chukchi Sea have demonstrated that this area was exundated until 11 000 radiocarbon years BP (Elias *et al.* 1992) when the Bering land bridge was submerged. Although the submerged Chukchi and Siberian seas were then very shallow, they significantly increased the area of the Arctic Ocean prone to sea ice formation. Secondly, Teller (1990) showed that runoff to the Arctic Ocean increased by about 20% at the same time because of the capture of what is now the headwater region of the Mackenzie River watershed. Both events mark the beginning of the Younger Dryas, and we suggest that increase of freshwater runoff and surface area of the Arctic Ocean, together with the weak inflow of fresh Pacific surface water, would have favoured the formation of sea ice and its transport to the Atlantic via the East Greenland Current. Arctic sea ice drift would thus constitute a new mechanism by which the freshwater budget of the North Atlantic may be modified, leading possibly to major changes in the efficiency of the Nordic Heat Pump.

Thanks are due to E. Jansen, N. J. Shackleton, B. Austin, J. Andrews, R. Bradley for helpful discussions and comments. This cork was supported by CNRS, CEA, INSU (PNEDC) and EEC grant No EV5V-CT92–0117.

This is CFR contribution No 1732.

References

BARD, E., ARNOLD, M., DUPRAT, J., MOYES, J. & DUPLESSY, J. C., 1987. Reconstruction of the last deglaciation: deconvolved records of $\delta^{18}O$ profiles, micropaleontological variations and accelerator mass spectrometric ^{14}C dating. *Climate Dynamics*, **1**, 101–112.

——, —— & 7 others 1994. The North Atlantic atmosphere-sea surface ^{14}C gradient during the Younger Dryas climatic event. *Earth and Planetary Science Letters*, **126**, 275–287.

BERGER, W. H., 1990. The Younger Dryas cold spell—A quest for cause, *Palaeogeography, Palaeoclimatology, Palaeoecology*, **89**, 219–237.

BOND, G., BROECKER, W. S., JOHNSEN, S., MCMANUS, LABEYRIE, J., & BONANI, G. 1993. Correlations between climatic records from North Atlantic sediments and Greenland ice. *Nature*, **365**, 143–147.

——, HEINRICH, H. & 12 others 1992. Evidence for massive discharges of icebergs into the North Atlantic ocean during the last glacial period. *Nature*, **360**, 245–249.

BOYLE, E. A. & KEIGWIN, L. D. 1987. North Atlantic thermohaline circulation during the last 20,000 years: link to high latitude surface temperature *Nature*, **330**, 35–40.

BROECKER, W. S., ANDREE, M., WOLFLI, W., OESCHGER, H., BONANI, G., KENNETT, J. P. & PETEET, D. 1988. The chronology of the last deglaciation: implications to the cause of the Younger Dryas event. *Paleoceanography*, **3**, 1–19.

CLIMAP PROJECT MEMBERS 1981. Seasonal reconstructions of the earth's surface at the last glacial maximum. *Geological Society of America Map and Chart Series, MC-36.*

COOPE, G. R. 1977. Fossil coleopteran assemblages as sensitive indicators of climatic changes during the Devensian (Last) cold stage. *Philosophical Transactions of the Royal Society, London, B*, **280**, 313–340.

CRAIG, H. & GORDON, L. I. 1965. Deuterium and oxygen 18 variations in the ocean and the marine atmosphere. *In*: TONGIORGI, E. (ed.) Stable isotopes in oceanographic studies and paleotemperatures. CNR, Pisa, 9–130.

DUPLESSY, J. C. 1970. Note préliminaire sur les variations de la composition isotopique des eaux superficielles de l'Océan Indien: la relation ^{18}O-salinité. *Compte Rendus de l'Académie des Sciences (Paris)*, **271**, 1075–1078.

——, BARD, E., LABEYRIE, L., DUPRAT, J., & MOYES, J. 1993. Oxygen isotope records and salinity changes in the Northeastern Atlantic Ocean during the last 18 000 years. *Paleoceanography*, **8**, 341–350.

——, CHENOUARD, L. & VILA, F. 1975. Weyl's theory of glaciation supported by isotopic study of Norwegian core K 11. *Science*, **188**, 1208–1209.

——, DELIBRIAS, G., TURON, J. L., PUJOL, C. & DUPRAT, J. 1981. Deglacial warming of the northeastern Atlantic Ocean: Correlation with the paleoclimatic evolution of the European continent, *Palaeogeography, Palaeoclimatology, Palaeoecology*, **35**, 121–144.

——, LABEYRIE, L., ARNOLD, M., PATERNE, M., DUPRAT, J. & VAN WEERING, T. C. 1992. Changes in surface salinity of the North Atlantic Ocean during the last deglaciation. *Nature*, **358**, 485–488.

——, JUILLET-LECLERC, A., MAITRE, F., DUPRAT, J. & SARNTHEIN, M. 1991. Surface salinity reconstruction of the North Atlantic Ocean during the last glacial maximum. *Oceanologica Acta*, **14**, 311–324.

ELIAS, S. A., SHORT, S. K. & PHILIPS, R. L., 1992. Paleoecology of late glacial peats from the Bering land bridge, Chukchi Sea shelf region, Northwestern Alaska. *Quaternary Research*, **38**, 371–378.

FAIRBANKS, R. G. 1989. A 17,000-year glacio-eustatic sea level record: influence of glacial melting rates on the Younger Dryas event and deep-ocean circulation, *Nature*, **342**, 637–642.

FILLON, R. H. & DUPLESSY, J. C. 1980. Labrador Sea bio-, tephro-, oxygen isotopic stratigraphy and Late Quaternary paleoceanographic trends. *Canadian Journal of Earth Sciences*, **17**, 831–854.

HILLAIRE-MARCEL, C., DE VERNAL, A., BILODEAU, G. & WU, G. 1994. Isotope stratigraphy, sedimentation rates, deep circulation, and carbonate events in the Labrador Sea during the last 200 ka. *Canadian Journal of Earth Sciences*, **31**, 63–89.

IMBRIE, J. & KIPP, N. G. 1971. A new micropaleontological method for quantitative paleoclimatology: application to a late Pleistocene Caribbean core. *In*: K. K. TUREKIAN, (ed.) *The Late Cenozoic Glacial Ages*, Yale University Press, 71–181.

——, MCINTYRE, A. & MIX, A. C. 1989 Oceanic response to orbital forcing in the Late Quaternary: observational and experimental strategies. *In*: BERGER, A. SCHNEIDER S. H. & DUPLESSY, J. C. (eds) *Climate and Geosciences, a Challenge for Science and Society in the 21st Century*, Reidel, Dordrecht, 121–164.

JANSEN, E. 1985. Rapid changes in the inflow of Atlantic water into the Norwegian Sea at the end of the last glaciation. *In*: BERGER, W. H. & LABEYRIE, L. D. (eds) *Abrupt Climatic Change*. Reidel, Dordrecht, 299–310.

—— & VEUM, T. 1990. Evidence for two-step deglaciation and its impact on North Atlantic deep-water circulation. *Nature*, **343**, 612–616.

JOHNSON, R. G. & MCCLURE, B. T. 1976. A model for northern hemisphere continental ice sheet variation. *Quaternary Research*, **6**, 325–353.

JONES, G. A. & KEIGWIN, L. D. 1988. Evidence from Fram Strait (78°N) for early deglaciation. *Nature*, **336**, 56–59.

KEIGWIN, L. D. & LEHMAN, S. J. 1994. Deep circulation changes linked to Heinrich event 1 and Younger Dryas in a middepth North Atlantic core. *Paleoceanography*, **18**, 185–194.

KELLOGG, T. B., DUPLESSY, J. C. & SHACKLETON, N. J. 1978. Planktonic foraminiferal and oxygen isotopic stratigraphy and paleoclimatology of Norwegian Sea deep-sea cores. *Boreas*, **7**, 61–73.

KOÇ, N. K., JANSEN, E. & HAFLIDASON, H. 1993. Paleoceanographic reconstruction of surface ocean conditions in the Greenland, Iceland and Norwegian seas through the last 14 ka based on diatoms. *Quaternary Science Reviews*, **12**, 115–140.

LABEYRIE, L., DUPLESSY, J. C., DUPRAT, J., JUILLET-LECLERC, A., MOYES, J., MICHEL, E., KALLEL, N. & SHACKLETON, N. J. 1992. Changes in the vertical structure of the North Atlantic Ocean between glacial and modern times. *Quaternary Science Reviews*, **11**, 401–413.

LEHMAN, S. J., JONES, G., KEIGWIN, L. D., ANDERSEN, E., BUTENKO, G. & OSTMO, S. R., 1991. Initiation of Fennoscandian ice sheet retreat during the last deglaciation. *Nature*, **349**, 513–516.

MANGERUD, J. 1987. The Allerod/Younger Dryas boundary. *In*: BERGER, W. H. & LABEYRIE, L. D. (eds) *Abrupt climatic changes—Evidence and implications*. Reidel, Dordrecht, 163–171.

——, LIE, S. E., FURNES, H., KRISTIANSEN, I. L. & LOMO, L. 1984. A Younger Dryas ash bed in western Norway and its possible correlation with tephras in cores from the Norwegian Sea and the North Atlantic. *Quaternary Research*, **21**, 85–104.

MERCER, J. H. 1969. The Allerod oscillation: a European climatic anomaly? *Arctic and Alpine Research*, **1**, 227–234.

MIX, A. C. & FAIRBANKS, R. G. 1985. North Atlantic surface-ocean control of Pleistocene deep-ocean circulation. *Earth and Planetary Science Letters*, **73**, 231–243.

NORDDAHL, H. & HAFLIDASON, H. 1992. The Skogar tephra, a Younger Dryas marker in North Iceland. *Boreas*, **21**, 23–41.

ROOTH, C. 1982. Hydrology and ocean circulation. *Progress in Oceanography*, **7**, 131–149.

RUDDIMAN, W. F. & GLOVER, L. K. 1975. Subpolar North Atlantic circulation at 9300 BP: faunal evidences. *Quaternary Research*, **5**, 361–389.

—— & MCINTYRE A. 1973. Time-transgressive deglacial retreat of polar waters from the North Atlantic. *Quaternary Research*, **3**, 117–130.

—— & —— 1981. The north Atlantic Ocean during the last deglaciation. *Palaeogeography, Palaeoclimatology, Palaeoecology*, **35**, 145–214.

—— & —— 1984. Ice-age thermal response and climatic role of the surface Atlantic Ocean, 40°N to 63°N. *Geological Society of America Bulletin*, **95**, 381–396.

SARNTHEIN, M., JANSEN, E. & 7 others 1992. $\delta^{18}O$ time-slice reconstruction of meltwater anomalies at Termination I in the North Atlantic between 50° and 80°N. *In*: BARD, E. & BROECKER, W. S. The last deglaciation: Absolute and Radiocarbon chronologies. Nato ASI Series, **12**, Springer, Heidelberg, 183–200.

——, ——, WEINELT, M. *et al.* Variations in Atlantic surface ocean paleoceanography 50°–85°N: a time-slice record of the last 545,000 years. *Paleoceanography*, **10**, 2063–2094.

SCOTT, D. B., MUDIE, P. J. and 6 others 1989, Lithostratigraphy, biostratigraphy, and stable isotope stratigraphy of cores from ODP leg 105 site surveys, Labrador Sea and Baffin Bay. *In*: SRIVASTAVA, S. *et al.* (eds) *Proceedings of the Ocean Drilling Program, Scientific Results*, **105**, 561–582.

TAYLOR, K. C., LAMORY, G. W. & 9 others 1993. The 'flickering switch' of late Pleistocene climate change. *Nature*, **361**, 432–436.

TELLER, J. T. 1990. Meltwater and precipitation runoff to the North Atlantic, Arctic and Gulf of Mexico from the Laurentide ice sheet and adjacent regions during the Younger Dryas. *Paleoceanography*, **5**, 897–905.

VAN DER HAMMEN, T. 1957. The stratigraphy of the Late Glacial. *Geologie en Mijnbouw*, **19**, 250–254.

VEUM, T., JANSEN, E., ARNOLD, M., BEYER, I. & DUPLESSY, J. C. 1992. Water mass exchange between the North Atlantic and the Norwegian Sea during the past 28 000 years. *Nature*, **356**, 783–785.

Late glacial–Holocene sea surface temperatures and gradients between the North Atlantic and the Norwegian Sea: implications for the Nordic heat pump

NALÂN KOÇ[1], EYSTEIN JANSEN[1], MORTEN HALD[2] &
LAURENT LABEYRIE[3]

[1] *Department of Geology, University of Bergen, Allegt. 41, N-5007 Bergen, Norway*
[2] *Department of Geology IBG, University of Tromsø, Tromsø, Norway*
[3] *Centre des Faibles Radioactivités, Laboratoire mixte CNRS-CEA,*
91198 Gif sur Yvette Cedex, France

Abstract: A S–N transect of sediment cores is used to (a) determine the millenial scale variability of sea surface temperatures (SSTs) and (b) the strength of the S–N SST gradients in the North Atlantic. The results show that the initial warming of the surface North Atlantic after the Last Glacial Maximum occurred synchronously between 50° N and 63° N at 13.4 ka, but was delayed by 1000 years at 72° N. All cores indicate that the Bølling–Allerød period was a climatically unstable time interval punctuated by several SST coolings. However, the magnitudes of these brief coolings were strongly subdued in the North Atlantic compared with the eastern Norwegian Sea. Plotting SSTs on a S–N transect indicates the presence of a strong (9°C) gradient (the Arctic front) between the Norwegian Sea and the North Atlantic throughout the Bølling-Allerød period. This gradient became even stronger (15°C) during the Younger Dryas, and nearly disappeared during the Early Holocene. The observed SST gradients have implications for the magnitude of the oceanic heat pump and atmospheric circulation patterns of the late glacial period.

The general circulation of the oceans generates a horizontal transport of energy from the tropics to the polar regions. In the North Atlantic, the Gulf Stream is the primary cause of the poleward flux of warm water to the high latitudes. It supplies between 50 and $100 \, W/m^2$ of heat to the north and, and once cooled, these waters sink to become a major source of deep water in the world ocean.

The distribution of sea surface temperatures (SSTs) in the North Atlantic shows a strong gradient—the Arctic Front—which extends northeastwards from the mid-Atlantic coast of North America to the Norwegian Sea in the vicinity of Spitzbergen (Hurdle 1986). At middle and high latitudes the eastern Atlantic is much warmer than the western Atlantic due to the northwards flow of the Gulf Stream on the eastern side and outflow of the cold East Greenland Current on the western side. This asymmetry contributes to the mild winter climates of western Europe.

The Gulf Stream changed its northward position considerably during the Late Quaternary, influencing the poleward heat flux and the position of the oceanic fronts (steep SST gradients). During the Last Glacial Maximum, the Gulf Stream did not flow northwards to its modern position, but turned almost straight eastwards without extending into the Norwegian Sea (CLIMAP Project Members 1981). Winter sea ice extended equatorward of 50° N and as a consequence the North Atlantic deep water ventilation was diminished and the core of ventilated deep water became shallower than today (Oppo & Lehman 1993; Sarnthein *et al.* 1994).

The pulsating nature and the abruptness of the glacial to post-glacial transition are well documented in ice core (e.g. Dansgaard *et al.* 1982; 1989; Oeschger *et al.* 1984), land (e.g. Mangerud *et al.* 1974; Watts 1980; Mangerud 1987; Atkinson *et al.* 1987; Paus 1989; 1990) and deep-sea records (e.g. Ruddiman *et al.* 1977; Ruddiman & McIntyre 1981*a*; 1981*b*; Duplessy *et al.* 1981; 1986; Jansen & Bjørklund 1985; Mix & Ruddiman 1985; Bard *et al.* 1987; Broecker *et al.* 1988; Lehman & Keigwin 1992; Koç Karpuz & Jansen 1992). Some theories proposed to explain such abrupt climatic shifts and the existence of climate instability call for a rapid reorganization of the surface and deep ocean circulation of the North Atlantic (Rind *et al.* 1986; Broecker & Denton 1989). The modelling studies of Rind *et al.* (1986) indicated the possibility that the high-amplitude climate change in this region over short time-scales of less than a few hundred years has been caused by variations in North Atlantic Ocean heat flux.

Here, we investigate the temporal and spatial variability of North Atlantic SSTs since the late

From Andrews, J. T., Austin, W. E. N., Bergsten, H. & Jennings, A. E. (eds), 1996, *Late Quaternary Palaeoceanography of the North Atlantic Margins*, Geological Society Special Publication No. 111, pp. 177–185.

glacial period to determine (a) the millenial scale variability of SSTs and (b) the strength of the Nordic heat pump. Time series studies of high resolution palaeoclimatic changes will improve our understanding of the causes and mechanisms of climatic change. Quantification of the strength of the Nordic heat pump, reflected in SSTs, would help to validate model simulations of climate variability.

Materials and methods

The temporal and spatial variability of late glacial and Holocene SSTs were analysed from a set of cores along a S–N transect; DSDP Site 609, core SU90-33, core HM 79-6/4 and core 88-T-2 (Fig. 1 Table 1). Today the cores lie under the northward flowing North Atlantic Drift, the northward branch of the Gulf Stream flowing into the Norwegian Sea. They were retrieved from the North Atlantic drifts or Norwegian Sea deep sea fans where sedimentation rates are high, varying between 7 and 120 cm/ka. These high sedimentation rates are essential to capture the abrupt, short-lived climatic events of the late glacial period. The chronology of the cores is based on a series of ^{14}C accelerator mass spectrometry (AMS) dates and ash layers (Table 2 Fig. 2) (Broecker *et al.* 1990; Bond *et al.* 1992; Koç Karpuz & Jansen 1992; Hald in press). Core 88-T-2 does not extend further than 11 930 years BP. The degla-

Table 1. *Core locations*

Core	Latitude	Longitude	Water depth (m)
DSDP Site 609	49°53.0′ N	24°14.0′ W	3884
SU 90-33	60°34.4′ N	22°05.1′ W	2400
HM79-6/4	62°58.0′ N	02°42.0′ E	850
88-T-2	71°55.3′ N	14°21.5′ E	1500

cial record of this core was extended by making a composite record through correlation with core NP90-57 from the same site (Hald in press). An age of 10 200 years BP was assigned to the inception of the Holocene in DSDP Site 609 as it was not tightly constrained by AMS dates. The chronology of core SU90-33 is based on the stable oxygen isotope stratigraphy (L. Labeyrie, unpub-lished data) and is based on visual correlation of its SST record with the other cores.

Transfer functions, using the statistical methods of Imbrie & Kipp (1971) on diatom species were used for estimating downcore summer SSTs. The SST record of core HM 79-6/4 has been published previously (Koç Karpuz & Jansen 1992). The SST estimates for the North Atlantic cores, DSDP Site 609 and core SU 90-33, are based on a new diatom transfer function, which has a better coverage of the North Atlantic than

Table 2. *Age model for the cores*

Depth (cm)	Corrected age
88-T-2	
10	2 080 ± 90
72	6 480 ± 100
135	8 990 ± 110
261	10 070 ± 115
308	11 035 ± 75
431	11 930 ± 150
NP 90-57	
372	12 425 ± 120
HM 79-6/4	
4.5	3 700 ± 70
80	5 065 ± 125
160	Saksun. ash 9100
250	Vedde ash 10 600
270	11 195 ± 160
305	12 325 ± 195
335	12 380 ± 105
390	13 165 ± 130
430	14 100 ± 155
DSDP Site 609	
22	5 020 ± 80
69	11 020 ± 190
74	12 350 ± 220
80	13 250 ± 90
84	14 590 ± 230

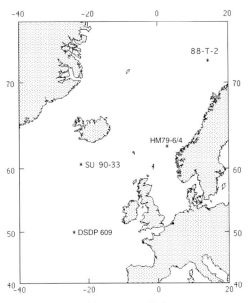

Fig. 1. Location of the cores studied.

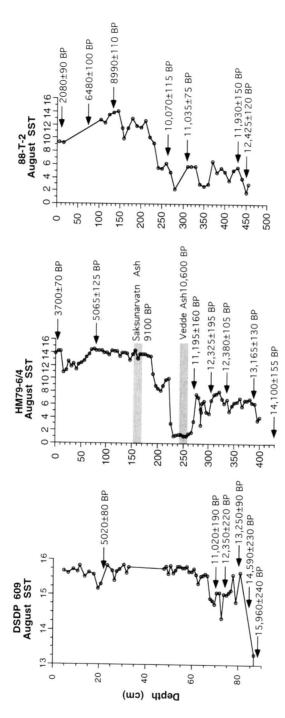

Fig. 2. Estimated summer sea surface temperature (SST in °C) records of the studied cores plotted against core depth. Also plotted are corrected ^{14}C accelerator mass spectrometry (AMS) dates and ash layers used in establishing the age model of the cores.

the previous function (Koç Karpuz & Schrader 1990). The new equation has a multiple correlation coefficient (adjusted for degrees of freedom) of 0.953 and standard error of estimate of ±1.2°C for summer SSTs. Details of this transfer function will be published elsewhere.

Millenial-scale SST changes since the late glacial period

The initial deglacial warming of the North Atlantic occurred at 13 400 years BP (^{14}C years) in both cores DSDP Site 609 and core HM 79-6/4 (Fig. 3). These identical ages indicate a very rapid northwards retreat of the polar front from 50°N to at least 63°N. The timing of the deglacial warming of the marine realm was also synchronous with that of the adjacent continents. Records of alpine glacier retreat from North America (Broecker & Denton 1989), the European Alps (Schluchter 1988) and Scandinavia (Mangerud 1980; Vorren *et al.* 1988) indicate that a similar warming occurred by about 13 500 years BP. The deglacial warming of site 88-T-2, located in the northern Norwegian Sea, did not take place until 12 450 years BP (Fig. 3). Before this time, the site was covered with sea ice, as deduced from the total absence of diatoms in the sediments of older age. This indicates that the northward penetration of the North Atlantic water to 72°N was delayed by about 1000 years compared with the southern Norwegian Sea.

After the initial warming, oceanic conditions exhibited high variability during the Bølling/Allerød interstadial complex (13 200–11 200 years BP). The high resolution record of core HM 79-6/4 shows that this period, characterized in general by warm SSTs, was punctuated by four progressively more severe SST minima: between 12 900 and 12 800 years BP (BCP I); 12 500 and 12 400 years BP (BCP II); 12 300 and 12 000 years BP (OD I); and 11 800 and 11 500 years BP (OD II) (Fig. 4) (Koç Karpuz & Jansen 1992). The Younger Dryas (YD) (11 200–10 200 years BP) cold period represents the most severe and most prolonged cold episode of the Bølling/Allerød series of climatic deteriorations. It was bounded by very rapid SST changes and characterized by Arctic–Polar conditions in the eastern Norwegian Sea (Koç *et al.* 1993). It has been proposed that these progressively more severe coolings documented within the Bølling/Allerød interstadial complex preconditioned the system for the YD cooling event (Koç Karpuz & Jansen 1992). These cooling events, especially OD II, are also captured to varying degrees in the other cores (Fig. 3). On the basis of a study of fluctuations of the percentage *N. pachyderma* sinistral in a high-resolution core, Troll 3.1 from the Norwegian Trench, Lehman & Keigwin (1992) also give evidence for OD I, OD II and YD with dates comparible with ours. Marine records hence show that the deglacial period was a climatically unstable time interval. There is also ample evidence from Scandinavia, in the form of glacial advances and/or palynological data, for these

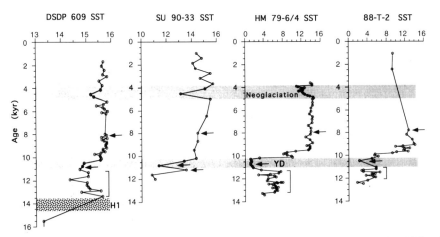

Fig. 3. Estimated summer sea surface temperature (SST) records of the studied cores plotted in °C for the last 14 ka in ^{14}C years. Note the different horizontal scales. Younger Dryas (YD) and the Neoglaciation events are shaded. Heinrich layer 1 (H1) is plotted from Bond *et al.* (1992). The arrows and the average of bracketed intervals denote the levels used for the construction of Fig. 5.

Table 3. *Correlation of Norwegian Sea late glacial climatic fluctuations with continental evidence from Scandinavia and North America*

HM 79-6/4	Scandinavia	North America
YD II (10 000–9600 years BP)	Glacier readvances dated to: 9900 ± 200 years BP 9600 ± 200 years BP 9300 ± 200 years BP	Emerson Phase (9900–9500 years BP)
YD (11 200–10 200 years BP)	Glacier readvance events: Tjtta (11 000-10 500 years BP) Tromsø-Lyngen (11 000–10 000 years BP) Ra moraines (10 800–10 600 years BP) Palynological evidence: Liastemmen (11 000–10 200 years BP) Utsira (11 000–10 000 years BP)	
OD II (11 800–11 500 years BP)	Palynological evidence: Liastemmen (11 700 years BP) Utsira (11 750 years BP)	Cass Phase (11 700 years BP) Sumas Stade (11 700–11 400 years BP)
OD I (12 300–12 000 years BP)	Glacier readvances in: Rogaland (12 380–11 970 years BP) Hordaland (12 400–12 000 years BP) Kristiansund (12 090 ± 100 years BP) Andøya (12 500–12 000 years BP) Palynological evidence: Liastemmen (12 250 years BP) Utsira (12 300–12 000 years BP)	Algona Phase (12 300 years BP)
BCP II (12 500–12 400 years BP)	Andøya (12 500–12 000 years BP)	
BCP I (12 900–12 800 years BP)		Port Huron Stadial (13 000 years BP)

deglacial cooling events (Andersen *et al.* 1982; Iversen 1954; Mangerud 1977; 1980; Paus 1989; 1990; Vorren *et al.* 1988) (Table 3).

High-resolution cores, DSDP Site 609, core HM79-6/4 and core 88-T-2, show that the warming into the Holocene took place in at least two steps (Fig. 3). The initial warming occurred at about 10 200 years BP. In the SE Norwegian Sea, core HM79-6/4 records that within less than half a ^{14}C century the SST increased 9°C from the cold (1°C) YD summer SSTs to the warm (10°C) interglacial summer SSTs (Fig. 4). However, within the next few centuries the SST dropped slightly to a post-glacial low (YD II) centred around 9800 years BP. The YD II event is recognized in cores DSDP Site 609, core HM79–6/4 and core 88-T-2. It is not observed in core SU90–33, most probably due to the lower resolution of this record. A series of glacier advances of the Scandinavian ice margin are dated to 9900, 9600 and 9300 years BP covering the same interval as the YD II (Denton & Hughes ʹ1981; Nesje *et al.* 1991).

The rather stable early Holocene SSTs were followed by a significant SST drop recorded in cores DSDP Site 609, SU90–33 and HM79-6/4 between 5000 and 3800 years BP (Fig. 3). During this time interval a climatic deterioration (Neoglacial cooling), resulting in the

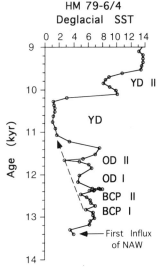

HM 79-6/4
Deglacial SST

Fig. 4. Estimated summer sea surface temperature (SST) record of HM 79-6/4 plotted in °C for the interval 9–14 ka in ^{14}C years (from Koç Karpuz & Jansen 1992). Deglacial SST fluctuations are labeled as BCP (Bølling Cold Period), OD (Older Dryas) and YD (Younger Dryas). The arrow denotes increasing instability with progressively more severe SST coolings towards the YD.

deforestation of mountain areas and in advances of some glaciers, was recorded from Scandinavia (Simonsen 1980; Selsing & Wishman 1984; Kullman 1987; Karlén 1988). The good correlation between land and ocean climatic events observed since the late glacial period points to highly coupled ocean–land climate changes.

Sea surface temperature gradients

The temperature trends as shown by the individual curves are generally consistent for the late glacial–Holocene North Atlantic and Norwegian Sea SSTs. All sites show the deglacial warming, the YD cooling, the early Holocene optimum and the Neoglacial cooling (Fig. 3). However, the amplitude of SST change is significantly different at individual sites, which indicates that distinct SST gradients existed during the late glacial period.

Summer temperatures at 50° N (DSDP Site 609) reached Holocene levels during the initial warming – the Bølling period – and decreased slightly (1°C) during the Allerød (Fig. 3). Further north, at the location of core H79-6/4 in the SE Norwegian Sea, summer SSTs were much lower (7°C) during the Bølling/Allerød interstadial complex (13 200–11 200 years BP) (Koç Karpuz & Jansen 1992). At 72° N, the oceanic warmth was not felt until the Allerød period as shown by core 88-T-2. As in the SE Norwegian Sea, summer SSTs did not reach the Holocene level during the Allerød period in the NE Norwegian Sea, either. Plotting deglacial (11–13 ka) SSTs on a S–N transect gives evidence for the existence of a strong front (Arctic Front) between the North Atlantic and the Norwegian Sea during the deglaciation (Fig. 5). The presence of the still

significantly large Scandinavian ice sheet might account for this steep gradient.

There was also a strong E–W gradient (Polar Front) in the Norwegian Sea, between the year long sea ice covered waters to the west and the seasonally open eastern Norwegian Sea during the deglacial period (Koç & Jansen 1994). Proximity to the sea ice margin and the oceanographic fronts made the eastern Norwegian Sea highly sensitive to climatic changes during the deglacial period, as evidenced in the SST records. The abrupt cooling events observed in the eastern Norwegian Sea records are in the order of 2–4°C coolings (Fig. 3). At DSDP Site 609 these events are highly subdued in magnitude – only two events of 1°C cooling are discerned during the Bølling/Allerød interstadial complex, indicating the diminishing sensitivity of the climate signals to the south. The Allerød to YD transition is also characterized by a much more intense cooling (6°C) than in the North Atlantic (0.5°C) and the YD to Holocene warming is likewise more pronounced in the north (9°C) than to the south (1°C). The SST gradient between the Norwegian Sea and the North Atlantic became even stronger during the YD period as the Polar Front migrated further eastwards in the Norwegian Sea (Fig. 5).

The strong northwards inflow of warm and saline North Atlantic Water during the early Holocene (the climatic optimum) reduced the SST gradient between the Norwegian Sea and the North Atlantic (Fig. 5). The sea ice margin and the accompanying Polar Front had retreated significantly towards a position along the northeastern part of Greenland. Arctic conditions were prevailing only along a narrow zone over the western Greenland basin. The western Iceland Sea was under subarctic condi-

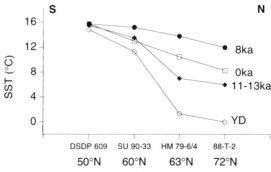

Fig. 5. Changes in summer summer sea surface temperatures (SSTs) along a S–N transect between 50° N and 72° N plotted for the deglacial period (11–13 ka), the Younger Dryas (YD), the Holocene climatic optimum (8 ka) and the present (0 ka). The present values are plotted from Dietrich (1969). The steep temperature gradient observed during the deglacial interval and the YD denotes the position of the Arctic Front.

tions, with the Arctic front located over the area, in contrast with the presence of polar conditions and the Polar Front at present (Koç *et al.* 1993). Today, the Norwegian–Greenland Sea SSTs are decreasing and the sea ice cover is extending eastwards as a result of decreasing northern hemisphere insolation (Koç & Jansen 1994). The present SST values of the Norwegian Sea lie between the early Holocene and the deglacial values for the area (Fig. 5). However, the S–N SST gradients have not changed significantly since the early Holocene.

Discussion

The presence of a strong front between the North Atlantic and the Norwegian Sea and the detection of abrupt climatic fluctuations in surface ocean temperatures during the Bølling/Allerød interstadial complex shows that the oceanic heat flux to the high latitudes was highly unstable during the last deglaciation. The sensitive areas are those north of *c.* 50° N. During the YD heat flux transport to the north was drastically reduced; the heat flux would be about 50 W/m^2 less than during the Holocene based on calculations of the present heat flux through the Iceland–Scotland gap (K. Simonsen, pers. comm. 1995). This is similar to the difference in insolation between the minimum and maximum summer insolation during the past 100 ka (Berger 1978). During the cold phases the northward advection of heat from the North Atlantic was diminished and much of the heat loss apparently occurred further south. This would influence the patterns of the atmospheric system and regional climate significantly, as also evidenced by the close coupling of the ocean and land records during the deglacial period. In general, we would expect a movement of the atmospheric Polar Front to the south and an advection of low pressure systems to follow a more zonal and southerly track than today over Europe during cold periods (COHMAP 1988). Time slice reconstructions of oxygen and carbon isotope distributions of surface and deep water indicate that during the YD cold phase the current patterns in both surface and deep waters of the northeast Atlantic and the Nordic seas were clearly meridional and at least partly overturning (Veum *et al.* 1992, Sarnthein *et al.* 1994, 1995). There is no evidence of a large-scale melting event which might have hampered the thermohaline circulation totally during this period. Hence the circulation type was similar to that of the present ocean, but the ocean carried much less heat to the high latitude

regions. We suggest that the high variability of the Nordic heat pump, as evidenced during the deglacial period, occurred with only subtle changes in circulation patterns, which would imply the possibility of large climatic effects without major shifts in the thermohaline circulation. This points to strong non-linearities in the ocean–atmosphere system. One reason this was so pronounced during the deglacial period is the possibility of strong ice sheet feedbacks, which influence both ocean circulation via wind fields and meltwater supply, and atmosphere circulation via albedo and wind field steering (Berger & Jansen in press). In the presence of still major ice masses, during a period of increasing insolation, we can foresee instabilities arising from the competition between glacial and interglacial modes of operation. If the strong climate instability recorded in ice cores for the last interglacial period were to be confirmed, this would give evidence for a much more sensitive Nordic heat pump.

We thank D. Kroon and J. Lloyd for careful reviews and suggestions for improvement of the draft manuscript. Special thanks go to A. Esmay for assistance with the statistics and Ocean Drilling Program for providing samples. This study was supported by grants from the Norwegian Research Foundation.

References

ANDERSEN, B. G., BØEN, F., RASMUSSEN, A., ROKOENGEN, K. & VALLEVIK, P. N. 1982. The Tjtta glacial event in southern Nordland, North Norway. *Norsk Geologisk Tidsskrift*, **62**, 39–49.

ATKINSON, T. C., BRIFFA, K. R. & COOPE, G. R. 1987. Seasonal temperatures in Britain during the past 22,000 years, reconstructed using beetle remains. *Nature*, **325**, 587–592.

BARD, E., ARNOLD, M., MAURICE, P., DUPRAT, J., MOYES, J. & DUPLESSY, J. C. 1987. Retreat velocity of the North Atlantic polar front during the last deglaciation determined by ^{14}C accelerator mass spectrometry. *Nature*, **328**, 791–794.

BERGER, A. 1978. Long term variations of daily insolations and Quaternary climatic changes. *Journal of Atmospheric Science*, **35**, 2362–2367.

BERGER, W. H. & JANSEN, E. On the origin of the Younger Dryas event: role of ice collapse and the super-fjord heat pump. *Proceedings of the Dutch Academy of Science*, in press.

BOND, G., HEINRICH, H. & 13 others. 1992. Evidence for massive discharges of icebergs into the North Atlantic ocean during the last glacial period. *Nature*, **360**, 245–249.

BROECKER, W. S. & DENTON, G. H. 1989. The role of ocean-atmosphere reorganizations in glacial cycles. *Geochimica Cosmochimica Acta*, **53**, 2465–2501.

——, ANDREE, M., WOLFLI, W., OESCHGER, H., BONANI, G., KENNETT, J. & PETEET, D. 1988. The chronology of the last deglaciation: implications to the cause of the Younger Dryas event. *Paleoceanography*, **3**, 1–19.

——, BOND, G., KLAS, M., BONANI, G. & WOLFLI, W. 1990. A salt oscillator in the glacial Atlantic? 1. The concept. *Paleoceanography*, **5**, 469–477.

CLIMAP PROJECT MEMBERS 1981. Seasonal reconstructions of the earths surface at the last glacial maximum. *Geological Society of America Map Chart Series*, **MC-36**.

COHMAP MEMBERS 1988. Climatic changes of the last 18,000 years: observations and model simulations. *Science*, **241**, 1043–1052.

DANSGAARD, W., CLAUSEN, H. B., GUNDESTRUP, N., HAMMER, C. U., JOHNSEN, S. F., KRISTINSDOTTIR, P. M. & REEH, N. 1982. A new Greenland deep ice core. *Science*, **218**, 1273–1277.

——, WHITE, J. W. C. & JOHNSEN, S. J. 1989. The abrupt termination of the Younger Dryas climate event. *Nature*, **339**, 532–533.

DENTON, G. H. & HUGHES, T. J. 1981. *The Last Great Ice Sheets*. Wiley, New York.

DIETRICH, G. 1969. Atlas of the hydrography of the northern North Atlantic Ocean. *Cons. Intern. pour l'exploration de la Mer*, 1–140.

DUPLESSY, J. C., ARNOLD, M., MAURICE, P., BARD, E., DUPRAT, J. & MOYES, J. 1986. Direct dating of the oxygen-isotope record of the last deglaciation by ^{14}C accelarator mass spectrometry. *Nature*, **320**, 350–352.

——, DELIBRIAS, G., TURON, J. L., PUJOL, C. & DUPRAT, J. 1981. Deglacial warming of the northeastern Atlantic Ocean: correlation with the palaeoclimatic evolution of the European continent. *Palaeogeography, Palaeoclimatology, Palaeoecology*, **35**, 121–144.

HALD, M. Rapid climatic shifts of the northern Norwegian Sea during the last deglaciation and the Holocene. *Paleoceanography*, in press.

HURDLE, B. G. 1986. *The Nordic Seas*. Springer, New York.

IMBRIE, J. & KIPP, N. G. 1971. A new micropalaeontological method for quantitative micropalaeontology: application to a late Pleistocene Carribean core. *In*: TUREKIAN, K. (ed.) *Late Cenozoic Glacial Ages*. Yale University Press, New Haven, 71–181.

IVERSEN, J. 1954. The Late-Glacial flora of Denmark and its relation to climate and soil. *Danmarks Geologiske Undersogelse Afh. Raekke* 2, **80**, 87–119.

JANSEN, E. & BJØRKLUND, K. 1985. Surface ocean circulation in the Norwegian Sea 15,000 BP to present. *Boreas*, **14**, 243–257.

KARLÉN, W. 1988. Scandinavian glacial and climatic fluctuations during the Holocene. *Quaternary Science Reviews*, **7**, 199–209.

KOÇ, N. & JANSEN, E. 1994. Response of the high-latitude North-ern Hemisphere to orbital climate forcing: Evidence from the Nordic Seas. *Geology*, **22**, 523–526.

——, —— & HAFLIDASON, H. 1993. Paleoceanographic reconstructions of surface ocean conditions in the Greenland, Iceland and Norwegian seas through the last 14 ka based on diatoms. *Quaternary Science Reviews*, **12**, 115–140.

KOÇ KARPUZ, N. & JANSEN, E. 1992. A high-resolution diatom record of the last deglaciation from the SE Norwegian Sea: documentation of rapid climatic changes. *Paleoceanography*, **7**, 499–520.

—— & SCHRADER, H. 1990. Surface sediment diatom distribution and Holocene palaeotemperature variations in the Greenland, Iceland and Norwegian Sea. *Paleoceanography*, **5**, 557–580.

KULLMAN, L. 1987. Sequences of Holocene forest history in the Scandes, inferred from megafossil *Pinus sylvestris*. *Boreas*, **16**, 21–26.

LEHMAN, S. J. & KEIGWIN, L. D. 1992. High resolution record of the North Atlantic drift 14–8 kyr BP: implications for climate, circulation and ice sheet melting. *Nature*, **356**, 757–762.

MANGERUD, J. 1977. Late Weichselian marine sediments containing shells, foraminifera, and pollen, at Çgotnes, Western Norway. *Norsk Geologisk Tidsskift*, **57**, 23–54.

——1980. Ice-front variations of different parts of the Scandinavian ice sheet, 13,000–10,000 years BP. *In*: LOWE, J. J., GRAY, J. M. & ROBINSON, J. E. (eds) *Studies in the late glacial of North-West Europe*. Pergamon, New York, 23–30.

——1987. The Allerød/Younger Dryas boundary. *In*: BERGER, W. H. & LABEYRIE, L. D. (eds) *Abrupt Climatic Change-Evidence and Implications*. Riedel, Dordrecht, 163–171.

——, ANDERSEN, S. T., BERGLUND, B. E. & DONNER, J. J. 1974. Quaternary stratigraphy of Norden, a proposal for terminology and classification. *Boreas*, **3**, 109–128.

MIX, A. C. & RUDDIMAN, W. F. 1985. Structure and timing of the last deglaciation: oxygen isotope evidence. *Quaternary Science Reviews*, **4**, 59–108.

NESJE, A., KVAMME, M., RYE, N. & LØVLIE, R. 1991. Holocene glacial and climate history of the Jostedalsbreen region, Western Norway; evidence from lake sediments and terrestrial deposits. *Quaternary Science Reviews*, **10**, 7–114.

OESCHGER, H., BEER, J., SIEGENTHALER, U., STAUFFER, B., DANSGAARD, W. & LANGWAY, C. C. 1984. Late glacial climate history from ice cores. *In*: HANSEN, J. E. & TAKAHASHI, T. (eds) *Climate Processes and Climate Sensitivity*, Geophysics Monograph Series, **29**, AGU, Washington, 299–306.

OPPO, D. W. & LEHMAN, S. J. 1993. Mid-depth circulation of the subpolar North Atlantic during the Last Glacial Maximum. *Nature*, **259**, 1148–1152.

PAUS, A. 1989. Late Weichselian vegetation, climate, and floral migration at Liastemmen, North Rogaland, south-western Norway. *Journal of Quaternary Science*, **4**, 223–242.

——1990. Late Weichselian and early Holocene vegetation, climate, and floral migration at Utsira, North Rogaland, southwestern Norway. *Norsk Geologisk Tidsskrift,* **70**, 135–152.

RIND, D., PETEET, D., BROECKER, W., MCINTYRE, A. & RUDDIMAN, W. 1986. The impact of cold North Atlantic sea surface temperatures on climate: implications for the Younger Dryas cooling (11–10 k). *Climate Dynamics,* **1**, 3–33.

RUDDIMAN, W. F. & MCINTYRE, A. 1981*a*. The North Atlantic Ocean during the last deglaciation. *Palaeogeography Palaeoclimatology Palaeoecology,* **35**, 145–214.

—— & ——1981*b*. The mode and mechanism of the last deglaciation: oceanic evidence. *Quaternary Research,* **16**, 125–134.

——, SANCETTA, C. D. & MCINTYRE, A. 1977. Glacial/interglacial response rate of subpolar North Atlantic waters to climatic change: the record in oceanic sediments. *Philosophical Transactions of the Royal Society of London, Series B,* **280**, 119–142.

SARNTHEIN, M., JANSEN, E. & 3 others. Variations in Atlantic surface ocean palaeoceanography, 50°–80° N: a time-slice record of the last 30,000 years. *Paleoceanography,* **10**, 1063–1094.

——, WINN, K., JUNG, S. J. A., DUPLESSY, J.-C., LABEYRIE, L., ERLENKEUSER, H. & GANSSEN, G. 1994. Changes in east Atlantic deepwater circulation over the last 30,000 years: eight time slice reconstructions. *Paleoceanography,* **9**, 209–267.

SCHLUCHTER, C. 1988. The deglaciation of the Swiss-Alps: a palaeoclimatic event with chronological problems. *Bulletin Assoc. Fr. Etude Quat.,* 141–145.

SELSING, L. & WISHMAN, E. 1984. Mean summer temperatures and circulation in a southwest Norwegian mountain area during the Atlantic period, based upon changes of the alpine pine-forest limit. *Annals of Glaciology,* **5**, 127–132.

SIMONSEN, A. 1980. Verti kale variasjoner i Holocen pollensedimentasjon i Ulvik, Hardanger. *AmS Varia,* **8**, 1–68.

VEUM, T., JANSEN, E., ARNOLD, M., BEYER, I. & DUPLESSY, J.-C. 1992. Water mass exchange between the North Atlantic and the Norwegian Sea during the past 28,000 years. *Nature,* **356**, 783–785.

VORREN, T., VORREN, K.-D., ALM, T., GULLIKSEN, S. & LØVLIE, R. 1988. The last deglaciation (20,000 to 11,000 BP) on Andya, northern Nor-way. *Boreas,* **17**, 41–77.

WATTS, W. A. 1980. Regional variation in the response of vegetation of late glacial climatic events in Europe. *In*: LOWE, J. J., GRAY, J. M. & ROBINSON, J. E. (eds) *Studies in the Late Glacial of North-West Europe.* Pergamon, New York, 1–22.

Late glacial sedimentology, foraminifera and stable isotope stratigraphy of the Hebridean Continental Shelf, northwest Scotland

W. E. N. AUSTIN* & D. KROON

Department of Geology and Geophysics, University of Edinburgh, West Mains Road, Edinburgh EH9 3JW, UK
* Present address: Environmental Research Centre, Department of Geography, University of Durham, Science Laboratories, South Road, Durham DH1 3LE, UK

Abstract: The detailed stratigraphies of two shallow marine cores from the Hebridean shelf of northwest Scotland are presented. The results provide evidence on the timing of deglaciation from about 15.2 ka BP, with evidence of cold, low salinity water persisting on the shelf until at least 13.5 ka BP. After 13.5 ka BP, probably shortly before 13.0 ka BP, warm shallow shelf seas were established and persisted throughout much of the interstadial. There is some evidence for climatic instability during the interstadial and for a cooling trend from after 11.6 ka BP. Glacial isostatic rebound of the shelf seems to have kept pace with eustatic sea level rise until about 11 ka BP.

The fully developed conditions of the Younger Dryas stadial are not observed until 11 ka BP. For the first time from the marine record the constituent tephra peaks of North Atlantic Ash Zone 1 are resolved into a sequence of eruptive events and demonstrate that extensive sea ice transgressed the western UK continental shelf throughout the Younger Dryas. The climatic conditions of the Younger Dryas persist until an initial, precursor warming at 10.2 ka BP, followed by a marked warming of about 8°C and fully established early Holocene temperatures before 10 ka BP. Many of the changes recorded through nearly 5 m of sediments accumulated during the Younger Dryas can be related to changing relative sea levels and source supply.

Changes within the North Atlantic during the last glacial to present interglacial transition reflect the complexity and apparent non-linearity of climate response to insolation driven changes. Much discussion has focused on the mechanisms which might act to drive these changes, but the general problem has been to fully resolve these records. The problem of correlating the terrestrial and marine records remains acute – at the limit of resolution of the radiocarbon method and yet the newly emerging ice core records of Greenland (Dansgaard *et al.* 1989) point to major climatic reorganization taking place within tens of years (Taylor *et al.* 1993). The fact that most of these climatic records appear to be linked mainly to changes within the surface North Atlantic (Lehman & Keigwin 1992; Bond *et al.* 1993; McManus *et al.* 1994; Zahn 1994; Fronval *et al.* 1995) is not in dispute, yet of all the records for this important period of earth history, the marine records often show the poorest temporal resolution.

Efforts to improve the temporal resolution of marine records have focused on sites of high sediment accumulation rate. These locations are mostly the North Atlantic drifts (e.g. Robinson & McCave 1994) and the continental slope sequences (e.g. Bard *et al.* 1987) of the North Atlantic margins. Few detailed, multi-proxy records of this period have come from the

continental shelves, with the exception of studies such as Hald & Vorren (1987). Perhaps this is not surprising when we consider that such records, which occur at present day water depths of generally less than 200 m, must accomodate eustatic sea level changes of over 100 m (Fairbanks 1989). In addition, the depositional environments of the continental shelves are highly dynamic and exhibit significant facies changes, particularly in response to regional deglaciation (Boulton 1990).

Our approach, therefore, has been to identify and discuss the most significant changes recorded in the continental shelf deposits of the Hebridean margin. The sedimentology and benthic foraminiferal stratigraphy, including some preliminary stable isotope stratigraphy, are documented in an attempt to reconstruct the palaeoenvironmental evolution through the late glacial period in relation to the decay of the British ice sheet, eustatic and relative sea-level change and oceanographic evolution of the NE Atlantic.

Modern oceanography: reflecting the NE Atlantic state

The general circulation pattern of the upper waters of the Atlantic, north of 40° N, are of a cyclonic gyre (McCartney & Talley 1982),

From Andrews, J. T., Austin, W. E. N., Bergsten, H. & Jennings, A. E. (eds), 1996, *Late Quaternary Palaeoceanography of the North Atlantic Margins*, Geological Society Special Publication No. 111, pp. 187–213.

known as Subpolar Mode Water (SPMW). The
temperature and salinity characteristics of these
waters reflect a progressive cooling and freshening of the original North Atlantic Central Water
as it crosses from the western Atlantic, enters
the European Basin, circulates northwards and
subsequently sinks to form North Atlantic Deep
Water (NADW) (Dietrich 1969; Harvey 1982;
Ellett *et al.* 1986).

Today, the continental shelf water mass of the
Hebridean Shelf (Cartwright *et al.* 1980; Booth
& Ellett 1983; Hill & Simpson 1988) maintains a
distinctive identity from that of the Rockall
Channel (Dickson *et al.* 1986) due to restricted
mixing brought about by well-developed seasonal thermocline fronts and a well-constrained
along-slope current (Huthnance 1986). In fact,
the northwest European continental shelf seas

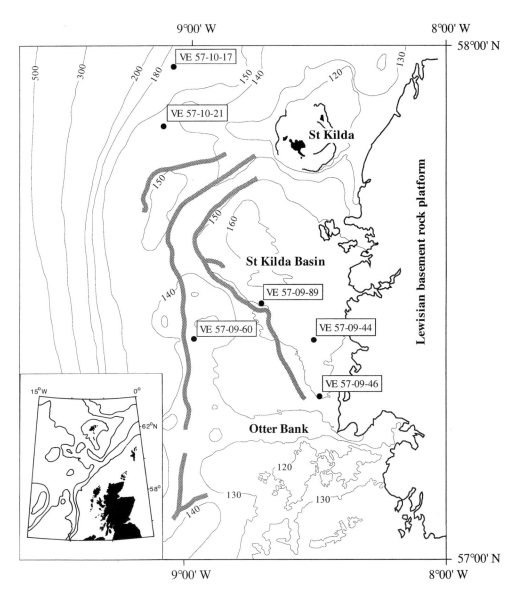

Fig. 1. Location Map. Bathymetry (m.) and core sites. Inset map shows the regional setting in relation to
NW Scotland. Heavy line = limits of exposed Lewisian basement rock platform. Thick, patterned line = morainal
bank complex (after Selby, 1989).

are generally distinguished by the formation of pronounced frontal systems during the summer months. Palaeotidal modelling studies of Quaternary continental shelves (e.g. Scott & Greenberg 1983; Belderson et al. 1986; R. M. Austin 1991) suggest that sea level plays an important part in the evolution of shelf sea fronts, together with a number of other factors such as energy dissipation across the shelf. Therefore it seems highly likely that the modern oceanographic conditions which today act to restrict shelf–ocean mixing may have differed significantly during the lowstands of the Quaternary.

Shelf geometry and morphology: an expression of glaciation

The area investigated consists of the Hebridean margin (Fig. 1), specifically the continental shelf to the west of the Outer Hebrides. This area forms a part of the northwest European passive continental margin.

The St Kilda Basin is a shallow depression on the middle to outer shelf (Fig. 1), up to 30 km across and over −160 m OD at its deepest. To the south it is bounded by the Otter Bank, a broad, east–west aligned ridge rising about 10 m above the surrounding sea bed to depths of between −120 and −130 m OD. To the north it is bounded by the St Kilda platform, corresponding to the limits of a Tertiary intrusive igneous complex (Harding et al. 1984). A 'cliff-line' is reported from the western side of this platform, with a further marine eroded rock-cut platform at a depth of −120 m to the west of it (Sutherland 1984). To the east, the basin is bounded by the rough, uneven and westwards sloping Lewisian basement rock platform of the inner shelf. To the west it is bounded by a low outer shelf bank, which rises up to −130 m OD.

Regional mapping by the British Geological Survey (BGS) of the shelf to the west of the Outer Hebrides has led to the delineation of a number of seismostratigraphic units (Selby 1989; Stoker et al. 1993). It is suggested that a Late Devensian ice sheet extended to its maximum western position as delineated by a series of morainal banks on the outer shelf. This ice sheet is thought to have been grounded to the morainal bank limit, while further offshore to the west there is evidence to suggest contemporaneous glacial marine deposition, based upon an AMS radiocarbon date of 22 480 ± 300 years BP from the marine bivalve *Portlandia lenticula* at a depth of c. 4.4 m in vibrocore 57/-10/21 (Fig. 1). This evidence supports the Hebridean ice limits outlined in Stoker et al.

(1993), as proposed by Von Weymarn (1979), Peacock (1984), Sutherland & Walker (1984) and Selby (1989).

North of the St Kilda Basin, Peacock et al. (1992) suggest that marine seismic evidence points to the ice margin extending to the St Kilda Plateau. However, there appears to have been only limited local glaciation of the island itself at this time (Sutherland et al. 1984). Further east, the Outer Hebrides themselves, with the possible exception of northern Lewis (Sutherland & Walker 1984), were glaciated during the last glacial maximum (Peacock 1991).

Materials and methods

Core recovery and sampling procedures

The materials analysed were collected by the BGS during the autumn of 1985. Navigation over the Hebridean Shelf relied soley on the Decca Mainchain system. The continuous wave Decca Hebridean (8E) chain, operating at 68% probability levels up to 10°00′ W, is defined as providing a full daylight fix repeatability accuracy of less than 100 m. Poorer fix repeatability accuracy occurs on summer and winter nights, so that at the time of sampling fix errors should be less than between 240–330 m (Selby 1989). Sampling was undertaken using the BGS MkII electronic vibrocorer, which generally gives good recovery in most sediment types and provides a core up to 6 m long, with an 83 mm diameter (Weaver & Schultheiss 1990).

Recovered cores were split into 1 m sections and capped before to cold storage. Core casings were subsequently split using a high-speed router; this produces minimal internal disturbance. Core sections were cut using an electro-osmotic knife, before detailed description and logging (Selby 1989; W. E. N. Austin 1991).

While avoiding material from around the casing, which in vibrocores is prone to down-core smearing (Austin 1994), sub-samples were removed and dried to constant weight at 40°C. After rehydration with distilled water for 24 hours, the sediments were wet sieved at 63 μm and the coarse fractions dried to constant weight at 40°C. Before foraminiferal counting the dry residues, often containing a large proportion of quartz sand, were concentrated by the heavy liquid separation technique (Feyling-Hanssen 1958; Feyling-Hanssen et al. 1971). Counts of >300 benthic specimens were made from the resulting 'light fraction' and total abundances calculated as numbers per unit weight of dry sediment processed. For further details of these techniques and their fuller implications, see W. E. N. Austin (1991).

Stable isotope analyses

Foraminiferal stable isotope measurements were carried out on a VG Isotech Prism isotope ratio mass spectrometer, with the generation of CO_2 from purified ortho-phosphoric acid at a constant reaction temperature of 90°C. Monospecific foraminiferal samples were picked from the washed residues (>63 μm), using between 5 and 10 tests of *Cibicides lobatulus* and between 40 and 60 tests of *Cassidulina reniforme*. Before analysis these samples were cleaned with alcohol in an ultrasonic bath. Typical sample weights were 0.15 ± 0.05 mg. Concurrently analysed Silver Mine calcite (SM) powdered standards (mean $= 0.15$ mg) yielded typical standard deviations of $\delta^{18}O = \pm 0.11$‰ and $\delta^{18}C = \pm 0.07$‰. All stable isotope results are quoted by the delta (δ) notation relative to the Pee Dee Belemnite (PDB) reference carbonate.

Tephra analyses

Preliminary results of tephra analyses are based on dry residue counting of glass shards from the sieved size range >250 μm. Shards can be differentiated into: (1) clear, winged morphologies; (2) brown, often vesicular morphologies; and (3) pumice-like morphologies. Details of the geochemical analyses are presented elsewhere (Hunt *et al.* 1995; Austin *et al.* 1995).

Measurement of organic carbon/nitrogen

Sediment subsamples were treated with sulphurous acid (1 ml, 5% v/v), freeze-dried and pelleted in tin foil before analysis in a Carlo-Erba NA1500 elemental analyser. Total organic carbon (TOC) measurements exclude the initial carbonate acid digestion step. The analytical precision of this method is ± 3.35% for organic carbon (OC) and ± 7.74% for organic/total nitrogen based on six replicates.

Determination of calcium carbonate content

A simple back-titration method was used to determine the calcium carbonate content, modified from Grimaldi *et al.* (1966). Approximately 0.5 g of dry sediment was weighed accurately, treated with an excess of acid (25 ml of 0.5 M HCl solution) and 0.5 ml of bromophenol blue indicator added. This solution was then back-titrated against a 0.35 M NaOH solution until a yellow to violet end-point was reached. The calcium carbonate content of the sediment sample is determined by the following equation (weight in grams, volume in litres):

$$\%CaCO_3$$
$$= 100[(\text{vol. HCl} \times \text{molarity HCl}$$
$$\times 1.007225)$$
$$- (\text{vol. NaOH} \times \text{molarity NaOH})]$$
$$\times (2 \times \text{sample weight})^{-1} \times 100$$

Results

Lithostratigraphy

Vibrocore 57/-09/89 (57°30.11′ N, 08°42.52′ W, 155 m water depth) was recovered from the margins of a morainal bank complex (Fig. 1), which delimits the western side of the St Kilda Basin. It consists of a highly variable lithological sequence (Fig. 2), essentially comprising a dark grey (5Y 3/1, 5Y 4/1, 5Y 4/2) muddy diamicton interspersed with clayey, silty and sandy horizons.

Bulk sediment particle diameter measurements illustrate the variability within this sequence particularly well (Fig. 2). On this basis, five major lithological units are recognized. From the base of the core to about 300 cm comprises a fairly massive diamicton rich in subangular, predominantly gneissic clasts up to 7.5 cm in length. Clast size and frequency tend to be higher towards the base of the core. A marked decline in sand content above 300 cm to about 250 cm is associated with a decline in clast size and frequency. From 250 cm to about 190 cm there is a marked increase in sand content, with values of nearly 80% at about 220 cm. A progressive decline in sand content from about 200 cm to a minimum at 160 cm continues until 100 cm, above which there is a gradual coarsening upwards to the top of the core.

The OC content is highly variable, ranging from a maximum of 0.65% weight at 290 cm to a minimum of 0.13% weight at 225 cm. However, the overall pattern of change appears to be closely related to the grain size changes, so that higher OC content correlates with a low sand, high silt/clay content and lower OC content with higher sand content. The total nitrogen (TN) content is less variable and generally less than 0.1% weight. The overall pattern does illustrate a positive covariance with OC. The carbon/

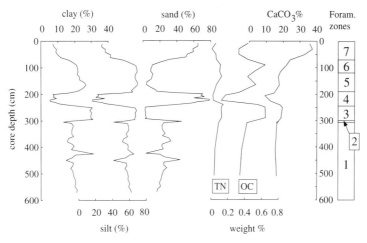

Fig. 2. Summary of core 57/-09/89 showing grain size, total nitrogen (TN), organic carbon (OC) and calcium carbonate (all expressed as dry weight %).

nitrogen (C/N) ratios are generally high, but exhibit no clear pattern of change through the core.

The calcium carbonate content of this core is low (<20%) up to about 100 cm, above which there is a gradual increase to nearly 40% at the top of the core (Fig. 2). The lowest values are observed at about 200 cm, corresponding to a minimum in OC and maximum sand content.

Vibrocore 57/-09/46 (57°19.30′ N, 08°30.04′ W, 156 m water depth, Fig. 1) was recovered from the seismically laminated sediments of the basin. It consists of 5.79 m of sediment with two lithological units separated by a gradational

'boundary' at about 85 cm. The lower unit consists of an homogenous, dark grey (5Y 4/1) soft sandy–silty–clay, with a gradual increase in the fine sand content upwards (Fig. 3). The upper unit consists of coarser, shelly sands and shows the continuation of the coarsening upwards trend exhibited within the lower unit. The marked increase in sand content, and associated decline in silt content, begins from about 150 cm and continues to the top of the core.

The organic carbon content of the core is low, with a maximum value of 0.55% at the bottom of the core. Values exhibit a gradual decline upwards through the core to a depth of

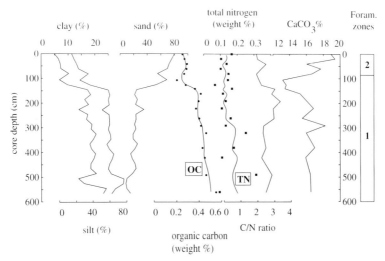

Fig. 3. Summary of core 57/-09/46 showing grain size, total nitrogen (TN), organic carbon (OC) and calcium carbonate (all expressed as dry weight %).

c. 160 cm and then a rapid fall to a minimum value of 0.2% at 105 cm. A small increase in OC is observed towards the top of the core. Total nitrogen values are more variable, particularly below 300 cm. Above 300 cm there appears to be little change in the average nitrogen content, with values remaining slightly above 0.1%. The C/N ratios are highly variable, but a three-point running average of OC and TN contents (Fig. 3) indicates that the highest C/N ratios occur from c. 300 to c. 150 cm. A marked decline in C/N ratios is observed above c. 160 cm. As in core 57/-09/89, the same general relationship exists between OC content and sediment grain size. The same pattern of declining TN values also appears to be positively correlated with the silt and clay content, although no marked decline is visible above c. 160 cm, as in the OC record.

The calcium carbonate content of this core remains low throughout (Fig. 3), from a high of about 20% at a depth of 20 cm to a low of about 13% at 105 cm. The lowest carbonate contents

are observed between 150 and 100 cm; there is a marked increase in carbonate content upwards to the top of the core.

Dating, tephra layers and sediment accumulation rates

The chronology of these two cores is based upon 12 molluscan accelerator mass spectrometer (AMS) radiocarbon ages (Table 1). For the purposes of this study we have used the modern surface ocean reservoir correction of 405 ± 40 years determined for British coastal waters by Harkness (1983). Therefore, all ages quoted are in radiocarbon years BP and have a marine ^{14}C reservoir age correction of 405 years applied. Icelandic tephra from vibrocore 57/-09/46 provide a means of quantifying the marine ^{14}C reservoir ages during the Younger Dryas period and we present evidence to support a significant increase in reservoir age (700 years) at this time (Austin et al. 1995).

Table 1. *AMS radiocarbon ages from the Hebridean shelf; 405 year marine ^{14}C reservoir correction applied (Harkness 1983)*

Laboratory Number	Species	Core depth (m)	Conventional age (^{14}C yr BP ±1σ)	Corrected age[a] (^{14}C yr BP ±1σ)
VE 57/-09/89				
OxA-2780	*Timoclea ovata*	0.50-0.60	5960±80	5555±90
OxA-2871	*Nuculoma belloti*	0.70-0.75	11040±110	10635±120
OxA-2782	*Parvicardium ovale*	1.94-2.00	11440±120	11035±130
OxA-2783	*Nucula nucleus*	2.25-2.35	12030±120	11625±130
OxA-2784	*Portlandia arctica*	2.50-2.55	13920±140	13515±150
OxA-2785	*Portlandia arctica*	3.10	15650±160	15245±170
VE 57/-09/46				
OxA-2786	*Acanthocardia echinata*	0.47-0.51	10380±100	9975±110
OxA-2787	*Nuculoma belotti*	1.05-1.30	10580±100	10175±110
TO-3127	*Nuculoma belotti*	2.06-2.09	10610±70	10205±80
TO-3128	*Nuculoma tenuis*	2.30-2.33	10970±70	10565±80
OxA-2788	*Nuculoma belotti*	4.80-5.00	11420±120	11015±130
TO-3126	*Nuculana pernula*	5.65-5.68	11400±70	10995±80
VE 57/-10/21				
OxA-1322	*Portlandia lenticula*	4.30-4.55	22480±300	

The dating of vibrocore 57/-09/89 was intended (Peacock *et al.* 1992) to prove the age of the major lithological and faunal boundaries. All the dates provide a conformable sequence and young towards the top of the core, from $15\,245 \pm 170$ years BP at 310 cm, to 5555 ± 90 years BP at *c.* 55 cm. Two major hiatuses can be inferred and occur at core depths of *c.* 250 and 75 cm (Fig. 4). The former may span nearly 2000 years, with much of the late glacial interstadial sediments either missing or highly compressed from after $13\,515 \pm 150$ years BP until some time before $11\,625 \pm 130$ years BP. The second hiatus spans nearly 5000 years, with much of the early Holocene record lost from some time after $10\,635 \pm 120$ years BP to before 5555 ± 90 years BP. The section of the core between *c.* 230 cm and 75 cm appears to have high sediment accumulation rates, with the Younger Dryas sequence accumulating at an average of 0.3 cm/year.

Vibrocore 57/-09/46 provides a higher resolution, but shorter time record than 57/-09/89. The sequence of dates is essentially conformable and in depositional order through the core, apart from a slight reversal from $10\,995 \pm 80$ years BP at 566.5 cm to $11\,015 \pm 130$ years BP at 490 cm. However, the latter overlap at one standard deviation and this reversal is not considered to be significant. The youngest dates from this core are 9975 ± 110 years BP at *c.* 50 cm and $10\,175 \pm 110$ years BP at *c.* 117 cm. In calculating the

accumulation rates for this core we have followed the approach of Austin *et al.* (1995) and derived an age–depth relationship based on a best-fit second-order polynomial curve ($r^2 = 0.94$)

Conventional ^{14}C age

$$= 10\,212 + 3.146 \text{ (depth cm)}$$

$$- 1.695 \times 10^{-3} \text{ (depth cm)}^2.$$

The fitted curve (Fig. 5) suggests that sediment accumulation rates were considerably higher during the early part of the Younger Dryas, with calculated rates of nearly 1.7 cm/year at 570 cm and less than 0.3 cm/year above 100 cm. On the basis of this age–depth curve we calculate the marine radiocarbon age of the peak in rhyolitic glass shards to be nearly 11 000 years BP, while terrestrial macrofossils suggest ages of *c.* 10 300 years BP. Thus the difference in these ages, about 700 years, indicates that reservoir ages differed substantially from modern values during the Younger Dryas. However, although this fact does have important implications for comparing climatic time series dated by ^{14}C, further investigations to determine the temporal and spatial variability are required before the new Younger Dryas reservoir age correction can be applied. In addition to the easily identified rhyolitic tephra of the Vedde Ash (e.g. Bard *et al.* 1994; Austin *et al.* 1995), we have also stratigraphically resolved basaltic tephra peaks corresponding to at least two other distinct eruptive events. The latter are thought to represent the constituent members of North Atlantic Ash Zone 1 (NAAZ1) (Kvamme *et al.* 1989). Although it is beyond the scope of this paper to deal in detail with the tephra of NAAZ1, we have plotted their depth distribution in core 57/-09/46 (Fig. 5) to demonstrate that individual eruptive events can be stratigraphically resolved and dated from this highly expanded sequence.

Benthic foraminiferal assemblages

The results of the micropalaeontological analyses are presented for each of the cores analysed and are summarized in Figs 8–11 and Tables 2 and 3. Counts are based on the sieved fraction $>63\,\mu$m and are all based upon >300 specimens. Full count data and taxonomic descriptions are available in W. E. N. Austin (1991). Taxonomic determinations are mostly based on Feyling-Hanssen (1964) and Feyling-Hanssen *et al.* (1971).

Fig. 4. Lithology and AMS radiocarbon ages, core 57/-09/89. Accumulation rates are based on linear extrapolation. Horizontal bars, corresponding to marked lithological changes, represent core hiatuses. Standard deviations of the measured ages typically fall within the area of each sample marker.

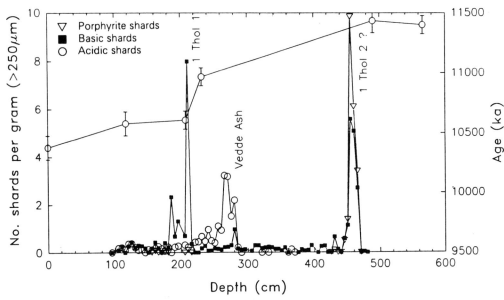

Fig. 5. AMS radiocarbon ages and tephra distribution, core 57/-09/46. Further details of the tephra are given by Hunt *et al.* (1995) and Austin *et al.* (1995). The best-fit curve defines the following age–depth relationship:

$$\text{conventional } {}^{14}\text{C age} = 10\,212 + 3.146 \text{ (depth cm)} - 1.695 \times 10^{-3} \text{ (depth cm)}^2$$

Foraminiferal zonation can be thought of as a form of classification and as the data are both quantitative and multivariate it is possible to use numerical methods of classification. Three numerical techniques have been used: the constrained single-link clustering method (Conslink of Gordon & Birks 1972) and two binary divisive procedures (SPLITLSQ and SPLITINF programmes of Birks & Gordon 1985). In general, the foraminiferal zone boundaries corrspond to the lithological boundaries and are very well defined by marked assemblage changes. Further quantification of the foraminiferal faunas, in an attempt to summarize the downcore changes, is provided by principal components analysis (PCA) and the first axis scores are plotted and discussed in the following pages. The sign of the PCA first axis scores differ from the two cores studied, in relation to the same prevailing climatic conditions, because of the different species used in the PCA. The most diagnostic taxa – that is, those used in the numerical zonation and PCA, are illustrated (Figs 6 & 7).

Vibrocore 57/-09/89

The foraminiferal assemblages of core 57/-09/89 are summarized in Figs 8 and 9. A summary of

the foraminiferal assemblages and palaeoenvironmental interpretations for this core is provided in Table 2. Seven assemblage zones are defined and these are largely coincident with the marked and well-defined lithological changes (see section on core properties and Fig. 2). Details of the corresponding molluscan zonations for these cores can be found in Peacock *et al.* (1992).

Zone 1. The dominant species of this zone are *Elphidium excavatum* forma *clavata* and *Cassidulina reniforme*, with common accessory species including *Cibicides* gr. *lobatulus*, *Nonion orbiculare*, *Astrononion gallowayi* and *Islandiella helenae*. The zone appears to be fairly variable in terms of species percentage composition, the number of species and faunal diversity (Walton 1964). Benthic foraminiferal sums are moderate (generally less than 200 specimens per gram) as are numbers of planktonic foraminifera expressed by a low planktonic/benthic ratio (Fig. 9).

Zone 2. Based on a single sample with a very rich foraminiferal assemblage dominated by *C. reniforme*, *E. excavatum* forma *clavata*, *Spiroplectammina wrightii*, *C.* gr. *lobatulus* and

Table 2. *Faunal summary and palaeoenvironmental interpretations of foraminiferal assemblage zones, vibrocore 57/-09/89*

Foram. Zone	Core depth (cm)	Dominant Species	Common Accessory Species	Palaeoenvironment
Zone 1	579 - 91cm	Cassidulina reniforme, Elphidium excavatum forma clavata	Cibicides gr. lobatulus, Elphidium albiumbilicatum, Nonion labradoricum	Cold (<2°C), glacial marine. high sediment accumulation rates.
Zone 2	91 - 00cm	Spiroplectammina wrightii	Cibicides gr. lobatulus, Cassidulina laevigata, Rosalina praegeri, Trifarina angulosa, Stainforthia fusiformis	Warm (>9°C), increasing water depths. stronger currents, increased N. Atlantic influence.

Table 3. *Faunal summary and palaeoenvironmental interpretations of foraminiferal assemblage zones, vibrocore 57/09/46*

Foram. Zone	Core depth (cm)	Dominant Species	Common Accessory Species	Palaeoenvironment
Zone 1	575 - 305cm	Elphidium excavatum forma clavata, Cassidulina reniforme	Cibicides gr. lobatulus, Nonion orbiculare, Astrononion gallowayi, Islandiella helenae, Cassidulina laevigata, Bulimina gr. marginata	Proximal glacial marine, possibly reworked and mixed foraminiferal assemblages
Zone 2	305 - 300cm	Cassidulina reniforme, Elphidium excavatum forma clavata, Spiroplectammina wrightii, Cibicides gr. lobatulus, Cassidulina laevigata	Ammonia batavus, Bolivina difformis, Bulimina gr. marginata, Rosalina praegeri, Stainforthia fusiformis, Trifarina angulosa	Origin uncertain? Possibly representing a brief warm interval? Reworked assemblages
Zone 3	300 - 245cm	Elphidium excavatum forma clavata, Cassidulina reniforme	Elphidium asklundi, Nonion orbiculare, Islandiella helenae, I. norcrossi, Nonion labradoricum	Shallow, cold and lowered salinity. Increasingly distal glacial marine
Zone 4	245 - 190cm	Cibicides gr. lobatulus, Ammonia batavus, Stainforthia fusiformis	Cassidulina laevigata, Bulimina gr. marginata, Rosalina praegeri, Spiroplectammina wrightii	Warm, shallow marine. High energy environment, strong currents.
Zone 5	190 - 120cm	Elphidium excavatum forma clavata, Cassidulina reniforme	Elphidium albiumbilicatum, Islandiella helenae, I. norcrossi, Nonion labradoricum	Cold water, increasing water depths and high sediment accumulation rates.
Zone 6	120 - 70cm	Cassidulina reniforme, Elphidium excavatum forma clavata	Nonion labradoricum, Cassidulina laevigata, Bolivina difformis, Bulimina gr. marginata, Cibicides gr. lobatulus, Rosalina praegeri, Spiroplectammina wrightii	Cold water faunas dominate a mixed assemblage, evidence of bioturbation.
Zone 7	70 - 00cm	Cassidulina laevigata	Bolivina difformis, Bulimina gr. marginata, Cibicides gr. lobatulus, Hyalinea balthica, Rosalina praegeri, Spiroplectammina wrightii, Trifarina angulosa	Warm waters, increasing water depths, strong currents, greater N.Atlantic influence.

Cassidulina laevigata. The common accessory species are outlined in Table 2. High diversity (*c.* 40 species), low dominance (<15%), a marked increase in the epifaunal/infaunal ratio (see Murray 1991) and the planktonic/benthic ratio characterize this zone. The benthic sum is also high, with about 650 benthic specimens per gram.

Zone 3. Dominated by the same species as Zone 1, *E. excavatum* forma *clavata* and *C. reniforme*, this zone is distinguished by its common accessory species: *Elphidium asklundi*, *Nonion orbiculare*, *N. labradoricum*, *I. helenae* and *I. norcrossi*. The number of species present (*c.* 20) is low, as is faunal diversity, which reaches its lowest value throughout the core. Faunal dominance is high and increases through the zone to a maximum core value of nearly 60% at the top of Zone 3. The epifaunal/infaunal ratios and planktonic/benthic ratios are low throughout, as are the benthic sums which fall to their lowest core values of *c.* 30 specimens per gram.

Zone 4. Marked assemblage changes help to define this zone, which is dominated by *C.* gr. *lobatulus*, *Ammonia batavus* and *Stainforthia fusiformis*. The common accessory species are: *C. laevigata*, *Bulimina* gr. *marginata*, *Rosalina praegeri* and *S. wrightii*. Faunal diversity is high but variable, exhibiting a marked increase from Zone 3 wheras the faunal dominance is generally low. Epifaunal/infaunal ratios are very diagnostic of Zone 4 reaching a maximum 0.8 at 214 cm. The variability observed in the epifaunal/infaunal ratios of this zone arise largely from significant changes in the abundance of the infaunal species *S. fusiformis*; the latter closely parallels grain size changes within this part of the sequence. Planktonic/benthic ratios are higher than Zone 3 values, but remain generally low and variable about a mean zonal value of 0.1. Benthic sums, however, exhibit a marked increase, with up to 1250 specimens per gram.

Zone 5. A return to assemblages dominated by *E. excavatum* forma *clavata* and *C. reniforme* characterizes the onset of this zone. Unlike Zone 3, the common accessory species of this zone are slightly modified and include *E. albiumbilicatum*, *I. helenae*, *I. norcrossi* and *N. labradoricum*. Lower diversity and higher species dominance characterizes Zone 5, together with the lowest epifaunal/infaunal ratios of the entire sequence. Planktonic/benthic ratios remain very low, although the benthic sums are generally variable and considerably higher than those of Zone 3.

Zone 6. *C. reniforme* and *E. excavatum* forma *clavata* remain the dominant taxa, but the common accessory species have a very different composition to those of Zone 5 (Table 2). Faunal diversity is generally high but very vari-able throughout this zone, whereas the faunal dominance is low. Epifaunal/infaunal ratios are elevated from Zone 5 as are the planktonic/benthic ratios, the latter exhibiting the first significant increase within the sequence. Benthic sums are also elevated from those of Zone 5 with a maximum of *c.* 600 specimens per gram at 95 cm.

Zone 7. A very different assemblage charac-terizes the uppermost section of the core, with *C. laevigata* as the dominant species. The common accessory species are those of Zones 4 and 6 without species such as *N. labradoricum*, but with some additional elements such as *Trifarina angulosa* and *Hyalinea balthica*. Faunal diversity is slightly lower than zone 6 and faunal dominance remains fairly low (*c.* 20%). Epifaunal/infaunal ratios continue to rise, reaching *c.* 0.6 at the top of the core, as do planktonic/benthic ratios which almost reach 1.0. More significant, however, is the sudden increase in benthic sum, which at 25 cm reaches over 18 000 specimens per gram.

Fig. 6. **1**, *Eggerelloides scabrum* (Williamson) side view ×32. **2, 3**, *Siphotextularia flintii* (Cushman), **2**, Side view of megalospheric generation ×48. **3**, Side view of microspheric generation ×28. **4**, *Quinqueloculina stalkeri* Loeblich and Tappan side view ×68, **6**, *Bolivina difformis* (Williamson). **5**, Side view ×93. **6**, Side view ×56. **7, 8**, *Bolivina pseudoplicata* Heron-Allen and Earland. **7**, Side view ×66. **8**, Side view ×62. **9**, *Cassidulina laevigata* d'Orbigny side view ×66. **10, 11**, *Cassidulina obtusa* Williamson. **10**, Side view ×91. **11**, Side view ×83. **12**, *Cassidulina reniforme* Nørvang side view ×66. **13**, *Islandiella helanae* Feyling-Hanssen and Buzas side view ×37. **14, 15**, *Globocassidulina suglobosa* (Brady). **14**, Oblique apertural view ×120. **15**. Peripheral view ×119. **16, 17**, *Stainforthia (Fursenkoina) fusiformis* (Williamson). **16**, Side view of adult specimen ×33. **17**, Side view of juvenile specimen ×120. **18**, *Stainforthia loeblichi* (Feyling-Hansen) side view ×33. **19**, *Bulimina marginata* d'Orbigny side view ×53. **20, 21**, *Uvigernina peregrina* Cushman. **20**, Side view ×26. **21**, Oblique side view ×68. **22, 23**, *Trifarina angulosa* (Williamson). **22**, Side view ×35. **23**, Side view ×34.

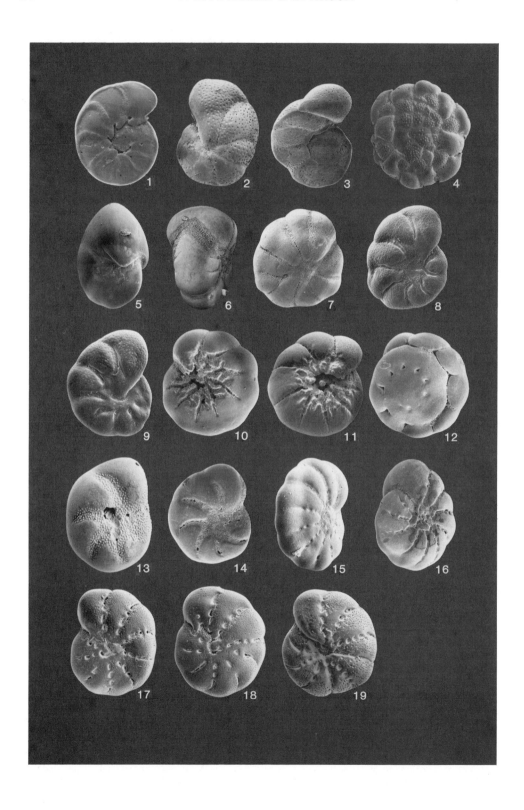

Vibrocore 57/-09/46

Vibrocore 57/-09/46 contains, as discussed earlier, a far more expanded sediment sequence which should, according to the radiocarbon ages, record the equivalent of Zones 5–7 from vibrocore 57/-09/89. However, only two foraminifera zones are recognized from this core (Figs 10 & 11). A summary of the foraminiferal assemblages and palaeoenvironmental interpretations for this core is provided in Table 3. Zone 1 of this core is equivalent to Zone 5 whereas Zone 2 is equivalent to Zone 7 of vibrocore 57/-09/89. The bioturbated and mixed assemblages of Zone 6 from vibrocore 57/-09/89 have no equivalent zone in this core and this supports the radiocarbon chronology which suggests that the Younger Dryas–Holocene transition is intact.

Zone 1 (579–91 cm). The dominant species are *C. reniforme* and *E. excavatum* forma *clavata*, while common accessory species include *C.* gr. *lobatulus*, *E. albiumbilicatum* and *N. labradoricum*. However, all these taxa exhibit a certain degree of variability throught the zone, most notably *N. labradoricum* which begins to increase from *c.* 500 cm, reaches its maximum values between 350 and 170 cm, and then declines upwards across the zone 1/2 boundary. Faunal diversity through this zone is also variable, with the highest values at the bottom of the zone, decreasing until about 350–300 cm, stabilizing and then increasing rapidly across the Zone 1/2 boundary. Faunal dominance follows a vaguely similar pattern, except that values decline from >40% to *c.* 20% across the Zone 1/2 boundary. Epifaunal/infaunal ratios follow a similar pattern to faunal diversity through the zone. Planktonic/benthic ratios remain fairly constant throughout, with a zonal mean of slightly less than 0.1. Similarly, benthic sums exhibit the same pattern, with a zonal average of about 200 specimens per gram.

Zone 2 (91–0 cm). *S. wrightii* is the dominant species, with common accessory species including *C.* gr. *lobatulus*, *C. laevigata*, *R. praegeri*, *T. angulosa* and *S. fusiformis*. Faunal diversity is high throughout, whereas the faunal dominance shows a marked increase upwards through the zone, increasing from 20% at the zonal boundary to over 40% at the top of the core. Epifaunal/infaunal ratios exhibit increasing values upwards through the zone, as do the planktonic/benthic ratios, although the latter show a reversal centred at about 40 cm. Benthic sums increase steadily upwards through the zone, reaching a maximum of nearly 3000 specimens per gram at 7.5 cm.

Stable isotope stratigraphy

Stable isotope analysis of two benthic foraminiferal species were performed from core 57/-09/46 (Figs 12 & 13) and on one species from core 57/-09/89 (Fig. 14). *Cibicides lobatulus* is an epifaunal species known to live an attached mode of life on hard substrates; the genus is probably dominated by passive suspension feeders. *Cassidulina reniforme* is an infaunal species, free-living within muds and sands; it is probably a detritivore feeder (Murray 1991). The modern dirtribution patterns of these two species are fairly well known: *C. lobatulus* is eurythermal whereas *C. reniforme* is confined to higher latitudes and/or deeper waters. Thus for vibrocore 57/-09/46 where both species have been measured in parallel, *C. lobatulus* is present throughout the core, while *C. reniforme* shows a marked decline from about 10 200 years BP and is greatly reduced through the warm Holocene interval.

Oxygen isotope profiles for both species through the Younger Dryas sequence exhibit relatively stable values, close to 3.5‰ for *C. reniforme* and nearer 2.5‰ for *C. lobatulus* (Fig. 10). This difference, approximately 0.93‰, is considered a more reliable estimate than the 0.85‰ offset between these two species reported by Hald & Vorren (1987), simply because we have achieved greater parallel sample comparison ($n = 22$). Hald & Vorren (1987) report the oxygen isotopic disequilibrium between *C. lobatulus* and bottom water to be -0.8 ± 0.2‰. This implies that *C. reniforme* calcifies close to

---

Fig. 7. **1**, *Hyalinea balthica* (Schroeter) side view ×39. **2, 3**, *Cibicides lobatulus* (Walker and Jacob). **2**, Ventral view ×20. **3**, Dorsal view ×34. **4**, *Planobulina distoma* Terquem ventral view ×39. **5**, *Nonion labradoricum* (Dawson) oblique side view ×25. **6, 7**, *Nonion orbiculare* (Brady). **6**, Oblique peripheral view ×34. **7**, Side view ×34. **8, 9**, *Astrononion (Laminonion) gallowayi* Loeblich and Tappan. **8**, Side view ×41. **9**, Side view ×64. **10–12**, *Ammonia batavus* (Hofker). **10**, Ventral view ×34. **11**, Ventral view ×37. **12**, Dorsal view ×34. **13, 14**, *Elphidium albiumbilicatum* (Weiss). **13**, Side view ×73. **14**, Side view ×73. **14**, Side view ×50. **15, 16**, *Elphidium asklundi* Brotzen. **15**, Oblique side view ×26. **16**, Oblique side view ×22. **17–19**, *Elphidium excavation* (Terquem) forma *clavata* Cushman. **17**, Side view ×41. **18**, Side view ×47. **19**, Side view ×39.

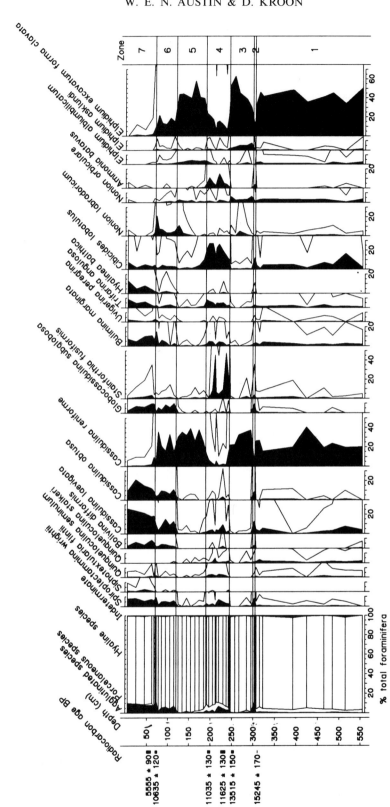

Fig. 8. Summary benthic foraminiferal diagram, core 57/-09/89. (×10 exaggeration indicated)

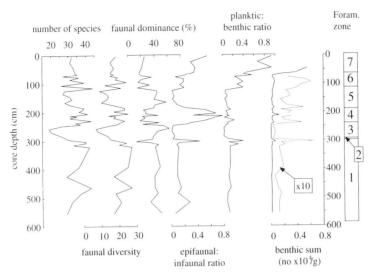

Fig. 9. Summary of faunal parameters, core 57/-09/89.

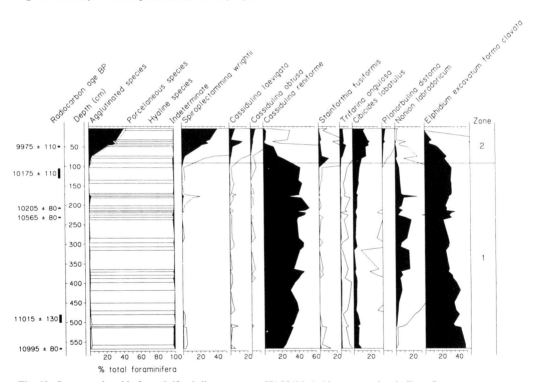

Fig. 10. Summary benthic foraminiferal diagram, core 57/-09/46. (×10 exaggeration indicated)

equilibrium with the ambient bottom water, possibly offset by +0.13 ± 0.2‰ according to our data.

Carbon isotope profiles for both these species are typically less variable than the corresponding $\delta^{18}O$ profiles from core 57/-09/46 (Fig. 15) Through the Younger Dryas interval, however, the plots show that both species exhibit a step-like change in their $\delta^{13}C$ at a core depth of about 350 cm, corresponding to 10 700 years BP.

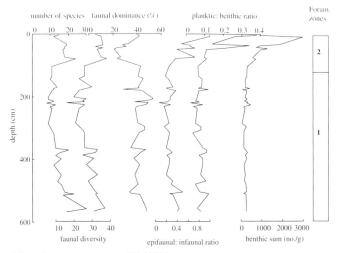

Fig. 11. Summary of faunal parameters, core 57/-09/46.

Cibicides lobatulus δ^{13}C values become slightly more negative, from an average 1.2‰ below 350 cm, to an average 1.0‰ just above. *Cassidulina reniforme* δ^{13}C values exhibit a corresponding change at the same core depth, but towards more positive values from an average −1.2‰ below 350 cm to −0.93‰ above. There is a very slight, but significant, progression in both species towards more positive δ^{13}C through the latter part of the Younger Dryas, whereas *C. lobatulus* exhibits markedly more positive δ^{13}C values through much of the

Holocene. The mean *C. lobatulus* δ^{13}C values are about 1.2‰, whereas the mean *C. reniforme* δ^{13}C values are about −1.0‰ (Fig. 15).

Discussion

Deglaciation and eustatic sea level

The evidence for grounded ice on the middle shelf to the west of the Outer Hebrides has been discussed earlier. A number of cores from this shelf contain diamicts which are thought to be associated with deposition from this ice sheet (W. E. N. Austin 1991): VE 57/-09/21, VE 57/-09/89 and VE 57/-09/60 (Fig. 1). Changes within a glacial marine depositional context as a response to local deglaciation are presented for vibrocore 57/-09/89 and the subsequent interaction of local isostacy and global eustacy discussed.

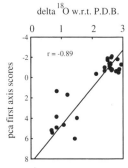

Fig. 12. δ^{18}O, first axis PCA scores and ^{14}C ages, core 57/-09/46. Closed squares, *C. lobatulus*; closed diamonds, *C. reniforme*. Note typical standard deviations of δ^{18}O = ±0.11‰.

Fig. 13. Covariance plot of first PCA scores vs. δ^{18}O of *C. lobatulus*, core 57/-09/46. Linear regression plotted as solid line.

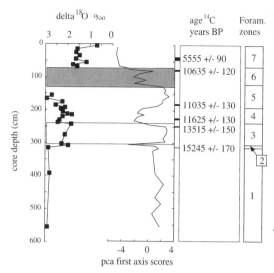

Fig. 14. $\delta^{18}O$, first axis PCA scores and ^{14}C ages, core 57/-09/89. Upper (dark) shaded area represents core depth influenced by bioturbation (Austin 1994). Lower (light) shaded area represents core depth influenced by deglacial meltwater. Note typical standard deviations of $\delta^{18}O = \pm 0.11‰$.

Critical to this discussion is the timing of deglaciation in NW Scotland in relation to global eustatic sea-level change. Peacock & Harkness (1990) provide an invaluable review of the radiocarbon ages throughout this period. In this respect it should be noted that it is the history of Laurentide ice sheet decay that largely

determines global eustatic sea levels during the Quaternary period. Bowen (1991) states that the British and North American ice sheets are likely to have been in phase for much of the Quaternary. However, during the critical late glacial period these ice sheets were out of phase and the British Devensian (Weichselian) ice sheets led the global eustatic sea-level cycle during their decay. Boulton (1990) has emphasized the phase relationship of ice sheet decay and its implications to regional sea-level history and glacial marine facies architecture.

Glacial marine sediments and benthic foraminiferal assemblages

Vibrocore 57/-09/89 is located on the eastern limits of the morainal bank complex (Fig. 1) and provides an opportunity to examine the lithological and faunal response associated with the early deglaciation of the Hebridean Shelf. Zone 1 at the base of the core is interpreted as a subglacial deposit (Peacock *et al.* 1992) which accumulated during or near to the time of maximum extent of the Hebridean ice sheet, which is thought to have been located slightly further west. However, it is equally possible that Zone 1 sediments represent proximal glacial marine deposition and that these deposits were accumulating before 15.2 ka BP. Neither the faunal assemblages nor the sediments themselves allow us to distinguish the precise depositional origin of Zone 1. This is a

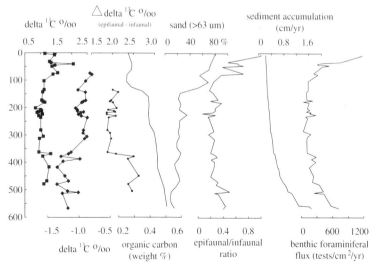

Fig. 15. Epifaunal–infaunal $\delta^{13}C$ differences, core 57/-09/46, plotted with other sedimentological and faunal parameters. Closed squares, *C. lobatulus*; closed diamonds, *C. reniforme*.

common problem associated with diamicts which are largely derived from the melting of glacier ice rich in marine debris entrained during movement over marine deposits (see discussion in Hald & Vorren 1987; Austin & McCarroll 1992).

Related to this question is the observation that planktonic/benthic ratios are higher in Zone 1 than Zones 3/4/5 (Fig. 9). It is a matter of observation that planktonic foraminifera are not abundant in surface sediments from the UK continental shelf and planktonic/benthic ratios exhibit well-defined gradients declining inshore from the shelf break (Murray 1991). How then does Zone 1 record higher planktonic/benthic ratios than the subsequent intervals; given that by the end of Zone 5 (c. 10.8 ka BP) there has been a rise in eustatic sea level of nearly 40 m (Fairbanks 1989)? One possibility is that glacial isostatic loading during the glacial maximum generated relatively deeper water over the shelf at this time. Such mechanisms, which produce highly unstable marine ice margins, have been argued for the deglaciation of the Irish Sea Basin (Eyles & McCabe 1989). However, it is unlikely that the Outer Hebrides ice sheet, here at its western extremity, would have generated sufficient isostatic loading of the crust. Sediment reworking is a more probable explanation, consistent with the proximal glacial marine interpretation of this zone. Furthermore, given that the highest planktonic/benthic ratios of both cores coincide with temperate water

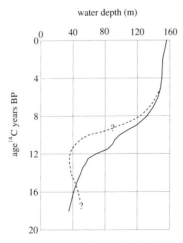

Fig. 16. Relative and global sea levels. Solid line, present-day water depth (156 m) minus eustatic sea level (data from Fairbanks 1989). Broken line, relative sea-level changes based on tentative water depth reconstructions.

benthic foraminiferal assemblages, it is interesting to note their greater abundance in Zone 1 than Zones 3 or 5. The latter further supports the hypothesis that Zone 1 represents proximal glacial marine deposits, containing both *in situ* proximal glacial marine assemblages and reworked temperate assemblages derived from shelf sediments originally deposited during a pre-glacial maximum highstand. Zone 2 is problematic, as the thin band of well-sorted sands containing mixed warm and cold assemblages, is very difficult to interpret.

Deglaciation: a regional response to glacier decay?

Marine records have largely been concerned with the timing and movements of the North Atlantic oceanic fronts, particularly the Arctic Front (sometimes incorrectly termed Polar Front), as these are readily recognized in the stratigraphic record (e.g. CLIMAP 1976; 1981). Determining the extent and timing of ice sheet decay from the oceanic record can be more difficult, except that deep ocean benthic carbonate records seem to preserve a well-defined glacial/interglacial difference in $\delta^{18}O$ of about 1.25‰ which has been attributed to a global ice volume effect (Duplessy *et al.* 1970). In the case of the last deglaciation the ice volume effect accounts for about 1.1‰ (Labeyrie *et al.* 1987; Shackleton 1987). Given that the surface ocean exhibits greater variability in salinity and temperature, the open ocean planktonic record can be difficult to interpret in terms of providing specific information regarding the history of melting of any given ice sheet. However, nearer to the source of glacial meltwater release it becomes possible to detect the timing and extent of ice sheet decay (Lloyd *et al.* this volume; Hald *et al.* this volume).

The transition to Zone 3 at or very soon after 15 245 ± 170 years BP, represents a critical period in terms of the timing of the deglaciation of the St Kilda Basin. The fine-grained sediments, high organic carbon contents, shift to more negative $\delta^{18}O$ values and high arctic, low diversity/high dominance foraminiferal assemblages (Fig. 2, 6, 7 and 12) all point to a period of glacier retreat, meltwater influence and high sediment flux. This cold, low salinity period appears to have persisted until at least 13 515 ± 150 years BP, after which time there is a marked climate warming. It would appear, therefore, that the major deglaciation of this part of the continental shelf of NW Scotland began some time around 15.2 ka BP and was over by 13.5 ka BP, or soon afterwards.

The sediments and foraminiferal assemblages at this time indicate a strong regional response to ice sheet decay and retreat in a shallow marine setting. The sediments become very fine grained and have a much reduced ice-rafted debris content, suggesting increasingly distal glacial marine deposition after 15.2 ka BP. High bulk sediment organic carbon contents imply rapid burial and preservation, as do the very low epifaunal/infaunal ratios, low planktonic/benthic ratios and low foraminiferal concentrations (Fig.7). Positive PCA first axis scores, which coincide with well developed arctic foraminiferal assemblages dominated by *E. excavatum* forma *clavata* and *C. reniforme*, indicate cold summer bottom waters, probably close to 0°C (Hald *et al.* 1994). These cold waters coincide with negative *C. lobatulus* δ^{18}O values throughout the zone (Fig. 14), further supporting evidence for low salinity, cold waters derived from glacier melt persisting on the shelf until after 13.5 ka BP. Indeed, perhaps the most surprising feature of the record is that a well-defined deglacial signal seems to have persisted for nearly 2000 years. These interpretations are consistent with those of Peacock *et al.* (1992).

Initial warming and climate instability

The first indications of the late glacial climatic warming are difficult to define in the cores examined, but must post-date 13.5 ka and pre-date 11.6 ka BP. However, new dating evidence from the slope region immediately west of the Hebridean Shelf (author's unpublished data) suggests that significant surface ocean warming [planktonic foraminiferal reconstructed summer sea surface temperatures (SST) > 11°C] had already been established by 13 020 ± 115 years BP (AMS dated monospecific *Globigerina bulloides*). Other North Atlantic records, for example nearby core V23-81 (54°15' N, 16°50' W, 2393 m) (Broecker *et al.* 1988, Jansen & Veum 1990), exhibit full warm conditions by about 12.9 ka BP. Another nearby core NA87-22 (55°30' N, 14°42' W, 2161 m) (Duplessy *et al.* 1992; this volume) records a very similar chronology, with warm (summer SST = 14°C) waters present by 13.0 ka BP. Further south, in core SU 81-18 (37°46' N, 10°11' W, 3135 m) Duplessy *et al.* (1992; this volume) demonstrate a similar chronology, with summer SSTs of >14°C established soon after 13 ka BP. Further offshore, Koç *et al.* (this volume) suggest that the entire surface waters of the North Atlantic between 50° N and 63° N experienced a synchronous initial warming at 13.4 ka BP. These ages, with the exception of the latter, all cluster at

about 13 ka BP and are consistent with those discussed from the Stornoway borehole 78/4 by Graham *et al.* (1990) and elsewhere from Scotland by Peacock & Harkness (1990).

The foraminiferal assemblages of the Hebridean continental shelf provide PCA first axis scores that appear to be very closely matched to known late glacial temperature variations (Fig. 14). During the interstadial period these scores have negative values, clearly distinguishing this warm interval from the positive values of Zones 1, 3 and 5 (well-defined cold intervals). These values do not, however, become as negative as those of the Holocene interval post-dating about 5.5 ka BP. One possibility is that the benthic foraminiferal assemblages (and PCA scores) are influenced by reworking during the lowstand that characterizes the interstadial; certainly there would have been many exposures of muddy diamicts rich in cold water foraminiferal assemblages. Alternatively, it may suggest that interstadial summer bottom water temperatures were lower than those of the late Holocene. There is no faunal evidence for lowered salinities on the shelf at 11.6 ka BP or during the late Holocene, but there is a 1.0‰ difference in the δ^{18}O of *C. lobatulus* between these intervals. If, at 11.6 ka BP, about 0.8‰ of the global ice volume signal was still to be returned to the world's oceans, then it seems likely that interstadial temperatures were perhaps only 1°C or possibly 2°C cooler than the present day summer bottom water values of 9°C. The global ice volume contribution to the δ^{18}O record is calculated on the basis of 0.011‰ per metre change in sea level (Fairbanks & Mathews 1978) and an eustatic sea level at this time of −70/75 m (Fairbanks 1989).

Much discussion has focused on climate instability during the late glacial interstadial (see, for example, Koç *et al.* this volume). The data available here point to a highly dynamic environment from 11.6 to 11.0 ka BP, with significant lithological, faunal and isotopic variability (Figs 2, 8 & 14). The coarse-grained nature of the sediments are reflected by relative abundance peaks in *Ammonia batavus* and *C.* gr. *lobatulus*. Perhaps most striking, however, are the twin peaks of the infaunal dwelling benthic foraminifera *Stainforthia fusiformis* centred on 235–240 and 211–213 cm (Fig. 10), which coincide with slightly finer grained sediments. Andrews *et al.* (1990) report similar abundance peaks of *S. fusiformis* from the SE Baffin Shelf (referred to as *Fursenkoina fusiformis*), which they correlate with disaerobic (lowered oxygen concentration) intervals. One possibility is that the very shallow St Kilda Basin became periodically semi-isolated from the outer shelf, possibly in response to complex glacio-isostatic readjustment of the crust, and that at these times the water column became strongly stratified leading to lowered bottom water oxygen concentrations and higher abundance of *S. fusiformis*. The more positive $\delta^{18}O$ of *C. lobatulus* may result from relatively colder bottom water temperatures due to this seasonal stratification or possibly from higher salinities as suggested by Duplessy *et al.* (1992) for this period. Increased isolation of the basin would also have weakened current activity and resulted in the deposition of the generally finer grained sediments.

Relative sea levels: global eustacy versus glacial isostacy

The shallow shelf seas which can be inferred from the foraminiferal assemblages of Zone 4, with water depths no greater than about 40 m (Peacock *et al.* 1992; Peacock this volume), suggest that the isostatic response (uplift) following the deglaciation of NW Scotland was sufficient to keep pace with eustatic sea level rise (Fairbanks 1989) throughout the late glacial interstadial. With a present day water depth of −156 m OD at the site, an eustatic sea level of about −70/80 m at 11 ka BP, and a palaeo-water depth of perhaps between 30 and 40 m then an isostatic component of about 40–50 m is implied. This inferred sea-level history is portrayed graphically in Fig. 16. These results are consistent with the shorelines predicted from models of glacio-hydro-isostatic rebound (Lambeck 1995).

The evidence from the foraminiferal record for water depths less than about 40 m is not unequivocal, simply because the known depth ranges of most of these taxa are large. However, the fairly high relative abundances of *Ammonia batavus* do support the interpretation of palaeo-water depths of less than 60 m (Murray 1991). The shallow shelf seas that are thought to have persisted throughout this period may also help to explain why the early interstadial record comprises coarse grained and very well sorted sands (Fig. 2) or may even be absent (Fig. 4 possible erosive hiatus at 245 cm core depth). High current velocities and exposure to the lowered wave base would have severely limited sediment accumulation at the site of core 57/-09/89, located at the western margin of the St Kilda Basin. High relative abundances of the attached species *C. gr. lobatulus* further support the notion of enhanced bottom current activity during this interval.

Climate deterioration and the Younger Dryas stadial

Evidence from core 57/-09/89 points to climatic deterioration, although not unidirectional, from 11.6 ka onwards. By 11 ka BP the benthic foraminiferal assemblages are indicative of well-established arctic conditions and suggest summer bottom water temperatures of less than 1–2°C (Hald *et al.* 1994). This reconstruction is tentatively supported by the Barents Sea benthic foraminiferal bottom water temperature transfer function (Poole *et al.* 1994), which generates values of between 1 and 2°C throughout Zone 5 (the early Younger Dryas) of this core. Although this method may not be wholly suitable for reconstructing palaeotemperatures from NW Scotland, given that the calibration data set is based soley on modern surface samples (Hald & Steinsund 1992; Steinsund *et al.* in press), we suggest that conditions prevailing during the Younger Dryas may have analogies with the present day Barents Sea. This transition to arctic conditions is rapid and, allowing for some smoothing of the record by bioturbation processes, was probably accomplished in less than 100 years. Both this core and core 57/-09/46, located more centrally within the St Kilda Basin, provide very similar records of fine-grained sediments with occasional ice-rafted debris dominated by *E. excavatum* forma *clavata* and *C. reniforme*. However, both records show some faunal variability, most notably an increase in relative abundance of *N. labradoricum* to a maximum at about 10.8 ka BP (see Knudsen & Austin this volume).

Stable oxygen isotopes (Figs 12 & 14) show only limited variability during the Younger Dryas, with the $\delta^{18}O$ of *C. lobatulus* close to 2.8‰ throughout. Given that the Younger Dryas–Holocene difference in the $\delta^{18}O$ of *C. lobatulus* on the shelf is about 2.0‰ and that the difference in $\delta^{18}O$ of *N. pachyderma* (sin.) offshore is about the same (Jansen & Veum 1990), then both shelf and offshore records support the reconstructed Younger Dryas–Holocene warming of about 8°C. As modern summer bottom water temperatures on the Hebridean shelf are between 9 and 10°C (Lee & Ramster 1981) and Younger Dryas reconstructions suggest values of 1–2°C, an 8°C warming is reasonable and the 2.0‰ difference implies no significant meltwater influence during the Younger Dryas (see, for example, discussion by Duplessy *et al.* this volume). The global ice volume effect during this very rapid warming interval is not a significant factor in the above calculations; however, Fairbanks (1989) has demonstrated that there is a period of accelerated sea-level rise at about this time.

With regard to the reconstructed Younger Dryas summer bottom water temperatures of 1–2°C, it is interesting to note that immediately offshore of the shelf break, in cores from the Hebridean slope, planktonic foraminiferal reconstructed summer SSTs are about 6°C (author's unpublished data). However, further offshore on the Rockall Plateau, core NA87-22 provides Younger Dryas summer SSTs of about 10°C (see Duplessy et al. 1992, this volume). We interpret the shelf waters of the St Kilda Basin to have been seasonally stratified during the summer months, producing a surface to bottom temperature gradient of up to 4°C. Reconstructed summer bottom water temperature estimates of 1–2°C suggest that the very near-surface waters of the shelf had a summer temperature of up to about 6°C, while winter surface temperatures fell to <2°C. By implication, there was no significant surface water temperature gradient across the shelf break. At the present day, Booth & Ellett (1983) report dense, winter-cooled waters persisting on the Hebridean shelf beneath the summer thermocline; these may well act to reduce on/off shelf exchanges.

When considering the Younger Dryas (11–10 ka BP) $\delta^{18}O$ values of C. lobatulus, we note that they are very similar to the pre-15.2 ka BP values of about 2.8‰. This is surprising when considering that deep sea records such as V23-81 exhibit N. pachyderma (sin.) $\delta^{18}O$ of nearly 1.0‰ between these intervals (Jansen & Veum 1990). Strong covariance between the benthic and planktonic $\delta^{18}O$ signals in V23-81 and the fact that the benthic 'overshoot' during Termination 1A (Duplessy et al. 1981) cannot be explained solely by a temperature effect, suggest (Jansen & Veum 1990) that the planktonic $\delta^{18}O$ shift and 'overshoot' were also the result of deglacial meltwater input to the North Atlantic. As our records, like those of V23-81 and other North Atlantic cores, do not exhibit well-defined meltwater influence until after 15.2 ka BP (see earlier discussion), the pre-15.2 ka BP $\delta^{18}O$ values of C. lobatulus suggest that Younger Dryas Hebridean shelf waters had summer bottom water temperatures about 1–2°C warmer than those of the last glacial maximum, given a global ice volume contribution of 40 m to eustatic sea level (~0.44‰) between these intervals. From our estimates of Younger Dryas summer bottom water temperatures of 1–2°C (see earlier), glacial maximum summer bottom water temperatures must have been close to 0°C. This contrasts with the NA87-22 summer SST record (Duplessy et al. this volume), which exhibits a net 4°C warming from 6°C at 14.5 ka BP to 10°C at 11 ka BP.

Younger Dryas sediment accumulation: the role of basin focusing

If the tests of C. lobatulus are recording $\delta^{13}C$ close to the dissolved inorganic carbon (DIC) of bottom waters, much as the closely related deep-sea genera Cibicidoides and Planulina are thought to do (Duplessy et al. 1970; Shackleton 1974; Belanger et al. 1981; Graham et al. 1981; Vincent et al. 1981), then it would appear that there is a change in the bottom water DIC through the Younger Dryas and a marked change across the Younger Dryas–Holocene boundary. Changes in the global carbon reservoirs during the glacial/interglacial transitions are well known (Shackleton 1986; Shackleton et al. 1983) and are thought to reflect the redistribution of carbon among the active carbon reservoirs, i.e. upper ocean, deep ocean, forests, terrestrial humus, marine humus and $CaCO_3$ in deep sea sediments (Broecker & Peng 1992; Goslar et al. 1995).

However, in view of the infaunal life habitat of C. reniforme we believe that the considerably depleted $\delta^{13}C$ values are a record of sediment pore water geochemistry rather than overlying bottom water chemistry. The $\delta^{13}C$ offset between these two species ranges between 1.85 and 2.62‰, with an average 2.08‰. These values are in general agreement with those of Hald & Vorren (1987); the average difference quoted by the latter was 2.3‰. Although typical pore water $\delta^{13}C$ profiles do exhibit a trend towards more negative values with increasing depth below the sediment/water interface (McCorkle et al. 1990), the average depth at which this species lives within the sediment is unknown.

By combining the $\delta^{13}C$ profiles of C. lobatulus and C. reniforme as a record of the epifaunal–infaunal difference (Fig. 13), we illustrate the pronounced change at 350 cm in core 57/-09/46, which is dated to 10 700 years BP. The interpretation of this record is difficult, as none of the physical or chemical parameters determined from this core exhibits a similar change at the same core depth. As discussed earlier, there are well-defined, progressive changes through this core interval in sediment grain size distribution, organic carbon, total nitrogen and sediment accumulation rates. However, flux estimates, particularly for organic carbon and benthic foraminifera, do illustrate elevated values below 350 cm. The most probable explanation for this 'event' is a combination of factors including changing sediment grain size (hence sediment porosity), particulate organic carbon flux, and sediment accumulation rate.

The downcore organic carbon content may reflect its preservation as a consequence of sediment accumulation changes (Müller & Suess 1979; Lee 1994), rather than its rain rate to the sediment. At sediment accumulation rates approaching 1 cm year^{-1} the burial efficiency of the total carbon flux preserved in the sediments approaches values of 90% or more (Henrichs & Reeburgh 1987). The increased clay content of the core is also closely correlated with a higher carbon flux, particularly below 500 cm. Keil *et al.* (1994) have suggested that carbon adsorbed onto clay mineral surfaces may be less prone to bacterial degradation and in this way can be preserved in marine sediments. The role of sediment porosity may also influence the record; note the excellent negative correlation between OC and percentage sand (Fig. 3), so that the OC of coarser sediments is more readily oxidized. The benthic foraminiferal flux may therefore be a better measure of the nutrient flux to the sediment, as the latter should not be influenced by preservational factors to the same extent as OC.

It is noteworthy that benthic foraminiferal flux to the sediment is indeed higher below about 350 cm in core 57/-09/46 (Fig. 3), suggesting that there may have been enhanced particulate OC contribution to the sediment through the early Younger Dryas. We suggest that this enhanced organic carbon flux resulted in the depletion of $\delta^{13}C$ of pore water DIC. It appears that the infaunal species *C. reniforme* was greatly influenced by this change in pore water DIC and that it does not faithfully record the chemistry of the overlying bottom waters (see earlier results). In this respect, some care should be exercised when interpreting the *C. lobatulus* $\delta^{13}C$ record: the change to slightly more negative values above 350 cm corresponds to a gradual transition to coarser, more porous(?) sediments and it is possible that this change facilitates some enhancement of pore water/bottom water exchange.

High rates of sediment accumulation during the Younger Dryas are consistent with sediment focusing into the central depression of the St Kilda Basin. Why rates of sediment accumulation changed so rapidly during this interval are not clear. One possible explanation is that the source sediments available from the surrounding shelf were rapidly remobilized during the early stages of this cold phase. This might explain why the early Younger Dryas sediments contain a relatively high clay and silt content, reflecting the most readily transportable grain size components. This size fraction would also have been rich in organic material, much of it derived from the erosion of terrestrial deposits containing carbon with a highly depleted $\delta^{13}C$ signature. As eustatic sea level continued to rise throughout the Younger Dryas, and the depth of the wave base rose with it, then progressively less winnowing of the surrounding shelf sediments would have led to lower sediment accumulation rates.

Younger Dryas climate instability: an oscillating North Atlantic Arctic Front?

There is some evidence in these records for climate instability before the main climatic amelioration which defines the early Holocene warming in this region. This precursor event is dated between 10 205 and 10 175 years BP in vibrocore 57/-09/46. A significant abundance peak of *Spiroplectammina wrightii* coincides with a small but significant shift to more negative $\delta^{18}O$ values in both *C. lobatulus* and *C. reniforme*. Does this imply a 'false-start' to climate amelioration, suggesting that the system was highly dynamic, or does it reflect the proximity and variability in southern extent of the North Atlantic Arctic Front?

As the North Atlantic Arctic Front retreated northwards at the end of the Younger Dryas, then its greater proximity to the site would have led to a stronger climate signal associated with the very steep temperature gradients found across it (Bard *et al.* 1987). Of course, the best example of this phenomenon is seen during the final northward retreat of the front at about 10.1 ka BP, when the full climatic gradient passed northwards very rapidly. If the Younger Dryas Arctic Front was characterized by variability in its southern extent, reaching its maximum at about 40° N (CLIMAP 1976; 1981), then it is possible that this precursor event represents one of many such oscillations.

On first inspection, it appears that our data do not support the conclusions reached by Koç *et al.* (1993), whereby they reconstruct a seasonally sea ice free corridor extending along western Norway from 13.4 ka BP onwards, based on results from core HM79-6/4 (62°58.0′ N, 02°42.0′ E). However, as we now demonstrate, there were short-lived intervals during the Younger Dryas when weak incursions of North Atlantic surface waters extended northwards past western Britain and these may be responsible for the conditions reported by Koç *et al.* (1993).

Early Holocene warming

The transition from Younger Dryas to Holocene is clearly defined by the foraminiferal assemblages of core 57/-09/46 (Fig. 10). The faunal changes across this boundary are consistent with a significant climatic amelioration, as qualified by examining the first PCA axis scores (Fig. 12). The amplitude of the negative $\delta^{18}O$ shift exhibited by *C. lobatulus* is up to 2.0‰ at its greatest, implying an equivalent temperature increase of nearly 8°C. The faunal indication of warming is dated between 10 175 and 9975 years BP, although the isotopic swing appears to be complete in about half this time. Evidence from the Greenland ice cores suggests that this warming may have been completed in 50 years (Dansgaard *et al.* 1989), or possibly even less (Taylor *et al.* 1993). This implies slightly lower temporal resolution in the Hebridean marine record, although the combined effects of bioturbation and sediment reworking appear to be no more than about 100 years.

The Holocene record itself, as with most of the exposed shelf seas of northern Britain, is poor and generally represented by less than 100 cm of sediment. These sediments are predominantly well-sorted, coarse sands and silts which appear to have been greatly influenced by enhanced current activity during the early Holocene transgression. Core 57/-09/89, for example, appears to contain a major hiatus at the Younger Dryas–Holocene boundary, with nearly 5000 radiocarbon years represented by a core interval of only 10 cm (Fig. 4). Rapidly increasing relative sea levels through the early Holocene, responding to eustatic sea-level rise (Fig. 16), are reflected by the increasing planktonic to benthic ratios in all the cores examined from this region (W. E. N. Austin 1991). Although Fig. 16 suggests that the glacio-isostatic components of crustal readjustment are complete by about 6 ka BP, it is not possible, given the difficulties of reconstructing water depths, to accurately determine when the two curves become coincident.

Conclusions

The late glacial foraminiferal records of the Hebridean Shelf suggest that there are palaeoceanographically valuable inventories of climate change preserved in the sediments of these and similar North Atlantic shelf sites. The records from the St Kilda Basin illustrate the importance of site, not only in the context of obtaining long records of sediment accumulation, but also in selecting sites of rapid, continuous sediment accumulation. Sediment focusing into this shallow, semi-enclosed, mid-shelf basin is the key feature which distinguishes it from other shelf regions.

A number of features which are consistent with the general pattern and timing of North Atlantic palaeoceanographic evolution are also recognized in these shelf records, notably: the timing of earliest significant meltwater influence at 15.2 ka BP; earliest interstadial climate warming after 13.5 ka BP; climate instability during the late glacial interstadial; climate deterioration from 11.6 ka BP; fully developed Younger Dryas stadial by 11 ka BP; climate instability during the Younger Dryas stadial; and very rapid climate warming (*c.* 8°C) between 10.2 and 10 ka BP

During the last deglaciation of the Hebridean shelf we observe several features not generally recognized in the open ocean North Atlantic records. The shallow shelf setting, close proximity to a decaying ice sheet margin and remarkably high sediment accumulation rates provide additional insights into the interaction between climate change, glacial isostacy and global eustacy. However, details of the timing of deglaciation of northern Britain are limited, except that it is possible to state that the last major ice sheets had largely disappeared by *c.* 13 ka BP (Lowe & Walker 1984). Terrestrial records from NW Europe exhibit a broadly consistent pattern of fairly rapid climatic warming at about 13 ka BP (Walker *et al.* 1994).

It is apparent therefore that the NW European ice sheets, and likewise climates, were strongly influenced by changes in North Atlantic surface circulation (Lehman & Keigwin 1992) as were changes in air temperature over the Greenland ice sheet (Dansgaard *et al.* 1989). In turn, these surface ocean circulation changes have been related to the formation of North Atlantic deep water and invoke abrupt reorganization of the system during the late glacial period (Broecker *et al.* 1985; Rind *et al.* 1986; Berger & Vincent 1986). One very interesting feature of the North Atlantic late glacial marine records is the timing of poleward heat flux through enhanced thermohaline circulation as opposed to the first evidence of major deglaciation. As discussed earlier, the melting histories of the Late Weichselian ice sheets were not in phase. The evidence from this study points to the initiation of melting from the NW Scottish ice sheet at about 15.2 ka BP, before significant North Atlantic warming, although the onset of Laurentide ice sheet melting appears to coincide with the onset of warm conditions in the surface waters of the North Atlantic at about 13 ka BP (Broecker *et al.* 1988; Fairbanks 1989).

We suggest that North Atlantic Heinrich Event 1 (Heinrich 1988; Bond *et al.* 1992), although dominated by a North American Laurentide ice sheet source (Andrews *et al.* 1993; 1994), has close parallels in the deglaciation of many relatively unstable ice sheets grounded on the continental shelves of the North Atlantic region. These maritime ice sheets, while lacking the volume of ice (12×10^6 km²) stored in the Laurentide ice sheet, were probably very sensitive to changes in eustatic sea-level rise and their disintegration may have been triggered by the attainment of a critical threshold in relative sea level. Fronval *et al.* (1995) suggest that the Laurentide and Fennoscandian ice sheets may have reacted largely in phase on a millenial time-scale. However, although this may be true of the disintegration of the rather sensitive maritime margins of these ice sheets, it does not apply to the main deglacial episodes.

Dowdeswell *et al.* (1995) have attempted to estimate the duration of the North Atlantic Heinrich events and suggest the most likely interval is between 250 and 1250 years. The duration of the deglacial signal on the Hebridean shelf is from 15.2 to 13.5 ka BP. However, given the regional setting of the Outer Hebrides ice sheet, we believe that the initial break-up of grounded ice in the overdeepened St Kilda Basin must have taken place very rapidly as the ice sheet began to 'float'. Ongoing investigations (author's unpublished data) further west on the Hebridean continental slope will reveal the timing of this break-up event and place the regional deglaciation of NW Scotland in a wider North Atlantic context.

Additionally, few records have resolved the detail of climate variability during the Younger Dryas, particularly from the marine environment. However, records from the Greenland ice cores provide new insights into the frequency of variability associated with abrupt climate change. Taylor *et al.* (1993) demonstratate the nature of rapid climate variation in the GISP2 ice core during the last deglaciation by reporting electrical conductivity measurements (ECM). The ECM signals are thought to reflect changes in the net balance of acids and bases in the ice, as a response to changes in the quantity of airborn dust, in turn reflecting climate or weather patterns. These high frequency climate features, although not fully understood, serve to illustrate the nature of rapid climate change. This so-called 'flickering switch' (Taylor *et al.* 1993) between glacial and near-interglacial conditions, sometimes at periods of

less than a decade, is thought to be related to a re-ordering of atmospheric circulation. Atmospheric circulation is strongly influenced by temperature gradients at mid- to high latitudes and an oscillating North Atlantic Arctic Front, as we have demonstrated, certainly has an important role in determining the spatial and temporal location of these steep temperature gradients.

Without a latitudinal transect of equally high-resolution marine records, it is not possible to determine whether this precursor warming event described from 10.2 ka BP is one of many roughly equal climatic oscillations, as suggested by the variability of the Younger Dryas δ^{18}O signal from the GRIP ice core (S. Johnsen, pers. comm. 1994), or whether it represents a significant Younger Dryas climate feature. Given the high frequency of variability of late glacial climates suggested by the ECM record of the GISP2 ice core (Taylor *et al.* 1993), it seems likely that the interpretation of very high resolution marine records will need to account for hitherto unresolved oscillations in the latitudinal extent of the North Atlantic Arctic Front. The North Atlantic continental margins promise to play an important part in providing the high temporal resolution required to resolve these features.

We conclude that the high sediment accumulation rates within the semi-enclosed St Kilda Basin preserve an excellent late glacial record with a very high temporal resolution. Such records appear to be strongly influenced by regional climates, but at the same time preserve a record of North Atlantic surface ocean changes. The strongest climate signals are derived from the rapid changes in sea surface conditions arising from the repeated passage of the North Atlantic Arctic Front adjacent to northwest Scotland. Benthic foraminifera and stable isotope analyses provide excellent tracers of these palaeoceanographic events. We believe that these results illustrate the potential which future studies of shelf-dwelling benthic foraminifera may have in developing a combined quantitative palaeotemperature and δ^{18}O approach to water mass reconstruction.

This manuscript was greatly improved by the constructive reviews of K. L. Knudsen, M. Hald and D. Peacock. We thank C. Taylor for her invaluable technical assistance. W.E.N.A. thanks J. Scourse and C. Evans for their support during the initial stages of this research and acknowledges receipt of a BP/RSE research fellowship. The BGS kindly allowed us access to core and seismic data. This work was funded through NERC's Special Topic: NEAPACC (GST/02/723 and GST/02/1174).

References

ANDREWS, J. T., ERLENKEUSSER, H., TEDESCO, K., AKSU, A. & JULL, A. J. T. 1994. Late Quaternary (Stage 2 and 3) meltwater and Heinrich Events, northwest Labrador Sea. *Quaternary Research*, **41**, 26–34.

——, EVANS, L. W., WILLIAMS, K. M., BRIGGS, W. M., ERLENKEUSER, H., HARDY, I. & JULL, A. J. T. 1990. Cryosphere/ocean interactions at the margin of the Laurentide Ice Sheet during the Younger Dryas Chron: S.E. Baffin Shelf, Northwest Territories. *Palaeoceanography*, **5**, 921–935.

——, TEDESCO, K. & JENNINGS, A. E. 1993. Heinrich events: chronology and processes, east-central Laurentide Ice Sheet and northwest Labrador Sea. *In*: PELTIER, W. R. (ed.) *Ice in the Climate System*. Springer, Berlin, 167–186.

AUSTIN, R. M. 1991. Modelling Holocene tides on the NW European continental shelf. *Terra Nova*, **3**, 276–288.

AUSTIN, W. E. N. 1991. *Late Quaternary benthonic foraminiferal stratigraphy of the western UK continental shelf*. PhD Thesis, University of Wales.

——1994. Disturbed foraminiferal stratigraphies – a cautionary "tail". *Cushman Foundation Special Publication*, **32**, 155–159.

—— & MCCARROLL, D. 1992. Foraminifera from the Irish Sea glacigenic deposits at Aberdaron, western Lleyn, North Wales: palaeoenvironmental implications. *Journal of Quaternary Science*, 7, 311–317.

——, BARD, E., HUNT, J. B., KROON, D. & PEACOCK, J. D. 1995. The ^{14}C age of the Icelandic Vedde Ash: implications for Younger Dryas marine reservoir age corrections. *Radiocarbon*.

BARD, E., ARNOLD, M. & 7 others 1994. The North Atlantic atmosphere–sea surface ^{14}C gradient during the Younger Dryas climatic event. *Earth and Planetary Science Letters*, **126**, 275–287.

——, ——, MAURICE, P., DUPRAT, J., MOYES, J. & DUPLESSY, J. C. 1987. Retreat velocity of the North Atlantic polar front during the last deglaciation determined by ^{14}C accelerator mass spectrometry. *Nature*, **328**, 791–794.

BELANGER, P. E., CURRY, W. B. & MATTHEWS, R. K. 1981. A core top evaluation of the paleoceanographic utility of benthic foraminiferal isotopic ratios. *Palaeogeography, Palaeoclimatology and Palaeoecology*, **33**, 205–220.

BERGER, W. H. & VINCENT, E. 1986. Deep-sea carbonates: reading the carbon isotope signal. *Geologisches Rundschan*, **75**, 249–269.

BIRKS, H. J. B. & GORDON, A. D. 1985. *Numerical Methods in Quaternary Pollen Analysis*. Academic, London.

BOND, G. & 13 others 1992. Evidence for massive discharges of icebergs into the glacial Northern Atlantic. *Nature*, **360**, 245–249.

——, BROECKER, W. S., JOHNSEN, S., MCMANUS, J., LABEYRIE, L., JOUZEL, J. & BONANI, G. 1993. Correlations between climate records from North Atlantic sediments and Greenland ice. *Nature*, **365**, 143–147.

BOOTH, D. A. & ELLETT, D. J. 1983. The Scottish continental slope current. *Continental Shelf Research*, **2**, 127–146.

BOULTON, G. S. 1990. Sedimentary and sea level changes during glacial cycles and their control on glacimarine facies architecture. *In*: DOWDESWELL, J. A. & SCOURSE, J. D. (eds) *Glacimarine Environments: Processes and Sediments*. Geological Society, London, Special Publications, **53**, 15–52.

BOWEN, D. Q. 1991. Time and space in the glacial sediment system of the British Isles. *In*: EHLERS, J., GIBBARD, P. L. & ROSE, J. (eds) *Glacial Deposits in Great Britain and Ireland*. Balkema, Rotterdam, 3–11.

BROECKER, W. S. & PENG, T. H. 1992. *Tracers in the Sea*. Eldigio Press, Palisades.

——, ANDREE, M., WOLFI, W., OESCHGER, H., BONANI, G., KENNETT, J. & PETEET, D. 1988. The chronology of the last deglaciation: implications to the cause of the Younger Dryas event. *Paleoceanography*, **3**, 1–19.

——, PETEET, D. M. & RIND, D. 1985. Does the ocean–atmosphere system have more than one stable mode of operation? *Nature*, **315**, 21–25.

CARTWRIGHT, D. E., HUTHNANCE, J. M., SPENCER, R. & VASSIE, J. M. 1980. On the St Kilda shelf tidal regime. *Deep Sea Research*, **27**, 61–70.

CLIMAP PROJECT MEMBERS 1976. The surface of Ice-Age Earth. *Science*, **191**, 1131–1137.

——1981. Seasonal reconstructions of the earth's surface at the Last Glacial Maximum. *Geological Society of America: Map and Chart Series*, **MC-36**, 1–18.

DANSGAARD, W., WHITE, J. W. C. & JOHNSEN, S. J. 1989. The abrupt termination of the Younger Dryas climate event. *Nature*, **339**, 532–534.

DICKSON, R. R., GARBUTT, P. A. & PILLAI, V. N. 1980. Satellite evidence of enhanced upwelling along the European continental slope. *Journal of Physical Oceanography*, **10**, 813–819.

DIETRICH, G. 1969. *Atlas of the Hydrography of the Northern North Atlantic Ocean*. International Council for the Exploration of the Sea, Service Hydrographique, Charlottenlund.

DOWDESWELL, J. A., MASLIN, M. A., ANDREWS, J. T. & MCCAVE, I. N. 1995. Iceberg production, debris rafting, and the extent and thickness of Heinrich layers (H-1, H-2) in North Atlantic sediments. *Geology*, **23**, 301–304.

DUPLESSY, J. C., DELIBRIAS, G., TURON, J. L., PUJOL, C. & DUPRAT, J. 1981. *Palaeogeography, Palaeoclimatology and Palaeoecology*, **35**, 121–144.

——, LALOU, C. & VINOT, A. C. 1970. Differential isotopic fractionation in benthic foraminifera and paleotemperature reassessed. *Science*, **168**, 250–251.

——, LABEYRIE, L., ARNOLD, M., PATERNE, M., DUPRAT, J. & VAN WEERING, T. C. E. 1992. Changes in surface salinity of the North Atlantic Ocean during the last deglaciation. *Nature*, **358**, 485–488.

——, —— & PATERNE, M. North Atlantic sea surface conditions during the Younger Dryas cold event. *This volume*.

ELLETT, D. J., EDWARDS, A. & BOWERS, R. 1986. The hydrography of the Rockall Channel – an overview. *Proceedings of the Royal Society of Edinburgh*, **88B**, 61–81.

EYLES, N. & MCCABE, A. M. 1989. The Late Devensian (<22,000 BP) Irish Sea Basin: the sedimentary record of a collapsed ice sheet margin. *Quaternary Science Reviews*, **8**, 307–351.

FAIRBANKS, R. G. 1989. A 17,000-year glacio-eustatic sea level record: influence of glacial melt rates on the Younger Dryas event and deep-ocean circulation. *Nature*, **342**, 637–642.

—— & MATHEWS, R. K. 1978. *Quaternary Research*, **10**, 181–196.

FEYLING-HANSSEN, R. W. 1958. Mikropaleontologiens teknikk. *Norges Geologiske Undersøkelse*, **203**, 35–48.

——1964. Foraminifera in Late Quaternary deposits from the Oslofjord area. *Norges Geologiske Undersøkelse*, **225**.

——, JØRGENSEN, J. A., KNUDSEN, K. L. & ANDERSEN, A. L. L. 1971. Late Quaternary foraminifera from Vendsyssel, Denmark and Sandnes, Norway. *Bulletin of the Geological Society of Denmark*, **21**, 67–317.

FRONVAL, T., JANSEN, E., BLOEMENDAL, J. & JOHNSEN, S. 1995. Oceanic evidence for coherent fluctuations in Fennoscandian and Laurentide ice sheets on millenium timescales. *Nature*, **374**, 443–446.

GORDON, A. D. & BIRKS, H. J. B. 1972. Numerical methods in Quaternary palaeoecology. I. Zonation of pollen diagrams. *New Phytologist*, **71**, 961–979.

GRAHAM, D. K., HARLAND, R., GREGORY, D. M., LONG, D. & MORTON, C. 1990. The biostratigraphy and chronostratigraphy of BGS Borehole 78/4, North Minch. *Scottish Journal of Geology*, **26**, 65–75.

GRAHAM, D. W., CORLISS, B. H., BENDER, M. L. & KEIGWIN, L. D. 1981. Carbon and oxygen isotopic disequilibria of recent deep-sea benthic foraminifera. *Marine Micropaleontology*, **6**, 483–497.

GRIMALDI, F. S., SHAPIRO, L. & SCHNEPFE, M. 1966. Determination of carbon dioxide in limestone and dolomite by acid-base titration. *US Geological Survey, Prof. Paper*, **550**, 186–188.

HALD, M. & STEINSUND, P. I. 1992. Distribution of surface sediment benthic foraminifera in the southwestern Barents Sea. *Journal of Foraminiferal Research*, **22**, 347–362.

—— & VORREN, T. O. 1987. Stable isotope stratigraphy and paleoceanography during the last deglaciation on the continental shelf off Troms, northern Norway. *Paleoceanography*, **2**, 583–599.

——, STEINSUND, P. I, DOKKEN, T., KORSUN, S., POLYAK, L. & ASPELI, R. 1994. Recent and Late Quaternary Distribution of Elphidium excavatum f. clavatum in Arctic Seas. *Cushman Foundation Special Publication*, **32**, 141–153.

——, DOKKEN, T. & HAGEN, S. Paleoceanography on the European Arctic margin during the last deglaciation. *This volume*.

HARDING, R. R., MERRIMAN, R. J. & NANCARROW, P. H. A. 1984. *St Kilda: an Illustrated Account of the Geology*. Report of the British Geological Survey, **16**.

HARKNESS, D. D. 1983. The extent of natural ^{14}C deficiency in the coastal environment of the United Kingdom. *Proceedings of the First International Symposium on C-14 and Archaeology, PACT*, **8**, 351–364.

HARVEY, J. G. 1982. θ-S relationships and water masses in the eastern North Atlantic. *Deep-Sea Research*, **29**, 1021–1033.

HEINRICH, H. 1988. Origin and consequences of cyclic ice rafting in the northeast Atlantic Ocean during the past 130,000 years. *Quaternary Research*, **29**, 142–152.

HENRICHS, S. M. & REEBURGH, W. S. 1987. *Journal of Geomicrobiology*, **5**, 191–237.

HILL, A. E. & SIMPSON, J. H. 1988. Low-frequency variability of the Scottish Coastal Current induced by along-shore pressure gradients. *Estuarine, Coastal and Shelf Science*, **27**, 163–180.

HUNT, J. B., FANNIN, N. G. T., HILL, P. G. & PEACOCK, J. D. 1995. The tephrochronology and radiocarbon dating of North Atlantic, Late-Quaternary sediments: an example from the St. Kilda Basin. *In*: SCRUTTON, R. A., STOKER, M. S., SHIMMIELD, G. B. & TUDHOPE, A. W. (eds) *The Tectonics, Sedimentation and Palaeoceanography of the North Atlantic Region*. Geological Society, London, Special Publications, **90**, 227–248.

HUTHNANCE, J. M. 1986. The Rockall slope current and shelf-edge processes. *Proceedings of the Royal Society of Edinburgh*, **88B**, 83–101.

JANSEN, E. & VEUM, T. 1990. Evidence for two-step deglaciation and its impact on North Atlantic deep-water circulation. *Nature*, **343**, 612–616.

KEIL, R. G., MONTLUÇON, D. B., PRAHL, F. G. & HEDGES, J. I. 1994. *Nature*, **370**, 549–552.

KNUDSEN, K. L. & AUSTIN, W. E. N. Lateglacial Foraminifera. *This volume*.

KOÇ, N., JANSEN, E. & HAFLIDASON, H. 1993. Paleoceanographic reconstructions of surface ocean conditions in the Greenland, Icelandic and Norwegian Seas through the last 14 ka based on diatoms. *Quaternary Science Reviews*, **12**, 115–140.

——, ——, HALD, M. & LABEYRIE, L. *This volume*.

KVAMME, T., MANGERUD, J., FURNES, H. & RUDDIMAN, W. F. 1989. Geochemistry of Pleistocene ash zones in cores from the North Atlantic. *Norsk Geologisk Tiddskrift*, **69**, 251–272.

LABEYRIE, L., DUPLESSY, J. C. & BLANC, P. L. 1987. Variation in deep water temperatures for the last 125,000 years. *Nature*, **327**, 477–482.

LAMBECK, K. 1995. Late Devensian and Holocene shorelines of the British Isles and North Sea from models of glacio-hydro-isostatic rebound. *Journal of the Geological Society*, **152**, 437–448.

LEE, C. 1994. Kitty litter for carbon control. *Nature*, **370**, 503–504.

LEE, A. J. & RAMSTER, J. W. (eds) 1981. *Atlas of the Seas around the British Isles*.

LEHMAN, S. J. & KEIGWIN, L. D. 1992. Sudden changes in North Atlantic circulation during the last deglaciation. *Nature*, **356**, 757–762.

LLOYD, J., KROON, D. & LABAN, C. Deglaciation history and paleoceanography of the Spitsbergen margin since the last glacial maximum. *This volume.*

—— & WALKER, M. J. C. 1984. *Reconstructing Quaternary Environments*. Longman, London.

MCCARTNEY, M. S. & TALLEY, L. D. 1982. The subpolar mode water of the North Atlantic Ocean. *Journal of Physical Oceanography*, **12**, 1169–1188.

MCCORKLE, D. C., KEIGWIN, L. D., CORLISS, B. H. & EMERSON, S. R. 1990. The influence of microhabitats on the carbon isotopic composition of deep-sea benthic foraminifera. *Paleoceanography*, **5**, 161–185.

MCMANUS, J. F., BOND, G. C., BROECKER, W. S., JOHNSEN, S., LABEYRIE, L. & HIGGINS, S. 1994. High-resolution climate records from the North Atlantic during the last interglacial. *Nature*, **371**, 326–329.

MURRAY, J. W. 1991. *Ecology and Palaeoecology of Benthic Foraminifera*. Longman, London.

MÜLLER, P. J. & SUESS, E. 1979. Productivity, sedimentation rate, and sedimentary organic matter in the oceans—I. Organic carbon preservation. *Deep Sea Research*, **26**, 1347–1362.

PEACOCK, J. D. 1984. *The Quaternary Geology of the Outer Hebrides*. Reports of the British Geological Survey, **16**(2).

—— Marine Molluscan proxy data applied to Scottish Late-glacial and Flandrian sites: strengths and limitations. *This volume.*

—— & HARKNESS, D. D. 1990. Radiocarbon ages and the full-glacial to Holocene transition in seas adjacent to Scotland and southern Scandinavia: a review. *Transactions of the Royal Society of Edinburgh: Earth Sciences*, **8**, 385–396.

——, AUSTIN, W. E. N., SELBY, I., HARLAND, R., WILKINSON, I. P. & GRAHAM, D. K. 1992. Late Devensian and Holocene palaeoenvironmental changes on the Scottish Continental Shelf west of the Outer Hebrides. *Journal of Quaternary Science*, **7**, 145–161.

POOLE, D. A. R., SÆTTEM, J. & VORREN, T. O. 1994. Foraminiferal stratigraphy, palaeoenvironments and sedimentation of the glacigenic sequence southwest of Bjørnøya. *Boreas*, **23**, 122–138.

RIND, D., PETEET, D., BROECKER, W., MCINTYRE, A. & RUDDIMAN, W. 1986. The impact of cold North Atlantic sea surface temperatures on climate: implications for the Younger Dryas cooling (11–10 k). *Climate Dynamics*, **1**, 3–33.

ROBINSON, S. G. & MCCAVE, I. N. 1994. Orbital forcing of bottom-current enhanced sedimentation on Feni Drift, NE Atlantic, during the mid-Pleistocene. *Paleoceanography*, **9**, 943–972.

SCOTT, D. B. & GREENBERG, D. A. 1983. Relative sea-level rise and tidal development in the Fundy tidal system. *Canadian Journal of Earth Science*, **20**, 1554–1564.

SELBY, I. 1989. *Quaternary Geology of the Hebridean Continental Margin*. PhD Thesis, Nottingham University.

SHACKLETON, N. J. 1974. Attainment of isotopic equilibrium between ocean water and the benthonic foraminifera genus Uvigerina: Isotopic changes in the ocean during the last glacial. *CNRS Colloques Internationaux*, **219**, 203–209.

——1987. Relationship between ice volume and the oxygen isotope record in benthic foraminifera. *Quaternary Science Reviews*, **6**, 183–190.

——, HALL, M. A., LINE, J. & CANG SHUXI. 1983. Carbon isotope data in core V19-30 confirm reduced carbon dioxide concentration in the ice age atmosphere. *Nature*, **306**, 319–322.

STEINSUND, P. I., POLYAK, L., HALD, M., MIKHAILOV, V. & KORSUN, S. Distribution of calcareous benthic foraminifera in recent sediments of the Barents and Kara Seas. *Journal of Foraminiferal Research*, in press.

STOKER, M. S., HITCHEN, K. & GRAHAM, C. C. 1993. *United Kingdom Offshore Regional Report: the Geology of the Hebrides and West Shetland Shelves, and Adjacent Deep Water Areas.* HMSO for the British Geological Survey, London.

SUTHERLAND, D. G. 1984. The submerged landforms of the St Kilda Archipelago, western Scotland. *Marine Geology*, **58**, 435–442.

—— & WALKER, M. J. C. 1984. A Late Devensian ice-free area and possible interglacial site on the Isle of Lewis, Scotland. *Nature*, **309**, 701–703.

——, BALLANTYNE, C. K. & WALKER, M. J. C. 1984. Late Quaternary glaciation and environmental change on St Kilda, Scotland, and their palaeoclimatic significance. *Boreas*, **13**, 261–272.

TAYLOR, K. C., LAMOREY, G. W. & 6 others. 1993. The 'flickering switch' of late Pleistocene climate change. *Nature*, **361**, 432–436.

VINCENT, E., KILLINGLEY, J. S. & BERGER, W. H. 1981. Stable isotope composition of benthic foraminifera from the equatorial Pacific. *Nature*, **289**, 639–643.

VON WEYMARN, J. 1979. A new concept of glaciation in Lewis and Harris. *Proceedings of the Royal Society of Edinburgh*, **77B**, 97–105.

WALKER, M. J. C., BOHNCKE, S. J. P., COOPE, G. R., O'CONNELL, M., USINGER, H. & VER-BRUGGEN, C. 1994. The Devensian/Weichselian Late-glacial in northwest Europe (Ireland, Britain, north Belgium, The Netherlands, northwest Germany). *Journal of Quaternary Science*, **9**, 109–118.

WALTON, W. R. 1964. Recent foraminiferal ecology and paleoecology. *In*: IMBRIE, J. & NEWELL, N. D. (eds) *Approaches to Paleoecology*. Wiley, New York, 151–237.

WEAVER, P. P. E. & SCHULTHEISS, P. J. 1990. Current methods for obtaining, logging and splitting marine sediment cores. *In*: HAILWOOD, E. A. & KIDD, R. B. (eds) *Marine Geological Surveying and Sampling*. Kluwer Academic, Dordrecht, 85–100.

ZAHN, R. 1994. Core correlations. *Nature*, **371**, 289–290.

Marine mollescan proxy data applied to Scottish late glacial and Flandrian sites: strengths and limitations

J. D. PEACOCK

18 McLaren Road, Edinburgh EH9 2BN, UK

Abstract: Knowledge of modern benthonic marine molluscs found in shallow water enables their distribution to be correlated with hydrographic conditions and the derived proxy data applied to late Quaternary assemblages. The application of such data for bottom temperature, minimum sea surface temperature and minimum salinity to four Flandrian and Late glacial sites shows that it is possible to follow changes in these parameters with time, in some cases in considerable detail. The chief limitations are that faunas from some boreholes and sections are sparse and of low diversity and that few taxa are restricted to narrow ranges of temperature and/or salinity. Where fossils of stenothermal and stenohaline species are absent from a profile, faunal analysis inevitably yields a less than precise picture of conditions. It is possible to give only generalized constraints on water depth because this is not a prime factor controlling the distribution of molluscs on the seafloor today. The palaeoenvironmental analysis of the four sites is briefly discussed in a wider context.

Estimates of Quaternary palaeoenvironmental parameters based on planktonic fauna and flora, particularly surface temperature and salinity, are now commonplace in the study of deep sea cores (e.g. Koc Karpuz *et al.* 1990). In the nearshore situation, however, planktonic taxa other than dinoflagellates (Harland *et al.* 1978) are rare or absent. Consideration must therefore be given to the fossil remains of benthonic organisms whose distribution is controlled by the much greater variation in water mass characteristics and food supply in the shallow water environment, and by additional parameters such as competition, predation, substrate lithology and the degree of shelter (Barnes & Hughes 1982).

The value of molluscs and other components of the macrofauna as proxies for temperature and salinity is inevitably related to the confidence that can be placed in the present day distributional limits of the animals and the available hydrographic data at such limits. For instance, care needs to be taken that both the hydrographic and distributional data cover a limited period, as northward and eastward spreading of species, probably as a consequence of rising temperature, has been recorded in the Barents Sea during the the first half of the 20th century (Zenkevitch 1963), and more recently in British seas (McKay 1995; Southward 1995). Another factor that needs to be considered when examining fossil assemblages is whether or not these are the remains of communities similar to those of today. Though this cannot be assumed, it is known that 13–32% of molluscan genera that usually yield fossils are likely to be preserved in modern arctic fjord and continental shelf situations and much useful information is preserved (Aitken 1990).

Water depth as such is not an independent parameter, being consequent on many factors such as the base of the photic zone (below which food supply and cover are limited), the position of the thermocline, and the nature of the sediment and/or bedrock on the seafloor. The last is related in turn to energy levels that vary according to coastal configuration, tidal currents and degree of exposure. A few molluscs, for instance *Littorina* spp., live chiefly in the intertidal zone (but see later). Others, though widely distributed, may be common only within a limited depth range (Peacock 1993). In a fossil assemblage where such species are abundant in both number and diversity, there is thus the possibility of providing very approximate upper and lower limits for the water depth in which the enclosing sediments were laid down.

In the following account, proxy values of temperature, salinity and depth published for northeastern Atlantic molluscs (Peacock 1993) are applied to four Scottish shelf and nearshore sites (Fig. 1) and their strengths and limitations discussed chiefly on a site-specific basis. Values for water depth have been referred to in the text where appropriate, but not plotted in the figures. All marine shell ages quoted are based on an apparent age for seawater of 405 ± 40 years (Harkness 1983). The nomenclature for zoographical subdivisions follows that of Feyling-Hanssen (1955).

Inchinnan

The site (Fig. 1A and 1B) lies on the south side of the River Clyde to the west of Glasgow (Browne *et al.* 1977). Raised marine deposits of

From Andrews, J. T., Austin, W. E. N., Bergsten, H. & Jennings, A. E. (eds), 1996, *Late Quaternary Palaeoceanography of the North Atlantic Margins*, Geological Society Special Publication No. 111, pp. 215–228.

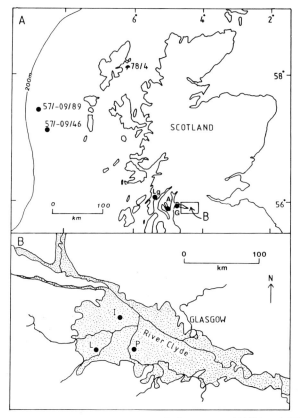

Fig. 1. (A) Location of Sites. Stornoway 78/4 Borehole and vibrocores 57/-09/46 and 57/-09/89. A, Ardyne; G, Garvel Park; and Lg, Lochgilphead. (B) Map of the Glasgow area showing localities discussed in the text. I, Inchinnan; L, Linwood; and P, former claypits near Paisley. The area underlain by late glacial marine deposits is stippled (modified from Browne & McMillan 1989).

late glacial interstadial age (LGI) with surface levels between 10 and 40 m OD are widespread in this area, their thickness varying from 2 to 3 m to over 20 m (Bishop & Coope 1977; Browne & McMillan 1989). The sediments exposed at the site itself may be taken as representative of parts of the area, particularly when combined with descriptions of former clay pits (Crosskey & Robertson 1869), temporary sections (Anderson 1948) and borehole cores (Browne & McMillan 1989).

At Inchinnan (Figs 2 and 3), marine conditions were probably established following deglaciation well before the adjusted radiocarbon date of 12 520 years BP (Browne *et al.* 1977; Browne & McMillan 1989), but deposition of the sandy silt that forms most of the section probably ceased about 12 000 years BP, towards the end of a period when the sea level was falling rapidly as a consequence of glacio-isostatic readjustment (Peacock *et al.* 1978; Browne &

McMillan 1989). Species numbers decline upwards from 27 at 11.6 m OD to 2 at 13.4 m and the minimum salinity declines as stenohaline species (*Yoldiella lenticula*, *Margarites helicinus*) disappear.

Mid-boreal to lusitanian taxa are absent from this section, though present in very small numbers at a locality some 400 m ENE (Peacock 1989). Here the temperate species *Abra alba* yielded a radiocarbon age of 12 435 years BP, close to that for the base of the section under discussion (12 520 years BP).

Some data (Gurjanova 1929 in Zenkevitch 1963; Rasmussen 1973) suggest that *Lacuna vincta* and *L. parva* (which are present at 11.6 m OD in the section) are associated with high minimum summer sea surface temperatures (MSSSTs); a minimum of approximately 14°C for the former and 16°C for the latter (Peacock 1993). However, the distributional records and hydrographic data from the NE Atlantic area as

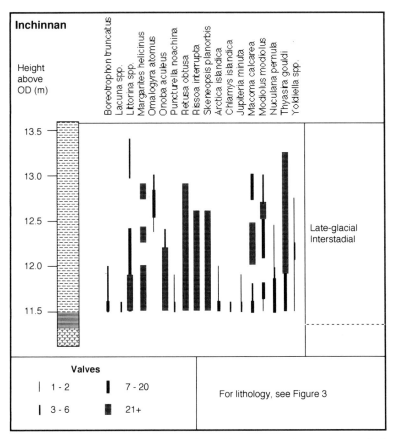

Fig. 2. Molluscs from Inchinnan. Modified from Peacock (1989), *Quaternary Science Reviews*, **8**, fig. 4A and reproduced with permission. Copyright Elsevier Science Limited.

a whole (Saetre 1973; Ockelman & Neilson 1981; Lee & Ramster 1981; Seaward 1990) are in keeping with lower MSSSTs; probably about 11°C for both species, and this more conservative figure is adopted here. Bottom temperatures are constrained to less than 8°C by the presence of *Yoldiella lenticula* and *Y. solidula*, suggesting the development of a marked summer thermocline at shallow depths, similar to that in East Greenland fjords today (Ockelmann 1958). There is a clear decline in MSSST upward in the section (Fig. 3) as weakly thermophilous taxa (*Onoba semicostata*; *Lacuna* spp.) disappear, but without supporting evidence from other sites and from microfaunal analysis it is uncertain whether or not this corresponds to reality or is merely a reflection of the general upward decrease in species as the water became shallower and less saline (see later).

Below 12 m OD there are several species that normally live at water depths of more than 10 m (*Boreotrophon truncatus*, *Puncturella noachina*,

Chlamys islandica, *Jupiteria minuta*, *Yoldiella* spp.), but above this level there is only one species (*Thyasira gouldi*). This is taken as evidence for upward shallowing towards possibly intertidal conditions above 13.3 m OD. The association of normally intertidal littorinids with such deeper water taxa may be because the former are known to migrate below low water where there are cold winters (Zenkevitch 1963).

Records from the Linwood and Paisley areas as a whole suggest that most of the fauna was recovered from close to the base of the marine sediments (Crosskey & Robertson 1869; Robertson 1877; Bishop & Coope 1977; Graham *in* Browne & McMillan 1989). It is therefore likely that the generalized lists of molluscs in 19th century publications refer chiefly to such basal beds, for which a number of radiocarbon dates between 12 400 years BP and 13 100 years BP have been published (Peacock & Harkness 1990, table 1).

The basal deposits in the Paisley and Linwood areas (Fig. 1B) have yielded the mid-boreal to

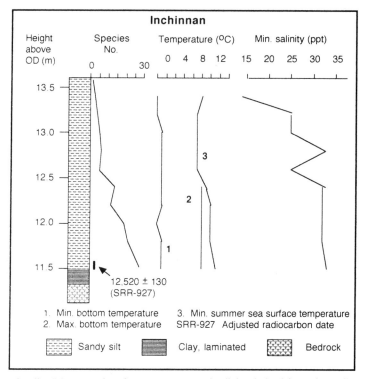

Fig. 3. Inchinnan, locality 7.3: proxy data for temperature and salinity derived from the molluscs in Fig. 2.

lusitanian taxa *Bittium reticulatum, Cylichna cylindracea, Nucula nucleus* and *Abra alba*, the last dated to 12 435 years BP at another nearby Inchinnan site (see earlier), and 12 600 and 12 400 years BP at Lochgilphead (Fig. 1A; Browne *et al.* 1977; Peacock & Harkness 1990, table 2). These records support the view that MSSST in the upper Clyde estuary may have reached or even locally exceeded 13°C early in the LGI, but also that temperatures throughout most of the water column were generally about 3°C lower than today (cf. Peacock 1983).

For the Clyde district as a whole, the fact that not all the thermophilous species occur in a particular section or borehole means that temperature estimates based on one site are unlikely to give a full picture, partly because of local spatial variations and incomplete stratigraphy. Moreover, short-term hydrographic fluctuations may be unrepresented in the data currently available. Species close to their northern limits on the west coast of the British Isles during the LGI may have reached the Clyde estuary only at intervals and the minimum temperature of 13°C attained only in favourable years.

St Kilda Basin

The two vibrocores described next were collected from the St Kilda Basin, west of the Outer Hebrides (Fig. 1A), about 15 to 30 km inside the maximum position reached by the Late Devensian ice sheet (Selby 1989; Peacock *et al.* 1992).

Vibrocore 57/-09/89

This vibrocore was collected from a morainal bank that forms the west side of the St Kilda basin (Selby 1989; Peacock *et al.* 1992). The basal 1.5 m (Units 1 and 2 Fig. 4) comprise the sediments of the morainal bank itself, here poorly sorted silt and sand with scattered dropstones interpreted as a high-arctic, proximal glaciomarine deposits laid down before the LGI. These are followed by bioturbated silt and clay with very scattered small pebbles (Unit 3 high-arctic, distal glaciomarine) and by poorly sorted silty sand and gravel with many shell fragments (Unit 4 boreal, shallow water environment). Unit 5 which is possibly high

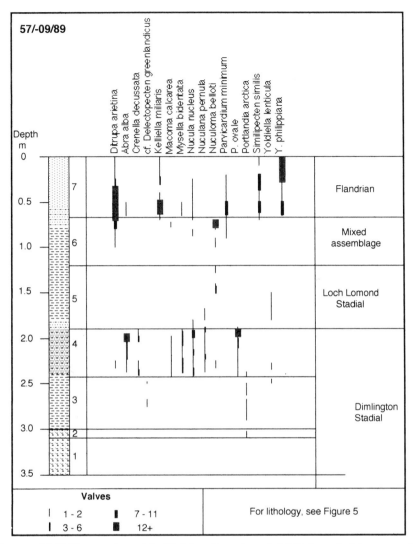

Fig. 4. Vibrocore 57/-09/89: macrofauna. Modified from Peacock *et al.* (1992) *Journal of Quaternary Science*, **7**, fig. 3 and reproduced with permission. Copyright John Wiley & Sons Ltd.

arctic according to the foraminifers (see Austin *in* Peacock *et al.* 1992), is lithologically similar to Unit 3. Unit 6 is transitional into the sand of Unit 7 (north temperate, deep water), which becomes increasingly carbonate-rich upwards.

Units 1 to 3 contain a sparse fauna of high-arctic affinities, chiefly *Portlandia arctica* and *Delectopecten greenlandicus*; these two species together suggest sea floor temperatures below 4°C, probably close to zero (Figs 4 and 5). The apparent fluctuations in salinity are solely due to the presence or absence of the stenohaline species *D. greenlandicus* in the sediment subsamples: it is

therefore unlikely that they are 'real' on this evidence alone. *Portlandia arctica* and *D. greenlandicus* are both found through a wide depth range, but the foraminiferal assemblage indicates shallow water (Austin *in* Peacock *et al.* 1992).

From the radiocarbon dates (Figs 4 and 5), Unit 4 was deposited during the last third of the LGI. About 20 species of molluscs were collected from the unit, including high-arctic to mid-boreal taxa (*Macoma calcarea, Nuculana pernula, Yoldiella lenticula*) and mid-boreal to lusitanian species (*Abra alba, Nucula nucleus*) that suggest MSSSTs of about 12–13°C. A

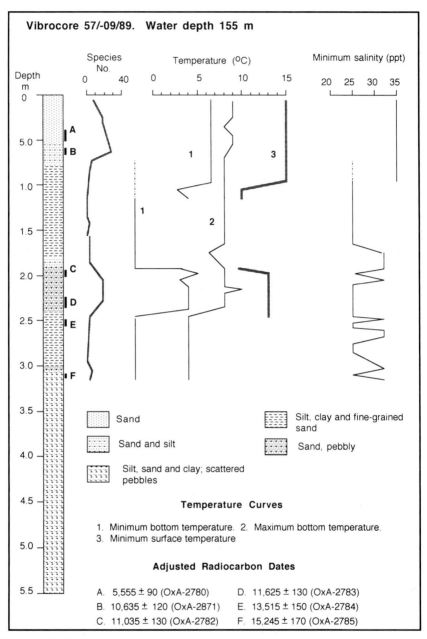

Fig. 5. Vibrocore 57/-09/89: proxy data for temperature and salinity.

significant feature is the presence of *Mysella bidentata* and *Nucula nucleus*, both of which are found today where seafloor temperatures are above 3–4°C. Shallow water is suggested by the occurrence together of *Abra alba* (most commonly found at depths of less than 60 m), *M. bidentata* (less than 45 m) and *Crenella* *decussata* (less than 30 m) as well as by the high energy conditions indicated by the lithology and microfauna.

Unit 5 with a lithology similar to that of Unit 3 was laid down during the Loch Lomond Stadial (LLS; Fig. 4). Stenothermal species are largely absent and the molluscan proxy data are based on a sparse, low diversity fauna (*Nucu-loma belloti*; *Yoldiella* spp.) with a relatively wide temperature tolerance (Fig. 5). The foraminiferal evidence suggests an increase in water depth compared with Unit 4 (Austin *in* Peacock *et al.* 1992), but the mollusca are those with a wide depth range.

At the late glacial–Flandrian boundary between 0.70 and 1.15 m (Unit 6) the fauna is a mixture of cold- and warm-tolerant species brought about by bioturbation. As the present day distributions of some species do not overlap, it is possible to plot proxy data for both (Fig. 5). From 0.70 m upwards (Unit 7, Flandrian) the fauna indicates full marine salinity with MSSSTs similar to that today. Relatively deep water, possibly similar to that at present (155 m) is indicated by the occurrence in quantity of the

bivalves *Parvicardium minimum* and *Kelliella miliaris*. Such deep water accounts for the narrow range of bottom temperature (7.5–9°C).

Vibrocore 57/-09/46

This vibrocore (Figs 1 and 6) penetrated over 5.7 m of deposit attributed chiefly to the LLS. The gaps in data in Figs 6 and 7 are the result of paucity of molluscan remains and the lack of borehole material, particularly between 0.80 and 1.00 m. Small gaps between 0 and 0.80 m are not shown on Fig. 7.

Between 1.00 and 5.70 m depth the molluscan fauna is almost identical to that from the LLS section in 57/-09/89 (Unit 4), being dominated by *Nuculoma belloti* and *N. tenuis*, together with

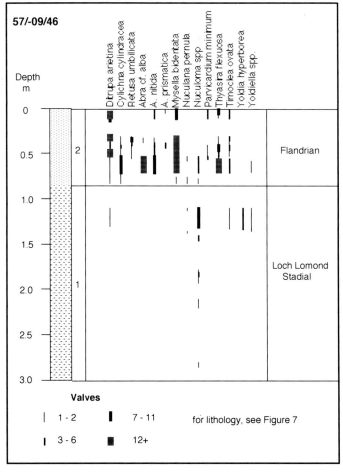

Fig. 6. Vibrocore 57/-09/46: macrofauna. Modified from Peacock *et al.* (1992) *Journal of Quaternary Science*, **7**, fig. 8 and reproduced with permission. Copyright John Wiley & Sons Ltd.

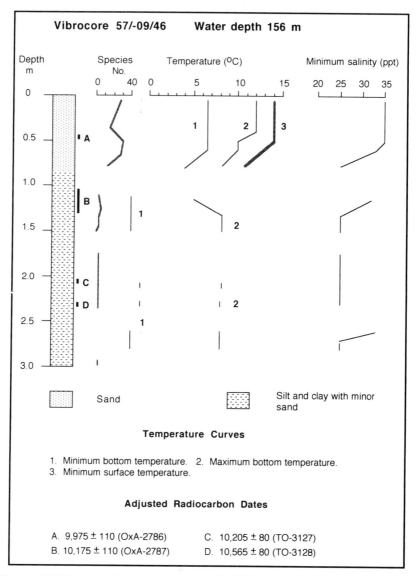

Fig. 7. Vibrocore 57/-9/46: proxy data for temperature and salinity.

minor *Retusa obtusa, Nuculana pernula, Yoldiella lenticula* and *Y. solidula*. The occurrence of *Yoldia hyperborea* between 1.05 and 1.30 m suggests maximum bottom temperatures of less than 5°C at this level, but an increase in the food supply (Ockelmann 1958). Though the molluscs are chiefly boreo-arctic species with a broad temperature tolerance (see comment for 57/-09/89), the microfaunal, microfloral and lithological evidence suggests arctic conditions, probably with seasonal sea ice (Peacock *et al.* 1992 and later discussion). As in 57/-09/89, the molluscs in the

section which is correlated with the Loch Lomond Stadial give little indication of water depth.

Above 0.72 m in the vibrocore the molluscan fauna is of boreal, shallow water type that would be associated with temperatures similar to those in the area at the present day. The presence and abundance of *Mysella bidentata, Abra alba* and *A. prismatica* between 0.72 and 0.32 m implies contemporaneous water depths of less than 60 m but the abundance of *Parvicardium minimum* suggests water depths of more than 40 m. The conclusion that water deths were a little less than 60 m is supported by the analysis of the ostracod fauna and dinoflagellate cysts (Peacock *et al.* 1992).

Stornoway Borehole 78/4

The borehole is located about 9 km SE of Stornoway in the Outer Hebrides (Fig. 1). The biostratigraphic data and radiocarbon dates

showed it to have intersected sediments of early Flandrian to Dimlington Stadial age, terminating in Jurassic strata (Graham *et al.* 1990). Thirty-eight subsamples were examined for molluscs, a similar number for foraminifers and ostracods, and about twice this number for dinoflagellates. The molluscs have been re-examined by the author and the results presented in Figs 8 and 9.

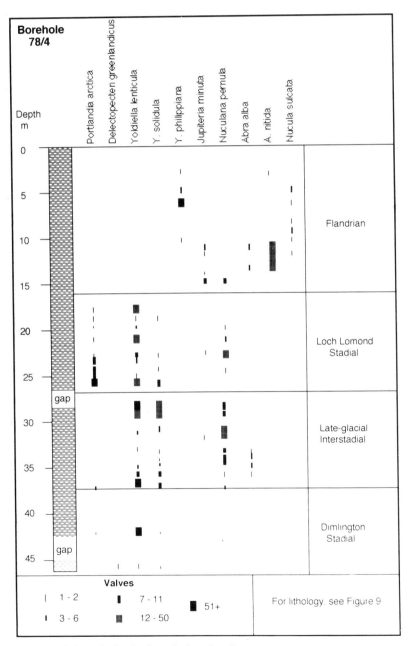

Fig. 8. Stornoway Borehole 78/4: distribution of selected molluscs.

The full potential of this general locality for Quaternary studies has yet to be realized as the rate of deposition of the late glacial part of this core, about 5–6 m per thousand years, is greater than that of one of the highest resolution cores so far examined from the northeast Atlantic over the same time span (Troll 3.1, northern North Sea, Lehman *et al.* 1991; Lehman & Keigwin 1992).

No mollusc was found between the base of the Quaternary succession at 57 m depth and a depth of 47 m in the borehole (Fig 8 and 9), but the lithology and the restricted microfauna (dominant *Elphidium clavatum* and cold-water ostracods including *Cytheropteron pseudomontrosiense*) suggest glaciomarine conditions and a salinity below 30 ppt (Graham *et al.* 1990).

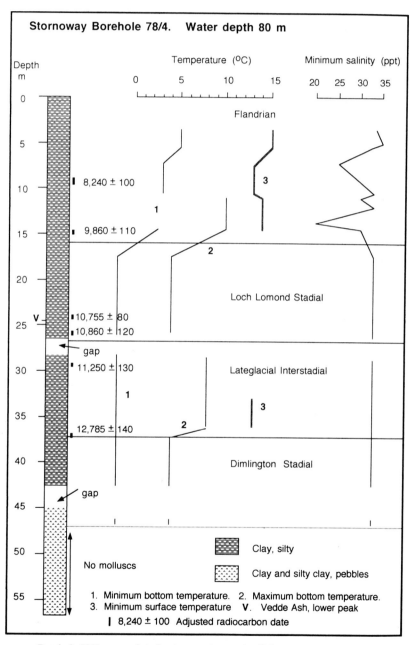

Fig. 9. Stornoway Borehole 78/4: proxy data for temperature and salinity.

Above this level the presence of *Yoldiella lenticula* together with fragments of *Portlandia arctica*, *Delectopecten greenlandicus* (at 46 m) and a continuation of the cold-water microfauna suggest salinities approaching normal marine, but with maximum water temperatures remaining below 4°C. The macrofauna here (and indeed throughout the borehole) is generally of offshore aspect, but otherwise gives little indication of water depth.

The LGI section of the borehole, which appears to be complete, is noteworthy for the continuation of indications of low bottom water temperature (less than 8°C) and near-normal marine salinity, both being provided by the remains of *Yoldiella lenticula* and *Y. solidula*. However, the abundant macrofauna above 38 m in the borehole may be consequent on a greatly augmented food supply and the presence of the mid-boreal to lusitanian bivalve *Abra alba* between 33 and 37 m suggests that the MSSST approached 13°C from time to time early in the period (Fig. 9; see also discussion of the Inchinnan area). This analysis of the low-diversity macrofauna is supported by the microfauna and microflora, which indicate a continuation of cold-water conditions, with the possibility of a milder marine climate early and late in the Interstadial (Graham *et al.* 1990).

The LLS is marked by the return of *Portlandia arctica* (maximum water temperature below 4°C), but there is little otherwise to differentiate the macrofauna, the microfauna and the microflora from those of the LGI, though there is a suggestion of a slight upward amelioration above a level of 22 m in the borehole (incoming of *Bulimina marginata* into the microfauna, if not due to bioturbation or contamination).

Excepting a sample taken immediately above the boundary with the late glacial sediment, the Flandrian macrofauna implies that marine temperatures were close to those at present in the area, though the apparent fluctuations in salinity (Fig. 8) may be the result of the fortuitous absence of stenohaline species at some levels. The species of *Yoldiella* formerly reported as *Y. lenticula* in this part of the borehole has been re-identified as *Y. philippiana*, a temperate taxon with a northern limit today at Lofoten on the Norwegian coast (Warén 1989).

Discussion

This account shows that it is possible to follow fluctuations of temperature and salinity with time at individual sites, often in detail, but that the estimation of depth is not always practical. It has also highlighted problems relating to the palaeoenvironment, the quality of the proxy data currently available and the sample size.

In the inferred arctic marine palaeoenvironments, the low diversity and generally sparse macrofaunas in the muddy sediments mean that the presence or absence of cold stenothermal and/or stenohaline species is critical to interpretation. This is particularly so for the Loch Lomond Stadial, where only one common cold stenothermal species, *Portlandia arctica*, is generally available. Another species, *Delectopecten greenlandicus*, apparently became locally extinct at the start of the LGI. *Portlandia arctica* is known from several western Scottish sites assigned to the Loch Lomond Stadial, for instance Ardyne (Fig. 1A; Peacock *et al.* 1978) and Garvel Park (Fig. 1A; Scott & Steel 1883; Peacock 1986) as well as Stornoway. It is thus uncertain from molluscan evidence alone whether or not the Loch Lomond Stadial faunas in the St Kilda vibrocores reflect a slightly less cold environment than those closer to the Scottish coast. Such slightly higher temperatures would agree with those reported for the same time interval in adjacent parts of the North Atlantic (Duplessy this volume). However, there is a general indication from the microfauna and dinoflagellate flora for very low temperatures, particularly during the earlier part of the Stadial, and higher temperatures during the later part (Austin *in* Peacock *et al.* 1992)

A further example is forthcoming from the LGI section of the Stornoway 78/4 Borehole (Figs 8 and 9) in which the presence of a generally cold-water microfauna and microflora (Graham *et al.* 1990) emphasized the macrofaunal evidence that water temperatures were apparently lower at the Stornoway site during the latter part of the Interstadial than at the locality of vibrocore 57/-09/89 on the continental shelf (Fig. 5) and at others on the coast of western Scotland, such as Lochgilphead (Peacock *et al.* 1977) and Ardyne (Peacock *et al.* 1978). There is thus some evidence for contemporaneous regional differences in water temperature during the late glacial period. From the foregoing it is clear that support from microfaunal evidence is valuable where stenothermal molluscs are absent, particularly where it is possible to infer values for temperature (e.g. Murray 1991).

Measures of minimum salinity at late glacial sites, and probably also at Flandrian sites, are likewise dependent on the presence or absence of a few molluscan taxa such as the stenohaline *Yoldiella* spp, particularly where the samples available for analysis are small. Inferences of maximum salinity from marine molluscs are likely to be limited because most estuarine taxa found in polar and temperate waters are euryhaline, tolerating both brackish and fully marine conditions: only a few, such as *Hydrobia ventrosa*, are normally found in salinities below 25 ppt (Graham 1988). Thus even where a large and diverse macrofauna has been obtained, such as from Inchinnan, it may only be possible to plot a trend of minimum salinity, though this may well reflect 'real' changes in salinity to a greater or lesser degree. Under such conditions, the molluscan data needs to be supplemented by that from other sources, such as the ostracod and diatom families which range from fully marine to fresh water (Robinson 1978; Kjemperud 1981).

Although this discussion suggests that the type of proxy data under review can give a broad picture of conditions, it is most usefully considered together with information from other sources, such as microfaunal and sedimentological analysis. In addition, proxies for temperature and salinity could be augmented by trace element and stable isotope analysis. Stable isotope analysis of carbon and oxygen has been successfully applied to benthonic foraminifers from the Norwegian Trench and the Scottish continental shelf and slope (e.g. Lehman *et al.* 1991). Little work of this type has, however, been carried out to date on the shells of benthonic marine molluscs found in borehole cores and sections adjacent to the northwest European seaboard (e.g. Donner & Nord, 1986), though its value has been demonstrated elsewhere (e.g. Andrews 1973; Boomer 1993). Such analysis, though possibly subject to problems caused by kinetic isotope effects in fast-growing taxa (Mitchell *et al.* 1994), could clearly overcome some of the discussed limitations, using the shells of common species as well as those of stenothermal and stenohaline species (for calibration purposes). Moreover, such analysis could provide a record of seasonality (Hillaire-Marcel 1981) and a platform for comparison with stable isotope determinations on microfauna.

Conclusions

(1) Molluscan proxy data applied to late glacial to Flandrian successions provides an outline of conditions, with detail preserved in some parts. As such it can provide a valuable addition to palaeoenvironmental studies.
(2) Cold or warm stenothermal molluscs are few. Where these occur, the results probably approach reality, but where they are absent, support may be needed from other sources.

(3) Depth can normally be estimated only within broad limits (ten to a few tens of metres). Such estimates, however, can be useful constraints on changes of sea level with time.
(4) Except where there is a rich fauna, analysis is likely to give a low figure for minimum salinity.
(5) Mid-boreal to lusitanian molluscs (temperate indicators) occur in the early late glacial interstadial, but have not been recorded at all localities where they might have been expected. This may be a function of sample size, features of the former environment such as bottom conditions, and fluctuations in the marine climate beyond the resolution of the data.

I am grateful to E. N. K. Clarkson and I. P. Wilkinson for reading through earlier drafts of the paper and suggesting alterations, and to the editors of *Quaternary Science Reviews* and *Journal of Quaternary Science* for permission to publish, respectively, Figs 2; 4 and 6. I also thank the two referees (H. P. Sejrup and an unnamed referee) for further useful comments

References

AITKEN, A. 1990. Fossilization potential of Arctic fjord and continental shelf benthic macrofaunas. *In*: DOWDESWELL, J. A. & SCOURSE, J. D. (eds) *Glacimarine Environments: Processes and Sediments*. Geological Society, London, Special Publications, **53**, 155–176.

ANDERSON, F. W. 1948. The fauna of the '100 feet beach' clays. *Transactions of the Geological Society of Edinburgh*, **14**, 220 – 229.

ANDREWS, J. T. 1973. Late Quaternary variations in oxygen and carbon isotopic compositions in Canadian arctic marine bivalves. *Palaeogeography, Palaeoclimatology, Palaeoecology*, **14**, 187–192.

BARNES, R. S. K. & HUGHES, R. N. 1982. *An Introduction to Marine Ecology*. Blackwell Scientific, Oxford.

BISHOP, W. W. & COOPE, G. R. 1977. Stratigraphical and faunal evidence for Lateglacial and Early Flandrian environments in south-west Scotland. *In*: GRAY, J. M. & LOWE, J. J. (eds) *Studies in the Scottish Lateglacial Environment*. Pergamon, Oxford, 61–88.

BOOMER, I. 1993. Palaeoenvironmental indicators from late Holocene and contemporary Ostracoda of the Aral Sea. *Palaeogeography, Palaeoclimatology, Palaeoecology*, **103**, 141–153.

BROWNE, M. A. E. & McMILLAN, A. A. 1989. *Quaternary geology of the Clyde Valley*. British Geological Survey Research Report, **Sa/89/1**.

——, HARKNESS, D. D., PEACOCK, J. D. & WARD, R. G. 1977. The date of deglaciation of the Paisley–Renfrew area. *Scottish Journal of Geology*, **13**, 301–303.

CROSSKEY, H. W. & ROBERTSON, D. 1869. The Post-Tertiary fossiliferous beds of Scotland: Paisley. *Transactions of the Geological Society of Glasgow*, **3**, 334 – 341.

DONNER, J. & NORD, A. G. 1986. Carbon and oxygen stable isotope values of shells of *Mytilus edulis* and *Modiolus modiolus* from the Holocene raised beaches of the Varanger Peninsula, North Norway. *Palaeogeography, Palaeoclimatology, Palaeoecology*, **56**, 35–50.

FEYLING-HANSSEN, R. W. 1955. Stratigraphy of the marine Late Pleistocene of Billefjorden, Vestspitsbergen. *Skrifter Norsk Polarinstitutt*, **107**, 1–186.

GRAHAM, A. 1988. Molluscs: Prosobranch and Pyramidellid Gastropods. *In*: DERMACK, D. M. & BARNES, R. S. K. (eds) *Synopses of the British Fauna (New Series)*. 2nd edn. E. J. Brill/W. Backhuys, Leiden.

GRAHAM, D. K., HARLAND, R., GREGORY, D. M., LONG, D. & MORTON, A. C. 1990. The biostratigraphy and chronostratigraphy of BGS Borehole 78/4, North Minch. *Scottish Journal of Geology*, **26**, 65–75.

HARKNESS, D. D. 1983. The extent of natural 14C deficiency in the coastal environment of the United Kingdom. *Proceedings of the First International Symposium on C-14 and Archaeology, Pact 8IV.9*, 351–364.

HARLAND, R., GREGORY, D. M., HUGHES, M. J. & WILKINSON, I. P. 1978. A late Quaternary bio- and climatostratigraphy for marine sediments in the north-central part of the North sea. *Boreas*, **7**, 91–96.

HILLAIRE-MARCEL, C. 1981. Paléo-océanographie isotopique des mers post-glaciaires du Québec. *Palaeogeography, Palaeoclimatology, Palaeoecology*, **35**, 63–119.

KJEMPERUD, A. 1981. Diatom changes in sediments of basins possessing marine/lacustrine transitions in Frosta, Nord-Trondelag, Norway. *Boreas*, **10**, 27–38.

KOC KARPUZ, N. & SCHRADER, H. 1990. Surface sediment diatom distribution and Holocene paleotemperature variations in the Greenland, Iceland and Norwegian Sea. *Paleoceanography*, **5**, 557–580.

LEE, A. J. & RAMSTER, J. W. 1981. *Atlas of the Seas around the British Isles*. Ministry of Agriculture, Food and Fisheries, HMSO, Southampton.

LEHMAN, S. J. & KEIGWIN, L. D. 1992. Sudden changes in North Atlantic circulation during the last deglaciation. *Nature*, **356**, 757–762.

——, JONES, G. A., KEIGWIN, L. D., ANDERSEN, E. S., BUTENKO, G. & ØSTMO, S. R. 1991. Initiation of Fennoscandian ice-sheet retreat during the last deglaciation. *Nature*, **349**, 513–516.

MCKAY, D. 1995. *Calliostoma granulatum* in Scottish waters. *Porcupine Newsletter*, **5**, 257.

MITCHELL, L., FALLICK, A. E. & CURRY, G. B. 1994. Stable isotope and carbon compositions of mollusc shells from Britain and New Zealand. *Palaeogeography, Palaeoclimatology, Palaeoecology*, **111**, 207–216.

MURRAY, J. W. 1991. *Ecology and Palaeocology of Benthic Foraminifera*. Longman Group UK, London.

OCKELMANN, K. W. 1958. The zoology of East Greenland: marine Lamellibrachiata. *Meddelelser om Grønland*, **122**(4), 1–256.

—— & NIELSEN, C. 1981. On the biology of the prosobranch *Lacuna parva* in the Øresund. *Ophelia*, **20**, 1–16.

PEACOCK, J. D. 1983. A model for Scottish interstadial marine palaeotemperature 13,000 to 11,000 BP. *Boreas*, **12**, 73–82.

——1986. A reassessment of the probable Loch Lomond stade marine molluscan fauna at Garvel Park, Greenock. *Scottish Journal of Geology*, **23**, 93–103.

——1989. Marine molluscs and Late Quaternary environmental studies with particular reference to the Late-glacial period in Northwest Europe: a review. *Quaternary Science Reviews*, **8**, 179–192.

——1993. Late Quaternary marine mollusca as palaeoenvironmental proxies: a compilation and assessment of basic numerical data for NE Atlantic species found in shallow water. *Quaternary Science Reviews*, **12**, 263–275.

—— & HARKNESS, D. D. 1990. Radiocarbon ages and the full-glacial to Holocene transition in seas adjacent to Scotland and southern Scandinavia: a review. *Transactions of the Royal Society of Edinburgh: Earth Sciences*, **81**, 385–396.

——, AUSTIN, W. E. N., SELBY, I., GRAHAM, D. K., HARLAND, R. & WILKINSON, I. P. 1992. Late Devensian and Flandrian palaeoenvironmental changes on the Scottish continental shelf west of the Outer Hebrides. *Journal of Quaternary Science*, **7**, 145–161.

——, GRAHAM, D. K. & GREGORY, D. M. 1978. Late-glacial and post-glacial marine environments at Ardyne, Scotland, and their significance in the interpretation of the Clyde sea area. *Report of the Institute of Geological Sciences*, **78/17**, 1–25.

——, ——, ROBINSON, J. D. & WILKINSON, I. P. 1977. Evolution and chronology of Lateglacial marine environments at Lochgilphead, Scotland. *In*: GRAY, J. M. & LOWE, J. J. (eds) *Studies in the Scottish Lateglacial Environment*. Pergamon, Oxford, 89–100.

RASMUSSEN, E. 1973. Systematics and ecology of Isefjord marine fauna (Denmark). *Ophelia*, **11**, 1–507.

ROBERTSON, D. 1877. Notes on a Post-Tertiary deposit of shell-bearing clay on the west side of the railway tunnel at Arkleston, near Paisley. *Transactions of the Geological Society of Glasgow*, **5**, 281–287.

ROBINSON, E. 1978. The Pleistocene. *In*: BATE, R. & ROBINSON, E. (eds) *A Stratigraphical Index of British Ostracoda*. Geological Journal Special Issue No. 8, 451–472.

SAETRE, R. 1973. Temperatur og saltholdighetsnormaler i norske kystfarvann. *Fiskets Gang*, **8**, 166–172.

SCOTT, T. & STEEL, J. 1883. Notes on the occurrence of *Leda arctica* (Gray); *Lyonsia areanosa* (Møller), and other organic remains in the post-Pliocene clays of Garvel Park, Greenock. *Transactions of the Geological Society of Glasgow*, **7**, 274–283.

SEAWARD, D. R. 1990. *Distribution of the Marine Molluscs of North West Europe*. Nature Conservancy Council, Peterborough.

SELBY, I. 1989. *Quaternary geology of the Hebridean continental margin*. PhD Thesis, Nottingham University.

SOUTHWARD, A. J. 1995. A 'new' warm-water barnacle off Plymouth. *Porcupine Newsletter*, **5**, 251.

WARÉN, A. 1989. Taxonomic comments on some protobranch bivalves from the Northeastern Atlantic. *Sarsia*, **74**, 223–259.

ZENKEVITCH, L. 1963. *Biology of the Seas of the U.S.S.R.* Allen and Unwin, London.

Late glacial sea level and ocean margin environmental changes interpreted from biostratigraphic and lithostratigraphic studies of isolation basins in northwest Scotland

IAN SHENNAN, MAIRÉAD M. RUTHERFORD,
JAMES B. INNES & KEVIN J. WALKER

*Environmental Research Centre, Department of Geography, University of Durham,
Science Laboratories, South Road, Durham DH1 3LE, UK*

Abstract: Detailed biostratigraphic and lithostratigraphic analyses from isolation basins at Ardtoe, Rumach, Loch nan Eala and Fearnbeg, northwest Scotland, allow an interpretation of sea level movements and environmental changes within the Lateglacial Interstadial and Younger Dryas (13–10 ka BP). Microfossil analyses illustrate the gradual transition of the isolation basins from marine basins to freshwater lakes within an area of isostatic uplift. These data provide evidence for a fall in relative sea level in northwest Scotland from the mid-Lateglacial Interstadial to the early Holocene.

Pollen, diatom and dinoflagellate cyst (dinocyst) analyses link the oceanic record of major climate and oceanic circulation changes with the terrestrial biostratigraphic record. Movement of the oceanic Polar Front west and north during a period of relative climatic amelioration within the Lateglacial Interstadial and a corresponding change in the position of the North Atlantic Current may be inferred from the dinocyst record. This is followed by a relative cooling.

Recent studies of the sediments of isolation basins at Rumach (Shennan *et al.* 1993), Loch nan Eala (Shennan *et al.* 1994) and Ardtoe (Shennan *et al.* in press) are primarily focused on the reconstruction of relative sea-level changes from the Lateglacial Interstadial (13–11 ka BP) through to the late Holocene. Lithostratigraphic and microfossil analyses illustrate the gradual transition of the isolation basins from marine basins to freshwater lakes within an area of isostatic uplift. The basins at Rumach and Loch nan Eala (Fig. 1) reveal a continuous fall in relative sea level from +17.8 m OD at 11.8 ka BP to around +5 m OD around the opening of the Holocene. Only the lowest isolation basins, with sills below +6.3 m OD, record a subsequent early Holocene rise in sea level and a late Holocene relative fall. Farther south, at Ardtoe (Fig. 1), a relative fall in sea level at +20.6 m OD is dated 12 ka BP.

The principal objectives of the previous investigations were to test existing models of relative sea-level change. These models can be grouped into two main types: empirical models based on the interpretation of field data; and high-resolution mathematical models of glacial rebound from which relative sea-level changes are predicted. However, the rich biostratigraphic and chronostratigraphic data collected in the course of these investigations provide important information for the understanding of other environmental processes. These include the rate and nature of coastal changes; past tidal regimes;

constraints on the age of deglaciation from the Late Devensian (Late Weichselian) ice sheet maximum and the extent of Loch Lomond (Younger Dryas) Stadial glaciers; terrestrial vegetation changes 12–4 ka BP; oceanographic changes at the NE Atlantic margin; and an opportunity to link the terrestrial and oceanic records of environmental changes (Shennan *et al.* 1993; 1994; 1995*a*; in press).

In this paper we present previously unpublished data from isolation basins at Fearnbeg and Rumach to (i) evaluate the spatial and temporal components of late glacial relative sea-level movements; and (ii) attempt to link the records of oceanographic changes obtained from ocean bottom cores with those from isolation basins.

Methods

Samples for microfossil analyses were prepared using standard procedures, as described by Moore *et al.* (1991) and Palmer & Abbott (1986). Nomenclature follows Moore *et al.* (1991) for pollen, Hartley (1986) for diatoms and Harland (1983) for dinocysts (see Appendix). Diatom species are summarized according to halobian classification (Vos & de Wolf 1993). All biostratigraphic diagrams have been produced using the TILIA programme of Grimm (1993). Raw microfossil counts are available from I. Shennan.

From Andrews, J. T., Austin, W. E. N., Bergsten, H. & Jennings, A. E. (eds), 1996, *Late Quaternary Palaeoceanography of the North Atlantic Margins*, Geological Society Special Publication No. 111, pp. 229–244.

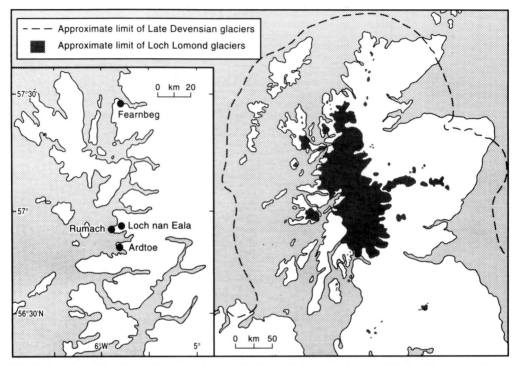

Fig. 1. Location of the sites at Fearnbeg, Rumach, Loch nan Eala and Ardtoe; and the Late Devensian (Late Weichselian) and Loch Lomond Stadial (Younger Dryas) ice limits (modified after Bowen *et al.* 1986).

Sites investigated

Fearnbeg

This isolation basin (National Grid Reference NG73805965, Fig. 2) is the most northerly studied to date, on the northeast coast of the Applecross peninsula, facing Loch Torridon. A sequence of clastic and organic sediments accumulated within a shallow depression behind a rock sill at +5.7 m OD. Stratigraphical analysis of two transects across the basin has shown the following lithological sequence over bedrock; a basal grey sandy silt overlain in turn by a *limus*, stratified organic sandy silt, red/brown sand, stratified silty clay, upper *limus*, a bryophytic peat and then a turfa peat to the present surface. The sequence of five major stratigraphic units (clastic–limnic–clastic–limnic–peat) is comparable with those recorded in the basins at Ardtoe (Shennan *et al.* in press), Rumach Iochdar and

Rumach Meadhonach (Shennan *et al.* 1993). Radiocarbon and microfossil data were obtained from a 50 mm piston core taken at the deepest part of the basin. Investigations to date only cover the lower, late glacial, section of the sequence.

Fearnbeg 93/1: diatoms. The diatom data from Fearnbeg are shown in Fig. 3a. The lower sandy silt is of marine origin, dominated by polyhalobous and mesohalobous species: these include *Cocconeis scutellum, Achnanthes delicatula, Paralia sulcata, Rhabdonema minutum, Navicula forcipata, Diploneis interrupta* and *Amphora marina*. At 595 cm the sediment becomes more organic and the diatoms show a decrease in the polyhalobous species, as first mesohalobous and then oligohalobous species rise. This represents the transition to a freshwater lake which is complete by the top of the diagram where halophobous species, such as *Tabellaria flocculosa*, rise. During

Fig. 2. (a) Fearnbeg site map. The stratigraphic cross-section in (b) follows the line of the transect across the basin. North is to the top of the figure. MHWS, mean high water of spring tides. Selected contours (10, 20, 30 m OD) shown. (b) Stratigraphic cross-section of Fearnbeg. Symbols: *turfa* peat (diagonal line); organic *limus*, with minor clastic component (cross-hatching); clastic sediment, sand, silt and clay (white); solid rock or borehole stopped by coarse gravel in deepest parts of the basin (brickwork).

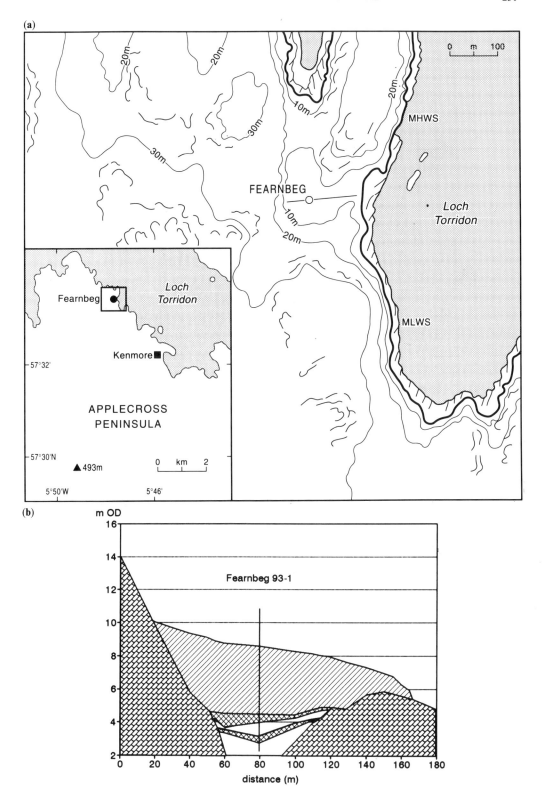

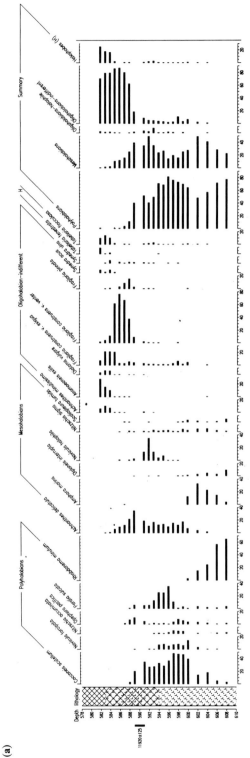

Fig. 3. (a) Fearnbeg diatoms. All species are expressed as percentage total diatom valves (%TDV). Only species which reach 5% TDV are shown as individual graphs, but all species counted are included in the four summary curves at the right of the diagram. Lithology symbols after Troels-Smith (1955).

(a)

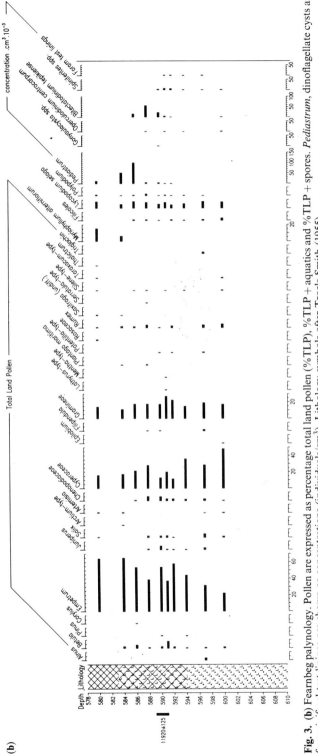

Fig. 3. (b) Fearnbeg palynology. Pollen are expressed as percentage total land pollen (%TLP), %TLP + aquatics and %TLP + spores. *Pediastrum*, dinoflagellate cysts and foraminiferal test linings are shown as concentrations (individuals/cm³). Lithology symbols after Troels-Smith (1955).

this transition the diatoms record the change from a complete connection to the sea throughout the tidal cycle, to regular connection only at high tide, and finally only occasional ingress of marine water during storm surges. This pattern is directly comparable with those observed in previous studies (e.g. Shennan *et al.* in press).

The transition is radiocarbon dated 11 920 ± 125 years BP (SRR-5171) and represents a fall in relative sea level across the sill at +5.7 m OD.

Fearnbeg 93/1: palynology. The transition from a marine basin to a freshwater lake is clearly portrayed by the decline in dinocysts as freshwater algae, *Pediastrum*, frequencies rise, followed by pollen of *Myriophyllum alterniflorum* (Fig. 3b). The marine dinocyst assemblages are discussed further in a later section. The land pollen assemblage is dominated throughout by *Empetrum*, Gramineae and Cyperaceae. This assemblage is consistent with the radiocarbon date for a Lateglacial Interstadial age for the isolation of the basin.

Rumach IV and Rumach V

At Rumach (Fig. 4; grid reference NM63708535) there is a series of infilled basins ranging in altitude from around +40 m OD down to present sea level. Shennan *et al.* (1993) show that Rumach Meadhonach, sill altitude +17.8 m OD, was isolated from the sea at 11 820 ± 145 years BP (UB-3643), and Rumach Iochdar, sill altitude +9.3 m OD, at 10 755 ± 90 years BP (SRR-4862). In both these basins the isolation contact is represented by a lithological change from predominantly clastic sediment to an organic limnic unit. Diatom analyses, in each basin comparable with those described from Fearnbeg, confirm the transition from marine water to a freshwater lake. In each basin the organic limnic unit is overlain by a predominantly clastic unit, shown by radiocarbon and pollen analyses to have formed during the Younger Dryas (Loch Lomond Stadial). Organic limnic and semi-terrestrial peat units, up to 6 m thick, complete the sequence in each basin.

The basins designated Rumach IV and V lie at intermediate altitudes between Rumach Iochdar and Rumach Meadhonach. At present Rumach IV is separated from Rumach V by a sill at +13.8 m OD. Rumach V currently drains over a sill, at +11.8 m OD, through an artificial road cutting. It has not proved possible to find any documentary evidence about the construction of the road but from the nature of the road, cutting, the artificial drainage channel and the biostratigraphic and radiocarbon data described in the following we conclude that the basins did not drain naturally over the present sill. There is one natural sill from Rumach IV westwards, towards the open Atlantic coast, at +16.32 m OD, and a second sill at approximately +16.26 m OD eastwards from Rumach V to Rumach Iochdar, and then to the very sheltered embayment of Loch nan Ceall. In this scenario the sill between Rumach IV and V never operated as a threshold between either basin and the sea, but would have an effect on water circulation and sediment accumulation within the basins.

Detailed stratigraphic analysis along two transects in Rumach IV reveals over 6 m of sediment in the centre of the basin (Fig. 4). Typically a basal grey silt clay is overlain by an organic *limus*, a grey silt clay and a limnic detrital peat layer which grades into a thick herbaceous peat to the present day surface. A broadly comparable sequence is found in the centre of Rumach V. However, the transition from the basal clastic unit to the lowest organic limnic deposit is much more gradual than in either Rumach IV or other isolation basins studied to date. There is a distinctive 0.2 m dark brown laminated organic clay unit. The overlying sequence follows the same as that described for Rumach IV.

Rumach IV and V: diatoms. Below 610 cm in Rumach IV core 93-F5 (Fig. 5a) the diatom assemblage is dominated by polyhalobous forms *Paralia sulcata*, *Rhabdonema minutum* and *Scoliotropis latestriata*. The isolation process is clearly underway by 610 cm, shown by increased frequencies of the oligohalobous-indifferent species *Fragilaria pinnata* and *F. virescens*. Further changes in water salinity are illustrated by the temporary peaks of the mesohalobous species *Navicula halophila* and *Achnanthes delicatula* before the final stage of the isolation process, marked by the freshwater assemblages, including a number of halophobous species, at 595 cm.

The diatom assemblages from Rumach V core 93–1 (Fig. 5b) are comparable with those from Rumach IV 93-F5. The increased frequencies of *Fragilaria pinnata* and *F. virescens* within the polyhalobous-dominated assemblage are clearly seen, as are the temporary peaks of the mesohalobous species *Navicula halophila* and *Achnanthes delicatula*. *Cocconeis scutellum* is more frequent than in Rumach IV, and immediately before the final isolation there is a temporary peak of *Navicula avenacea*, an oligohalobous-halophile species. A few mesohalobous species are consistently present in low frequencies after the final isolation.

(a)

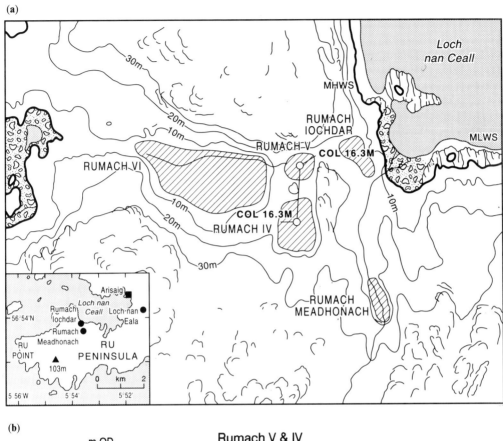

(b)

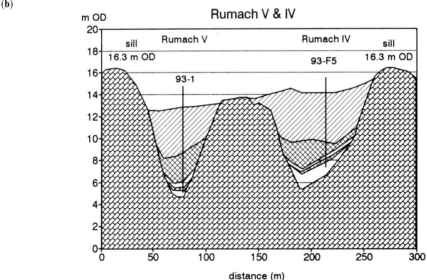

Fig. 4. (a) Rumach site map. The stratigraphic section in (b) follows the line across Rumach IV and V. North is to the top of the figure. MHWS, mean high water of spring tids. MLWS, mean low water of spring tides. Selected contours (10, 20, 30 m OD) shown. (b) Stratigraphic cross-sections of Rumach IV and V. Symbols: *turfa* peat (diagonal line); organic *limus*, with minor clastic component (cross-hatching); clastic sediment, sand, silt and clay (white); solid rock or borehole stopped by coarse gravel in deepest parts of the basin (brickwork).

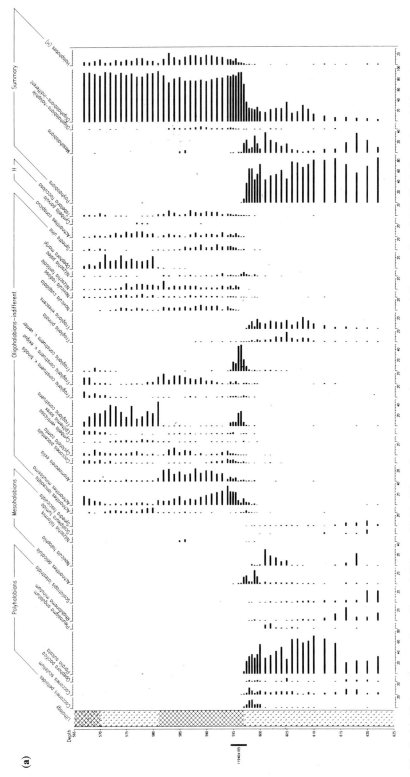

Fig. 5. (a) Diatom diagram from Rumach IV, core 93-F5. All species are expressed as percentage total diatom valves (%TDV). Only species which reach 5% TDV are shown as individual graphs, but all species counted are included in the five summary curves at the right of the diagram. Lithology symbols after Troels-Smith (1955).

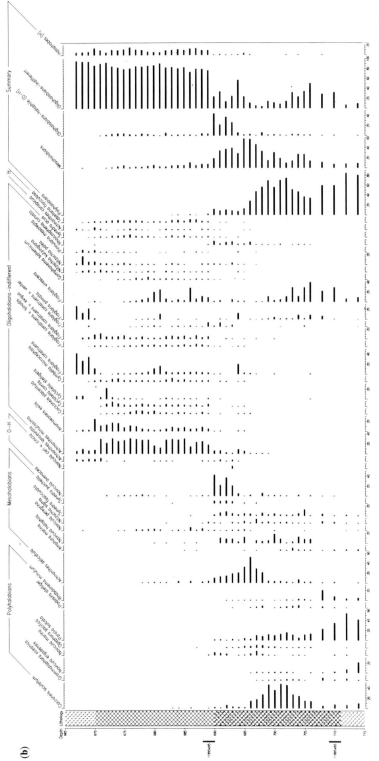

Fig. 5. (b) Diatom diagram from Rumach V core 93-1. All species are expressed as percentage total diatom valves (%TDV). Only species which reach 5% TDV are shown as individual graphs, but all species counted are included in the five summary curves at the right of the diagram. Lithology symbols after Troels-Smith (1955).

We conclude that the diatom assemblages from the two basins support the hypothesis that both basins were isolated at the same time, across both the sill at +16.3 m OD to the west of Rumach IV and the other sill of this altitude to the east of Rumach V. This view is supported by the three statistically indistinguishable radiocarbon dates (Fig. 5a and 5b). As the sea level fell across both sills at *c.* +16.3 m OD the effectiveness of water mixing between the two basins was reduced due to the rock sill between them at +13.8 m OD. During the final stages of the isolation the deepest water in Rumach V may have become stratified, accounting for the differences in diatom assemblages. This would also allow for the rapid organic sediment accumulation indicated by the indistinguishable radiocarbon dates within Rumach V. The continued presence of a stratified layer of brackish water may explain the occurrence of mesohalobous diatoms after the isolation. Kjemperud (1986) describes comparable examples of stratification from isolation basins in Norway.

The intercalated clastic unit in each basin (Fig. 4) is unequivocally of freshwater origin (Fig. 5a, 570–581 cm; Fig. 5b, above 670 cm). In terms of lithostratigraphic position and sediment content it is directly comparable with clastic units described from the isolation basins at Rumach Meadhonach and Rumach Iochdar (Shennan *et al.* 1993) and Ardtoe (Shennan *et al.* in press), forming during the Younger Dryas.

Recovery of pollen and dinocysts was poor from both Rumach IV and V and the full diagrams are not reproduced as a minimum pollen sum of 200 was not attainable for every level. The dinocyst data are presented in the later section. At the isolation contact in both basins the pollen assemblage is dominated by Gramineae, Cyperaceae and *Empetrum* with low or absent *Juniperus* and *Rumex*. These assemblages support the Lateglacial Interstadial age indicated by the radiocarbon assays and sustain the view that the basins were isolated at the same time. Furthermore, they suggest that the isolation occurred slightly after that at Rumach Meadhonach, where the pollen assemblages across the isolation contact shows falling *Juniperus* and *Rumex* frequencies. This age difference must lie within the error terms of the radiocarbon assays from the basins (see earlier).

Late glacial relative sea level change

Isolation basins at Ardtoe (Shennan *et al.* in press), Loch nan Eala (Shennan *et al.* 1994) and Rumach (Shennan *et al.* 1993) provide evidence for late glacial relative sea-level change which can be evaluated alongside the new data presented in this paper. All the index points record a fall in relative sea level and are shown in Fig. 6. The Holocene record from the isolation basins at Loch nan Eala and raised coastal marshes elsewhere in the area are described by Shennan *et al.* (1995a, 1995b).

The basins at Loch nan Eala and Rumach are less than 4 km apart and can be discussed as one group to assess the temporal pattern of relative sea-level change 10–12 ka BP. They reveal a continuous fall in relative sea level from *c.* 12 ka BP through to the opening of the Holocene. There is no evidence for a rise in relative sea level during the Younger Dryas (Loch Lomond Stadial), as described for some other parts of Scotland (e.g. Firth & Haggart 1989; Sissons 1983; Sutherland 1988). This contrast is discussed further elsewhere (Shennan *et al.* 1995a; in press).

Ardtoe and Fearnbeg are, respectively, 15 km south and 65 km north of Rumach. Therefore these data illustrate the spatial differences in relative sea-level change since about 11.9 ka BP, arising from the effects of glacio- and hydro-isostatic processes. An 11–12 m displacement between Fearnbeg and Rumach, and a further 3–4 m with Ardtoe (which could be partly attributed to the older radiocarbon age) is consistent with reconstructions of ice sheet dimensions at the Late Weichselian maximum and during deglaciation (Andersen 1981; Bennett & Boulton 1993; Bowen *et al.* 1988). As the isolation basin data provide well-constrained age and altitude parameters on relative sea level, previously unavailable for the late glacial, they can be used to test numerical models of earth rheology and ice sheet interactions (e.g. Lambeck 1993; 1995) as reported by Shennan *et al.* (1995a).

Dinocyst distribution in late glacial sediments

Fluctuations between relative colder and warmer climatic conditions within the Lateglacial Interstadial may be inferred from vegetation records as indicated by pollen analysis. Sample preparations from isolation basins in northwest Scotland have been shown to yield dinocysts, in addition to pollen assemblages, both before and throughout the isolation event. The combination of marine dinocysts and non-marine pollen provides a link between the marine and terrestrial record. Such records help to pinpoint the precise isolation of the basins and to define the nature of the isolation and the subsequent marine influences (storm events) into the basins.

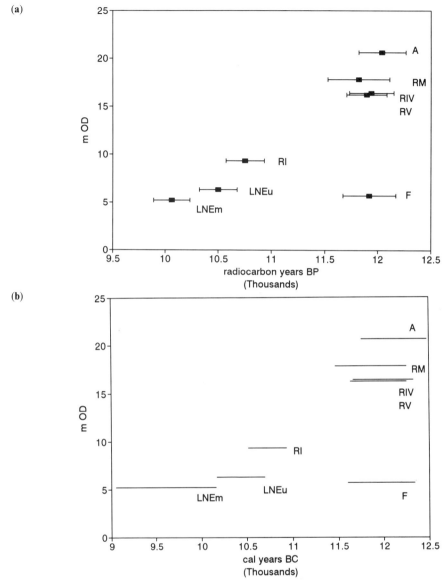

Fig. 6. (a) Relative sea-level index points from Ardtoe (A), Rumach Meadhonach (RM), Rumach IV (RIV), Rumach V (RV), Rumach Iochdar (RI), Loch nan Eala upper basin and main basin (LNEu, LNEm) and Fearnbeg (F). RIV and RV refer to the same sill height, but are offset in the figure for clarity. Calibrated radiocarbon ages are shown in **(b)**. Each index point represents a relative fall in sea level at the altitude of the sill. The indicative meanings of these types of index points are discussed in Shennan *et al.* (in press).

The systematic description of dinocysts in Quaternary sediments around the coast of Britain (Harland 1983; Reid 1972; 1975; 1978; Reid & Harland 1977) has resulted in a *corpus* of data which illustrates the preferential habitats of certain dinocysts in coastal waters and on the continental shelf. The work of Dale (1983) has contributed to a growing knowledge about the

ecology of dinocysts, as has the work of Williams (1971), Wall *et al.* (1977) and Harland (1983) on the distribution of cysts in bottom sediments from the North Atlantic Ocean and adjacent seas. Ecological information from extant species allows an interpretation of the palaeoenvironments to reconstruct palaeoclimates and, from that, to build a climatostratigraphy. The North

of the Younger Dryas (determined palynologically and lithologically) upsection provides a further control on the stratigraphical interpretation of the assemblages.

This assemblage is interpreted as indicative of the possible influence of the North Atlantic Current (NAC) offshore northwest Scotland at this time. A well documented transition from dinocysts indicative of colder, arctic conditions to those indicative of more temperate conditions between 13–11 ka BP has been interpreted, in terms of palaeoceanography, to indicate the passage of the oceanic Polar Front across the northwestern part of the Atlantic and the retreat of ice-dominated waters from the Atlantic and North Sea (Harland 1988). The dominance of *O. centrocarpum* to near monospecific proportions within the Ardtoe section is indicative of north-temperate to arctic environments. Palaeoceanographic reconstructions for the period 13–11 ka BP (for example, Ruddiman & McIntyre 1981) illustrate the migration of the oceanic Polar Front north and west during this time and the introduction of warmer, more temperate NAC waters. The mechanism of withdrawal of the oceanic Polar Front and advance of the NAC is not known in detail. It may be that the movements were progressive rather than expressed in one rapid phase, neither were transitions between positions of the currents necessarily instantaneous. High resolution dinocyst data has the potential for contributing to models of oceanographic change.

At Fearnbeg, the dinocyst assemblage is characterized by low numbers of *Spiniferites* spp., *Gonyaulacysta* spp. and *Operculodinium centrocarpum*. Around the isolation contact the dinocyst assemblage is dominated by *Bitectatodinium tepikiense*. The isolation contact at Fearnbeg has provided a radiometric date of 11 920 ± 125 years BP (SRR-5171).

A similar pattern emerges at Rumach V where *Bitectatodinium tepikiense* again dominates the dinocyst assemblage within the isolation interval which has a radiocarbon age of 11 895 ± 95 years BP (SRR-5168). *Operculodinium centrocarpum* is consistently present but in lower numbers. Dinocyst recovery in Rumach IV is very poor and may be linked to faster sedimentation rates at this site and/or a greater influx of more clastic fractions into the basin.

The overall pattern of dinocyst recovery in terms of stratigraphy would appear to be:

(1)   *c.* 11 920 years BP: assemblages poorer in dinocyst recovery; dominance of *B. tepikiense* but with *O. centrocarpum* still

present, indicating the influence of colder, more arctic water but with the ameliorating effects of the NAC still present. Meltwater effects may have acted to reduce salinity levels to less than fully marine.

(2)   >*c.* 12 040 years BP: assemblages dominated by *O. centrocarpum*, indicating the influence of temperate water, i.e. the NAC.

Although the radiocarbon ages from the isolation basins overlap, the pollen assemblage zone data and the relative altitudes of the isolation basins support the chronological sequence indicated (further discussion in Shennan *et al.* in press).

The most dramatic switch in dinocyst assemblages documented in the literature from the North Atlantic and the North Sea highlights the upsection transition from *B. tepikiense* to *O. centrocarpum* but dated only in a broad band (13–11 ka BP) (Harland 1988). Unfortunately, the few samples deeper than those yielding *O. centrocarpum* at Ardtoe do not yield dinocyst assemblages. This may be due to the coarser nature of the lithology at these depths. At the other sites, only the organic rich samples around the isolation contacts are productive for dinocysts.

Climatic reconstructions (Walker *et al.* 1994) based on faunal and floral assemblages for the period 13–11 ka BP show that the downturn in climate after the thermal maximum followed a step-like pattern; the general pattern to emerge is one of slow deterioration towards the Younger Dryas cold phase with a series of short-lived, warmer events.

The pattern which emerges from the few records of dinocysts at the isolation basin sites may be interpreted, with caution, to indicate evidence for a relatively warm period, followed by a return to colder conditions. These assemblage fluxes occur over a very small time scale – perhaps within 100 years. The data from the isolation basins indicate a relatively warm conditions before 12 040 ± 110 years BP followed by a relatively cooler event, assigned ages of around 11 920 ± 125 years BP and 11 895 ± 95 years BP. This trend is in agreement with the schematic climate reconstruction of Walker *et al.* (1994) which show relative warming pre-12 ka BP, with stepwise cooling 12–11 ka BP (Fig. 7).

Lehman & Keigwin (1992), describing sudden changes in North Atlantic circulation during the last deglaciation, indicate faunal (foraminiferal) evidence for two cooling episodes prior to the Younger Dryas. The older event may be correlated with events from Denmark and

Sweden and is assigned an age within the interval 12–11.8 ka BP. They also conclude that cold oscillations persisted for periods of 200–700 radiocarbon years and the transitions between cold and warm states were extremely rapid, taking no more than 40 years.

Conclusions

Previous research has demonstrated that dinocyst associations are linked with palaeoceanographic regimes and can be used to indicate relative influences of polar and temperate water masses. The research presented in this paper shows that this sensitivity to water temperature, when allied to other types of detailed biostratigraphic evidence, can provide a reliable proxy record of climate change which can be related to the late glacial chronology established by relative pollen analysis and radiocarbon dating. This linkage of dinocyst associations and palaeoceanographic regime may be of sufficiently high resolution to indicate fluxes over short time-scales. Certainly dinocyst assemblages combined with co-occurring diatom and pollen assemblages may be used to monitor the marine–non-marine transition within isolation basins and thus elucidate sea-level history and coastal environmental change. Further detailed work, in particular determining a complete dinocyst stratigraphic record from the Lateglacial Interstadial through to the Younger Dryas, would help elucidate the stepwise cooling from the thermal maximum (13–12.5 ka BP) to 11 ka BP.

This research is supported by contracts from the European Community: 'Relative Sea-Level Changes and Extreme Flooding Events Around European Coasts' contract number EV5V-CT93–0266 and 'Climate Change, Sea-Level Rise and Associated Impacts in Europe' contract number EPOC-CT90-0015. The radiocarbon dates were provided by NERC, radiocarbon allocations 455/0591 and 554/1293. The authors thank all the landowners for granting access to the sites; J. Lloyd, A. Long, S. Haslett and I. Sproxton for help in the field; F. Davies for the laboratory preparations; R. Harland and D. Smith for their valuable comments on the original version; S. Allan for the cartographic work; and M. Powell for the production of the final version. This paper is a contribution to IGCP Project 367.

Appendix: dinoflagellate cyst taxa

Operculodinium centrocarpum (Deflandre and Cookson) Wall 1967
Bitectatodinium tepikiense Wilson 1973

Spiniferites Mantell 1850
Gonyaulacysta Deflandre 1964 ex Morris and Sargeant 1965

References

ANDERSEN, B. G. 1981. Late Weichselian ice sheets in Eurasia and Greenland. *In*: DENTON, G. H. & HUGHES, T. J. (eds) *The Last Great Ice Sheets*. Wiley, New York, 1–65.

BENNETT, M. R. & BOULTON, G. S. 1993. Deglaciation of the Younger Dryas or Loch Lomond Stadial ice-field in the northern Highlands, Scotland. *Journal of Quaternary Science*, **8**, 133–145.

BOWEN, D. Q., ROSE, J., MCCABE, A. M. & SUTHERLAND, D. G. 1986. Correlation of Quaternary glaciations in England, Ireland, Scotland and Wales. *Quaternary Science Reviews*, **5**, 299–340.

DALE, B. 1983. Dinoflagellate resting cysts: 'benthic plankton'. *In*: FRYXELL, G. R. (ed.) *Survival Strategies of the Algae*. Cambridge University Press, 69–136.

DE VERNAL, A., MUDIE, P. J., HARLAND, R., MORZADEC-KERFOURN, M., TURON, J. & WRENN, J. H. 1992 Quaternary organic-walled dinoflagellate cysts of the North Atlantic Ocean and adjacent seas: ecostratigraphy and biostratigraphy. *In*: HEAD, M. J. & WRENN, J. H. (eds) *Neogene and Quaternary Dinoflagellate Cysts and Acritarchs*. American Association of Stratigraphic Palynologists Foundation, Dallas, 289–328.

EDWARDS, L. E. & ANDRLE, V. A. S. 1992. Distribution of selected dinoflagellate cysts in modern marine sediments. *In*: HEAD, M. J. & WRENN, J. H. (eds) *Neogene and Quaternary Dinoflagellate Cysts and Acritarchs*. American Association of Stratigraphic Palynologists Foundation, Dallas, 259–288.

GRIMM, E. 1993. *TILIA: a Pollen Program for Analysis and Display*. Illinois State Museum, Springfield.

FIRTH, C. R. & HAGGART, B. A. 1989. Loch Lomond Stadial and Flandrian shorelines in the inner Moray Firth area, Scotland. *Journal of Quaternary Science*, **4**, 37–50.

HARLAND, R. 1983. Distribution maps of recent dinoflagellate cysts in bottom sediments from the North Atlantic Ocean and adjacent seas. *Palaeontology*, **26**, 321–387.

——1988. Quaternary dinoflagellate cyst biostratigraphy of the North Sea. *Palaeontology*, **31**, 877–903.

——1994. Dinoflagellate cysts from the glacial/postglacial transition in the northeast Atlantic Ocean. *Palaeontology*, **37**, 263–283.

HARTLEY, B. 1986. A check-list of the freshwater, brackish and marine diatoms of the British Isles and adjoining coastal waters. *Journal of the Marine Biological Association, UK*, **66**, 531–610.

KJEMPERUD, A. 1986. Late Weichselian and Holocene shoreline displacement in the Trondheimsfjord area, central Norway. *Boreas*, **15**, 61–82.

LAMBECK, K. 1993. Glacial rebound of the British Isles—II. A high-resolution, high-precision model. *Geophysical Journal International*, **115**, 960–990.

——1995. Late Devensian and Holocene shorelines of the British Isles and North Sea from models of glacio-hydro-isostatic rebound. *Journal of the Geological Society of London*, **152**, 437–448.

LEHMAN, S. J. & KEIGWIN, L. D. 1992. Sudden changes in North Atlantic circulation during the last deglaciation. *Nature*, **356**, 757–762.

MOORE, P. D., WEBB, J. A. & COLLINSON, M. E. 1991. *Pollen Analysis*. Blackwell, London.

PALMER, A. J. M. & ABBOTT, W. H. 1986. Diatoms as indicators of sea-level change. *In*: VAN DE PLASSCHE, O. (ed.) *Sea-level Research: a Manual for the Collection and Evaluation of Data*. Geo Books, Norwich, 457–488.

REID, P. C. 1972. Dinoflagellate cyst distribution around the British Isles. *Journal of the Marine Biological Association, UK*, **52**, 939–944.

——1975. A regional sub-division of dinoflagellate cysts around the British Isles. *New Phytologist*, **75**, 589–603.

——1978. Dinoflagellate cysts in the plankton. *New Phytologist*, **80**, 219–229.

—— & HARLAND, R. 1977. Studies of Quaternary dinoflagellate cysts from the North Atlantic. *American Association of Stratigraphical Palynologists; Contribution Series*, **5A**, 147–169.

RUDDIMAN, W. F. & MCINTYRE, A. 1981. The North Atlantic Ocean during the last deglaciation. *Palaeogeography, Palaeoclimatology, Palaeoecology*, **35**, 145–214.

SHENNAN, I., GREEN, F. M. L., INNES, J. B., LLOYD, J. M., RUTHERFORD, M. M. & WALKER, K. Evaluation of rapid relative sea-level changes in northwest Scotland during the late glacial-interglacial transition: evidence from Ardtoe and other isolation basins. *Journal of Coastal Research*, in press.

——, INNES, J. B., LONG, A. J. & ZONG, Y. 1993. Late Devensian and Holocene relative sea-level changes at Rumach, near Arisaig, northwest Scotland. *Norsk Geologisk Tidsskrift*, **73**, 161–174.

——, ——, —— & ——1994. Late Devensian and Holocene relative sea-level changes at Loch Nan Eala, near Arisaig, northwest Scotland. *Journal of Quaternary Science*, **9**, 261–283.

——, ——, —— & ——1995a. Late Devensian and Holocene relative sea-level changes in northwestern Scotland: new data to test existing models. *Quaternary International*, **26**, 97–123.

——, ——, —— & ——1995b. Holocene relative sea-level changes and coastal vegetation history at Kentra Moss, Argyll, northwest Scotland. *Marine Geology*, **124**, 43–59.

SISSONS, J. B. 1983. Shorelines and isostasy in Scotland. *In*: SMITH, D. E. & DAWSON, A. G. (eds) *Shorelines and Isostasy*. Academic Press, London, 209–226.

SUTHERLAND, D. G. 1988. Glaciation and sea-level change in the south west Highlands. *In*: DAWSON, A. G. (ed.) *INQUA Field Excursion and Symposium on Late Quaternary Sea Levels and Crustal Deformation*. Coventry Polytechnic, Coventry, 15–27.

TROELS-SMITH, J. 1955. Characterization of unconsolidated sediments. *Danmarks Geologiske Undersogelse, Series IV*, **3**, 38–73.

VOS, P. C. & DE WOLF, H. 1993. Diatoms as a tool for reconstructing sedimentary environments in coastal wetlands; methodological aspects. *Hydrobiologia*, **269/270**, 285–296.

WALKER, M. J. C., BOHNCKE, S. J. P., COOPE, G. R., O'CONNELL, M., USINGER, H. & VERBRUGGEN, C. 1994. The Devensian/Weichselian late-glacial in northwest Europe (Ireland, Britain, north Belgium, The Netherlands, northwest Germany). *Journal of Quaternary Science*, **9**, 109–118.

WALL, D., LOHMANN, G. P. & SMITH, W. K. 1977. The environmental and climatic distribution of dinoflagellate cysts in modern marine sediments from regions in the North and South Atlantic Oceans and adjacent seas. *Marine Micropalaeontology*, **2**, 121–200.

WILLIAMS, D. B. 1971. The occurrence of dinoflagellates in marine sediments. *In*: FUNNELL, B. M. & RIEDEL, W. R., (eds) *Micropalaeontology of Oceans*. Cambridge University Press, Cambridge, 231–243.

Late Weichselian environmental changes of the southern Kattegat, Scandinavia, inferred from diatom records

HUI JIANG[1] & KJELL NORDBERG[2]

[1] Department of Quaternary Geology, Lund University, Tornavägen 13 S-223 63, Lund, Sweden

[2] Department of Oceanography, Earth Sciences Centre, Göteborg University, S-413 81, Göteborg, Sweden

Abstract: The diatom stratigraphy of a high-resolution sediment core, dated by the tandem accelerator mass spectrometry (AMS) ^{14}C method, records the environmental changes of the Late Weichselian in the southern Kattegat. Five diatom assemblage zones, with two subzones, are distinguished during the Allerød and Younger Dryas chronozones. Fresh water diatoms dominate the assemblages throughout the core. Salinities, particular the surface water salinity during the whole period, were much lower than that of today. Between 11 500 and 11 300 years BP, the occurrence of abundant freshwater planktonic species with only a few brackish water and marine species suggests an environment strongly affected by a great amount of meltwater discharged from the Baltic Ice Lake via the Öresund Strait. The period from the late Allerød to the early Younger Dryas between 11 300 and 10 600 years BP is characterized by an incursion of cold, saline water into the southern Kattegat with the strongest phase between 11 300 and 10 900 years BP, mirrored by increasing marine diatoms, especially sea ice species. Climatic amelioration took place at about 10 650 years BP, which occurred synchronously with a hydrographic change in the southern Kattegat. Relatively warm marine water, mixed with cold marine water, flowed into the Kattegat, although its impact on the southern Kattegat was small. Towards the end of this stage, the influence of saline water on the southern Kattegat became weaker, and a large amount of meltwater was discharged from the Baltic Ice Lake, which resulted in the surface water salinity decreasing greatly. An earlier change in the drainage pathway of the Baltic Ice Lake, from the Öresund Strait to south central Sweden, took place between 11 200 and 10 900 years BP. This was suggested by fewer planktonic freshwater diatoms and low sediment accumulation rates and/or a hiatus.

The Skagerrak and Kattegat area is an epicontinental part of the North Sea and links the Baltic Sea to the North Sea. The inflow of normal saline water from the Skagerrak and the outflow of hyposaline water from the Baltic Sea, as well as water discharge from the Swedish mainland, carry a large amount of sediments into the Kattegat. Study of the palaeoceanography of the southern Kattegat during Late Weichselian can help us to not only understand the history of the current patterns in the area, but also provide information about the drainage history of the Baltic Ice Lake. The Late Weichselian litho/biostratigraphy and geological development of offshore Kattegat have been studied by Mörner (1969), Miller (1982), Fält (1982), Knudsen & Nordberg (1987), Bergsten & Nordberg (1992), Seidenkrantz & Knudsen (1993) and Bergsten (1994). Diatoms are found wherever there is moisture and sufficient light for photosynthesis and therefore they are good indicators of various environments. So far, however, there are few diatom data available for the southern Kattegat. Diatom analysis of sediments covering c. 1000 years of the late part of the Late Weichselian from the southern Kattegat can provide us with high-resolution records to infer palaeoenvironmental changes in this area such as current patterns, salinity and the drainage history of the Baltic Ice Lake.

Oceanography and geography

The Kattegat is hydrographically situated in the transition zone between the normal saline North Sea and the low saline Baltic Sea (Fig. 1). The general circulation is characterized by the outflow of hyposaline Baltic water along the surface and the inflow of water of nearly normal salinity confined to the deeper parts of the Kattegat (Fig.1). The outflow of the Baltic water through the Danish–Swedish straits and the Kattegat is today a major driving mechanism for the southward inflow of saline water into the Kattegat and the western Baltic (Stigebrandt 1983). The surface water salinity ranges between 10 and 30‰ from south to north. The deep water salinity is constant from north to south with salinities between 30‰ and 34‰. Seasonal

From Andrews, J. T., Austin, W. E. N., Bergsten, H. & Jennings, A. E. (eds), 1996, *Late Quaternary Palaeoceanography of the North Atlantic Margins*, Geological Society Special Publication No. 111, pp. 245–260.

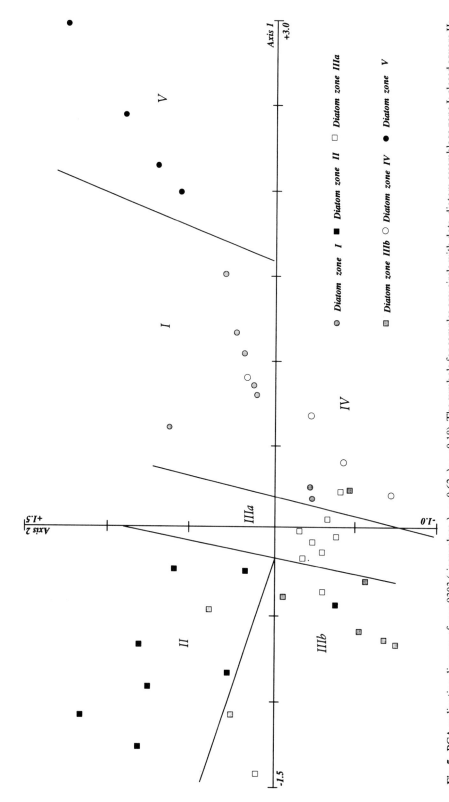

Fig. 5. PCA ordination diagram of core 9303 (eigenvalues $\lambda_1 = 0.62$, $\lambda_2 = 0.18$). The symbols for samples are: circle with dots, diatom assemblage zone I; closed square II; open square, IIIa; square with dots, IIIb; open circle, IV; and closed circle, V.

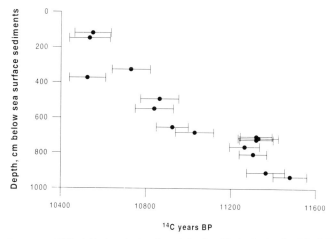

Fig. 6. AMS dates from core 9303 plotted against sediment depth with single standard deviation. A correction for the reservoir effect of sea water was made by subtracting 400 years from the obtained ^{14}C age.

Diatom assemblage from the surface sediments

Diatom analysis on the surface samples (041-98, 041-124, 041-156 and 041-162) near core 9303 gave completely different diatom composition (Table 4; Fig. 4). The assemblage consists mainly of marine diatoms and includes as the main species *Paralia sulcata*, *Thalassionema nitzschioides*, *Cymatosira belgica* Grunow and *Thalassiosira* species that are only found in the two topmost samples of the vibrocore in small numbers. *Fragilariopsis cylindrus*, the most common marine species in the core, is not found in the surface samples. Brackish water species are abundant and contain *Cocconeis costata* Gregory, *Tabularia tabulata* (C.A. Agardh) Snoeijs, *Achnanthes delicatula* Kützing Grunow and *Catenula adhaereni* (Mereschkowsky) Mereschkowsky, of which the first three species are also commonly found in the vibrocore. There are only a few freshwater species in the surface samples with an increase in abundance towards the south.

Chronostratigraphy and sediment accumulation rates

The ^{14}C measurements allow the establishment of a chronology for core 9303 (Fig. 6; Table 2). The dating at 583 cm is obviously too old and is therefore not used. The remaining data set basically shows continuously younger ages upwards and an abrupt change in sediment accumulation rates is observed close to 700 cm. The average sediment accumulation rates below 703 cm and above 650 cm are between 8 and 14 mm/year, and the rates between 703 and 650 cm are relatively low, only around 2 mm/year. There is an alternative interpretation of the ^{14}C data. Instead of just a change in sediment accumulation rates, a hiatus lasting about 200 radiocarbon years at about 700 cm can be suggested. In that case, the sediment accumulation rate is about 7 mm/year between 650 and 703 cm.

The sediments of core 9303 represent parts of the Allerød and Younger Dryas chronozones. Radiocarbon datings of shells at three different

Table 4. *Diatom living habitat and salinity groupings from the surface samples*

Sample No.	041-98	041-124	041-156	041-162
Marine plankton	17.6	7.9	28.2	21.2
Marine non-plankton	41.2	35.0	41.6	29.2
Brackish water plankton	5.9	12.9	2.0	14.4
Brackish water non-plankton	29.4	26.3	16.8	22.9
Freshwater plankton	1.2	2.9	2.0	0.53
Freshwater non-plankton	4.7	15.0	9.4	11.7

* Numbers are percentages.

tolerate greatly freshened surface water. Secondly, the Baltic Ice Lake was the most likely source for an allochthonous freshwater flora. So far no record shows the evidence that freshwater planktonic diatoms were abundant in the Baltic Ice Lake during this period (Abelmann 1985).

11 300–10 900 years BP (802–622 cm)

Cold marine water with high salinity from the Skagerrak flowed into the southern Kattegat much stronger than before, as mirrored by the presence of more sea ice species *Fragilariopsis cylindrus* together with abundant mollusc shells of *Portlandia arctica*. The abrupt decrease of planktonic freshwater diatoms implies less meltwater from the Baltic Ice Lake via the Öresund Strait. However, the water discharged from the rivers along the Swedish west coast still had some influence on the diatom flora in the southern Kattegat as the number of non-planktonic fresh water diatoms remained the same. The meltwater outflow from the Baltic Ice Lake and the rivers along the Swedish west coast might be one of the drivers for the incursion of cold marine water from the Skagerrak into the southern Kattegat, which resulted in inflow of saline bottom water as the Baltic Current does today (Stigebrandt 1983). It may be also the climatic cooling that strengthens the circulation as the thermohaline circulation of the oceans is due to an increase of density at the upper surface, either directly by cooling or indirectly when ice freezes out, ejecting salt and thus increasing the density of the remaining water. The sediment accumulation rates between 700 and 622 cm are relatively low; a hiatus representing about 200 radiocarbon years at about 700 m might even occur. The low sediment accumulation rates can be attributed to the climatic cooling, which resulted in significantly less meltwater from the Baltic Ice Lake, and consequently fewer sediments deposited in the southern Kattegat. It can also be interpreted that the sediment deposition during this period might have had, instead of the Öresund Strait, a different pathway such as north of Mt Billingen (south central Sweden) as suggested by Donner (1969) and Björck (1979).

10 900–10 650 years BP (622–273 cm)

The impact of cold marine water on the southern Kattegat became weaker, and consequently the salinity in the southern Kattegat was lower than before, reflected by the decrease of marine species such as *Fragilariopsis cylindrus*. The strength of the cold marine water incursion during this stage also varied with the strongest phase in the late period mirrored by the changes in the numbers of marine diatoms. There was almost no variation in the composition of marine diatoms, implying that the marine water flowing into the southern Kattegat remained cold. The increasing freshwater diatoms, low diatom concentrations and high accumulation rates suggest a relatively strong influence of meltwater on the southern Kattegat again. It is also worth mentioning that non-planktonic freshwater species achieved their maximum abundances (44–67%). They may be physically attached to the substratum by means of mucous stipes or pads, or may lie free as a film on mud or sand (Hendey 1964). Therefore they usually live in shallow water because they need light to keep them growing, as most plants do. It is difficult to explain these diatoms as authochthonous freshwater flora living in relatively deep water with a saline water layer at the bottom. Instead, they were probably carried into the southern Kattegat by the rivers along the Swedish west coast. This suggests that meltwater discharged from the rivers along the Swedish west coast also had some effect on the southern Kattegat.

10 650–10 500 years BP (273–122 cm)

There was an obvious change in the current circulation in the Skagerrak, possibly also in the North Atlantic area during this period. Instead of only cold marine water, relatively warm water mixed with cold marine water flowed into the Kattegat, as reflected by the presence of a cosmopolitan species *Thalassionema nitzschioides*, although the impact of marine water on the southern Kattegat was much weaker than before. In the GIN Sea, *Thalassionema nitzschioides*, together with *Paralia sulcata* and *Proboscia alata* (Brightwell) Sundström, represent the Norwegian–Atlantic Current (Koç Karpuz & Schrader 1990). The high number of freshwater planktonic species can be attributed to the discharge of a huge amount of meltwater from the Baltic Ice Lake via the Öresund Strait. This resulted in the surface water salinity in the southern Kattegat decreasing greatly, especially towards the end of this stage, although there was still a brackish–saline water layer at the bottom as during 11 500–11 300 years BP. The sediment accumulation rates were high, accompanied by extremely low diatom concentrations and poor diatom preservation. This evidence seems to hint at a climatic amelioration.

Correlation and discussion

Allerød/Younger Dryas climatic oscillation

The Allerød/Younger Dryas climatic oscillation has been recorded from the Swedish west coast and adjacent regions, Norwegian Sea and the circum-Atlantic region although the origin of this event is still enigmatic (Duplessy *et al.* 1992; Koç Karpuz & Jansen 1992; Lehman & Keigwin, 1992; Veum *et al.* 1992; Alley *et al.* 1993; Berglund *et al.* 1994). Bergsten & Nordberg (1992) made a stratigraphic investigation of 38 piston and vibrocores in the southern Kattegat. A cold phase, between 11 500 and 10 600 years BP was recorded by decreased sediment accumulation rates and an increased abundance of salt demanding foraminiferal species, and a climatic warming close to 10 500–10 600 years BP suggested by more temperate mollusc and fora-miniferal faunas. Koç Karpuz & Jansen (1992) found that between 11 200 and 10 200 years BP, during the Younger Dryas, arctic and polar conditions prevailed in the SE Norwegian Sea with a summer sea surface temperature of about 1°C and winter sea ice cover. Two periods with especially strong sea ice influence and polar conditions (as mirrored by the sea ice diatom assemblage with *Nitzschia grunowii*, *N. cylindrus* and *Thalassiosira hyalina*) were documented at the beginning and at the end of the Younger Dryas period. The middle Younger Dryas was characterized by the Arctic Water assemblage and less influence of the Sea Ice assemblage, indicating a slightly less cold period. Berglund *et al.* (1984), based on the analysis of pollen, plant macrofossils and insect remains, concluded that the Allerød/Younger Dryas transition at *c.* 11 000 years BP represented a sudden and distinct climatic deterioration with response in soil and vegetation. This deterioration coincided with a distinct readvance of the Scandinavian inland ice (Berglund 1979; Björck & Digerfeldt 1984) and this Younger Dryas cold phase had a length of only *c.* 500 ^{14}C years (Björck 1979; Berglund *et al.* 1984). A fossil insect record from southern Sweden (Lemdahl 1991) suggests that temperate conditions prevailed at *c.* 11 800 years BP with average summer temperatures of 15–18°C. A gradual climatic deterioration started at *c.* 11 600 years BP and arctic conditions became established with mean summer temperatures of 10–13°C at *c.* 10 800 years BP. A slight amelioration occurred around 10 500 years BP and a marked climatic warming started at approximately 10 200 years BP with mean summer temperatures rising to 14–16°C. Diatom analysis

from core 9303 suggests that sea water in the Skagerrak and the Kattegat during 11 500–11 300 years BP was cold. A stronger incursion of cold saline water into the southern Kattegat was registered during 11 300–10 650 years BP with the strongest phase between 11 300 and 10 900 years BP when the water temperature was even lower than before, in-ferred by increase of sea ice species *Fragilariopsis cylindrus*. After *c.* 10 650 years BP, *Fragilariopsis cylindrus* almost disappeared and, instead, the cosmopolitan species *Thalassionema nitzschioides* occurred, reflecting a relatively high water temperature. This also agrees with freshwater diatom data, in which planktonic species domi-nate, suggesting a huge amount of meltwater discharged from the Baltic Ice Lake triggered by climatic amelioration.

Drainage history of the Baltic Ice Lake

The development of the Baltic Sea since the last deglaciation has been the focus for at least a century of research in the circum-Baltic countries (Björck 1995). One of the main questions under debate is the drainage history of the Baltic Ice Lake during the last deglaciation. There seems to be a consensus of opinion that the first outlet for the Baltic Ice Lake meltwater was situated in the Öresund area (Agrell 1976; Björck 1979; Bergsten & Nordberg 1992). According to the data from the Kattegat, Bergsten & Nordberg (1992) suggested that the Öresund Strait functioned as an outlet from approximately 12 700 years BP until *c.* 10 300 years BP when a sudden change in the drainage pathway of the Baltic Ice Lake, from the Öresund Strait to north of Mt Billingen, south central Sweden, took place. On the other hand, Donner (1969) and Björck (1979) suggested that such a change in the drainage pathway of the Baltic Ice Lake, for the first time, occurred at *c.* 11 200 years BP when the water level of the Baltic Ice Lake was rapidly lowered. Inter- and extrapolated shorelines in the Baltic and along the Swedish west coast were both situated 5–10 m below the Öresund bedrock sill at *c.* 11 000 years BP (Björck & Digerfeldt 1991). In the early Younger Dryas, the Mt Billingen drainage pathway was blocked by the advancing ice sheet and the Baltic Ice Lake water was once again dammed, with the Öresund Strait as the renewed outlet (Björck 1995). Björck (1995) gives a detailed list of the arguments for and against the drainage at Mt Billingen at *c.* 11 200 years BP and concludes that the hypothesis for an earlier drainage change is most likely.

If meltwater from the Baltic Ice Lake was drained continuously via the Öresund Strait between 12 700 and 10 300 years BP and there was no drainage change during this period, the changes in numbers of freshwater planktonic diatoms could reflect the variations in the strength of the meltwater outflow from the Baltic Ice Lake, caused mainly by climatic oscillation. Hence the small number of freshwater planktonic species between 11 300 and 11 000 years BP might indicate a colder period, which resulted in less meltwater flowing into the southern Kattegat from the Baltic Ice Lake and consequently low sediment accumulation rates. The increase of sea ice species also suggests a cold climate during this period.

Comparing the diatom assemblage between 11 200 and 10 900 years BP with those of 11 300–11 200 and 10 900–10 650 years BP, we find that the sea ice species are the main marine species during the whole period and there is no big difference in the composition of marine diatoms although the numbers of marine diatoms especially sea ice species between 11 200 and 10 900 years BP are higher than those in the previous and following periods. We think that such a climatic cooling could not have generated a great change in sediment accumulation rates. It is more likely that there was a dramatic environmental change in connection with a shift of the drainage pathway. As the Baltic Ice Lake drainage via Öresund is suggested by abundant freshwater planktonic diatoms and high sediment accumulation rates in the southern Kattegat (see zone I), it seems reasonable to explain few freshwater planktonic diatoms and low sediment accumulation rates with a change in the drainage pathway from the Öresund Strait to south central Sweden. If there was a hiatus, it can also be interpreted as a result of a drainage change. According to Björck & Digerfeldt (1991) and Bergsten & Nordberg (1992), the Öresund Strait no longer functioned as outlet of the Baltic Ice Lake at about 10 300 years BP. A large land bridge existed between Sweden, Denmark and the continent. The accumulation of sediments suddenly ceased in the southern Kattegat (Bergsten & Nordberg 1992). Simultaneously the opening of a passage, the catastrophic lowering by about 25 m of the Baltic Ice Lake and the establishment of a drainage pathway for the Baltic Ice Lake across south central Sweden took place (Donner 1969; Björck 1979; Björck & Digerfeldt 1984; Svensson 1989). The same situation might also have occurred at the end of the Allerød Chronozone as the water level of the Baltic Ice Lake may have been rapidly lowered (5–10 m) at about

11 200 years BP (Björck 1979; Svensson 1989) when there was a similar hiatus in the southern Kattegat.

Conclusion

(1) Five diatom assemblage zones can be distinguished, of which one has been subdivided into two subzones, indicating that the southern Kattegat underwent five main environmental periods in the late Allerød and Younger Dryas. The salinities, in particular the surface water salinity, in the southern Kattegat during the whole period were much lower than that of today based on the comparison of diatom assemblages between core 9303 and the recent surface sediments adjacent to the vibrocore.

(2) Freshwater diatoms dominate the assemblage with only a few brackish water and marine species during the late Allerød (11 500–11 300 years BP), which suggests an environment strongly influenced by the meltwater outflow. Abundant fresh water planktonic species, high accumulation rates and dropstones suggest that a large amount of meltwater with abundant sediments was discharged from the Baltic Ice Lake into the southern Kattegat via the Öresund Strait. The water column in the southern Kattegat was highly stratified by a brackish–saline water layer at the bottom and a greatly freshened water layer on the top. The impact of marine water was weak as only a few marine diatoms were found. The presence of sea ice species, although small in numbers, implies that the temperature of marine water flowing into the Kattegat at that time was cold.

(3) The period from the late Allerød to the early Younger Dryas between 11 300 and 10 650 years BP is characterized by a relatively strong incursion of cold saline water into the southern Kattegat with the strongest phase between 11 300 and 10 900 years BP, mirrored by increasing marine diatoms, especially sea ice species. Both climatic cooling and the meltwater outflow from the Baltic Ice Lake can be possible drivers for the strong incursion of cold marine water from the Skagerrak into the southern Kattegat.

(4) An earlier change in the drainage pathway of the Baltic Ice Lake, from the Öresund Strait to south central Sweden, took place at about 11 200 years BP. It was suggested

by fewer freshwater planktonic diatoms, low sediment accumulation rates and/or a hiatus.

(5) Climatic amelioration occurred at about 10 650 years BP. Instead of dominating cold marine water, relatively warm marine water mixed with cold marine water flowed into the Kattegat, although the impact of this marine water on the southern Kattegat was small. The highest numbers of planktonic freshwater diatoms, extremely low diatom concentrations, and high sediment accumulation rates in the uppermost four samples indicate the discharge of a huge amount of meltwater from the Baltic Ice Lake via the Öresund Strait. The salinities, especially surface water salinity, decreased greatly. There was still a brackish–saline water layer at the bottom as during the period 11 500–11 300 years BP.

We acknowledge S. Björck for his enthusiastic and valuable comments and discussions. H. Håkansson, G. Digerfeldt, B. Stabell and two anonymous referees critically read the manuscript and we are grateful for many valuable comments. M. Gustafsson and P. I. Sehlstedt assisted during the coring onboard the research vessel *Svanic*; F. Klingberg, Swedish Geology Survey, provided us with surface sediment samples; I. Snowball checked the English; and T. Persson gave technical support. To all these people we are very thankful. Financial support by the Geological Survey of Sweden (Nordberg) and the Swedish Natural Science Research Council (NFR) (Nordberg Grant No. G-GV 9874-302 and Björck Grant No. S-FO 4637-320) is gratefully acknowledged.

References

ABELMANN, A. 1985. *Palecologic and Ecostratigraphic Investigations of Diatom Assemblages in Holocene Sediments of the Central Baltic Sea.* Berichte-Reports, Geologisch-Paläontologisches Institut der Universitäa Kiel, **Nr. 9**.

AGRELL, H. 1976. The highest coastline in south-eastern Sweden. *Boreas*, **5**, 143–154.

ALLEY, R. B., MEESE, D. A. & 9 others 1993. Abrupt increase in Greenland snow accumulation at the end of the Younger Dryas event. *Nature*, **362**, 527–529.

BATTARBEE, R. W. & KNEEN, M. J. 1982. The use electronically counted microspheres in absolute diatom analysis. *Limnology and Oceanography*, **27**, 184–188.

BERGLUND, B. E. 1979. The deglaciation of southern Sweden 13 500–10 000 B. P. *Boreas*, **8**, 89–118.

——, BJÖRCK, S., LEMDAHL, G., BERGSTEN, H., NORDBERG, K. & KOLSTRUP, E. 1994. Late Weichselian environmental change in southern Sweden and Denmark. *Journal of Quaternary Science*, **9**, 127–132.

——, LEMDAHL, G., LIEDBERG-JÖNSSON, B. & PERSSON, T. 1984. Biotic response to climatic changes during the time span 13,000–10,000 B.P. — a case study from SW Sweden. *In*: MÖRNER, N.-A. & KARLÉ, W. (eds) *Climatic Changes on a Yearly to Millennial Basis.* Reidel, Dordrecht, 25–36.

BERGSTEN, H. 1994. A high-resolution record of late glacial and early Holocene marine sediments from southwestern Sweden; with special emphasis on environmental changes close to the Pleistocene–Holocene transition and the influence of fresh water from the Baltic basin. *Journal of Quaternary Science*, **9**, 1–12.

——, H. & NORDBERG, K. 1992. Late Weichselian marine stratigraphy of the southern Kattegat, Scandinavia: evidence for drainage of the Baltic Ice Lake between 12,700 and 10,300 years BP. *Boreas*, **21**, 223–252.

BJÖRCK, S. 1979. *Late Weichselian stratigraphy of Blekinge, SE Sweden, and water level changes in the Baltic Ice Lake.* PhD Thesis, **7**, University of Lund, Department of Quaternary Geology.

——, 1995. A review of the history of the Baltic Sea, 13.0–8.0 ka BP. *Quaternary International*, **27**, 19–40.

—— & DIGERFELDT, G. 1984. Climatic changes at Pleistocene/Holocene boundary in the Middle Swedish endmoraine zone, mainly inferred from stratigraphic indications. *In*: MÖRNER, N.-A. & KARLÉN, W. (eds) *Climatic Changes on a Yearly to Millennial Basis.* Reidel, Dordrecht, 37–56.

—— & —— 1991. Allerød–Younger Dryas sea level changes in southwestern Sweden and their relation to the Baltic Ice Lake development. *Boreas*, **20**, 115–133.

DONNER, J. J. 1969. A profile across Fennoscandia of Late Weichselian and Flandrian shore-lines. *Societas Scientarum Fennica. Commentationes Physico-Mathematicae*, **36**, 1–23.

DUPLESSY, J. C., LABEYRIE, L., ARNOLD, M., PATERNE, M., DUPRAT, J. & VAN WEERING, T. C. E. 1992. Changes in surface salinity of the North Atlantic Ocean during the last deglaciation. *Nature*, **358**, 485–489.

FRYXELL, G. A. & HASLE, G. R. 1972. *Thalassiosira eccentrica* (Ehrenb.) Cleve, *T. symmetrica* sp. nov., and some related centric diatoms. *Journal of Phycology*, **8**, 297–317.

FÄLT, L. M. 1982. *Late Quaternary sea-floor deposits off the Swedish west coast.* PhD Thesis. Department of Geology, Chalmers University of Technology and University of Gothenburg Publ., **A37**.

HASLE, G. R., 1978. Some *Thalassiosira* species with one central process (Bacillariophyceae), *Norw. J. Bot.*, **25**, 77–110.

——, VON STOSCH, H. A. & SYVERTSEN, E. E. 1983. Cymatosiraceae, a new diatom family. *Bacillaria*, **6**, 9–156.

HENDEY, N. I. 1964. *An introductory Account of the Smaller Algae of British Coastal Waters. Part V. Bacillariophyceae (Diatoms).* HMSO, London.

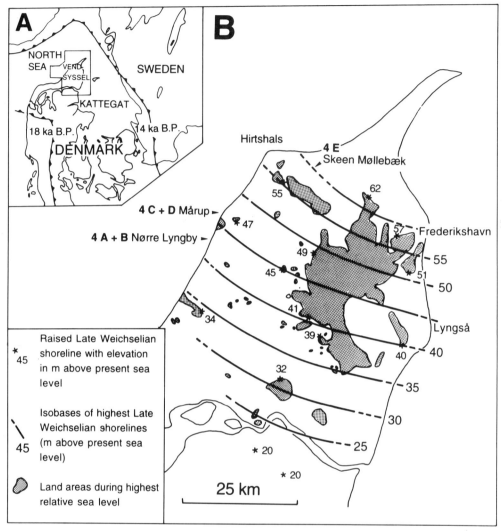

Fig. 1. (**A**) Denmark and southern Sweden with Weichselian maximum (*c.* 18 ka BP) and ice position *c.* 14 ka BP (ice positions after Lagerlund & Houmark-Nielsen 1993). (**B**) Vendsyssel: isobases of highest Late Weichselian shorelines and land–sea configuration during highest relative sea level. 4A–E indicate sections discussed in this paper. Land–sea configuration after Jessen (1918).

The Zirphaea beds rest on the Younger Yoldia clay or older deposits, not on the Upper Saxicava sand. Foraminiferal studies indicate that the Upper Saxicava sand and the Zirphaea beds are contemporary (Knudsen 1978). This contemporaneity is clearly shown by the ecological evaluation of ^{14}C dated mollusc assemblages (Petersen 1984*a*).

Classical sea-level history

The classical picture of the Late Weichselian sea-level history is based on Jessen's (1899; 1918)

work. The three lowermost stratigraphic units were thought to have been deposited during a major transgression–regression cycle, whereas the Zirphaea beds were ascribed to represent a shorter and slightly younger cycle superimposed on the major cycle (Fig. 2).

In contrast with the general opinion, Andersen (1961) suggested that a maximum transgression reaching more that 90 m above the present sea level occurred before deglaciation and that deglaciation took place during regression; Mörner (1969) sketched sea-level curves for Vendsyssel indicating a rapid fall of *c.* 10 m

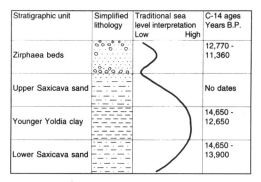

Stratigraphic unit	Simplified lithology	Traditional sea level interpretation		C-14 ages Years B.P.
		Low	High	
Zirphaea beds				12,770 - 11,360
Upper Saxicava sand				No dates
Younger Yoldia clay				14,650 - 12,650
Lower Saxicava sand				14,650 - 13,900

Fig. 2. Classical stratigraphy and sea-level history plus ^{14}C ages. Stratigraphic units after Jessen (1918), lithology after Jessen (1899; 1918), sea-level interpretation inferred from Hansen (1965), ^{14}C ages after Tauber (1966), Krog & Tauber (1974), Knudsen (1978) and Aaris-Sørensen & Petersen (1984).

about 15 ka BP and a following more or less continuous and moderate regression.

A modern and detailed relative sea-level curve for Vendsyssel, based on palaeoecological evaluation of ^{14}C dated marine molluscs (Petersen 1984a; A in Fig. 3), covers the time span 14600 to 11 200 a BP

Isostatic revision of the classical relative sea-level curve

The relative sea-level curve by Petersen (1984a) has, however, a pronounced weakness. The data used for its construction originate from localities which have experienced different amounts of isostatic uplift since time of deposition and the curve is thus in danger of being skewed. To

reduce this problem Petersen's data are here corrected in relation to a fixed level of isostatic uplift using the isobases in Fig. 1B (Table 1). Because the majority of the data come from the northern areas, the 60 m isobase is chosen as the reference level. The resulting sea-level curve (B in Fig. 3) is thus valid in the transect Hirtshals–Frederikshavn.

According to the revised sea-level curve the period from *c.* 15 000 to 11 000 years BP can be di-vided into six events, starting with deglaciation and followed by five events of changing relative sea level (Fig. 3).

Sedimentological evaluation of the Late Weichselian sea-level events

The main features of new sedimentological data from classical localities in NW Vendsyssel (Fig. 1B) are presented to test the relative sea-level events in a sedimentological and sequence stratigraphic context. To facilitate comparison between the sedimentologically significant sea-level events and the events from the ecologically based sea-level curve (B in Fig. 3), the numbering of events introduced in Fig. 3 is maintained here.

Events 1 to 3: deglaciation and progressive sedimentation under a high relative sea level

At Nørre Lyngby (sections 4A and 4B in Fig. 4) and Mårup (sections 4C and 4D) marine sediments fill depressions in the glacial landscape. Sections 4B and 4D are located central in these depressions, whereas 4A and 4C are located in marginal positions.

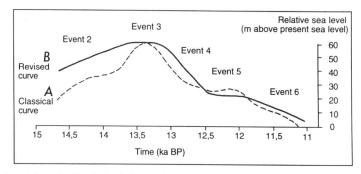

Fig. 3. Isostatic revision of a classical relative sea-level curve. The classical palaeoecologically based sea-level curve by Petersen (1984a) (curve A) is corrected to a fixed level of isostatic uplift using the isobases in Fig. 1B. The 60 m isobase is used as reference level. The revised curve (curve B) is valid in the transect Hirtshals–Frederikshavn.

Table 1. *Data, primary sources and corrections used to outline the relative sea level curves B (in Fig. 3) and C (in Fig. 10)*

Sample No.	[14]C age (years BP)	Lithology	Fauna	Locality	Coordinates	Area	Elevation (masl)	Isobase (masl)	Corrected elevation (masl)	Reference
K-2670	14 650 ± 190	L.S.-Y.Y.	A.S.	Nørre Lyngby	57°25′ N 09°45′ E	SW	1, 6	42	20	3
K-2671	14 270 ± 180	Y.Y.	A.D.	Nørre Lyngby	57°25′ N 09°45′ E	SW	8	42	26	3, 4
K-1052	14 080 ± 240	Y.Y.	A.D.	Skeen Møllebæk	57°33′ N 10°07′ E	NW	12	60	12	2*
K-858	13 900 ± 220	L.S.	A.S.	Lønstrup Klint	57°28′ N 09°47′ E	SW	22	47	35	1*
K-1053	13 610 ± 220	Y.Y.	A.D.	Skeen Møllebæk	57°33′ N 10°07′ E	NW	15	60	15	2*
K-903	13 010 ± 190	Y.Y.	A.D.	Dybvad	57°17′ N 10°22′ E	SE	16	42	34	1*
K-1468	12 770 ± 190	Z.	B.S.	Vangen	57°32′ N 10°12′ E	NW	15	60	15	2
K-891	12 650 ± 180	Y.Y.	A.D.	Bindslev	57°32′ N 10°12′ E	NW	12	60	12	1*
K-897	12 520 ± 180	Z.	B.S.	Skeen Møllebæk	57°33′ N 10°07′ E	NW	8	60	8	1*
K-1318	12 460 ± 190	Z.	B.S.	Kjul Å	57°35′ N 10°01′ E	NW	7	58	9	2
K-1688	12 400 ± 180	?U.S./Z.?	B.S.	Råholt	57°27′ N 10°31′ E	NE	25	60	25	2
K-1357	12 340 ± 190	Z.	B.S.	Kjul Å	57°35′ N 10°01′ E	NW	7	58	9	2
K-899	12 240 ± 180	Z.	B.S.	Skeen Møllebæk	57°33′ N 10°07′ E	NW	10	60	10	1*
K-860	12 230 ± 170	Z.	B.S.	Skeen Møllebæk	57°33′ N 10°07′ E	NW	7	60	7	1*
K-861	12 190 ± 170	Z.	B.S.	Skeen Møllebæk	57°33′ N 10°07′ E	NW	11	60	11	1*
K-1320	12 130 ± 190	Z.	B.D.	Kjul Å	57°35′ N 10°01′ E	NW	6	58	8	2
K-1689	12 120 ± 180	Z.	B.S.	Skeen Mølle	57°33′ N 10°07′ E	NW	9	60	9	2*
K-859	12 030 ± 130	?U.S./Z.?	B.S.	Borgbakke	57°27′ N 10°31′ E	NE	20	60	20	1*
K-1687	12 020 ± 180	?U.S./Z.?	B.S.	Borgbakke	57°27′ N 10°31′ E	NE	20	60	20	2
K-1470	11 980 ± 190	Z.	B.D.	Tværsted Å	57°35′ N 10°11′ E	NW	3	62	1	2
K-1471	11 950 ± 190	Z.	B.D.	Tværsted Å	57°35′ N 10°11′ E	NW	3	62	1	2
K-1319	11 950 ± 190	Z.	B.S.	Kjul Å	57°35′ N 10°01′ E	NW	5, 5	58	8	2
K-1248	11 710 ± 180	Z.	B.S.	Kjul Å	57°35′ N 10°01′ E	NW	7	58	9	2
K-2575	11 360 ± 170	Z.	B.S.	Sindallund	57°27′ N 10°31′ E	NE	4	60	4	5

Lithology: L.S., Lower Saxicava sand; U.S., Upper Saxicava sand; Y.Y., Younger Yoldia clay; and Z., Zirphaea beds.
Fauna: A.D., arctic deep water (>20 m); A.S., arctic shallow water (0–20 m); B.D., boreal deep water (>20 m); B.S., boreal shallow water (0–20 m). Ecological evaluations after Petersen (1984a).
Areas: SW, The Nørre Lyngby–Mårup area; NW, The Hirtshals–Skeen Møllebæk area; NE, The Frederikshavn area; SE, The Lyngså area (Fig. 1B).
References: 1, Tauber (1966); 2, Krog & Tauber (1974); 3, Knudsen (1978); 4, Abrahamsen & Readman (1980); 5, Aaris-Sørensen & Petersen (1984); *, Elevation after Petersen (1984a). The ^{14}C ages are not corrected for isotopic fractionation. This gives a 'built in' age correction of c. –410 years (Mangerud 1972) and the 'raw' [14]C ages are therefore directly comparable with ^{14}C ages of organic terrestrial material (Krog & Tauber 1974). For a discussion, see Lagerlund & Houmark-Nielsen (1993).

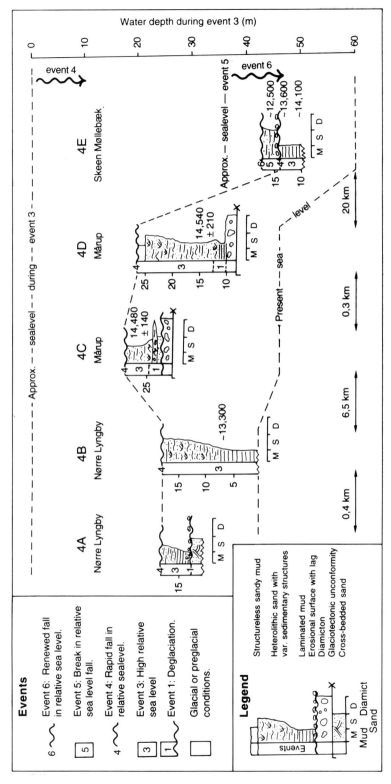

Fig. 4. Sedimentological evaluation of relative sea-level events. The five sections are arranged according to the water depth during event 3 (high relative sea level). Numbering of events is adapted from Fig. 3 (no evidence for a transgressive event 2 is found). Ages from section 4C and 4D are new AMS ^{14}C ages corrected for a reservoir age of 400 years (Table 2). Ages from section 4B and 4E are inferred from ^{14}C ages from Krog & Tauber (1974), Knudsen (1978) and Abrahamsen & Readman (1980). These ages have a 'built in' reservoir correction and they are therefore directly comparable with the reservoir corrected new AMS ^{14}C ages and with the ages of organic terrestrial material (Lagerlund & Houmark-Nielsen 1993; see also Table 1 for discussion).

Deglaciation. At Nørre Lyngby (section 4A in Fig. 4) glaciation and deglaciation are represented by an erosional surface formed in various sediments pre-dating the Weichsel maximum. A position near the ice margin is reflected in the scattered sand lenses in the lowermost part of the marine mud resting on the erosional surface (Fig. 5).

In the marginal section at Mårup (4C in Fig. 4) deglaciation is represented by various slumped subaqueous sand and diamicton beds (Fig. 6) resting on a diamicton interpreted as a subglacial till (Richardt unpublished data). Bioturbation commences immediately above the disturbed diamicton beds.

In the central section at Mårup (4D in Fig. 4) the subglacial till shows a gradual transition to laminated sandy mud, which in turn changes gradually to strongly bioturbated muddy sand with abundant marine macrofossils.

Deglaciation is in all three sections interpreted to have taken place under glaciomarine conditions.

Marine sedimentation. As stated earlier, the sand lenses in the lowermost part of the marine mud in section 4A are interpreted to be a result of a position proximal to the ice margin. The sand rich basal parts of the marine successions in sections 4C and 4D are interpreted to have the same origin and the rather abruptly fining upwards transitions to heterolithic muddy sand are thus reflecting retreat of the ice margin rather than transgression.

The major parts of the four sections 4A to 4D consist of coarsening upwards successions starting with offshore mud (sections 4A and 4B, Fig. 5) or marine heterolithic mud–sand packages (sections 4C and 4D, Figs 6 and 7). The successions coarsen to more sandy or even gravelly beds (Fig. 8). These successions are typical for the gradational-based shoreface successions of Plint (1988) deposited under 'normal regression' *sensu* Posamentier *et al.* (1992), i.e. during stable relative sea level, where sediment accumulation leads to a lowering of water depth and to prograding coastlines. This interpretation is adapted for all four sections, 4A to 4D.

The uppermost mud in section 4D may have been deposited after a substantial transgression, but a more simple explanation favoured here is deposition in a protected environment behind a spit bar system initiated from the island to the south of Mårup (Fig. 1B). No remains of such a spit bar system are left today due to recent coastal erosion, but elsewhere in Vendsyssel Late Weichselian spit bar systems more than 10 km long, isolating large embayments, have been found (Nielsen *et al.* 1988).

Sea-level history during events 1 to 3. In contrast with the classical interpretations, the above-mentioned successions are interpreted as representing deglaciation and progressive sedimentation under a stable high relative sea level. Minor falls or rises in relative sea level may have occurred during sedimentation, but there is no evidence of a major transgression. This means that the transgressive event 2 in Fig. 3 is questionable and that event 3 therefore had a longer duration than indicated on the sea level curve B in Fig. 3.

Fig. 5. Basal part of section 4A (Figs 1 and 4): marine mud resting on fluvial sand with erosional contact. Glaciation and deglaciation (event 1) are represented by the erosional surface. Marine mud is deposited during event 3 (high relative sea level). Sand ripples in the lower part of the mud are deposited due to a position near the ice margin. Pen 14 cm long.

Fig. 6. Basal part of section 4C (Figs 1 and 4): deglaciation sediments and marine heterolithic sand covering subglacial till. The succession represents deglaciation in a marine environment (event 1) and progressive sedimentation during event 3 (high relative sea level). Handle of trowel 13 cm long.

Events 4 to 6: forced regression

Several small sections in the Skeen Møllebæk area contain the same succession (section 4E in Fig. 4). The succession starts with offshore mud (Younger Yoldia clay). The offshore mud is truncated by a regional erosional surface, in some sections with a gravelly lag with abundant redeposited marine shells and covered by stratified marine sand (Zirphaea beds), in some sections with gravelly horizons. This succession is typical of the 'sharp-based shoreface succession' of Plint (1988), deposited during 'forced regression' *sensu* Posamentier *et al.* (1992), i.e. during a fall in relative sea level.

The erosional surface is formed during the fall in relative sea level, whereas the sandy packages resting on the erosional surface are deposited during break(s) in the relative sea-level fall. This means that in the Skeen Møllebæk sections event 4 (rapid fall in relative sea level) is represented by the erosional surface whereas event 5 (break in relative sea-level fall) is represented by the sandy beds.

In the four other sections a regional erosional surface representing event 4 is also present

(Fig. 4A–4D, Fig. 9), but here no sharp-based shoreface sand bodies were deposited during event 5 because these areas had already emerged from the sea during event 4 (Fig. 4).

Event 6 is represented by the uppermost erosional surface in the Skeen Møllebæk section, reflecting the renewed fall in relative sea level, that continued into the Holocene. The erosional surface is the sequence boundary separating the Late Weichselian sequence from the Holocene sequence.

Sea level history during events 4 to 6. The sedimentological and sequence stratigraphic interpretations above confirm the occurence of the relative sea level events 4, 5 and 6.

Outlining the new sedimentologically based relative sea-level curve

The sedimentologically significant sea-level events from above form the base of the outline of a new relative sea-level curve (C in Fig. 10). To date the sea-level events and estimate the

Fig. 8. Upper part of section 4B: marine heterolithic sand deposited at the end of event 3 (high relative sea level). Note the high sand–mud ratio compared with Fig. 7 and the low degree of bioturbation indicating a higher energy environment caused by lowered water depth and progradation of the coastline. Knife 22 cm long.

Fig. 7. Central part of section 4C (Figs 1 and 4): marine heterolithic sand with medium to high bioturbation dominated by equilibrium traces made by *Hiatella arctica* (note *in situ* shells). Deposited during event 3 (high relative sea level) without influence from the ice margin. Pen 14 cm long.

Event 1: deglaciation

Deglaciation took place before 14 650 years BP in Nørre Lyngby (K-2670) and before 14 500 years BP in Mårup (AAR-2133 and AAR-2134).

Event 2: transgression

As stated earlier, there is no evidence of a major transgression following deglaciation.

Event 3: high relative sea level

The positions of highest shorelines indicate a relative sea level *c.* 60 m above the present. This is supported by the presence of marine mud in section 4A. Sections 4A and 4B probably represent fully exposed marine environments and the (glacio-)marine mud therefore indicates at least 20–30 m of water depth (Boulton 1990),

relative sea level during the events ^{14}C ages from the study area, geomorphological data and supplementary sedimentological considerations are used. The 60 m isobase (Fig. 1B) is chosen as reference level of isostatic uplift. Because all data come from the western part of Vendsyssel, the new sedimentologically based sea level curve is only valid in NW Vendsyssel. Use of the curve in other areas will be discussed later.

K numbers (e.g. K-2670) given in the following refer to Copenhagen radiocarbon ages listed in Table 1. References are given in the table. AAR numbers (e.g. AAR-2134) refer to new Aarhus AMS radiocarbon ages listed in Table 2.

Fig. 9. Cliff face near section 4B (Figs 1 and 4): marine mud and sand deposited during event 3 (high relative sea level), truncated by a regional erosional surface formed during rapid fall in relative sea level (event 4). Cliff face ~18 m high.

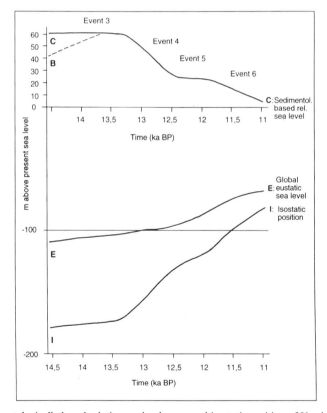

Fig. 10. New sedimentologically based relative sea-level curve and isostatic position of Vendsyssel 14.6–11 ka BP The new relative sea-level curve (C) is valid in the Hirtshals–Skeen Møllebæk area. Isostatic position (I) is calculated using the new relative sea level curve (C), a global eustatic curve (E) (Fairbanks 1989) and a constant geoid low (amounting 10 m).

Table 2. *New AMS ¹⁴C dates from the Lower Saxicava sand at Mårup (sections 4C and 4D)*

Sample No.	Section	Elevation (masl)	Isobase (masl)	Corrected elevation (masl)	¹⁴C age (years BP)	Reservoir corrected ¹⁴C age (years BP)	δ¹³C (‰) PDB
AAR-2132	4D	13	46	27	14 600 ± 140	14 200 ± 140	−0.4
AAR-2133	4D	15	46	29	14 940 ± 210	14 540 ± 210	−0.5
AAR-2134	4C	25	46	39	14 880 ± 140	14 480 ± 140	−0.6

All dates are obtained from paired shells of *Hiatella arctica*. AAR-2133 and AAR-2134 were collected in life position. AAR-2132 was redeposited. Elevations, isobases and corrected elevations are given in m above sea level. The ¹⁴C ages are given in conventional radiocarbon years before present and have been corrected for isotopic fractionation. The reservoir corrected ¹⁴C ages are calculated by subtracting a reservoir age of 400 years from the conventional ¹⁴C ages.

which points towards a relative sea level at least 60 m above the present (Fig. 4).

The high relative sea level persisted with possible minor fluctuations until *c.* 13 300 years BP In the Nørre Lyngby profile, 900 m north of section 4B, a level in the marine mud aged 14 270 years BP (K-2671) is covered by 8 m of marine mud which is erosively truncated at the top (Abrahamsen & Readman 1980). Lateral relations indicate that before erosion another *c.* 2 m of mud were deposited before transition to more sandy deposits. A calculated average rate of sedimentation of 1 cm/a estimates the age of the top of the mud to 13 300 years BP. There is no section at Nørre Lyngby with two ¹⁴C ages, but K-2670 (14 650 years BP) situated 1.2 m above the base of the marine mud (Knudsen 1978) and K-2671 (14 270 years BP) situated 5 m above the base of the marine mud (Abrahamsen & Readman 1980) point towards a rate of sedimentation around 1 cm/year. In a core from Rugbjerg, 2 km from Nørre Lyngby, Abrahamsen & Knudsen (1979) estimated the same rate of sedimentation, and in the Skeen Møllebæk area two ¹⁴C ages from the same profile (K-1052 and K-1053) also indicate an average rate of sedimentation around 1 cm/year.

Event 4: fall in relative sea level (forced regression)

The rapid fall in relative sea level (event 4) started around 13 300 years BP. In the Skeen Møllebæk area the end of the rapid fall is marked by the onset of deposition of the sharp-based shore-face sand-bodies (Zirphaea beds). This occurred at *c.* 12 500 years BP (K-897).

Event 5: break in relative sea-level fall

Event 5 lasted from *c.* 12 500 years BP (K-897) until *c.* 12 000 years BP (e.g. K-1689, K-1319).

The relative sea level during event 5 can be inferred from geomorphological data. A few kilometres to the southwest of Skeen Møllebæk a distinct shoreline separates the plateau with sharp-based shoreface deposits (Zirphaea beds) from higher areas with older Late Weichselian marine sedi-ments (Jessen 1899). This shoreline is situated *c.* 22 m above the present sea level and indicates a relative sea level of this magnitude during event 5.

Event 6: renewed fall in relative sea level

There is no data from the investigated area that indicates the rate of the renewed fall in relative sea level during event 6.

Reliability of the relative sea-level curves

Sources of error

All the relative sea-level curves discussed in this paper share the errors connected to the ¹⁴C ages. These include precision of the ages, radiocarbon plateaus and the risk of contaminated samples.

The two palaeoecologically based curves (curves A and B in Fig. 3) are vulnerable to errors associated with the ecological palaeo-bathymetry. Such errors might occur if some species are more dependent on the substratum than on the water depth. The type of substratum can be independent of water depth (e.g. exposed shoreface versus protected embayment).

The sedimentologically based curve (curve C in Fig. 10) is vulnerable to errors associated with sedimentological palaeobathymetry. However, in contrast with the ecologically based curves, sedimentary environments and palaeogeography are considered in the sedimentological sea level interpretations.

The existing ecologically based curve (A) suffers from the earlier mentioned uplift problem. Data come from areas which have experienced different amounts of isostatic uplift since the time of deposition. In the two other curves this problem is reduced by correcting all data using a fixed level of isostatic uplift. Because the isobases of the highest shorelines used for the correction are based on a limited amount of data, and because the isobases are furthermore probably diachronous, the correction introduces new sources of error. These problems are, however, considered to be of minor importance compared with the uplift problem of curve A.

The sedimentologically based curve (C) is less vulnerable to the problem of diachronous shorelines than curve B because it is based on data from a more restricted area. This point is especially important because the sea-level history of eastern and western Vendsyssel apparently differs significantly (see later).

The new sedimentologically based relative sea-level curve (C) is therefore considered to be the at present most reliable for the Late Weichselian Vendsyssel. As mentioned earlier, the curve only represents the overall trend in the relative sea level. Minor oscillations probably occurred throughout the Late Weichselian.

Relative sea-level history in eastern Vendsyssel

Only limited amounts of data are available from eastern Vendsyssel.

In the area around Frederikshavn (Fig. 1B) two distinct levels of shorelines are seen (Jessen 1899; 1918). One level represents the highest Late Weichselian relative sea level (c. 55–58 m above present sea level). A younger very pronounced level is located c. 20 m lower than the older shorelines.

In the Lyngså area (Fig. 1B) large spit systems formed during the Late Weichselian. The largest system is estimated to have been formed during at least 500 years with relatively stable sea level (Nielsen et al. 1988). Relative sea level during the formation of this spit system was approximately 20 m lower than maximum Late Weichselian sea level as determined from the highest shorelines. Time of formation is estimated to 13 100–12 500 years BP from ^{14}C ages from the em-bayment behind the spit systems (Nielsen et al. 1988).

These observations might indicate that eastern Vendsyssel experienced a relative sea-level history similar to that of western Vendsyssel, starting with high relative sea level followed by a (rapid) fall, a break in the fall and finally a renewed fall in relative sea level. The data do not make it possible to decide whether these events occurred simultaneously in the east and in the west. The amount of relative sea-level fall in eastern Vendsyssel (c. 20 m) differs significantly from the relative sea-level fall in western Vendsyssel (c. 35–40 m). The difference is dramatic considering that the distance between Skeen Møllebæk and Frederikshavn is only 25 km and that the highest shorelines are found at the same elevation in the two areas.

The reason of the difference is not clear, but the fact that Vendsyssel was probably deglaciated from the west towards the east (Fredericia 1988) might be part of an explanation. Neotectonic movements are also possible. Several workers (e.g. Knudsen 1978; Lykke-Andersen & Knudsen 1991; Lykke-Andersen 1992) have given examples that indicate neotectonic movements in Vendsyssel. Lykke-Andersen & Knudsen (1991) suggested that the centre of subsidence in the Kattegat basin shifted between the Saalian and the Eemian.

Use of the new relative sea-level curve (C) outside the Hirtshals–Skeen Møllebæk area

Because of the above-mentioned discrepancies between the eastern and western areas the new relative sea-level curve should not be used in eastern Vendsyssel.

In the southwestern area a simple first approximation will be to subtract the difference between the highest shoreline at the given locality and the highest shoreline at Skeen Møllebæk (60 m). Because the difference in isostatic depression probably decreased during isostatic uplift the relative sea-level curve should, however, have a less steep course in the south.

Delay of the isostatic rebound

Relative sea level is mainly controlled by eustasy, isostasy and geoidal changes (e.g. Boulton 1990). By using the new curve of relative sea level (C) and a global eustatic curve (Fairbanks 1989), and by assuming a practically constant geoid low amounting c. 10 m as indicated by Fjeldskaar (1991), it is possible to sketch the isostatic movements in NW Vendsyssel between 14 600 and 11 000 years BP (Fig. 10).

It is remarkable that rapid isostatic uplift apparently commenced as late as 13 300 years BP. The retreat of the Scandinavian ice sheet from the Main Stationary Line (Weichselian maximum) began c. 18 000 years BP (e.g. Houmark-

Nielsen 1987), Vendsyssel was deglaciated around 15 000 years BP, and the active ice margin was situated in Halland *c.* 100 km away at 14 000 years BP (Lagerlund & Houmark-Nielsen 1993). Well-documented glacial readvances from a southeasterly direction were earlier thought to have occurred between 14 000 and 13 000 years BP (Petersen 1984*b*), but they probably stagnated and left most of Denmark free of active ice before 14 000 years BP (Lagerlund & Houmark-Nielsen 1993).

Conclusions

(1) Sedimentological investigations in a sequence stratigraphic context also prove within the field of Quaternary geology to be a strong tool in constructing or revising relative sea-level history.

(2) A new sedimentologically based relative sea-level curve is considered to be the most reliable for the Late Weichselian NW Vendsyssel.

(3) The new sea-level curve shows deglaciation and progressive sedimentation during high relative sea level followed by (glacio-isostatically induced) forced regression with a major break in the relative sea level fall occurring *c.* 12 500–12 000 years BP

(4) The sea-level history is different in eastern and western Vendsyssel. A time transgressive deglaciation pattern and neotectonic movements might explain the differences.

(5) A time lag of at least 1300 years is demonstrated between the deglaciation of NW Vendsyssel and rapid isostatic uplift of the area.

The investigations were conducted under a PhD project financially supported by the Danish Natural Science Research Council and supervised by M. Houmark-Nielsen. J. Heinemeier at the AMS [14]C Dating Laboratory, University of Aarhus made the new ^{14}C datings which were financed by the Danish Natural Science Research Council. M. Houmark-Nielsen and L. A. Hansen critically read the manuscript. O. B. Berthelsen carried out the photographic work.

References

AARIS-SØRENSEN, K. & PETERSEN, K. S. 1984. A Late Weichselian find of polar bear (*Ursus maritimus* Phipps) from Denmark and reflections on the paleoenvironment. *Boreas*, **13**, 29–33.

ABRAHAMSEN, N. & KNUDSEN, K. L. 1979. Indication of a geomagnetic low inclination excursion in supposed Middle Weichselian interstadial marine clay at Rugbjerg, Denmark. *Physics of the Earth and Planetary Interiors*, **18**, 238–246.

—— & READMAN, P. W. 1980. Geomagnetic variations recorded in Older (>23.000 BP) and Younger Yoldia Clay (14.000 BP) at Nørre Lyngby, Denmark. *Geophysical Journal of the Royal Astronomical Society*, **62**, 329–344.

ANDERSEN, S. A. 1961. *Geologisk fører over Vendsyssel.* Historisk Samfund for Hjørring Amt, Populærvidenskabeligt Forlag, Copenhagen.

BOULTON, G. S. 1990. Sedimentary and sea level changes during glacial cycles and their control on glacimarine facies architecture. *In:* DOWDESWELL, J. A. & SCOURSE, J. D. (eds) *Glacimarine Environments: Processes and Sediments.* Geological Society Special Publication, **53**, 15–52.

FAIRBANKS, R. G. 1989. A 17,000-year glacio-eustatic sea level record: influence of glacial melting rates on the Younger dryas event and deep-ocean circulation. *Nature*, **342**, 637–642.

FJELDSKAAR, W. 1991. Geoidal-eustatic changes induced by the deglaciation of Fennoscandia. *Quaternary International*, **9**, 1–6.

FREDERICIA, J. 1988: Den hydrogeologiske kortlægning af Nordjyllands Amtskommune. *Danmarks Geologiske Undersøgelse, Intern Rapport*, **22**.

HANSEN, S. 1965. The Quaternary of Denmark. *In:* RANKAMA, K. (ed.) *The Quaternary.* Interscience Publishers, New York, 1–90.

HOUMARK-NIELSEN, M. 1987. Pleistocene stratigraphy and glacial history of the central part of Denmark. *Bulletin of the Geological Society of Denmark*, **36**, 1–189.

JESSEN, A. 1899. Beskrivelse til geologisk kort over Danmark. Kortbladene Skagen, Hirtshals, Frederikshavn, Hjørring og Løkken. *Danmarks Geologiske Undersøgelse, I. Række*, **3**.

——1918. Vendsyssels geologi. *Danmarks Geologiske Undersøgelse, V. Række*, **2**.

——1936. Vendsyssels geologi, 2. udg. *Danmarks Geologiske Undersøgelse, V. Række*, **2**.

KNUDSEN, K. L. 1978. Middle and Late Weichselian marine deposits at Nørre Lyngby, northern Jutland, Denmark. *Danmarks Geologiske Undersøgelse, II. Række*, **112**.

KROG, H. & TAUBER, H. 1974. C-14 chronology of Late- and Post-glacial marine deposits in North Jutland. *Danmarks Geologiske Undersøgelse, Årbog 1973*, 93–105.

LAGERLUND, E. & HOUMARK-NIELSEN, M. 1993. Timing and pattern of the last deglaciation in the Kattegat region, southwest Scandinavia. *Boreas*, **22**, 337–347.

LYKKE-ANDERSEN, A.-L. & KNUDSEN, K. L. 1991. Saalian, Eemian, and Weichselian in the Vendsyssel–Kattegat Region, Denmark. *In:* ANDERSEN, B. G. & KÖNIGSSON, L. K. (eds) *Late Quaternary Stratigraphy in the Nordic Countries 150,000–15,000. Striae*, **34**, 135–140.

LYKKE-ANDERSEN, H. 1992. Massebevægelser i Vendsyssels og Kattegats kvartære aflejringer. *Dansk Geologisk Forening, Årsskrift for 1990–91*, 93–97.

MANGERUD, J. 1972. Radiocarbon dating of marine shells, including a discussion of apparent age of recent shells from Norway. *Boreas*, **1**, 143–172.

MERTZ, E. L. 1924. Oversigt over de sen- og postglaciale Niveauforandringer i Danmark. *Danmarks Geologiske Undersøgelse, II. Række*, **41**.

MÖRNER, N. A. 1969. The Late Quaternary history of the Kattegat Sea and the Swedish west coast. Deglaciation, shorelevel displacement, chronology, isostasy and eustasy. *Sveriges Geologiska Undersökning, Ser. C*, **640**.

NIELSEN, L. H., JOHANNESEN, P. N. & SURLYK, F. 1988. A Late Pleistocene coarse-grained spit-platform sequence in northern Jylland, Denmark. *Sedimentology*, **35**, 915–937.

NUMMEDAL, D., PILKEY, O. H. & HOWARD, J. D. (eds) 1987. *Sea-Level Fluctuation and Coastal Evolution*. The Society of Economic Paleontologists and Mineralogists, Special Publications, **41**.

PETERSEN, K. S. 1984a. Late Weichselian sea-levels and fauna communities in northern Vendsyssel, Jutland, Denmark. *In*: MÖRNER, N. A. & KARLÉN, W. (eds): *Climatic Changes on a Yearly to Millennial Basis*. Reidel, Dordrecht, 63–68.

——1984b. Stratigraphical position of Weichselian tills in Denmark. *In*: KÖNIGSSON, L.-K. (ed.) *Ten Years of Nordic Till Research*. *Striae*, **20**, 75–78.

PLINT, A. G. 1988. Sharp-based shoreface sequences and "offshore bars" in the Cardium Formation of Alberta: their relationship to relative changes in sea level. *In*: WILGUS, C. W. *et al.* (eds) *Sea-Level Changes—an Integrated Approach*. The Society of Economic Paleontologists and Mineralogists, Special Publications, **42**, 357–370.

POSAMENTIER, H. W., ALLEN, G. P., JAMES, D. P. & TESSON, M. 1992. Forced regressions in a sequence stratigraphic framework: concepts, examples, and exploration significance. *American Association of Petroleum Geologists Bulletin*, **76**, 1687–1709.

——, SUMMERHAYES, C. P., HAQ, B. U. & ALLEN, G. P. (eds) 1993. *Sequence Stratigraphy and Facies Associations*. Special Publication of the International Association of Sedimentologists, **18**.

TAUBER, H. 1966. Danske kulstof-14 dateringsresultater. *Meddelelser fra Dansk Geologisk Forening*, **16**, 153–176.

WILGUS, C. K., HASTINGS, B. S., KENDALL, C. G. ST. C., POSAMENTIER, H. W., ROSS, C. A. & VAN WAGONER, J. C. (eds) 1988. *Sea-level Changes: an Integrated Approach*. The Society of Economic Paleontologists and Mineralogists, Special Publications, **42**.

Palaeoceanography on the European arctic margin during the last deglaciation

MORTEN HALD, TROND DOKKEN & SVEINUNG HAGEN

University of Tromsø, Department of Geology IBG, N-9037 Norway

Abstract: To reveal the palaeoceanographic and palaeoclimatic evolution related to the disintegration of the Barents Sea and Fennoscandian ice sheets, high-resolution sediment cores from the continental margin off western Svalbard, western Barents Sea and northern Norway were investigated. The location of these cores is below the axis of the Norwegian Current and beyond, but close to, glaciated continental areas. Hence they should sensitively reflect the palaeoceanography of the northernmost Norwegian Sea. Between , 14.5–19.5 and 22.5–29 ^{14}C ka, a high abundance of planktonic foraminifera and a small content of subpolar species indicate seasonally ice–free and slightly warmed surface water. This phenomenon is related to the advection of surface water of North Atlantic origin. The onset of the deglaciation is characterized by a marked low oxygen event dated to between 15 and 13 ka, interpreted to reflect a surface water freshening produced by meltwater and reduced oceanic mixing. After the onset of deglaciation, the surface ocean warmed in three rapid steps: (1) around 12.5 ka, indicated by increased abundances of planktonic foraminifera; (2) at 10.2 ka and at (3) 10–9.6 ka. The two latter steps are reflected by the increased abundance of subpolar planktonic foraminifera.

A variety of high resolution climatic records produced during the last decade have revealed the rate and pattern of atmospheric and oceanic warming following the last glaciation in the North Atlantic region (Dansgaard *et al.* 1989; 1993, Lehman *et al.* 1991; 1992, Koç *et al.* 1993). The impact of these changes at high northern latitudes is to some extent known from deep sea cores (Jones & Keigwin 1988; Hebbeln *et al.* 1994) or from the continental shelf (Vorren *et al.* 1978; Hald & Vorren 1987; Hald *et al.* 1989). However, as many of the deep sea cores have low resolution and the continental shelf records suffer from the lack of detailed age control, both the timing and structure of the palaeoceanographic evolution following the last glaciation is insufficiently known. The present paper presents a well dated high resolution record focusing on the palaeoceanographic evolution in time and space during the last glacial to interglacial transition, particularly discussing: (1) the surface ocean during the last glacial maximum; (2) meltwater fluxes; (3) the inflow of Atlantic Water during the deglaciation; (4) Younger Dryas ocean circulation; and (5) the ocean climate during the Holocene. To address these problems we analysed, planktonic foraminifera, oxygen isotopes, lithology and ^{14}C dates in four high resolution sediment cores from the shelf off northern Norway (69° N), off western Barents Sea (79°N), and off western Svalbard (78° N); (Fig. 1, Table 1). The cores are located (vertically) below the present inflow of warm and saline Atlantic Water and should reveal the extent and duration of oceanic climatic changes during the latest Quaternary.

Materials and methods

The sediment cores (Table 1, Fig. 1) were retrieved either by gravity or piston corer. Preparation of foraminiferal samples from the sediments generally followed the methods given by Feyling-Hanssen (1958) and Meldgaard & Knudsen (1979). Two to three hundred individual planktonic foraminifera from the 100–1000 μm fraction were identified to species level; the number of planktonic foraminifera per gram of dry bulk sediment and the percentages of the individual species were calculated (Figs 2–6). In core T-79-51/2 100–200 planktonic foraminifera were counted in the 125–1000 μm fraction, but this slight difference in procedures should not influence our comparisons.

The planktonic foraminifer *Neogloboquadrina pachyderma* was selected for oxygen isotope measurements (Figs 2–6). The samples were prepared following the procedures described by Shackleton & Opdyke (1973), Shackleton *et al.* (1983) and Duplessy (1978). Approximately 20 individual tests were picked per measurement. The isotope measurements were carried out at the Norwegian Geological Mass Spectrometer Laboratory at the University of Bergen and at the Centre des Faiblés Radioactivites, CNRS, Gif sur Yvette, France using Finnigan MAT 251 mass spectrometers. The average reproducibility at these laboratories is claimed to be ±0.07‰ for δ^{18}O and 0.06‰ for δ^{13}C.

Accelerator mass spectrometry (AMS) radiocarbon dates (Table 2) were measured at the Radiocarbon Laboratory of Uppsala, Sweden,

From Andrews, J. T., Austin, W. E. N., Bergsten, H. & Jennings, A. E. (eds), 1996, *Late Quaternary Palaeoceanography of the North Atlantic Margins*, Geological Society Special Publication No. 111, pp. 275–287.

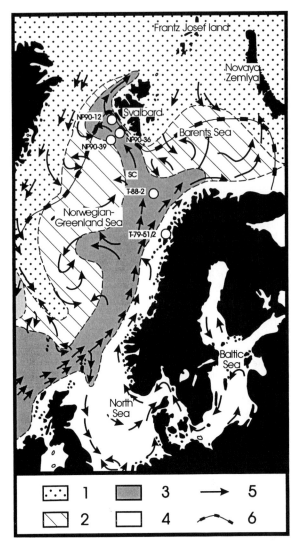

Fig. 1. Surface waters in the Norwegian Sea and adjoining seas modified from Mosby (1968). (1) Polar Water, (2) Arctic Water, (3) Atlantic Water (water in the Norwegian Current), (4) coastal, Baltic and North Sea water (water in the Norwegian Coastal Current), (5) surface currents and (6) sea ice border, April. Definition of the water masses are according to Hopkins (1991). Open circles show the core locations.

and at Centre des Faiblés Radioactivites, France and University of Colorado, Boulder. The material used for dating was either planktonic foraminifera or macrofossils.

Results

Dates

From the cores T-88-2 and NP90-57 we combined several planktonic foraminiferal species

(Table 2). In NP90-39 and NP90-12 we picked only left-coiling *N. pachyderma*. From core T-79-51/2 we used macrofossils that are considered to be *in situ* (Thomsen & Vorren 1986). Compared with macro fossils, there is a larger risk for the foraminiferal datings to be misleading due to pollution by younger or older carbo-nate by reworking or bioturbation (Jennings *et al.* this volume). All ages have been corrected for a marine reservoir effect of 440 years (Mangerud & Gulliksen 1975). For

Table 1. *Position, depth, length and coring device of the sediment cores investigated*

Core identifier	Latitude (°N)	Longitude (°E)	Depth (m)	Length (cm)	Corer	Area
NP90-12	78°24.47′	09°24.88′	628	335	Piston	Svalbard
NP90-36	77°37.04′	09°56.18′	1360	380	Piston	Svalbard
NP90-39	77°15.49′	09°05.58′	2119	600	Piston	Svalbard
T-88-2/NP90-57	71°59.29′	14°21.52′	1495	863*	Gravity/piston	W. Barents
T-79-51/2	69°18.00′	16°23.00′	505	350	Gravity	N. Norway

* Core length for this site is based on patching two cores (T-88-2 and NP90-57) from the same location by AMS, litho- and biostratigraphic correlation discussed by Hald (unpublished data).

each sediment core (Figs 2–6) we calculated sedimentation rates by linear extrapolation between the dated levels and by assuming that the core top is 0 years BP. In core T-88-2 the dating at 8120 ± 120 a (Table 2) is too young by c. 1 ka compared with the other dating in this core. The reason for this is difficult to explain. In core T-79-51/2 the date 8560 ± 80 is too old by >1 ka, which may indicate reworking. These misleading date are omitted from further discussions and applications. There is also a cluster of dates around 9000 years in this core within one sigma standard deviation. According to Kromer & Becker (1993) there is no radiocarbon plateau around this date which could explain this cluster, hence we interpret them as resulting from high sedimentation rates.

Lithostratigraphy

The sediments on the shelf off northern Norway (Fig. 2) have been divided into informal units and discussed in detail by Hald & Vorren (1984) and Vorren et al. (1984). Unit tC is a glaciomarine diamicton including iceberg-rafted debris (IRD), >1 mm grain fraction. Units tB and tA are dominated by pelite and sandy pelite, respectively. They lack IRD and are interpreted to represent open marine environments. On the Barents Slope (Fig. 3) two lithostratigraphic units are distinguished (Hald unpublished data): the diamicton in the lower part is related to glaciomarine processes or the formation of debris lobes during the late glacial (Laberg & Vorren 1993). The lithology of the sediments off

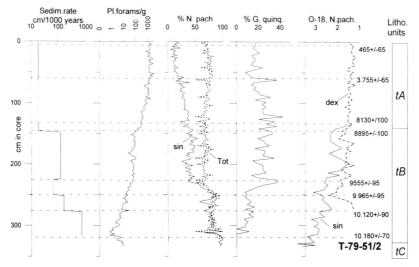

Fig. 2. Downcore analysis in core T-79-51/2 on the shelf off northern Norway showing: sedimentation rate (cm/1000 years); number of planktonic foraminifera per gram dry, bulk sediment; percentage *N. pachyderma* (broken line = sinistral + dextral *N. pachyderma* versus total planktonic foraminiferal fauna; solid line = *N. pachyderma* sinistral based on sinistral + dextral *N. pachyderma* = 100%); percentage *G. quinqueloba* of total planktonic fauna; $\delta^{18}O$ (‰ versus PDB) measured on sinistral *N. pachyderma*. The numbers on the curve to the right give the radiocarbon age. Lithostratigraphic units (Hald & Vorren 1984; Vorren et al. 1984) are shown in the column to the right. Fore core location, see Fig. 1.

Table 2. *Radiocarbon AMS datings*

Core identification	Mean core depth (cm)	Fossils dated	Age ^{14}C (years)	Error ^{14}C (years)	Laboratory identification
NP90-12	30	*N. pach (sin)*	11 940	±320	TUa-562
NP90-12	192	*N. pach (sin)*	13 315	±100	TUa-846
NP90-12	219.5	*N. pach (sin)*	14 760	±155	TUa-563
NP90-12	262.5	*N. pach (sin)*	17 245	±125	TUa-564
NP90-36	18.5	*N. pach (sin)*	7 975	±105	TUa-842
NP90-36	64.5	*N. pach (sin)*	8 855	±80	TUa-843
NP90-36	160	*N. pach (sin)*	11 730	±110	TUa-844
NP90-36	331	*N. pach (sin)*	15 595	±130	TUa-845
NP90-39	48.5	*N. pach (sin)*	7 855	±85	TUa-343
NP90-39	123.5	*N. pach (sin)*	13 100	±115	TUa-558
NP90-39	126.5	*N. pach (sin)*	14 495	±115	TUa-561
NP90-39	128.5	*N. pach (sin)*	15 135	±105	TUa-342
NP90-39	160.5	*N. pach (sin)*	19 375	±120·	TUa-557
NP90-39	186	*N. pach (sin)*	21 185	±160	TUa-559
NP90-39	246	*N. pach (sin)*	23 080	±200	TUa-341
NP90-39	269	*N. pach (sin)*	29 605	±645	TUa-560
T-88-2	12	Planktonic forams	2 080	±90	Gif
T-88-2	72	Planktonic forams	6 840	±100	Gif
T-88-2	136	Planktonic forams	8 990	±110	Gif
T-88-2	210	Planktonic forams	8 120	±120*	Gif
T-88-2	196	Planktonic forams	9 030	±105	TUa-465
T-88-2	168	Planktonic forams	9 465	±400	TUa-116
T-88-2	261	Planktonic forams	10 070	±115	TUa-464
T-88-2	308	Planktonic forams	11 035	±75	TUa-466
T-88-2	431	Planktonic forams	11 930	±150	Gif
NP90-57	372	Planktonic forams	12 425	±120	TUa-463
T-79-51/2	2	*Yoldiella* sp.	465	±65	TUa-1119
T-79-51/2	60	*Yoldiella* sp.	3 755	±65	TUa-948
T-79-51/2	134	*Yoldiella* sp.	8 130	±65	TUa-949
T-79-51/2	98	*Bathyarc. pectun*	8 560	±80*	Tua-1120
T-79-51/2	148	*Yoldiella* sp.	8 895	±100	TUa-950
T-79-51/2	226	*Yoldiella* sp.	9 555	±95	TUa-951
T-79-51/2	252	*Yoldiella lenticula*	9 965	±95	TUa-952
T-79-51/2	288	*Yoldiella* sp.	10 120	±90	TUa-1121
T-79-51/2	318	*Nuculana* sp.	10 180	±70	NSRL-2057

* Dates considered misleading.

Svalbard is under investigation (Andersen *et al.* unpublished data).

Planktonic foraminifers

We have identified six species of planktonic foraminifers in the sediment cores. These are: *Neogloboquadrina pachyderma* (Ehrenberg) (both the sinistral and dextral form), *Globigerina quinqueloba* Natland, *Globigerina bulloides* d'Orbigny, *Globigerina falconensis* Blow, *Globigerinata bradyi* Wiesener and *Globigerinita glutinata* (Egger). *N. pachyderma* is the most frequent at all the sites, followed by *G. quinqueloba*; the other species occur sporadically and less frequently.

On the shelf off northern Norway *N. pachyderma* constitutes close to 100% of the total planktonic foraminiferal fauna in the lower part of the core (Fig. 2). A stepwise reduction of sinistral form of *N. pachyderma* versus total *N. pachyderma* is seen; the first step occurs just after 10.18 ka and a second step between 9.97 and 9.56 ka. The third step is recorded at around the lithostratigraphic tA/tB boundary between 8.9 and 8.13 ka and a fourth step around 3.76 ka. *G. quinqueloba* constitutes 20–40% of the planktonic fauna. It has a marked increase between 9.97 and 9.56 ka and declines gradually after 8.13 ka, interrupted by some short-lived peaks, e.g. the maximum at 3.76 ka. The abundance of planktonic foraminifera (number per gram dry sediment) (Fig. 2) show one minimum around

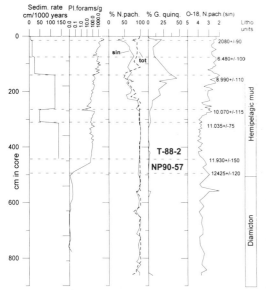

Fig. 3. Downcore analysis in core T-88-2/NP90-57 from the continental slope off the western Barents Sea showing: sedimentation rate (cm/1000 years); number of planktonic foraminifera per gram dry, bulk sediment, percentage sinistral *N. pachyderma* based on sinistral + dextral *N. pachyderma* equal to 100%; percentage *G. quinqueloba* of total planktonic fauna; $\delta^{18}O$ (‰ versus PDB) measured on sinistral *N. pachyderma*. The numbers on the curve to the right give the radiocarbon age. Lithostratigraphic units are shown in the column to the right. Fore core location, see Fig. 1.

On the Barents Sea slope (Fig. 3) planktonic foraminifera constitute less than 10% of the total (benthic + planktonic) foraminiferal fauna in the diamicton. At the onset of hemipelagic sedimentation there is an increase in planktonic foraminifera per gram by a factor of five to eight. The planktonic component has dominated the foraminiferal fauna since 12.5 ka. *Neogloboquadrina pachyderma* is the dominant species. The most striking feature in the planktonic fauna is the sudden shift in *N. pachyderma* sinistral (calculated versus sinistral + dextral *N. pachyderma* = 100%), dropping from 90% to less than 60% within less that 100 years at 10 ka. A broad minimum of *N. pachyderma* sinistral occurs around 9 ka and a second minimum around 2 ka. Also characteristic is the marked influence of *G. quinqueloba*, reaching 46% at *c.* 9 ka and a secondary maximum around 2 ka.

The foraminiferal content in the cores from the Svalbard margin (Figs 4–6) is dominated by planktonic species (>95% of the total foraminiferal fauna) and reveals large shifts in abundance (number of specimens per gram dry bulk sediment). Two marked maxima that we term HP1 and HP2 (Dokken *et al.* unpublished data) are recorded between 14.5–19.5 ka and 22.5–29 ka (Fig. 4) and a secondary maximum during the early Holocene. In cores NP90-36 and NP90-12 (Figs 5 & 6) only HP1 was penetrated. *Neogloboquadrina pachyderma* sinistral dominates the planktonic fauna, but in each of the abundance maxima there is a characteristic content of *G. quinqueloba*.

10.18 ka, a gradual increase between 10 and 9 ka and a marked increase after 8 ka. The latter increase corresponds to the lithostratigraphic tA/tB boundary.

Oxygen isotopes

In the cores from the Svalbard margin (Figs 4–6), before 15 ka, $\delta^{18}O$ measured on *N. pachyderma*

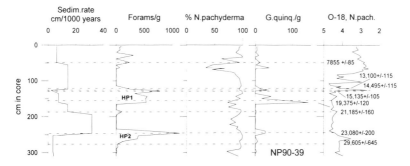

Fig. 4. Downcore analysis in core NP90-39 from the continental slope off Svalbard showing: sedimentation rate (cm/1000 years); number of foraminifera (benthic + planktonic) per gram dry bulk sediment; percentage sinistral *N. pachyderma* based on sinistral + dextral *N. pachyderma* equal to 100%; number of *G. quinqueloba* per gram dry, bulk sediment; $\delta^{18}O$ (‰ versus PDB) measured on sinistral *N. pachyderma*. The numbers on the curve to the right give the radiocarbon age. Fore core location, see Fig. 1.

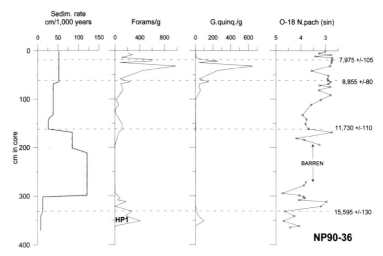

Fig. 5. Downcore analysis in core NP90-36 from the continental slope off Svalbard showing: sedimentation rate (cm/1000 years); number of foraminifera (benthic + planktonic) per gram dry, bulk sediment; percentage *G. quinqueloba* of total planktonic fauna; $\delta^{18}O$ (‰ versus PDB) measured on sinistral *N. pachyderma*. The numbers on the curve to the right give the radiocarbon age. Fore core location, see Fig. 1.

sinistral shows the highest values. We correlate these with oxygen isotope stage 2 (Martinson *et al.* 1987). A marked low oxygen isotope signal recorded between 15 and 13 ka (Figs. 4–6) that we term LOE 1 (low oxygen isotopic event). In core NP90-12 the first light $\delta^{18}O$ is dated to $14\,760 \pm 155$ years BP, whereas an in-core NP90-39 age of $15\,135 \pm 105$ years BP pre-dates the

onset of LOE 1. The $\delta^{18}O$ values drop back to heavy values again at $13\,100 \pm 115$ in core NP90-39 and at slightly before $13\,315 \pm 100$ in core NP90-12. A secondary, weaker minimum is recorded in two of the cores (Figs 3 and 4) around 12 ka. On the Barents slope in core 88-2 (Fig. 3) an undated mininum is record before 12.5 ka. We cannot exclude a correlation of this

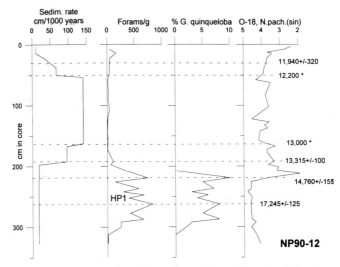

Fig. 6. Downcore analysis in core NP90-12 from the continental slope off Svalbard showing: sedimentation rate (cm/1000 years); number of foraminifera (benthic + planktonic) per gram dry, bulk sediment; percentage *G. quinqueloba* of total planktonic fauna; $\delta^{18}O$ (‰ versus PDB) measured on sinistral *N. pachyderma*. The numbers on the curve to the right give the radiocarbon age. Fore core location, see Fig. 1. Asterisks indicate ages based on oxygen isotope correlation.

signal with the 12 ka minimum in the Svalbard cores. How-ever, we believe that the Barents slope minimum is probably older.

A shift towards lighter values in the planktonic $\delta^{18}O$ occurs between 10.5 and 9.9 ka on the Barents slope (Fig. 3) and a stepwise reduction is recorded off northern Norway between 10.2 and 10 ka (Fig. 2). On the Barents slope this reduction is followed by several rapid shifts reaching a $\delta^{18}O$ minimum around 9 ka. Off northern Norway values close to modern are reached at 9.5 ka BP and on the Barents slope after 7.8 ka BP.

Discussion

Palaeoceanography during the last glacial maximum

The peaks in abundance of planktonic foraminifera HP1 and HP2, in the cores off Svalbard (Figs 4–6) are discussed in detail by Hebbeln et al. (1994) and Dokken et al. (unpublished data). They showed that the two abundance maxima were associated with increased amounts of subpolar planktonic foraminifera (e.g. G. quinqueloba Figs 4–6), coccoliths and IRD with a southern source. Based on these observations, they suggested that the HP zones represent periods of seasonally ice-free, highly productive surface waters and that a possible mechanism for establishing these conditions could be the inflow of Atlantic Water. Atlantic Water inflow also would create an important northern pathway for moisture, influencing the buildup of the Fennoscandian and Barents Sea ice sheets by promoting atmospheric conditions necessary for rapid ice growth, including nearby warm ocean and low northern summer insolation (Ruddiman et al. 1980).

Onset of deglaciation

We correlate the low oxygen isotopic event between 15 and 13 ka, LOE 1. with a similar light excursion found in the Fram Strait (Jones & Keigwin 1988) and Barents Sea margin (Weinelt et al. 1991; Sarnthein et al. 1992) and also in the Norwegian–Greenland Sea (Koç & Jansen 1994; Stein et al. 1994) and the Labrador Sea (Andrews et al. 1994). The light peak before 12.4 ka in core 88-2 on the Barents slope (Fig. 3) may also correlate with LOE 1. Jones & Keigwin (1988) originally suggested that the light $\delta^{18}O$ spike reflected low salinity meltwater produced by a sudden downdraw of a marine-based ice

sheet in the Barents Sea. However, the sedimentation rate data in this study and dating of the deglaciation of the Barents Sea Ice Sheet (see later) may indicate that such a downdraw was not synchronous or synonymous with a major deglaciation of the Barents Sea Ice Sheet (Hald & Andrews 1995).

Radiocarbon datings of the last deglaciation of the Barents Sea indicate that the southwestern part was deglaciated c. 13.3 ka (Vorren & Kristoffersen 1986; Hald et al. 1989), the central eastern parts by 13 ka (Polyak et al. in press) and the northeastern parts by 13.2 ka (Polyak & Solheim 1994). Although these dates are minimum dates for deglaciation, there is no evidence that the area was deglaciated much earlier than these estimates. Peak values of the LOE 1 are around 14.5 ka (in this study) and in the Fram Strait (Jones & Keigwin 1988) as well as the northern Norwegian Sea (Koç & Jansen 1994). This date is more than 1 ka before the minimum age for the deglaciation of this area.

During the LOE 1 the sedimentation rates are low (Figs 5 and 6) or reach a minimum (Fig. 4) and the flux of IRD (mineral grains $>500\,\mu m$) shows a slight increase, but are relatively low compared with after 13 ka (Elverhøi et al. unpublished data). This pattern may indicate incipient iceberg rafting corresponding to the LOE. However, the onset of the major sediment flux corresponds with the minimum ages of the deglaciation of the Barents Sea Ice Sheet.

The large signal of LOE 1 corresponds to a global sea level rise of only 5 mm/year (Fairbanks 1989). On the other hand, the large global meltwater events MWP 1a at 12 ka, and MWP 1b at 9 ka, with sea level rises of 38 mm/year and 26 mm/year (peak values), respectively (Fairbanks 1989), are less marked than LOE 1 in the oxygen isotopic record of both the Nordic Seas and the Labrador Sea. Thus, LOE 1 appears to not only reflect the volume of meltwater. Possible explanations are (a) reduced oceanic mixing, (b) light isotope sources or (c) melting of ice sheets from continental shelves which contribute virtually no signal to the global δ^{18} ice volume.

There are indications that the conveyer belt circulation in the North Atlantic region was reduced and/or shut off during the LOE 1 (Veum et al. 1992; Keigwin & Lehman 1994). This could lead to the storage of isotopically light water at the ocean surface, created partly by precipitation and partly by meltwater. Model experiments by Lehman et al. (1994) show a surface water freshening during the Younger Dryas cooling associated with a collapse of the conveyer belt. Mixing and downwelling of this freshwater occurs as the conveyer belt

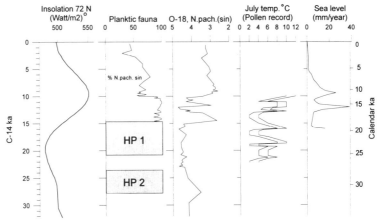

Fig. 7. Comparison of planktonic foraminiferal data including percentage *N. pachyderma* sinistral (from core T-88-2/NP90-57) and abundance peaks (from core NP90-39) and planktonic $\delta^{18}O$ (core NP90-39) to: June insolation at 72° N (W/m²); atmospheric temperature (°C) based on pollen stratigraphy from Andøya off Northern Norway (Vorren *et al.* 1988; Alm 1993) and global sea-level curve (mm/year) from Fairbanks (1989). The data are plotted against age, both U–Th corrected according to Bard *et al.* (1990) and ¹⁴C years.

circulation recovers. Light isotope sources may be a result of latitudinal depletion of $\delta^{18}O$ precipitated from water that will make the northernmost ice sheets more $\delta^{18}O$ depleted than those further south. The geographical distribution of the LOE 1 shows the lightest values off the western Barents Sea margin (Sarnthein *et al.* 1992; Hald & Andrews 1995). This area drains meltwater both from the Barents Sea and Fennoscandian ice sheets. Increasing $\delta^{18}O$ values both to the west, south and north may be due both to the meltwater routing patterns and variations in the isotopic source. If the low $\delta^{18}O$ is created by meltwater from thin, nearly buoyant parts of marine-based glaciers, the contribution to the global sea level rise is low. We also notice that there is a return to heavy glacial $\delta^{18}O$ after the LOE (Figs 4 and 5). This may indicate that LOE deglaciation, in a global context, was limited. It is difficult to differentiate between the importance of the various factors causing the LOE. At the present we favour a moderate incipient melting of the Barents Sea Ice Sheet around the peak LOE (14.5 ka).

The last deglaciation has been explained as the result of both orbital forcing and a more non-climatic destabilization of the large ice sheets. In Fig. 7 we compare the onset of deglaciation with the June insolation at 72° N and with the atmospheric temperature curve based on a pollen stratigraphy on Andøya, close to the core off northern Norway (Alm 1993; Vørren

et al. 1988). Before to the deglaciation, insolation was at a minimum between the HP zones and during early HP1. However, during the HP zones (HP2 and upper HP1) interpreted as ice-free, slightly warmed surface waters, insolation is a little higher. During HP1 when insolation was starting to rise, there were two episodes with a marked atmospheric warming indicated by the pollen record. This may indicate that orbitally forced warming was already under way before melting of the ice sheets started, and hence may indicate that a warming triggered or enhanced the deglaciation.

Surface ocean palaeoceanography 12.5–9.5 ka

The cores off Svalbard (Figs 4–6) are characterized by a very low content of planktonic foraminifera and the fauna is totally dominated by *N. pachyderma* sinistral. High sediment and meltwater fluxes probably created a less favourable and cold environment at this location. On the Barents slope (Fig. 3) there is a monospecific *N. pachyderma* sinistral planktonic assemblage during this interval. Hence temperatures were <5°C and variations below this temperature level cannot be quantified by using palaeotemperature transfer functions. However, the increased abundaces of planktonic foraminifera after 12.5 ka corresponding to the onset of hemipelagic sedimentation may reflect increased production that in turn may be a function of a surface water temperature increase within 0–5°C. This age is roughly equal with the onset of production of North Atlantic Deep Water (Charles & Fairbanks 1992; Veum *et al.* 1992), indicative of the establishment of a modern circulation pattern in the North Atlantic. This possible warming of the surface waters on the Barents slope correlates to the 'the Bølling Amelioration' of the pollen record on Andøya (Alm 1993) (Fig. 7). During the Younger Dryas we interpret low sedimentation rates and the minimum in forams/g on the Barents slope as indicative of a cooling, probably also an increased sea ice cover, hampering both sediment flux (decreased melting) and the production of planktonic foraminifera.

There are some indications in the δ^{18}O curves of our cores of meltwater spikes (Figs 3–5). In core NP90-39 off Svalbard and NP90-36 (Figs 4 and 5), the light excursion around 12 ka may correlate with the global meltwater spike MWP 1a (Fairbanks 1989). However, this excursion is absent in core NP90-12, probably due to a hiatus in the upper part of the core. In the Barents slope core T-88-2/NP-90-57 (Fig. 3) there is an undated spike before 12.5 ka BP that may potentially correlate with the early part of MWP 1a or, alternatively, the LOE 1.

In the core off northern Norway (Fig. 2) at the end of the Younger Dryas, the decease in *N. pachyderma* sinistral corresponds to a decline in δ^{18}O; both may indicate surface ocean warming. Applying either the oxygen isotope palaeotemperature equation of Shackleton

(1974) or planktonic foraminiferal transfer function (Johannesen 1987), this temperature increase is about 2°C. Following this increase is a two-step δ^{18}O decline not associated with a faunal shift. Thus this latter two-step decline may possibly be related to a surface water freshening. A δ^{18}O minimum occurs on the Barents slope at *c.* 10 ka (Fig. 3) and correlates chronologically with the global meltwater spike MWP 1b, dated between 10.5 and 8.5 ka BP (Fairbanks 1989). In the cores from both the Barents slope and off northern Norway this δ^{18}O minimum is followed by a marked temperature rise reflected by the reduction in *N. pachyderma* (sinistral) (Figs 2 and 3). This rise, corresponding to a temperature increase of 2–3°C, occurs very abruptly on the Barents slope (<100 years) and more gradually off northern Norway between 9.97 and 9.56 ka BP.

In Fig. 8 the inflow history of warm (>5°C) Atlantic Water, as reflected by the planktonic foraminiferal fauna, is mapped along a north–south transect in the North Atlantic–Norwegian Sea by comparing the distribution of *N. pachyderma* (sinistral) in three Norwegian Sea cores (Ruddiman *et al.* 1977; Lehman & Keigwin 1992; Veum *et al.* 1992). A stepwise warming of the surface ocean is indicated. The first step is in the south (Fig. 8a and 8b), characterized by a marked warming after 13.5 ka reaching modern temperature levels by 13.1 ka BP. In contrast, sea surface temperatures in the north (Fig. 8e) remained below 5°C until *c.* 9.6 ka BP. According to Lehman & Keigwin (1992), temperatures similar to those at present (13–14°C) existed

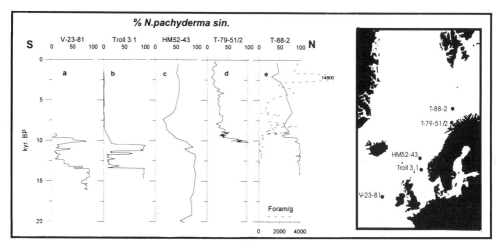

Fig. 8. Comparison of records of sinistral *N. pachyderma* from (**a**) Ruddiman *et al.* (1977), (**b**) Lehman & Keigwin (1992), (**c**) Veum *et al.* (1992) with the records off northern Norway (Fig. 2) and the Barents slope (Fig. 3). For the Barents slope, record T-88-2/NP90-57 and the number of foraminifera per gram are shown. A location map is shown to the right.

284

at the Troll 3.1 location between 13.1 and 11.7 ka BP (Fig. 8b). If so, a temperature gradient, larger than that of today (4–5°C) must have existed between 61° N and 72° N in the Norwegian Sea during this time interval. The first warming at the Barents slope, as indicated by the increase in foraminiferal abundance (Fig. 8e), occurs around 12.5 ka BP, almost 1 ka later than in the south. Core HM52-43 (Fig. 8c), located *c*. 64°30′ N, northwest of Troll 3.1. shows no clear evidence of warming before *c*. 12 ka BP. Together these data indicate a northward and westward time transgressive immigration pattern of warm Atlantic Water into the Norwegian Sea.

The second major warming occurs at the end of the Younger Dryas chronozone and is less time transgressive. There is a time lag of *c*. 500 years between the northern cores (Fig. 8d and 8e) and the southern Norwegian Sea (Fig. 8b), but this is not shown for the North Atlantic core (Fig. 8a). The more gradual warming indicated for core HM52-43 may be due to bioturbation, as sedimentation rates are fairly low in this core (less than 5 cm/1000 years, Veum *et al.* 1992).

The Holocene

The early Holocene is characterized by a marked rise of the subpolar species *G. quinqueloba*, reaching maximum values between 9.5 and 8 ka BP (Figs 2 and 3). This subpolar species is associated with the oceanic fronts of the Norwegian Sea, especially the Arctic Front separating the Atlantic and Arctic water masses (Johannesen *et al.* 1994). This rise in *G. quinqueloba* may indicate that the Arctic Front was located along the continental margin between northern Norway and Svalbard during the early Holocene. On the Barents slope (Fig. 3) the *G. quinqueloba* maximum, together with relatively high numbers of dextral *N. pachyderma*, gives the highest values for subpolar species in the planktonic foraminiferal fauna and indicate an early Holocene surface ocean temperature maximum.

This early Holocene temperature maximum occurs during the June solar insolation maximum (Fig. 7) when the insolation was >9% larger than at present (Kutzbach & Guetter 1986). An early Holocene temperature maximum has been found in both continental and marine records (see Crowley & North 1991 for a review). A temperature maximum is also postulated in general circulation models that show a net annual decrease in sea ice because of greatly enhanced summer heating (Kutzbach & Gallimore 1988; Mitchell *et al.* 1988). In accordance with the present study, thermophilus

mollusca from Svalbard (Salvigsen *et al.* 1992) and diatoms from the Iceland Sea area (Koç *et al.* 1993) indicate that early Holocene temperatures were as warm or slightly warmer than present. However, the records from the central Norwegian Sea (Koç *et al.* 1993) and continental records from Scandinavia based on the displacement of vegetation zones (Iversen 1944; Selsing & Wishman 1984) or glacier fluctuations (Karlèn 1988; Nesje *et al.* 1991), record a temperature optimum around 7 ka. This difference in timing for the Holocene temperature maximum indicates that in addition to insolation, local feedback mechanisms played a part. For the Iceland Sea area and the northern Norway–Svalbard continental margin, sea ice could be an important local factor as these areas are located closer to sea ice covered waters.

Off Svalbard *G. quinqueloba* disappears in the upper Holocene and the fauna is totally dominated by *N. pachyderma* sinistral. During the middle Holocene on the Barents slope, around 6.5 ka BP, the slight increase in *N. pachyderma* sinistral and the decline in *G. quinqueloba* suggest a cooling followed by increased influence of subpolar species around 2 ka BP indicating warming. Off northern Norway the sum of subpolar fauna remains relatively constant over the last 9 ka BP as the decline in *G. quinqueloba* is balanced by a decline in the polar *N. pachyderma* sinistral.

The more variable surface temperatures on the Barents slope compared with the results from off northern Norway may be caused by the proximity on the Barents slope of the present Arctic Front (Fig. 1). The annual sea surface temperature variability for the Barents Sea has been close to 2°C for the last 90 years (Loeng 1991). Modelling experiments (Ådlandsvik & Loeng 1991) have shown that this variability is mainly a function of influx of Atlantic Water. According to their model, high ocean temperatures occur during periods of relatively low air pressure, cyclonic circulation, low sea ice cover and increased influx of warm Atlantic Water. On the contrary, cold temperatures are associated with relatively high atmospheric pressure and decreased inflow of Atlantic Water. The observed surface palaeotemperature variations during the last 9.5 ka on the Barents slope are close to those observed in modern hydrographic measurements and thus could be explained by this model in terms of long-term persistence of one or the other atmospheric circulation types. According to Ådlandsvik and Loeng (1991), the switch between the cold and warm state and thus the cause for rapid fluctuations of the Barents Sea region is most likely to be due to variations in larger scale oceanic and atmospheric circulation.

Conclusions

(1) In isotope stage 2, during two periods, between 14.5–19.5 and 22.5–29 ka BP, respectively, we infer a moderate advection of Atlantic Water to the Svalbard margin 78° N of the Polar North Atlantic. This advection may have transported both moisture and heat to the European Arctic, the former responsible for a large ice buildup and the latter for later deglaciation.

(2) The onset of the deglaciation is reflected by a light planktonic $\delta^{18}O$ excursion between 15 and 13 ka BP. This is a regional northern hemisphere ocean signal indicative of a surface water freshening, caused by meltwater and reduced oceanic mixing.

(3) After the onset of deglaciation, the surface ocean warms in three rapid steps: around 12.5 ka BP; 10.2 ka BP; and 10–9.6 ka BP.

Funding was provided by the Norwegian Council for Research, the Nansen Fund, the Roald Amundsen Centre for Arctic Research, the University of Tromsø (UiTø) and the Norwegian Polar Institute (NPI). The sediment cores (T-88-2, T-79-51/2) were sampled during cruises by T. Vorren, UiTø, and by A. Solheim, NPI (cores NP90-12, NP-90-39 and NP-90-57). Laboratory analysis were carried out by M. Berntsen, I. Bottolfsen, T. K. Danielsen, J. H. Nilsen and M. Raste. L. Labeyrie (Centre Faibles Radioactivites, CNRS, France) and E. Jansen (University of Bergen) provided stable isotope measurements, J. C. Duplessy (Centre Faibles Radioactivites, CNRS, France) and the Radiocarbon Laboratory in Trondheim, Norway provided AMS datings. Analysis on core T-51-2 were performed at the Institute of Arctic and Alpine Research, University of Colorado, Boulder, as part of S. H.'s graduate thesis study under supervision by J. T. Andrews and A. Jennings. T. Andrews and A. Jennings also critically revised the paper and made many suggestions for improvements. To all these people and institutions we offer our sincere thanks.

References

ALM, T. 1993. Øvre Æårsvatn-palynostratigraphy of a 22,000 to 10,000 B.P. lacustrine record on a Andøya, northern Norway. *Boreas*, **22**, 71–188.

ANDREWS, J. T., ERLENKEUSER, H., TEDESCO, K., AKSU, A. & JULL, A. J. T. 1994. Late Quaternary (Stage 2 and 3) meltwater and Heinrich events, NW Labrador Sea. *Quaternary Research*, **41**, 26–34.

ÅDLANDSVIK, B. & LOENG, H. A study of the climatic system in the Barents Sea. *Polar Research*, **10**, 45–59.

BARD, E., HAMELIN, B., FAIRBANKS, R. G. & ZINDLER, A. H. 1990. Calibration of the ^{14}C timescale over the past 30,000 years using mass spectrometric U–Th ages from Barbados corals. *Nature*, **346**, 453–458.

CHARLES, C. D. & FAIRBANKS, R. G. 1992. Evidence from Southern Ocean sediments for the effect of North Atlantic deep-water flux on climate. *Nature*, **355**, 416–419.

CROWLEY, T. J. & NORTH, G. R. 1991. *Paleoclimatology*. Univeristy Press, New York.

DANSGAARD, W., JOHNSEN, S. J. & 9 others 1993. Evi-dence for general instability of past climate from at 250-kyr ice–core record. *Nature*, **364**, 218–220.

——, WHITE, J. W. C. & JOHNSEN, S. J. 1989. The abrupt termination of the Younger Dryas climate event. *Nature*, **339**, 532–534.

DUPLESSY, J. C. 1978. Isotopic studies. *In*: GRIBBIN, J. (ed.) *Climatic Change*. Cambridge University Press, 46–67.

FAIRBANKS, R. G. 1989. A 17,000-year glacio-eustatic sea level record: influence of glacial melting rates on the Younger Dryas event and deep-ocean circulation. *Nature*, **298**, 841–844.

FEYLING-HANSSEN, R. W. 1958. Mikropalaeontologiens teknikk. *Norges Geologiske Undersøkelse*, **203**, 35–48.

HALD, M. & ANDREWS, J. T. 1995. Response of the high latitude northern hemisphere to orbital forcing: evidence from the Nordic Seas—comment. *Geology*, **23**, 382–383.

—— & VORREN, T. O. 1984. Modern and Holocene foraminifera and sediments on the continental shelf off Troms, North Norway. *Boreas*, **13**, 133–154.

—— & —— 1987. Foraminiferal stratigraphy and environments of Late Weichselian deposits on the continental shelf off Troms, Northern Norway. *Marine Micropaleontology*, **12**, 129–160.

——, DANIELSEN, T. K. & LORENTZEN, S. 1989. Late Pleistocene and Holocene benthic foraminiferal distribution in the southwestern Barents Sea: paleoenvironmental implications. *Boreas*, **18**, 367–388.

HEBBELN, D., DOKKEN, T., ANDERSEN, E., HALD, M. & ELVERHØI, A. 1994. Moisture supply for northern ice-sheet growth during the Last Glacial Maximum. *Nature*, **370**, 357–360.

HOPKINS, T. S. 1991. The GIN Sea—a synthesis of its physical oceanography and literature review 1972–1985. *Earth-Science Reviews*, **30**, 175–318.

IVERSEN, J. 1944. *Viscum, Hedra* and *Ilex* as climatic indicators. *Geologiska Føreningens i Stockholm, Førhandlingar*, **66**, 463–483.

JOHANNESSEN, T. 1987. *Resente planktoniske foraminiferer fra Norskehavet, Islandshavet og Nordatlanteren. Taxonomi, faunafordeling og stabilisotopsammensetning*. Thesis, Univeristy of Bergen.

——, JANSEN, E., FLATØY, A. & RAVELO, A. C. 1994. The relationship between surface water and paleoclimatic proxies in surface sediments of the Greenland, Iceland, Norwegian Seas. *In*: ZAHN, R. et al. (eds) *Carbon Cycling in Glacial Ocean: Constraints on the Ocean's Role in Global Change*. NATO ASI Series, **117**, 61–85.

JONES, G. & KEIGWIN, L. D. 1988. Evidence from Fram Strait (78° N) for early deglaciation. *Nature*, **336**, 56–59.

KARLÈN, W. 1988. Scandinavian glacial and climatic fluctuations during the Holocene. *Quaternary Science Reviews*, **7**, 199–209.

KEIGWIN, L. D. & LEHMAN, S. J. 1994. Deep circulation change linked to HEINRICH event 1 and Younger dryas in a middepth North Atlantic core. *Paleoceanography*, **9**, 185–194.

KOÇ, N. & JANSEN, E. 1994. Response of the high-latitude Northern Hemisphere to orbital climate forcing: evidence from the Nordic Seas. *Geology*, **22**, 523–526.

——, —— & HAFLIDASON, H. 1993. Paleoceanographic reconstructions of surface ocean conditions in the Greenland, Iceland and Norwegian Sea through the last 14 ka based on diatoms. *Quaternary Science Reviews*, **12**, 115–140.

KROMER, B. & BECKER, B. 1993. German oak and pine ^{14}C calibration, 7200–9400 BC. *Radiocarbon*, **35**, 125–135.

KUTZBACH, J. E. & GALLIMORE, R. G. 1988. Sensitivity of a coupled atmosphere/mixed layer ocean model to changes in orbital forcing at 9000 B.P. *Journal of Geophysical Research*, **93**, 803–821.

—— & GUETTER, P. I. 1986. The influence of changing orbital parameters and surface boundary conditions on climate simulations for the past 18,000 years. *Journal of Atmospheric Science*, **43**, 1726–1759.

LABERG, J. S. & VORREN, T. O. 1993. A late Pleistocene submarine slide on the Bear Island Trough a Mouth Fan. *Geo-Marine Letters*, **13**, 227–234.

LEHMAN, S. J. & KEIGWIN, L. D. 1992. Sudden changes in North Atlantic circulation during the last deglaciation. *Nature*, **356**, 757–762.

——, JONES, G. A., KEIGWIN, L. D., ANDERSEN, E. S., BUTENKO, G. & ØSTMO, S. R. 1991. Initiation of Fennoscandian ice-sheet retreat during the last deglaciation. *Nature*, **349**, 513–516.

——, WRIGHT, D. G. & STOCKER, T. F. 1994. Transport into the deep ocean by the conveyer. *In: Global Environmental Change*. NATO ASI Series I, **12**, 187–209.

LOENG, H. 1991. Features of the physical oceanographic conditions of the Barents sea. *Polar Research*, **10**, 518.

MANGERUD, J. & GULLIKSEN, S. 1975. Apparent rediocarbon ages of recent marine shells off Norway, Spitsbergen and Arctic Canada. *Quaternary Research*, **5**, 263–273.

MARTINSON, D. G., NICKLAS, G. P., HAYS, J. D., IMBRIE, J., MOORE, T. C. & SHACKLETON, N. J. 1987. Age dating and the orbital theory of ice ages: development of a high-resolution 0 to 300,000 years chronostratigraphy. *Quaternary Research*, **27**, 1–29.

MELDGAARD, S. & KNUDSEN, K. L. 1979. Metoder til indsamling og opparbejding af prøver til foraminifer-analyser. *Dansk Natur, Dansk Skole*, 48–57.

MITCHELL, J. F. B., GRAHAME, N. S. & NEEDHAM, K. H. 1988. Climate simulations for 9000 years before present: seasonal variations and the effect of the laurentide Ice Sheet. *Journal of Geophysical Research*, **93**, 8282–8303.

MOSBY, H. 1968. Surrounding Seas. *In*: SØMME, A. (ed.) *Geography of Norden*. J. W. Cappelens Forlag, Oslo, 18–26, map 7.

NESJE, A., KVAMME, M., RYE, N. & LØVLIE, R. 1991. Holocene glacial and climate history of the Jostedalsbreen region, western Norway: evidence from lake sediments and terrestrial deposits. *Quaternary Science Reviews*, **10**, 296–298.

POLYAK, L. & SOLHEIM, A. 1994. Late and post-glacial environments in the northern Barents Sea west of Franz Josef Land. *Polar Research*, **13**, 197–207.

——, LEHMAN, S. J., GATAULLIN, V. & JULL, A. J. T. 1995. Two-step deglaciation of the southeastern Baretns Sea. *Geology*, **23**, 567–571.

RUDDIMAN, W. F., MCINTYRE, A., NIEBLER-HUNT, V. & DURAZZI, J. T. 1980. Oceanic evidence for the mechanism of rapid northern hemisphere glaciation. *Quaternary Research*, **13**, 33–64.

——, SANCETTA, C. D. & MCINTYRE, A. 1977. Glacial/interglacial response rate of sub-polar North Atlantic waters to climatic change: the record in oceanic sediments. *Philosophical Transactions of the Royal Society B*, **280**, 119–142.

SALVIGSEN, O., FORMAN, S. & MILLER, G. H. 1992. Thermophilus molluscs on Svalbard during Holocene and their paleoclimatic implications. *Polar Research*, **11**, 1–10.

SARNTHEIN, M., JANSEN, E. & 7 others 1992. $\delta^{18}O$ time-slice reconstruction of melt water anomalies at termination 1 in the North Atlantic between 50 and 80° N. *In*: BARD, E. & BROECKER, W. S. (eds) *The Last Deglaciation: Absolute and Radiocarbon Chronologies. Global Environmental Change*. NATO ASI Series, Series 1, Springer-Verlag, Berlin, Heidelberg.

SELSING, L. & WISHMAN, E. 1984. Mean summer temperatures and circulation in southwest Norwegian mountain area during the Atlantic period, based upon changes of the alpine pine-forest limit. *Annals of Glaciology*, **5**, 127–132.

SHACKLETON, N. J. 1974, Attainment of isotopic equilibrium between ocean water and the bentho-nic foraminifera genus *Uvigerina*: isotopic changes in the ocean during the last glacial. *Centre National de la Recherche Scientifique Collagues Internationaux*, **219**, 203–209.

—— & OPDYKE, N. D. 1973. Oxygen isotope and palaeomagnetic stratigraphy of equatorial Pacific core V28-238: oxygen isotope temperatures and ice volumes on a 10^5 year and 10^6 year scale. *Quaternary Research*, **3**, 39–55.

——, IMBRIE, J. & HALL, M. A. 1983. Oxygen and carbon isotope record of core V19-30: implications for the formation of deep water in the Late Pleistocene North Atlantic. *Earth and Planetary Science Letter*, **65**, 233–244.

STEIN, R., NAM, S. I., SCHUBERT, C., VOGT, C., FUTTERER, D. & HEINEMEIER, J. 1994. The last deglaciation event in the eastern central Arctic Ocean. *Science*, **264**, 692–696.

THOMSEN, E. & VORREN, T. O. 1986. Macrofaunal paleoecology and stratigraphy in late Quaternary shelf sediments off Northern Norway. *Palaeogeography, Palaeoclimatology, Palaeoecology*, **56**, 103–150.

VEUM, T. E., JANSEN, M., ARNOLD, I., BEYR, I. & DUPLESSY, J. C. 1992. Water mass exchange in the North Atlantic and the Norwegian Sea during the past 28,000 years. *Nature*, **356**, 783–785.

VORREN, T. O. & KRISTOFFERSEN, Y. 1986. Late Quaternary glaciation in the south western Barents Sea. *Boreas*, **15**, 51–59.

——, HALD, M. & THOMSEN, E. 1984. Quaternary sediments and environments on the continental shelf off Northern Norway. *Marine Geology*, **57**, 229–257.

——, STRASS, I. F. & LIND-HANSEN, O. W. 1978. Late Quaternary sediments and stratigraphy on the continental shelf off Troms and West Finnmark, Northern Norway. *Quaternary Research*, **10**, 340–365.

——, VORREN, K. D., ALM, T., GULLIKSEN, S. & LVLIE, R. 1988. The last deglaciation 20,000 to 11,000 BP) on Andøya, Northern Norway. *Boreas*, **17**, 41–77.

WEINELT, M., SARNTHEIN, M., VOGELSANG, E. & ERLENKEUSER, H. 1991. Early decay of the Barents Shelf Ice Sheet—spread of stable isotope signals across the eastern Norwegian Sea. *Norsk Geologisk Tidsskrift*, **71**, 137–140.

Deglaciation history and palaeoceanography of the western Spitsbergen margin since the last glacial maximum

J. LLOYD[1,*], D. KROON[1], C. LABAN[2] & G. BOULTON[2]

[1] *Department of Geology and Geophysics, University of Edinburgh, West Mains Road, Edinburgh EH9 3JW, UK*
[2] *Geological Survey of the Netherlands, Marine Geology Department, PO Box 157, 2000 AD Haarlem, The Netherlands*
* Present address: Department of Geography, University of Durham, South Road, Durham DH1 3LE, UK

Abstract: Two high resolution cores from the Spitsbergen margin were studied to increase the understanding of the palaeoceanography and deglaciation of the Spitsbergen continental margin. Planktonic and benthic foraminiferal $\delta^{18}O$ records along with foraminiferal abundance counts and dropstone analysis were used to interpret the palaeoceanography of the Spitsbergen margin and to link the marine record with deglaciation of the Barents Sea Ice Sheet. High foraminiferal and dropstone abundances during the Late Weichselian glacial maximum show that this period was characterized by seasonally ice-free conditions. The initial deglaciation recognized along the Spitsbergen margin is dated at 14.1 ka BP and represents the break up of the Barents Sea Ice Sheet, though some input from the Spitsbergen ice dome is likely. This initial deglaciation was produced by glacio-isostatic relative sea-level rise and/or by increased solar insolation after the minimum of the Late Weichselian. The first unequivocal deglaciation of Spitsbergen ice occurred at 13 ka, whereas the oceanographic regime was still dominated by polar waters. The beginning of the Holocene was heralded by a second deglaciation phase of the Spitsbergen ice mass. The first influx of North Atlantic waters causing rapid iceberg calving and melting was recorded at this time. Dropstone input virtually ended at approximately 9 ka BP when most glaciers had retreated beyond their present day positions. A short relatively cool episode produced by the retreat of the North Atlantic waters during the early Holocene was recorded along the Spitsbergen margin.

The history of the continental margin of Svalbard and its ice-cap are not clearly understood for the period since the last glacial maximum. This paper presents results from two high resolution cores from the continental slope of the Spitsbergen margin and attempts to link the marine record of meltwater events with the deglacial record of the Spitsbergen ice-cap. Meltwater events can be recognized from $\delta^{18}O$ measurements on planktonic foraminifera; the chronology of the cores is based on eight ^{14}C dates. Some aspects of the ice rafting history are also analysed from counts of dropstones seen in X-rays of the cores. Changes in the general palaeoceanographic regime of the area are identified from planktonic foraminiferal assemblages and surface water productivity is evaluated from absolute abundances of foraminifera in the cores.

The Late Weichselian glacial maximum on Spitsbergen is generally thought to have occurred between 18 and approximately 13 ka (Svendsen & Mangerud 1992). The maximum size of this ice mass is disputed. Some recon-structions show the whole Svalbard archipelago covered by the Barents Sea Ice Sheet (Grosswald 1980; Denton & Hughes 1981), whereas other research suggests that the west coast of Spitsbergen was ice-free during the whole of the Late Weichselian (Salvigsen 1977; 1979; Miller 1982; Miller *et al.* 1989; Forman 1989). More recent work has shown that ice tongues extended from the major outlet fjords a considerable distance onto the continental shelf and possibly even as far as the shelf edge (Mangerud *et al.* 1992; Svendsen *et al.* 1992). The initial deglaciation of the Spitsbergen margin has been ^{14}C dated at approximately 13–12.5 ka BP at various sections along the west coast of Spitsbergen (Svendsen *et al.* 1992, for the Isfjorden area; Landvik *et al.* 1992, for Bellsund; Mangerud & Svendsen 1990) There is much evidence that the outer coast was ice-free by 12–13 ka BP at the latest (Boulton *et al.* 1982; Forman *et al.* 1987; Forman 1989; Mangerud & Svendsen 1990; Lehman & Forman 1991; Mangerud *et al.* 1992). A further rapid melting event occurred at approximately 10 ka BP

From Andrews, J. T., Austin, W. E. N., Bergsten, H. & Jennings, A. E. (eds), 1996, *Late Quaternary Palaeoceanography of the North Atlantic Margins*, Geological Society Special Publication No. 111, pp. 289–301

(Mangerud *et al.* 1992; Svendsen *et al.* 1992); most glaciers terminated at or landward of their present positions by about 9 ka BP (Forman 1989; Sexton *et al.* 1992).

From the marine record Jones & Keigwin (1988) suggest initial disintegration of the Barents Sea Ice Sheet at 14.5 ka BP based on a meltwater spike identified in the Fram Strait. This is earlier than the disintegration of the Spitsbergen ice mass just described. Sarnthein *et al.* (1992) have described a series of meltwater events recognized in marine cores from the Norwegian–Greenland Sea. The first meltwater event they recognize has been dated at 13.6 ka BP at its peak (dated from near the Barents Shelf edge). They assume that this event correlates with the meltwater spike dated at 14.5 ka BP by Jones & Keigwin (1988) and agree that it represents disintegration of the Barents Sea Ice

Sheet. A second meltwater event was recognized culminating near 12.3 ka BP, also produced from the Barents Shelf. This event was also notable for the first influx of subpolar planktonic foraminifera into the southeastern Norwegian Sea. The Holocene circulation and temperature regime commenced close to 9 ka BP, with maximum warmth reached at approximately 7 ka BP. The high resolution records from the continental margin of Spitsbergen of this study will be compared with these marine data sets and the Spitsbergen terrestrial records.

Materials and methods

The two 10 cm diameter piston cores used in this study were taken from the continental slope off the western margin of Spitsbergen (Fig. 1).

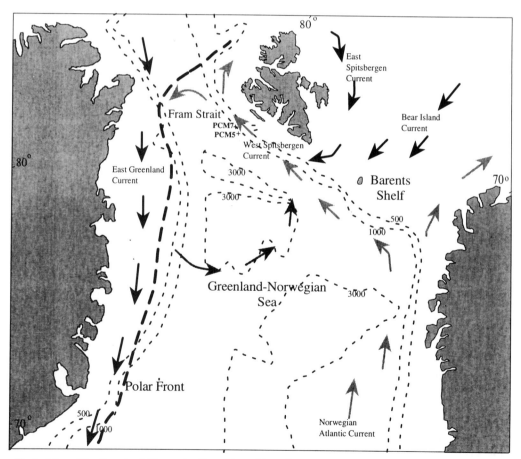

Fig. 1. Map of the Greenland–Norwegian Sea with position of cores PCM5 and PCM7 marked. The present day surface current regime is also shown; warm currents are depicted by lighter arrows, cooler currents by darker arrows. The approximate position of the Polar Front for the present day is also shown.

These cores were taken in 1988 during an expedition of the Geological Survey of the Netherlands, with the vessel *Hr. Ms. Tydeman* of the Hydrographic survey of the Netherlands. Core PCM7 (lat. 78°37′ N, long. 7°54′ E) was taken from a water depth of 1073 m along with a trip core (PCM7t), core PCM5 (lat. 78°29′ N, long. 7°43′ E) was taken from slightly further down the continental slope at a depth of 2139 m.

These cores lie under the northward flowing West Spitsbergen Current at the present day (the relatively warm, saline extension of the Norwegian Current). The present day surface oceanographic regime is shown in Fig. 1, along with the approximate position of the Polar Front.

Laboratory analysis

The cores were sub sampled at 5 cm intervals. Samples were then dried and weighed before being wet sieved at 63 μm. The residue was then dried for use in foraminiferal and oxygen isotope analysis. For oxygen isotope analysis specimens of the planktonic species *Neogloboquadrina pachyderma* (sinistral) (Ehrenberg) were picked from the >125 μm fraction (on average 5–10 specimens were used in the analysis). For the benthic oxygen isotope analysis several species had to be picked. For PCM5 *Eponides umbonatus* (Reuss) was measured (an average of 10–15 specimens needed per analysis), a correction factor of +0.47‰ has been made to these measurements (Belanger *et al.* 1981). For PCM7 two species were analysed, *Melonis barleeanum* (Williamson) (correction factor of +0.4‰, Streeter & Shackleton 1979, 4–6 specimens per analysis) and *Cassidulina teretis* (Tappan) (no correction factor used, Rokoengen *et al.* 1991, 10–15 specimens per analysis). Where two species are used in the same core different symbols are used for each. Samples were run on a VG Isogas Prism mass

spectrometer at the Scottish Research and Reactor Centre, East Kilbride. The precision of the oxygen isotope analyses was 0.08‰ (standard deviation for 100 analyses of a standard carbonate, SM1, conducted over several months).

The total abundance for both planktonic and benthic foraminifera was calculated on the >125 μm fraction. Counts of individual planktonic species were also made on this fraction. Where possible at least 300 specimens were counted from each sample; where abundances were too high the sample was accurately split. The fraction from 63–125 μm was scanned to check if a significant difference in assemblage was present between size fractions. For the total foraminiferal abundance values are expressed as number of specimens per gram of dry sediment; for the individual species counts percentage values have been calculated.

The abundance of dropstones was calculated from X-rays of the undisturbed half of each core. This has been reported for the whole of these cores by Lloyd *et al.* (1996). Counts of clasts with a greater than 2 mm diameter were assumed to be representative of dropstones; these were made over 2 cm slices of the cores.

Chronology

The chronology of the cores is based on eight AMS ^{14}C dates. Details are shown in Table 1. Two of the dates are from the trip core, PCM7t, five are from PCM7 and one is from PCM5. These dates are marked on the results shown in Figs 2 and 3. Both cores extend further back than shown here: PCM5 extends back to oxygen isotope stage 6 (the Early Saalian) and PCM7 extends back well into stage 3 (described by Lloyd *et al.* 1996), but only the sections relevant to this paper are shown here.

The oldest AMS date obtained is from 195 cm in PCM5, 22.0 ka BP. This coincides with a

Table 1. *Details of AMS dates from cores. A reservoir correction of 400 a has been subtracted from each value*

Core	Depth (cm)	Species measured	Weight (mg)	Laboratory code	Age (years BP)
PCM7t	2	*N. pachyderma* (s)	10	GrA-581	6 180 ± 35
PCM7t	100	*N. pachyderma* (s)	10	GrA-582	9 450 ± 40
PCM7	20	*N. pachyderma* (s)	18	GrA-569	8 065 ± 40
PCM7	70	*N. pachyderma* (s)	10	GrA-572	9 030 ± 40
PCM7	120	*N. pachyderma* (s)	11	GrA-571	8 595 ± 40
PCM7	150	*C. teretis*	22	GrA-564	12 410 ± 60
PCM7	250	*N. pachyderma* (s)	25	GrA-563	14 110 ± 70
PCM5	195	*N. pachyderma* (s)	20	OxA-3504	22 040 ± 320

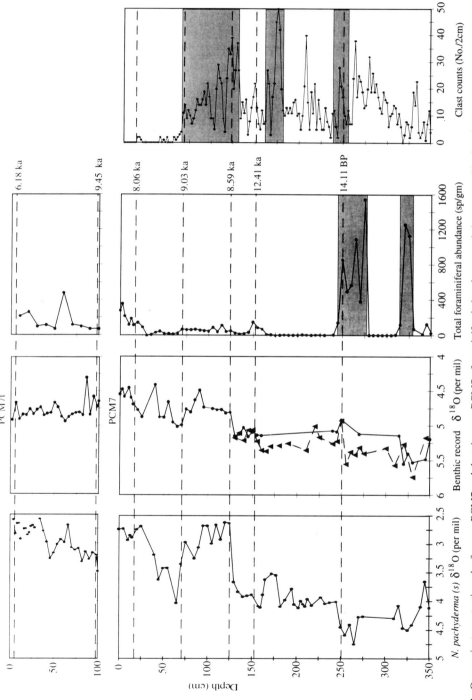

Fig. 2. Oxygen isotope stratigraphy for core PCM7 and the trip core, PCM7t, foraminiferal abundances and clast counts. Planktonic measurements are shown on the left, benthic measurements are from two speceis, *M. barleeanum* (circles) and *C. teretis* (triangles). The position of radiocarbon dates from the cores are also shown; a correction of 400 years has been subtracted from all dates.

section of heavy planktonic $\delta^{18}O$ values (Fig. 3). The next oldest date, 14.1 ka BP, is from 250 cm in PCM7, found at the end of a heavy $\delta^{18}O$ section (Fig. 2). The planktonic $\delta^{18}O$ records of PCM5 and PCM7 can be correlated. The section from 345 to 250 cm in PCM7 (Fig. 2), characterized by two prominent heavy $\delta^{18}O$ sections, correlates with the section from 205 to 130 cm in PCM5 (also with two prominent peaks in $\delta^{18}O$ values, Fig. 3). This correlation is also supported by the foraminiferal abundances, both cores having two spikes in abundance during the heavy $\delta^{18}O$ sections; these are shaded in Figs 2 and 3. This section represents the Late Weichselian glacial maximum, evidenced by the two AMS dates of 22.0 and 14.1 ka BP and the heavy 'glacial' planktonic $\delta^{18}O$ values. The plateau of planktonic $\delta^{18}O$ values approximately 4‰ seen from 245 to 130 cm in PCM7 can be correlated with the poor resolution section from 125 to 15 cm in PCM5.

The Holocene AMS datings in general cover a short time span; not including the date at the top of the trip core they range from 8.06 to 9.45 ka BP. There are definite problems with these dates: there is an age reversal and the date of 8.59 ka BP at 120 cm is younger than expected. The most likely explanation is that the Holocene section has been affected by reworking. The cores were recovered from the continental slope where gravitational processes have been active during the Holocene; these processes could have produced reworking over this section.

The results from cores PCM7 and PCM7t (its trip core) have been presented separately. Although the record from PCM7t should be preserved in PCM7, the ^{14}C dates and the results themselves suggest that a significant section of sediment is missing from the top of PCM7. This difference between the cores may have been produced by disturbance caused by the coring procedure. Both cores have a substantial proportion of the Holocene missing (from 6 ka BP to the present in PCM7t and from 8 ka BP to present in PCM7). PCM5 has an even larger section missing from approximately 10 ka BP to present. This was probably produced by erosion due to gravitational processes on the continental slope. X-Ray photographs of the cores have been examined; no obvious breaks in sedimentation were seen, though minor hiatuses may be present.

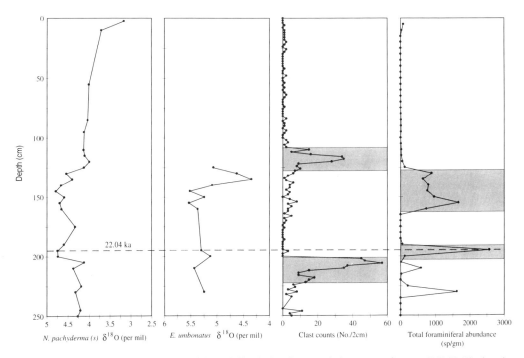

Fig. 3. Oxygen isotope stratigraphy, total foraminiferal abundance and clast counts for core PCM5. Planktonic measurements from *N. pachyderma* (s) are shown on the left, benthic measurements next to this from *E. umbonatus*. The position of radiocarbon date from this core is also shown; a correction of 400 years has been subtracted.

Results and interpretation

Late Weichselian glacial maximum

The peak of the Late Weichselian glacial maximum, oxygen isotope stage 2, can be recognized from the oxygen isotope signature of both planktonic and benthic foraminifera in both cores (seen in Figs 2 and 3). This interpretation has been verified by ^{14}C dates in PCM5, 22.0 ka BP at 195 cm, and PCM7, 14.1 ka BP at 250 cm. The isotopic evidence shows two events of increased planktonic δ^{18}O, one at 22 ka BP, and one immediately before 14.1 ka BP. Both these periods are characterized by high foraminiferal absolute abundances in both PCM5 and PCM7, up to 1000–2000 sp/g (shaded sections in Figs 2 and 3). The assemblage during these heavy isotope sections is almost 100% N. pachyderma (sinistral), the polar water species (shown in Fig. 4). The high foraminiferal abundances during these peak glacial periods imply productivity blooms caused by at least seasonally ice-free conditions along the Spitsbergen margin at these times. A thick sea ice cover would prevent solar insolation from reaching surface waters, thus reducing productivity to very low values, though it is known that N. pachyderma can live below sea ice (Carstens & Wefer 1992). These high glacial abundances are the opposite of foraminiferal abundances observed elsewhere in the Norwegian–Greenland Sea and Arctic Ocean (Sejrup et al. 1984; Kellogg 1980; Belyaeva & Khusid 1990), though more recently Hebbeln et al. (1995) recognized two similar high foraminiferal abundance peaks in a core just south of this study area (this is discussed in more detail later).

The dropstone abundance during these periods of high bioproductivity is variable, generally low in PCM5 but moderate to high in PCM7. It is assumed that an increase in dropstone abundance relates to an increase in iceberg calving and melting. The overall much higher proportion of dropstones found in PCM7 than PCM5 might relate to iceberg drift patterns favouring the site of PCM7. The occurrence of moderate to high dropstone counts during certain periods of high bioproductivity (260–275 and 325–335 cm in PCM7, Fig. 2) suggests that, at least some of the time, high productivity coincides with increased calving and melting.

The high nutrient supply necessary for the productivity blooms was almost certainly produced from melting sea ice and increased iceberg calving and melting, partially supported by the dropstone data. Ackley & Sullivan (1994) found that release of detritus and algae from melting

sea ice seeds ice edge blooms in phytoplankton around Antarctica at the present day. Nutrients are often concentrated in sea ice by the aeolian transport of terrestrial detritus (Smith et al. 1987), whereas calving icebergs commonly have a nutrient concentration an order of magnitude higher than ambient sea water (Jacobs et al. 1979). Upwelling of nutrient-rich deeper waters, also common at the margins of sea ice, would also promote increased productivity. Sancetta (1992) suggested nutrient supply from icebergs and upwelling and turbulence produced by icebergs to explain high primary productivity in glacial North Atlantic sediments rich in ice-rafted detritus. Smith et al. (1987) and Carstens & Wefer (1992) have studied phytoplankton biomass and productivity at the margins of sea ice in the Fram Strait, showing a peak in productivity and abundance at the sea ice margin; this productivity decreases rapidly under the ice and less rapidly towards open water.

The idea of a sea ice free Spitsbergen margin during peak glacial periods disagrees with the reconstructions produced by the CLIMAP Group for 18 ka BP for the northern North Atlantic, (CLIMAP Project Members 1976; McIntyre et al. 1976) showing permanent pack ice throughout the Norwegian–Greenland Sea. A seasonally ice-free Spitsbergen margin has been suggested before, however. Hebbeln et al. (1995) suggested an ice-free corridor reached the Spitsbergen margin in two periods during the Late Weichselian, 27–22.5 ka BP and 19.5–14.5 ka BP. They argued that this was caused by the northward flow of Atlantic water based on the occurrence of a subpolar foraminiferal assemblage and the presence of chalk fragments sourced from the North Sea. Their results show two periods of increased foraminiferal abundance which correlate with the abundance peaks identified in this study. However, the interpretation of faunal data from Hebbeln et al. (1995) is questionable. The actual percentage of 'subpolar' specimens is relatively small, below 10%, apart from one sample with 30%, and the estimated percentages may be too high because Globigerina quinqueloba (Natland) also occurs in polar waters (Carstens & Wefer 1992). The assemblage found is very much dominated by polar species, so if it does represent the influx of Atlantic water, then it must be a very minor inflow as the main subpolar species such as Globigerina bulloides (d'Orbigny) and right coiling varieties of N. pachyderma were not reported. The presence of chalk fragments is harder to explain, though they could have been carried up during a previous deglacial episode,

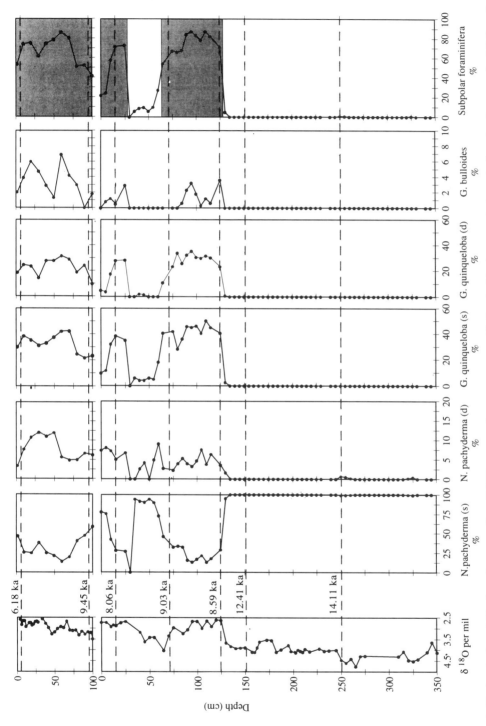

Fig. 4. Planktonic foraminiferal species counts from PCM7, expressed as percentages, with the planktonic oxygen isotope stratigraphy shown on the left for reference. The summary curve on the right, showing the percentage of subpolar foraminifera, includes specimens of *N. pachyderma* (s), *G. quinqueloba* (s and d) and *G. bulloides*. The position of radiocarbon dates are also marked.

deposited on the continental shelf and then reworked by locally derived icebergs during the glacial maximum. The faunal data from this study does not record an influx of subpolar foraminifera during these periods (Fig. 4). The smaller size fraction, 63–125 μm, was scanned to see if it contained the subpolar species *G. quinqueloba*, but it was dominated by near 100% *N. pachyderma* (sinistral). Thus we did not find any evidence of an influx of subpolar Atlantic water. The cores from this study are further north than core NP90-39 from Hebbeln *et al.* (1995) and this might explain why they do not record the subpolar influence of Atlantic waters.

Svendsen & Mangerud (1992) suggested seasonally ice-free conditions in the Norwegian Sea as a mechanism to provide the moisture supply necessary for rapid ice advance from 18 to 13 ka BP on Spitsbergen. During this period we see an increasing trend in dropstone abundance in PCM7 and, to a lesser extent, in PCM5; this relates to an increasing calving rate (Figs 2 and 3). We interpret this as a response of an increase in ice accumulation leading to ice advance onto the continental shelf and associated calving; a high calving rate does not necessarily relate to glacial retreat. The major dropstone peak in PCM5 just before to the Late Weichselian glacial maximum (Fig. 3) may relate to a deglacial event at the end of stage 3 or, perhaps, to a rapid accumulation event and advance of ice onto the shelf leading to increased calving rates. PCM7 shows a similar though less pronounced peak at this time.

This still leaves the problem of explaining the presence of ice-free conditions during the peak of the last glaciation. Perhaps an increase in wind stress coupled with low accumulation caused the break-up of sea ice along the shelf edge.

Initial deglaciation of the Barents Sea Ice Sheet at 14.1 ka BP

The initial deglacial event after the Late Weichselian glacial maximum is clearly seen in the oxygen isotope records of both PCM7 and PCM5; it is ^{14}C dated at 14.1 ka BP in PCM7 (Figs 2 and 3). This age is similar to the proposed initial break-up of the Barents Sea Ice Sheet and deglaciation of the Norwegian Continental Shelf at 15–14.5 ka BP (Jones & Keigwin 1988; Lehman & Forman 1991; Sarnthein *et al.* 1992). Koç & Jansen (1994) suggest that this initial deglaciation affected marine-based ice sheets over the whole of the

Nordic Seas, though the Barents Sea recorded the most intense meltwater transfer. The planktonic δ^{18}O shift over this initial step along the Spitsbergen margin was approximately 0.5‰; benthic δ^{18}O values for both cores also show a significant drop. The amplitude of the benthic shift is approximately 0.4‰, for PCM7, and considerably larger, 0.8–1.0‰, for PCM5.

This benthic isotopic shift is surprising; the ice volume effect at this time would be minimal, the influx of a new deep water mass is another possibility, but a more likely explanation is the production of dense meltwater brines which sink down the continental slope. This process has been described from present day Arctic continental shelves (Nansen Arctic Drilling Program Science Committee 1992); continued melting and re-freezing of sea ice causes an increase in the salinity of meltwater. Eventually this meltwater becomes so saline that cold very dense brines with a light δ^{18}O composition are produced, which sink.

The dropstone records of PCM5 and PCM7 both show an increase over this initial deglaciation, shaded in Figs 2 and 3. This suggests a major calving event, either from the local Spitsbergen ice mass, or icebergs carried north from the Barents Sea Ice Sheet. There is no foraminiferal evidence of an influx of North Atlantic waters at this time. The faunal assemblage is dominated by the polar species *N. pachyderma* (s), 99–100% (Fig. 4). The absolute abundances of planktonic foraminifera were low for this initial deglacial period (Figs 2 and 3), suggesting that the area was dominated by meltwater at this time. Carstens & Wefer (1992) found that planktonic foraminifera in the Arctic Ocean did not like living in meltwater-dominated surface waters and tended to live below the pycnocline.

The presence of a polar water foraminiferal assemblage over this initial deglaciation phase, (Fig. 4) suggests it is not due to influx of North Atlantic waters along the Spitsbergen margin. Jones & Keigwin (1988), Lehman *et al.* (1991) and Polyak *et al.* (1995) have suggested that the initial break-up of the Barents Sea Ice Sheet was due to a relative sea-level rise caused by isostatic lowering of the ice sheet bed. The exact timing of initial deglaciation of the Spitsbergen margin is unsure. Svendsen *et al.* (1992) have evidence from cores on the continental shelf of Spitsbergen suggesting that the ice sheet reached the shelf edge in glaciated troughs at the last glacial maximum. A radiocarbon-dated mollusc from the base of a marine sequence just above the interpreted Late Weichselian till suggests that deglaciation occurred at approximately 12.5 ka BP. This agrees with other data suggesting that the outer coast of Spitsbergen was ice-free by 12–13 ka BP at the latest (Forman 1989; Mangerud & Svendsen 1990; Lehman & Forman 1991; Mangerud *et al.* 1992). This is significantly later than the break-up of the Barents Sea Ice Sheet at 14.5 ka BP, and the initial meltwater spike identified in PCM7 and PCM5. It seems likely that the initial break-up of ice on the Barents Shelf coincided with some deglaciation from Western Spitsbergen; a glacio-isostatic sea-level rise would cause disintegration of ice on both the Barents Shelf and West Spitsbergen margin. The initial deglaciation from the West Spitsbergen margin must have been minor as it has not been identified from cores from the continental shelf. This supports the incorporation of a meltwater signal in the benthic foraminifera from the Spitsbergen continental slope.

Deglaciation of Spitsbergen ice at 13 ka BP

A significant spike of planktonic $\delta^{18}O$ values is seen from 180 to 160 cm in PCM7, beginning at approximately 13 ka BP. This spike suggests a further deglacial pulse recognized along the Spitsbergen margin. The fauna at this time is dominated by 100% polar species, so there is unlikely to have been a temperature effect on the $\delta^{18}O$ record; the global ice volume change may have produced a small reduction in values, but the dominant change must have been produced by meltwater. This section is also characterized by a dramatic increase in dropstone abundances seen in PCM7, shaded in Fig. 2. PCM5 shows neither of these changes; the record in PCM5 may finish before this event occurred. These two pieces of evidence suggest a major deglacial event took place at 13 ka BP leading to massive iceberg calving rates.

The major Barents Sea ice calving event is recorded earlier, at 14.1 ka BP, so this event most likely represents the initial break-up of the Spitsbergen ice mass. An approximate age can be assigned to this episode from the ^{14}C dates either side of it. Assuming a constant sedimentation rate between the dates of 12.4 ka BP at 150 cm and 14.1 ka BP at 250 cm this deglacial event can be dated at approximately 13–12.5 ka BP. This age fits in with the start of the Bølling–Allerød period, a warm episode that can be clearly seen in the Greenland ice core records (Johnsen *et al.* 1993). This warming was not strong enough to allow North Atlantic subpolar waters to extend as far north as Spitsbergen; no

subpolar foraminfera are recorded in PCM7. The age of this event also agrees closely with the suggested age of deglaciation across the Spitsbergen continental shelf of 12.4 ka BP suggested by Svendsen *et al.* (1992). Their date comes from a core midway across the continental shelf, but the initial deglaciation must have been before this if the ice was at the shelf edge. Therefore the age of 13 ka BP approximated for the start of this event from PCM7 is likely to be accurate. This provides evidence that Late Weichselian ice did reach the shelf edge at least offshore from Isfjorden (the largest outlet fjord from western Spitsbergen). This is also in general agreement with many other deglacial chronologies from the west Spitsbergen margin, suggesting that the outer coast became ice-free at approximately 13–12 ka BP (Svendsen *et al.* 1992, for the Isfjorden area; Landvik *et al.* 1992, for Bellsund; Boulton *et al.* 1982; Forman *et al.* 1987; Forman, 1989; Mangerud & Svendsen, 1990; Lehman & Forman, 1991; Mangerud *et al.* 1992). This deglaciation was not caused by the influx of warmer waters, but may have been induced by increased solar radiation receipt after the low values of the preceding glacial maximum, though Koç *et al.* (1993) and Sarnthein *et al.* (1992) suggest warmer North Atlantic waters invaded the southeastern Norwegian Sea at approximately 13.5 ka BP forming an ice-free corridor along the Norwegian coast. Alternatively, it may be the response of glacio-isostatic sea-level rise leading to break-up of a marine-based ice mass.

Deglaciation continued at a slower rate after this initial phase. Planktonic $\delta^{18}O$ values increased again, suggesting the presence of less meltwater, though still cold polar surface waters (100% polar fauna); dropstone numbers decreased reflecting lower calving rates. This situation remained during the Younger Dryas period until the dramatic changes experienced at the beginning of the Holocene.

Early Holocene subpolar water influx

The beginning of the Holocene was heralded by a major deglacial event, which can be recognized in all the data of this study at 130 cm in PCM7. Planktonic and benthic $\delta^{18}O$ values decrease markedly, a sudden influx of subpolar foraminfera is found along with an increase in absolute foraminiferal abundances and there is also an increase in dropstones (Figs 2 and 4). This initial period of subpolar water influence along the Spitsbergen margin lasted until approximately 9 ka (^{14}C date of 9.03 ka BP at 70 cm in PCM7;

Fig. 4). Unfortunately, the record of PCM5 ends at or before this deglacial event, so it is only clearly seen in PCM7. A planktonic $\delta^{18}O$ shift from approximately 4.0 to 2.6‰, a much larger shift than those of the previous two deglacial events, can be seen in Fig. 2. The benthic $\delta^{18}O$ record also shows a significant shift from 5.2 to 4.7‰. This deglacial event also marks the first influx of subpolar foraminifera into the area. The planktonic foraminiferal assemblage at this point changes from a monospecific assemblage of the polar species *N. pachyderma* (s) to a subpolar assemblage (Carstens & Wefer 1992) of *G. quinqueloba* (dextral and sinistral), *N. pachyderma* (d) and minor occurrences of *Globigerina bulloides* d'Orbigny as well as *N. pachyderma* (s). The oceanographic regime must have changed from a relatively stagnant situation dominated by polar surface waters from the Arctic to one with a northwards flowing current with a strong North Atlantic water component.

Carstens & Wefer (1992) report 60–70% subpolar foraminifera in the West Spitsbergen Current at the present day; this is slightly less than the 80% seen at the beginning of the Holocene in PCM7. This suggests that the influx of subpolar water seen at this time was probably stronger than the present day West Spitsbergen Current. This supports the inference of Svendsen & Mangerud (1992) that the early and mid-Holocene was warmer than the late Holocene on Spitsbergen.

The large increase in dropstones during this period suggests that this influx of subpolar waters led to major deglaciation and increased iceberg calving. Mangerud *et al.* (1992) and Svendsen *et al.* (1992) recognized a major deglaciation event in Isfjorden beginning at 10 ka BP, the beginning of the Holocene. It seems likely that this major event correlates with the event recognized in PCM7 at 130 cm. This therefore suggests that the ^{14}C date at the start of this period, 8.59 ka BP at 120 cm, is too young due to contamination, or possibly due to an hiatus within the core. The evidence from this study provides a mechanism for this deglaciation, an influx of relatively warm subpolar surface waters to the Spitsbergen margin.

Early Holocene cold phase

At approximately 9 ka BP the polar water assemblage increases to account for over 90% of foraminifera in PCM7, suggesting the retreat of subpolar North Atlantic waters (Fig. 4). This cooler period dominated by a polar water regime

lasted until approximately 8 ka (the age of this event is uncertain due to the poor ^{14}C dating during the Holocene). The planktonic foraminiferal abundances also drop over this period. Polar waters at this time were far less productive than during the Late Weichselian maximum. This is perhaps due to the absence of a major ice sheet on the nearby continental shelf coupled with low rates of sea ice production and melting. These factors would decrease the nutrient input to surface waters compared with peak glacial times. The cooler conditions such an oceanographic change would produce are supported by the $\delta^{18}O$ records of both planktonic and benthic foraminifera and the dropstone record (Fig. 2). The planktonic $\delta^{18}O$ values increase from 2.7 to approximately 3.5‰, whereas the benthic values increase from approximately 4.7 to 5.0‰. Dropstone abundances decrease at approximately 9 ka and are present in very low numbers thereafter. This suggests that iceberg production was reduced. Reduction in iceberg production at this time from the Spitsbergen ice mass agrees with the assertion by Sexton *et al.* (1992) that glaciers had retreated to or beyond their present day positions by 9 ka BP. This has been established for many of the fjords around Spitsbergen (Mangerud *et al.* 1992).

Mid Holocene climatic optimum, approximately 8–6 ka BP

From approximately 8 ka BP subpolar waters again invaded the area, producing an assemblage with 70% subpolar foraminifera and a corresponding increase in absolute planktonic abundances due to the increased productivity of North Atlantic sourced waters (Fig. 4). The $\delta^{18}O$ values of planktonic foraminifera decrease, supporting this interpretation, warmer surface waters causing a decrease in $\delta^{18}O$ values. There was no increase in dropstone abundance, suggesting that the isotope response was due entirely to the influx of warmer subpolar waters rather than meltwater.

The faunal data suggest a weakening of the subpolar water influence at the top of PCM7 and the base of the trip core, polar fauna increasing to 50–60%. The age of this increase is uncertain due to the doubt about the AMS date at the base of the trip core, though it must be younger than 8 ka BP (from the date at 20 cm in PCM7). The subpolar influence soon increases, however, rising to account for 60–80% of the assemblage for the rest of the trip core until 6.18 ka BP.

Timing and amplitude of Norwegian–Greenland Sea deglacial events

Sarnthein *et al.* (1992) investigated the meltwater anomalies in the Norwegian–Greenland Sea area during the last deglaciation. Similar deglacial events can be recognized from cores all over the area, though the planktonic $\delta^{18}O$ amplitude of events is different. The initial event interpreted as the break-up of the Barents Sea Ice Sheet has the largest amplitude just off the Barents Shelf (core M23259 of Sarnthein *et al.* 1992); this then decreases slightly southwards along the Norwegian margin and is even less pronounced along the Spitsbergen margin. This supports the idea of a predominantly clockwise circulation regime in the Norwegian–Greenland Sea when the Barents Sea Ice Sheet disintegrated (Sarnthein *et al.* 1992). There must have been some northward flowing current, however, possibly similar to the present day East Spitsbergen Current (Fig. 1), to produce the anomaly seen in the Fram Strait of this study and found by Jones & Keigwin (1988), unless this early event was produced by calving from the Spitbergen ice mass or outflow from the Arctic Ocean.

The next deglacial event, dated as Bølling from this study (13 ka BP) but slightly younger by Sarnthein as 12.3 ka BP, again has a larger amplitude off the Barents Shelf and in the southeastern Norwegian Sea. The higher amplitude in the southeastern Norwegian Sea is due to the influx of warmer North Atlantic waters to the area, as evidenced from the appearance of subpolar foraminifera (Sarnthein *et al.* 1992). Along the Spitsbergen margin the amplitude of the Bølling deglaciation was much smaller than that of the early Holocene event. This is not surprising as during the early Holocene North Atlantic waters actually reached the Spitsbergen margin for the first time during the deglaciation phase, so as well as a meltwater input there would have been a significant temperature effect reducing the $\delta^{18}O$ values. The planktonic $\delta^{18}O$ values are significantly lighter than recognized from further out in the Fram Strait by Jones & Keigwin (1988), core PS 21295, though PCM7 from this study is of a much higher resolution than PS 21295. This could be due to North Atlantic waters not extending as far out into the Fram Strait as core PS 21295; also the meltwater signal recorded in PCM7 would be further diluted once it reached PS 21295.

The significant cooling seen during the early Holocene (approximately 8–9 ka BP) along the Spitsbergen margin, with the retreat of North Atlantic water, does not seem to have been recorded elsewhere. This event may have been a local event, the North Atlantic waters only retreating a short distance south of Spitsbergen, and therefore not picked up in cores further south. The alternative is that some of the cores to the south are of a lower resolution over this period than PCM7 and did not pick up this event.

Conclusions

(1) During certain periods of the Late Weichselian glacial maximum, at approximately 22 ka BP and just before to the initial deglaciation at 14 ka BP, the Spitsbergen shelf edge was at least seasonally free of sea ice. Blooms in planktonic and benthic foraminiferal productivity were recorded; these were seeded by melting sea ice. No evidence of subpolar water influence is recorded at this time from cores PCM7 and PCM5.

(2) Initial deglaciation occurred at 14.1 ka BP, this most likely reflects the break-up of the Barents Sea Ice Sheet, though the possibility of input from the Spitsbergen ice mass cannot be excluded. There was no evidence of an influx of warmer subpolar waters during this intial phase of deglaciation, supporting the assertion by Jones & Keigwin (1988), Lehman *et al.* (1991) and Polyak *et al.* (in press) that the initial deglaciation of the Barents Sea was due to mechanical break-up.

(3) The initial deglaciation of the Spitsbergen ice mass began at approximately 13 ka BP, there was no associated influx of North Atlantic waters recognized with this event. It may have been caused by glacio-isostatic relative sea-level rise (as has been suggested for the Barents Sea Ice Sheet), or by the increase in solar insolation receipt after the minimum of the Late Weichselian.

(4) The first influx of subpolar North Atlantic waters into the area is recorded during the second deglacial phase of the Spitsbergen ice mass at the beginning of the Holocene. The faunal data suggest this period, until approximately 9 ka BP, was as warm if not warmer than the present day along the Spitsbergen margin.

(5) The influence of subpolar North Atlantic waters virtually disappeared for a period during the early Holocene (approximately 9–8 ka BP). The beginning of this phase also marks the reduction in iceberg production caused by retreat of glaciers landward of their present day positions (Sexton *et al.* 1992).

(6) From 8 until 6.18 ka BP (the end of the
records of this study) subpolar waters
again invaded the area. There is no
evidence of increased iceberg calving at
the beginning of this period, suggesting
that there was no major ice advance during
the preceding cold period.

Material for this study was obtained from the
Geological Survey of the Netherlands, collected in
1988 by the vessel *Hr. Ms. Tydeman* of the Hydrographic Survey of the Netherlands. The oxygen isotope
analysis was carried out at the Scottish Research and
Reactor Centre, East Kilbride. This research was
carried out while in receipt of an Natural Environment Research Council grant.

References

ACKLEY, S. F. & SULLIVAN, C. W. 1994. Physical
controls on the development and characteristics of
Antarctic sea ice biological communities—a
review and synthesis. *Deep-Sea Research*, **41**,
1583–1604.
BELANGER, P., CURRY, W. B. & MATTHEWS, R. K.
1981. Core-top evaluation of benthic foraminiferal isotopic ratios for palaeo-oceanographic
interpretations. *Palaeogeography, Palaeoclimatology, Palaeoecology*, **33**, 205–220.
BELYAEVA, N. & KHUSID, T. 1990. Foraminiferal
assemblages in sediments from the Mendeleev
Ridge, Arctic Ocean. *In*: BLEIL, U. & THIEDE, J.
(eds) *Geological History of the Polar Oceans:
Arctic Versus Antarctic*. Kluwer, Dordrecht,
447–454.
BOULTON, G. S., BALDWIN, C. T. & 12 others 1982. A
glacio-isostatic facies model for the Quaternary
events in Spitsbergen and the Arctic. *Nature*, **298**,
437–441.
CARSTENS, J. & WEFER, G. 1992. Recent distribution
of planktonic foraminifera in the Nansen Basin,
Arctic Ocean. *Deep-Sea Research*, **39**, 507–524.
CLIMAP PROJECT MEMBERS 1976. The surface of the
Ice Age Earth. *Science*, **191**, 1131–1144.
DENTON, G., H. & HUGHES, T., J. 1981. The Arctic
Ice Sheet: an outrageous hypothesis. *In*: DENTON,
G. H. & HUGHES, T. J. (eds) *The Last Great Ice
Sheets*. Wiley, New York, 437–467.
FORMAN, S. T. 1989. Late Weichselian glaciation and
deglaciation of Forlandsundet area, western
Spitsbergen, Svalbard. *Boreas*, **18**, 51–60.
——, MANN, D. H., MILLER, G. H. 1987. Late
Weichselian and Holocene relative sea level
history of Broggerhalvoya, Spitsbergen. *Quatern-
ary Research*, **27**, 41–50.
GROSSWALD, M. G. 1980. Late Weichselian ice sheets
of northern Eurasia. *Quaternary Research*, **13**,
1–32.
HEBBELN, D., DOKKEN, T., ANDERSEN, E., HALD,
M. & ELVERHOI, A. 1995. Moisture supply for
the northern ice-sheet growth during the Last
Glacial Maximum. *Nature*, **370**, 357–360.

JACOBS, S., GORDON, A. & AMOS, A. 1979. Effects of
glacial ice melting on the Antarctic surface water.
Nature, **277**, 469–471.
JOHNSEN, S., CLAUSEN, H. & 8 others 1993. Irregular
glacial interstadials recorded in the new Greenland ice core. *Nature*, **359**, 311–313.
JONES, G. & KEIGWIN, L. 1988. Evidence from Fram
Strait (78°N) for early deglaciation. *Nature*, **336**,
56–59.
KELLOGG, T. 1980. Paleoclimatology and paleo-
oceanography of the Norwegian and Greenland
Seas: glacial–interglacial contrasts. *Boreas*, **9**,
115–137.
KOÇ, N. & JANSEN, E. 1994. Response of the high-
latitude Northern Hemisphere to orbital climate
forcing: evidence from the Nordic Seas. *Geology*,
22, 523–526.
——, —— & HAFLIDASON, H. 1993. Paleoceano-
graphic reconstruction of surface ocean condi-
tions in the Greenland, Iceland and Norwegian
Seas through the last 14 ka based on diatoms.
Quaternary Science Reviews, **12**, 115–140.
LANDVIK, J. Y., BOLSTAD, M., LYCKE, A. K.,
MANGERUD, J. & SEJRUP, H. P. 1992. Weichselian
stratigraphy and palaeoenvironments at Bellsund,
western Spitsbergen. *Boreas*, **21**, 335–358.
LEHMAN, S. J. & FORMAN, S. L. 1991. Late Weichselian
glacial retreat in Kongsfjorden, west Spitsbergen,
Svalbard. *Quaternary Research*, **37**, 139–154.
——, JONES, G. A., KEIGWIN, L. D., ANDERSEN, E.
S., BUTNEKO, G. & OSTMO, S. R. 1991. Initi-
ation of Fennoscandian ice sheet retreat during
the last deglaciation. *Nature*, **349**, 513–516.
LLOYD, J. M., KROON, D., BOULTON, G. S., LABAN,
C. & FALLICK, A. 1996. Ice rafting history of the
Spitsbergen ice cap over the last 200 ka. *Marine
Geology*, **131**.
MANGERUD, J. & SVENDSEN, J. 1990. Deglaciation
chronology inferred from marine sediments in a
proglacial lake basin, western Spitsbergen, Sval-
bard. *Boreas*, **19**, 249–272.
—— & ——1992. The last interglacial–glacial period
on Spitsbergen, Svalbard. *Quaternary Science
Reviews*, **11**, 633–664.
——, BOLSTAD, M. & 8 others 1992. The last glacial
maximum on Spitsbergen, Svalbard. *Quaternary
Research*, **38**, 1–31.
MCINTYRE, A., KIPP, N., CROWLEY, T., KELLOGG,
T., GARDINER, J., PRELL, W. & RUDDIMAN, W.
1976. *Glacial North Atlantic 18,000 years ago: A
CLIMAP Reconstruction*. Geological Society of
America, Memoir, **145**, 43–76.
MILLER, G. H. 1982. Quaternary depositional epi-
sodes, western Spitsbergen, Norway: amino-
stratigraphy and glacial history. *Arctic and
Alpine Research*, **14**, 321–340.
——, SEJRUP, H. P., LEHMAN, S. J., FORMAN, S. L.
1989. Glacial history and marine environmental
change during the last interglacial–glacial cycle,
Western Spitsbergen, Svalbard. *Boreas*, **18**,
273–296.
NANSEN ARCTIC DRILLING PROGRAM SCIENCE
COMMITTEE 1992. *The Arctic Ocean Record: Key
to Global Change (Initial Science Plan)*, 1–102.

POLYAK, L., LEHMAN, S. J., GATAULLIN, V., JULL, A. J. 1995. *Two-step deglaciation of the southeastern Barents Sea. Geology*, **23**, 567–571.

ROKOENGEN, K., ERLENKEUSER, H., LOFALDLI, M., SKARBO, O. 1991. A climatic record for the last 12,000 years from a sediment core on the Mid-Norwegian continental shelf. *Norsk Geologisk Tidsskrift*, **71**, 75–90.

SALVIGSEN, O. 1977. Radiocarbon datings and the extension of the Weichselian ice sheet in Svalbard. *Norsk Polarinstitutt Arbok*, **1976**, 209–224.

——1979. The last deglaciation of Svalbard. *Boreas*, **8**, 217–227.

SANCETTA, C. 1992. Primary production in the glacial North Atlantic and North Pacific oceans. *Nature*, **360**, 249–251.

SARNTHEIN, M., JANSEN, E. & 7 others 1992. $\delta^{18}O$ time slice reconstruction of meltwater anomalies at termination I in the North Atlantic between 50 and 80°N. *In*: BARD, E. & BROECKER, W. S. (eds) *The Last Deglaciation: Absolute and Radiocarbon Chronologies (183–200)*. Springer, Berlin, Heidelberg.

SEJRUP, H. P., JANSEN, E., ERLENKEUSER, H. & HOLTEDAHL, H. 1984. New faunal and isotopic evidence on the Late Weichselian–Holocene oceanographic changes in the Norwegian Sea. *Quaternary Research*, **21**, 74–84.

SEXTON, D. J., DOWDESWELL, J. A., SOLHEIM, A. & ELVERHOI, A. 1992. Seismic architecture and sedimentation in northwest Spitsbergen fjords. *Marine Geology*, **103**, 53–68.

SMITH, W., BAUMANN, M., WILSON, D. & ALETSEE, L. 1987. Phytoplankton biomass and productivity in the marginal ice zone of the Fram Strait during summer 1984. *Journal of Geophysical Research*, **92**, 6777–6786.

STREETER, S. & SHACKLETON, N. 1979. Paleocirculation of the deep North Atlantic: 150,000 year record of benthic foraminifera and oxygen-18. *Science*, **203**, 168–171.

SVENDSEN, J. I. & MANGERUD, J. 1992. Paleoclimatic inferences from glacial fluctuations on Svalbard during the last 20,000 years. *Climate Dynamics*, **6**, 213–220.

——, ——, ELVERHOI, A., SOLHEIM, A. & SCHUTTENHELM, R. 1992. The Late Weichselian glacial maximum on western Spitsbergen inferred from offshore sediment cores. *Marine Geology*, **104**, 1–17.

Late glacial air temperature, oceanographic and ice sheet interactions in the southern Barents Sea region

TORE O. VORREN & JAN S. LABERG

Institute of Biology and Geology, University of Tromsø, N-9037 Tromsø, Norway

Abstract. Stratigraphic records from three areas (the Andøya area, the continental slope and the continental shelf of the southern Barents Sea) are used to evaluate the history of the late glacial Barents Sea Ice Sheet and the northern Fennoscandian Ice Sheet. Two late glacial maxima are indicated: one before 22 ka BP (LGM I) and the younger after 19 ka BP (LGM II). A major deglaciation phase was initiated during a warm spell between 16 and 15 ka BP. During a drawdown of marine based ice sheets about 14.5 ka BP large parts of the southern Barents Sea Ice Sheet decayed. This deglaciation was retarded between 13.7 and 13 ka BP. Most of the eastern and northern Barents Sea was deglaciated during the Bølling-Allerød interstadial complex. During the LGM II there was an ice stream in the Bear Island Trough with an estimated velocity at the front of about 2.5 km/year. An average accumulation rate of 0.3–0.4 m/year is estimated for the drainage area of the Bear Island Trough Ice Stream. A close interrelation exists between summer air temperatures and the waxing and waning phases of the northern Fennoscandian and southern Barents Sea ice sheets. It is suggested that most of the ice sheet decay was due to climatic warming, which caused thinning of the ice sheets, making them susceptible to decoupling from the sea bed and increased calving. The subsequent halts/readvances were due to climatic deteriorations caused by huge inputs of icebergs to the Norwegian Sea which cooled the surface water and in turn promoted sea ice preservation through the summer season and thereby increased the albedo.

There is ample evidence for multiple glaciations of the Barents Sea shelf during the Late Cenozoic (Solheim & Kristoffersen 1984; Vorren *et al.* 1988a; Sættem *et al.* 1992). Marine geological studies in the 1980s showed that the northern (Elverhøi & Solheim 1983) and southern Barents Sea (Vorren & Kristoffersen 1986) were glaciated during the Late Weichselian. The timing and mechanisms of the Late Weichselian glaciation and deglaciation of the Barents Sea Ice Sheet and its relation to the evolution of the northern part of the Fennoscandian Ice Sheet is still disputed.

We will use data from three areas (Fig. 1) to elucidate the Late Weichselian chronology, air temperature and relation between the Barents Sea Ice Sheet and the Fennoscandian Ice Sheet; namely from the onshore record on Andøya, the continental shelf of the southern Barents Sea and the depocentre on the continental margin. Our aim is to evaluate these and the deep sea record with respect to the interaction among the ice sheets, the air temperature and the palaeoceanography.

Andøya record

Owing to its close proximity to the continental shelf break, Andøya has the potential of recording most of the changing Late Weichselian environment. On the northern tip of Andøya (Fig. 2) four corings in lake basins have revealed a continuous record from 22 ka BP to the Holocene (Vorren, K.-D. 1978; Vorren *et al.* 1988b; Alm 1993). The four sites are strategically located with respect to the marginal moraines in the area, providing a time-stratigraphic frame-work for their formation as well as the most comprehensive and detailed Late Weichselian palaeoclimatic terrestrial record hitherto found in Fennoscandia.

Palaeotemperature curve from northern Andøya

Based mainly on pollen, spores and plant macrofossils and about 50 radiocarbon dates from the four coring sites (Fig. 2), an average July palaeotemperature curve (Fig. 3) was reconstructed for the period 22 to 10 ka BP (Vorren, K.-D. 1978; Vorren *et al.* 1988b; Alm 1993). There are several points of interest: the July temperature has generally increased towards the Holocene; there have been relatively abrupt changes in climate – a tendency for a saw-tooth shape is apparent; in addition to the Bølling–Allerød warm events, warm events occurred at 21–19, 18.3–17.9 and 16–15 ka BP; very cold events peaked around 18.8–18.5, 16.8–16, 13.7 (14.4)–12.8 ka BP and during the early Younger Dryas (10.8 ka BP).

From Andrews, J. T., Austin, W. E. N., Bergsten, H. & Jennings, A. E. (eds), 1996, *Late Quaternary Palaeoceanography of the North Atlantic Margins*, Geological Society Special Publication No. 111, pp. 303–321.

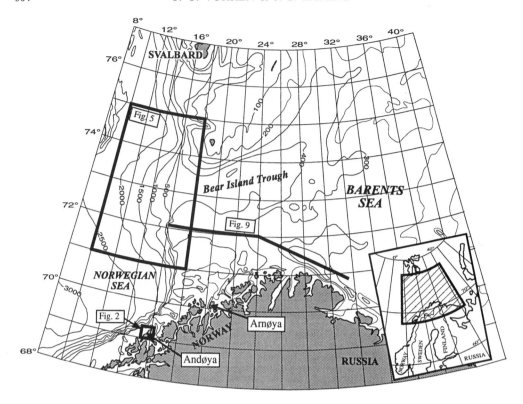

Fig. 1. Map of the southern Barents Sea and adjoining areas.

Glaciation curve

Based on the marine record in the Andfjorden Trough on the continental shelf, as well as the terrestrial record, Vorren *et al.* (1988*b*) constructed a time–distance diagram of glacial fluctuations for the area. Based on these and on new data from Alm (1993) supported by data from J. J. Møller *et al.* (1992) and Andreassen *et al.* (1985), we here present a revised time-distance diagram (Fig. 4). The basis for the diagram is described in the remainder of this section.

Dates from Arnøya (Andreassen *et al.* 1985) indicate that the coastal areas of northern Norway were deglaciated about 29 ka BP (Table 1) (see later). Subsequently the coastal areas were again glaciated. The new data from Øvre Æråsvatn (Fig. 2) show a continous stratigraphy from 22 ka BP onwards, demonstrating that this area has been ice free since 22 ka BP. This implies that the Late Weichselian maximum extent at Andøya as reconstructed by Vorren *et al.* (1988b) pre-dates 22 ka BP. After this advance (the late glacial maximum I, LGM I) there must have been a glacial recession. How far the

glacier front receded is unknown. The next advance reached the Kjølhaug end moraine (Fig. 2). This halt must have been brief as the post-glacial sedimentation in the proximally situated Lake Endletvatn commenced shortly after sedimentation in Nedre Æråsvatn. The next halt was at the Endleten moraine. This moraine coincides with a distinct shoreline drop from c. 36 to *c.* 29 m above sea level. The implication is that the glacier margin was situated at this position or oscillated proximally to it until Nedre Æråsvatn was isolated from the sea, i.e until about 15.5 ka BP (Vorren *et al.* 1988*b*). We denote the re-advances to the Kjølhaug and Endleten moraines as the late-glacial maximum II (LGM II). A two-fold Late Weichselian re-advance is also reported from the North Sea area (Sejrup *et al.* 1994).

A rapid deglaciation then occurred at least partly contemporaneous with the 16–15 ka BP warm spell (Fig. 3). During this deglaciation phase finely laminated clay sediments were deposited in the shelf trough of Andfjorden. This was interrupted by a halt/re-advance (the Flesen event), probably around 15–14.5 ka BP (Vorren *et al.* 1983).

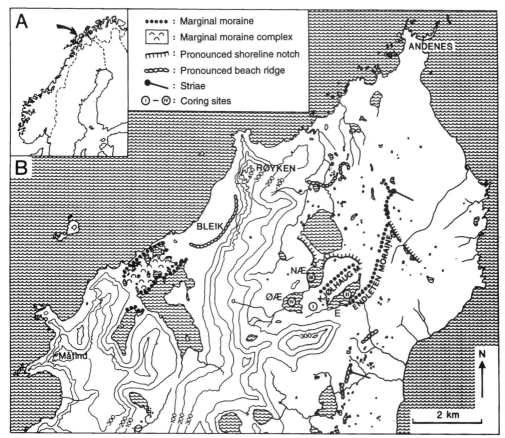

Fig. 2. Map of the northern tip of Andøya with coring sites I -IV, moraines and raised shoreline features. NÆ, Nedre Æråsvatn; ØÆ, Øvre Æråsvatn; and E, Endletvatn. Modified from Vorren *et al.* (1988*b*).

The last halt/re-advance reaching the shelf is identified by a high content of dropstones in the shelf trough sediments (Vorren *et al.* 1983). This event was originally suggested to have an age between 14 and 13 ka BP. A later dating of 13 730 ± 400 years BP (Table 2) just at the lower boundary of this high ice-rafted debris event by Thomsen & Vorren (1986) indicates that this event started about 13.7 ka BP.

Continental slope record

The Bear Island Trough Mouth Fan (TMF) acted as an important depocentre during the Late Cenozoic (e.g. Vorren *et al.* 1991; Riis & Fjeldskaar 1992; Eidvin *et al.* 1993, Laberg & Vorren in press). The Bear Island TMF has a maximum width and length of about 800 and 700 km, respectively (Figs 1 and 5).

High resolution seismic profiles from the middle part of the Bear Island TMF show a series of units, each of which consists of mound-shaped deposits that are elongate downslope and lensoid in cross-section. These are lobes deposited by debris flows. Each unit is separated from the others by a high amplitude reflector. The reflectors which separate the seismic units are inferred to reflect palaeo-fan surfaces formed during sediment-starved interstadials and inter-glacials, whereas the units comprise diamictons deposited during peak glacials (Laberg & Vorren in press).

Laberg & Vorren (in press) identified eight units. The two upper units (VII and VIII) are interpreted to have been deposited after 28 ka BP (see later). Individual debris lobes at the surface belonging to unit VIII have been mapped by high resolution seismics (Fig. 5) (Laberg & Vorren 1995), by SeaMARC II sidescan sonar

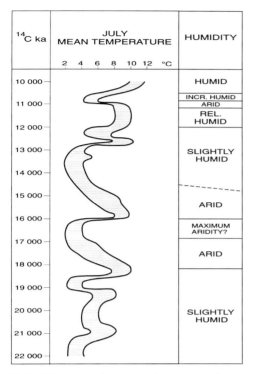

Fig. 3. July mean palaeotemperature curve and humidity on northern Andøya from 22 to 10 ka BP. Based on Vorren, K.-D. (1978); Vorren *et al.* (1988*b*) and Alm (1993) and adapted from Alm (1993).

(Fig. 6) (Vogt *et al.* 1993) and by GLORIA longrange sidescan sonar (Dowdeswell *et al.* in press). The debris flows are up to 100 km long, up to 24 km in width and 50 m thick, and the largest cover has an area of 1880 km² (Laberg & Vorren 1995).

On the upper slope the base of each lobe is erosional and the debris flow incorporated some slope material during its downslope movement. At the lower slope the debris lobes are well delineated at the base as well as at the margins (Fig. 7).

Laberg & Vorren (1995) systematically cored one of the debris lobes (debris lobe 4 on Fig. 5; see also Fig. 6). The stratigraphy comprises a lower grey diamicton and an upper Late Weichselian glacimarine and Holocene yellow brown mud. The lower diamicton is interpreted to represent the debris flow deposits. This is corroborated by its content of reworked shelf foraminifera and by lithological similarities to the shelf diamictons. Radiocarbon (AMS) dates on a reworked shell (*Bathyarca glacialis*) in the debris flow diamicton gave an age of 24 ka BP.

Data on *Neogloboquadrina pachyderma*, probably incorporated in the diamicton from the hemipelagic mud during downslope transport, gave an age of 17.5 ka BP. This supports the interpretation that the upper debris flows occurred during the LGM II.

The sketch in Fig. 8 is intended to show the main sedimentary processes on the shelf break and upper slope during the presence of an ice sheet at the shelf break. A glacigenic shelf diamicton was transported to the shelf break as a deforming till (Sættem *et al.* 1992; Elverhøi *et al.* 1993). There a till delta (Alley *et al.* 1989) or diamict apron (Hambrey *et al.* 1992) was accumulated. Oversteepening and/or build-up of excess pore pressure due to high sediment input were probably the reasons for sediment release. During the downslope transport, sediments were eroded and entrained on the upper fan. On average 18 km³ sediment were remobilized during each flow.

The volume of units VII and VIII is estimated to be 2357 km³. Unit VIII comprises about two-thirds of this, or about 1500 km³.

Continental shelf record

We will focus on the southern part of the large epicontinental Barents Sea (Fig. 1). This part is characterized by a broad east–west channel, the Bear Island Trough, which reaches a depth of 500 m and shallower banks to the south and north.

A schematic geoseismic profile (Fig. 9) across the southern Barents Shelf shows six main units in the east and four in the west. Sættem *et al.* (1992) have further subdivided the units in the west into seven units. Of particular interest in this context is unit 4W and its corresponding units. Unit 4W is divided into units E, F and G by Sættem *et al.* (1992). Unit E is found in local depressions. It comprises glaciomarine recessional sediments followed by Eemian bioturbated marine sediments and Lower-?Middle Weichselian stratified glaciomarine sediments. Units F and G include regional sheets of glacial diamictons dated by amino acid analysis to be younger than 30 ka BP. This conforms with radiocarbon datings of reworked shell fragments from unit 4W giving ages of 28 to 21.5 ka BP (Fig 10A) (Hald *et al.* 1990; Vorren *et al.* 1990). Thus unit 4W must be of this age or possibly slightly younger (because of the reworked nature of the shells). The implication of this stratigraphy is that probably no ice sheet reached the outer part of Bear Island Trough during the Early and Middle Weichselian (Sættem *et al.* 1992).

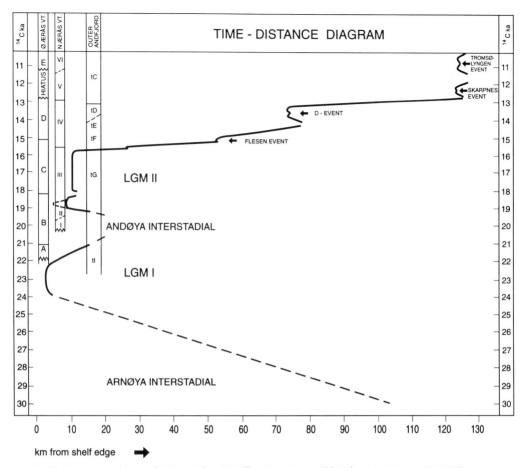

Fig. 4. Time-distance diagram for the Andøya/Andfjorden area. Modified from Vorren *et al.* (1988*b*).

Table 1. *Radiocarbon dates between 30 and 20 ka BP of shells from the southern Barents Sea area (sea Fig. 10A)*

Laboratory reference	Position Latitude	Longitude	Water depth (m)	¹⁴C Age (years BP)	Material	Depth in core (m)	Reference
T-8029A	60°15′ N	16°01′ E	–	21 800 ± 410	Pediastrum peat	13.875–13.94	1
T-3507	70°04′ N	20°45′ E	–	27 400 + 1500/−1200	Fragments of *M. truncata*		2
T-4020	70°03′ N	20°29′ E	–	29 000 + 4200/−2700	*Chlamys* sp., *P. arctica*, *P. lenticula*		2
T-4021	70°03′ N	20°29′ E	–	30 200 + 4100/−2700	Shell fragments		2
Ua304	76°19′ N	30°00′ E	280	28 080 ± 1125	Forams	0.45	3
Ua305	76°19′ N	30°00′ E	280	21 200 ± 825	Forams	1.75	3
Ua1136	75°19′ N	24°43′ E	110	22 400 ± 1095	Shell fragment	0.76	4
Ua1137	75°19′ N	24°43′ E	110	29 510 ± 1260	Shell fragment	0.76	4
Ua1138	75°19′ N	24°43′ E	110	30 140 ± 925	Shell fragment	0.76	4
Ua1054	71°37′ N	20°56′ E	315	21 110 ± 550	Shell fragments	17.74–17.78	5
Ua1053	74°29′ N	25°46′ E	335	21 615 ± 565	Shell fragments	42.01–42.07	5
Ua1050	72°24′ N	22°47′ E	423	24 880 ± 550	Shell fragments	21.75	5
Ua1049	73°16′ N	23°09′ E	418	27 320 ± 735	Shell fragments	70.25–70.35	5

From: 1, Alm (1993); 2, Andreassen *et al.* (1985); 3, Elverhøi *et al.* (1990); 4, Elverhøi *et al.* (1993); and 5, Hald *et al.* (1990). The dates of Elverhøi *et al.* (1993) have not been corrected for reservoir age.

Table 2. *Radiocarbon dates giving minimum ages of the last deglaciation of the southern Barents Sea shelf (see Fig. 10B)*

Lab- oratory reference	Position		Water depth (m)	^{14}C Age (years BP)	Material	Depth in core (m)	Reference
	Latitude	Longitude					
AA-12262	71°33′ N	41°40′ E	269	12 715 ± 95	Forams	17.0–17.5	1
T-2326	70°27′ N	17°40′ E	160	13 310 ± 110			2
AA-420	69°11′ N	16°21′ E	471	13 730 ± 400	*Y. intermedia*	3.70–3.80	3
T-4914	71°25′ N	22°54′ E	414	13 290 ± 290	*M. calcarea, N. pernula*	2.33	4
T-2209	71°22′ N	18°51′ E	270	13 550 ± 400	*A. crenata, H. arctica, M. calcarea*	0.36–0.56	5
T-3633	69°28′ N	16°14′ E	358	13 630 ± 1250	*Y. intermedia, Y. lenticula*		6

From: 1, Polyak *et al.* (1995); 2, Rokoengen *et al.* (1976); 3, Thomsen & Vorren (1986); 4, Vorren & Kristoffersen (1986); 5, Vorren *et al.* (1978); and 6, Vorren *et al.* (1983).

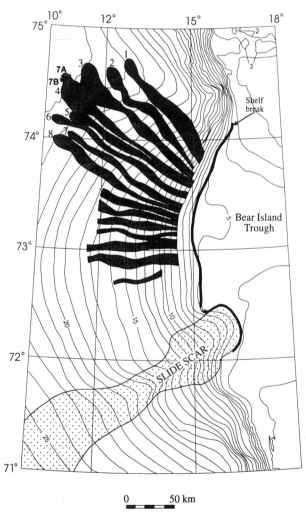

Fig. 5. Map showing debris lobes identified in the upper unit VIII on the Bear Island Trough Mouth Fan. The stippled area in the south represents a large slide scar. After Laberg & Vorren (1995).

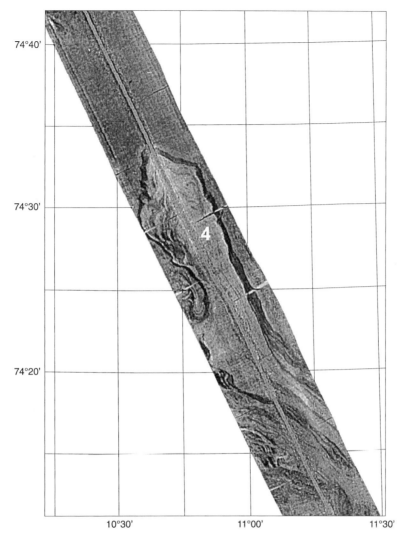

Fig. 6. SeaMARC II sidescan image showing the distal part of debris lobe 4 on Fig. 5. After Vogt *et al.* (1993).

Units F and G can be seismostratigraphically correlated with units VII and VIII on the continental slope respectively (Laberg & Vorren 1995). Sættem *et al.* (1992) indicated that the F/G boundary may reflect changes in the ice flow pattern. If the correlation with the slope stratigraphy is correct, we infer that units F and G probably represent two different glacial advances to the shelf break after 28 ka BP. Unit F was deposited during the LGM I, whereas unit G represents the LGM II.

Unit 5E in the east (Fig. 9) partly overlies (the older part of) unit 4W. Unit 5E has an internal transparent signature, a wide lateral extent and a thickness of up to 200 ms (TWT).

The isopachs show a pronounced thickness maximum close to the coast. Vorren *et al.* (1990) inferred that unit 5E was deposited in a distal glaciomarine environment in an embayment between the Fennoscandian and Barents Sea ice sheets. Most of the sediment was probably supplied by meltwater rivers from the south. The (semi)transparent signature of 5E indicates relatively fine-grained sediments with a small number of larger clasts. Deposition of suspended fines and some fallout from icebergs were probably the dominating sedimentary processes.

After the deposition of 5E this unit was clearly overridden and eroded by a glacial re-advance. This is shown by the morphology of its upper

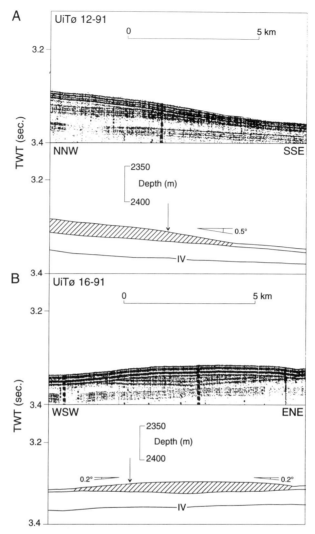

Fig. 7. Sparker profiles from the lower part of debris lobe 4 on Fig. 5. (**A**) Logitudinal profile; arrow indicates intersection with profile B; (**B**) transverse profile; arrow indicates intersection with profile A. See Fig. 5 for location. After Laberg & Vorren (1995).

surface (Vorren *et al.* 1990). Owing to its stratigraphic position, we suggest that Unit 5E was deposited during an ice-free period between the two late glacial maxima.

The extent of the LGM II re-advance is indicated by some moraine ridges in the southwestern Barents Sea (Fig. 10B) (Vorren & Kristoffersen 1986). The moraine ridges are 10–50 m high, 1–5 km broad and can be followed continuously for several tens of kilometres. One set was deposited in front of a lobe from the Fennoscandian Ice Sheet, the other is deposited at the southwestern margin of the Barents Sea Ice Sheet.

Growth and decay of the ice sheets

Pre-LGM I: the Arnøya Interstadial

The only dating of autochthonous fossils in the study area pre-dating the LGM I is from the inner part of Arnøya. The age was 29 ka BP (T-4020, Table 1, Fig. 10A). Reworked shell frag-ments of *Mya truncata* from a nearby area on Arnøya gave 27.4 ka BP (Andreassen *et al.* 1985). On the continental shelf there are several dates between 30 and 20 ka BP (Fig. 10A, Table 1). However, most of them are on reworked multi-species samples, thus giving a maximum

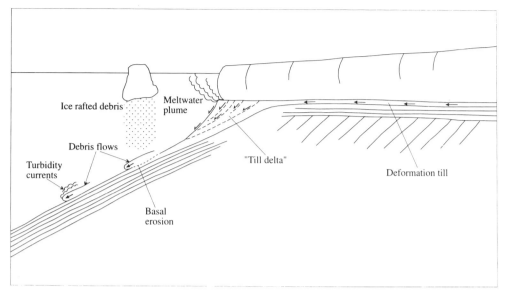

Fig. 8. Schematic model showing the main sedimentary processes at the shelf break and on the upper slope during the presence of the Late Weichselian Barents Sea Ice Sheet at the shelf break. After Laberg & Vorren (1995).

age. Apparently, only the dates from Elverhøi *et al.* (1993) are on single fragments. Based primarily on the Arnøya data we infer that the coastal areas of northern Norway and the southern Barents Sea were deglaciated about 29/27 ka BP. However, the fauna on Arnøya indicate high arctic conditions and glaciers in the nearby fjord areas at the end of this interstadial.

The Arnøya Interstadial seem to correspond to the Ålesund Interstadial in southwestern

Norway (Larsen *et al.* 1987) and at least part of the Kapp Ekholm Interstadial on Spitsbergen (Mangerud & Svendsen 1992).

LGM I

The stratigraphy from Andøya indicates that the Fennoscandian Ice Sheet was situated close to the shelfbreak in that area just before 22 ka BP.

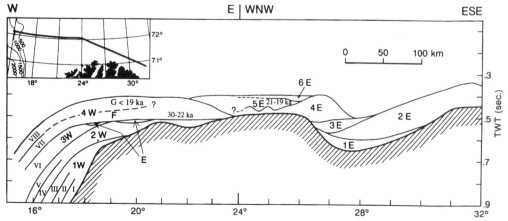

Fig. 9. Generalized geoseismic profile from the upper continental slope to the inner shelf (inset) showing the stratigraphical and lateral relationship of the different stratigraphic units in the upper, glacigenic sequence. Modified from Vorren *et al.* (1990).

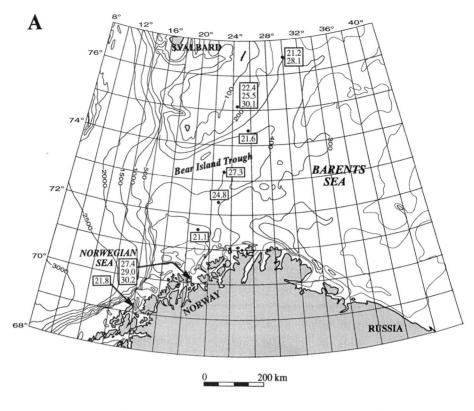

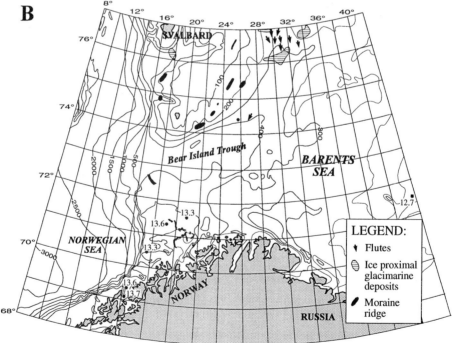

Fig. 10. (**A**) Radiocarbon datings between 30 and 20 ka BP in the southern Barents Sea (see Table 1).
(**B**) Marginal moraines (after Elverhøi & Solheim 1983; Vorren & Kristoffersen 1986), proximal glaciomarine deposits (after Elverhøi *et al.* 1993), glacial fluted surface (after Solheim *et al.* 1990) and radiocarbon dates (see Table 2) of shells in sediments not overidden by glaciers, giving minimum ages for deglaciation in the southern Barents Sea.

The seismic unit corresponding to this glacial advance is probably the lower part of unit 4W (unit F) of Sættem et al. (1992) and unit VII on the slope. Marine fossils in unit F show that much of the sediment was originally deposited in a marine/glaciomarine environment (Poole et al. 1994). However, a faint fissility indicates deformation/reworking, and Sættem et al. (1992) conclude that the diamicton of unit F is mostly a till indicating that the ice margin oscillated to the shelf-break.

Based on cores from the deep sea and continental slope west of Svalbard, Hebbeln et al. (1994) find an open water situation from 27 ka BP to 22.5 ka BP. At the end of this period the Barents Sea Ice Sheet had expanded 'into the ocean, and increased input of terrestrial material occurred'.

We infer that during the earliest part of the LGM I sedimentation occurred primarily in the outer and deeper part of the Bear Island Trough, probably mostly by settling of suspended sediment supplied by meltwater streams and icebergs. Iceberg scouring is seen at the base of the overlying unit 5E. During the later stages, when the ice front reached the shelf break, debris flow deposition occurred on the Bear Island TMF.

Considering the growth of the Fennoscandian Ice Sheet towards the LGM I geological evidence indicates that Fennoscandian Ice Sheet extended to the coast in southwestern Norway c. 28 ka BP, just after the Ålesund Interstadial (Larsen et al. 1987), as it probably also did in northern Norway just after the correlative Arnøya Interstadial (Andreassen et al. 1985). On Spitsbergen, on the other hand, Mangerud et al. (1992) do not find two late glacial maxima, and indicate that the glaciers on and around Svalbard were not much larger than today until it advanced to the LGM II.

The timing of the growth towards the LGM I is in phase with the decreasing summer insolation in the northern hemisphere (Berger & Loutre 1991). Relatively warm water advected into the Norwegian Sea as far north as Spitsbergen between 27 and 22.5 ka BP (Hebbeln et al. 1994). This would provide a regional moisture source for the build-up of the Barents Sea Ice Sheet towards the LGM I. Some indication of the duration of the LGM I is given by the amount of sediment transported to the continental slope. The sediment volume of unit VII (LGM I) is approximately half of that of unit VIII (LGM II). If the duration of the LGM II ice margin at the shelf-break was 3000 years (see later), other variables being equal, the duration of the LGM I ice margin at the shelf-break was about 1500 years.

LGM I/II interstadial: the Andøya Interstadial

The fossil data from Andøya indicate a high arctic climate between 22 and 21 ka BP. Between 21 and 19 ka BP a low to middle Arctic climate prevailed. The climate was slightly humid (Alm 1993).

In the southern Barents Sea the proximal glaciomarine seismic unit 5E (Fig. 9) is inferred to have been deposited during this interstadial. Three of the shell dates on the shelf fall into this period (Fig. 10A). The location of two of these in the inner Bear Island Trough may indicate that most of the trough was deglaciated during this interstadial (Fig. 11A). The frontal position of the glacier margin was probably unstable, and shortlasting advances across the proglacial sediments probably occurred (Vorren et al. 1990).

The cause of the Andøya Interstadial is not easy to understand. This interstadial occurred during a minimum in insolation and during a falling trend in the global eustatic sea level. A high input of terrigenous material seems to have taken place during this interstadial (Hebbeln et al. 1994), probably reflecting the decay of the southern part of Barents Sea Ice Sheet. This probably led to a cooling of the surface water and closer sea ice cover shutting off the nourishment of the ice sheets and starving them to recession. However, the triggering mechanism of this deglaciation phase is still not satisfactory explained.

The LGM II

As mentioned earlier, the end-moraines in the southwestern Barents Sea are interpreted to mark the extent of the LGM II in this area. Further north the large amount of late glacial sediment on the slope shows that the terminus of the Barents Sea Ice Sheet had reached the shelfbreak in front of the Bear Island Trough and the Storfjord Trough (Fig. 11B).

A high to middle arctic climate prevailed on Andøya between 19 and 16 ka BP, except for a 400 years warm spell between 18.3 and 17.9 ka BP. A gradual decrease in humidity is also indicated, culminating with maximum aridity between 16.8 and 16 ka BP. This may indicate that most of the growth of the ice sheets occurred during the earlier part of LGM II. Also during LGM II, offshore open water provided a moisture source for the build up of the ice sheets (Hebbeln et al. 1994).

The duration of the LGM II on Andøya is indicated to about 3500 years (19–15.5 ka BP)

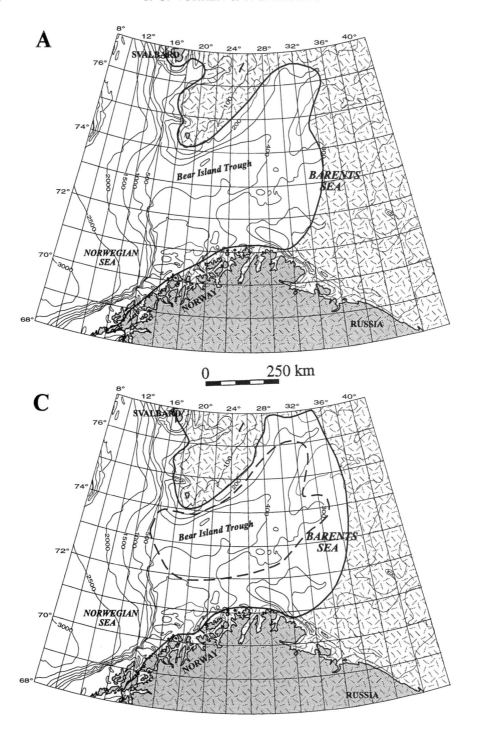

Fig. 11. Schematic development of the Barents Sea Ice Sheet during the late glacial. (**A**) Andøya Interstadial;
(**B**) LGM II (broken line encloses inferred deglaciated area during the first major marine drawdown);
(**C**) The D event (13.7–13 ka BP). (**D**) Younger Dryas.

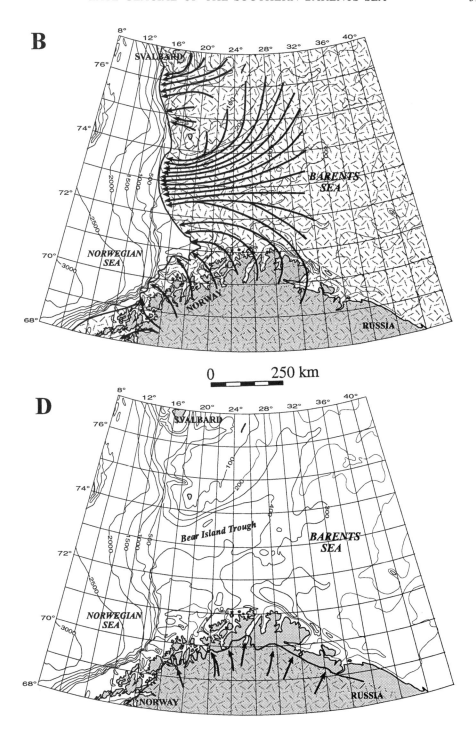

Fig. 11. Continued.

(Fig. 4). The initiation of the final deglaciation of the Barents Sea Ice Sheet is probably signalled in the Norwegian-Greenland Sea late glacial low oxygen isotope event (meltwater spike) identified by Jones & Keigwin (1988), Sarnthein *et al.* (1992), Koç & Jansen (1994), and Hebbeln *et al.* (1994) and dated to around 14.5 ka BP. Jørgensen (1994) indicates 14.8 ka BP as a minimum age of the ice recession of the outer shelf west of Svalbard. There are no unequivocal data to tell when the LGM II ice margin reached the shelf-break in the southwestern Barents Sea. We expect that more time was needed to build up the ice sheet in the southern Barents Sea and establish an ice stream in the Bear Island Trough than to expand the probably already existing outlets of the Fennoscandian Ice Sheet. As a first approximation we suggest that the Barents Sea Ice Sheet reached the shelf-break about 18 ka BP and stayed there until 15 ka BP, implying a duration of about 3000 years at the shelf-break.

The morphology and locus of sediment accumulation on the Bear Island TMF indicate that much of the southern part of the Barents Sea Ice Sheet drained through the Bear Island Trough (Fig. 11B). The amount of sediment transported to the continental slope can give a first approximation of the velocity and ice discharge of the ice stream.

The sediment flux through any cross-section normal to the direction of ice flow is the sum of the flux due to the deformation of any subglacial till layer, the flux carried by subglacial streams, and the flux carried by basal ice (e.g. Hooke & Elverhøi in press). Assuming: (1) that the sediment in the debris lobes is derived mainly from flux due to deformational transport of subglacial till; (2) that the porosity of the debris flow sediments is the same as in the deforming basal till layer; (3) that the total volume of the debris flows in unit VIII (corresponding to the LGM II) is 1500 km^3 ($= Q$) [see Equation (1)]; (4) that the thickness of the deforming basal till layer is 4 m ($= h$); (5) that the ice margin halted at the shelf-break for 3000 years ($= T$) during LGM II (18–15 ka BP); and (6) given the width of the Bear Island Trough Ice Stream was 150 km ($= w$), corresponding to the present width of the Bear Island Trough, we find the the speed of the basal ice ($= u$) from the equation $Q = kuwhT$, where k is a fraction which accounts for the decrease in deformation rate with depth in the till layer. A value of 1/3 for k will by used here (cf. Hooke & Elverhøi, in press).

The largest uncertainty is related to the thickness of the deforming basal till layer. Observed thicknesses of deforming till layers vary from less than a 1 m to over 6 m (Boulton

& Jones 1979; Hooke & Elverhøi in press). In the fluted area in the inner Bear Island Trough, Solheim *et al.* (1990) found a diamicton layer with shear strengths between 20 and 80 kPa, about 0.5 m thick, above a stiff diamicton. In the southwestern Barents Sea we have observed a dark grey diamicton of more than 1 m thickness having shear strengths in the range 15–30 kPa (cf. Vassmyr & Vorren 1990). Hooke & Elverhøi (in press) assume a thickness of 4 m in the outer part of Isfjordrenna off Spitsbergen. We will use the same value for the outer part of the Bear Island Trough. Then the speed of the basal ice is

$$u = 3 \cdot 1500/(150 \cdot 0.004 \cdot 3000) \text{ km/year}$$
$$= 2.5 \text{ km/year} \tag{1}$$

Although the value obtained is within the range of values for the velocity at the termini of modern glaciers, it is nevertheless fairly high. Ice stream B in Antarctica has a velocity of about 0.45 km/year (Alley *et al.* 1987) and the extremely rapid Jakobshavn Isbre on Greenland moves with a rate of up to 7 km/year (Echelmayer & Harrison 1990).

Assuming a width of 150 km for the Bear Island Trough Ice Stream and an average thick-ness of 0.5 km at the terminus, the ice discharge to the sea was 187.5 km^3/year or, in round numbers, 200 km^3/year. This is comparable with the discharge of rivers such as the Yukon (195 km^3/year), Niger (192 km^3/year) and Danube (206 km^3/year) (Milliman 1983).

The altitude of the glacial equilibrium line (ELA) during LGM II on Andøya is indicated by the average summer temperature which was *c.* 8°C lower than today. The elevation of the ELA depends mainly on the summer temperature and the precipitation. The modern glaciation limit is approximately 800 m asl as extrapolated from data given by Østrem (1964) and Andersen (1968). The modern ELA is lower (150–250 m) than the glaciation limit (Andersen 1968). The vertical atmospheric temperature gradient is about 0.7°C/100 m. If the snow precipitation was the same as today, 8°C lower summer temperature corresponds to a lowering of the ELA of 900–1000 m that is below the sea level during LGM II. However, the Andøya record indicate that the precipitation was lower during LGM II than today. Thus the depression of the ELA was probably less, but it seems safe to conclude that it was close to sea level.

Given that ELA was situated close to sea level, calving was the main ablation process of the northern Fennoscandian Ice Sheet as well as of the Barents Sea Ice Sheet during LGM II.

Knowing the drainage area feeding into the Bear Island Trough Ice Stream, we could estimate the steady-state accumulation rate that would be required to supply that ice. Vari-ous models have been proposed for the shape of the Barents Sea Ice Sheet. Based on post-glacial emergence pattern, Forman et al. (1995) have indicated that the Barents Sea Ice Sheet was the dominant load, and glacier coverage of Novaya Zemlya was comparatively limited. This may imply an ice divide centrally located in the Barents Sea as also indicated by the minimum model of Lambeck (1995). We speculate that an ice divide may have been located over the Central Bank, giving a drainage area similar to the pre-glacial fluvial drainage system reconstructed by Vorren et al. (1991). This implies a drainage area in the order of 500–600 000 km^2 for the Bear Island Trough Ice Stream. Based on this an average accumulation rate of 0.3–0.4 m/year is found.

First deglaciation phase

In the Andøya area, the retreat of the Fennos-candian Ice Sheet seems to have started during the 16–15 ka BP warm spell (Figs 3 and 4), whereas the first major drawdown of the marine based Barents Sea Ice Sheet started later, about 14.5 ka BP (Fig. 11C). The 16–15 ka BP warm spell, which also experienced low precipitation, probably resulted in a rise of the glacial ELA, causing a down-melting of the surface of the western Fennoscandian Ice Sheet as well as the southwestern periphery of the Barents Sea Ice Sheet. The smaller outlet glaciers of the Fennos-candian Ice Sheet reacted first. Thinning due to surface ablation eventually made the Bear Island Trough Ice Stream susceptible to decoupling from the bed and increased calving followed. Lehman et al. (1991) have given a similar explana-tion for the initial deglaciation of the marine-based part of the Fennoscandian Ice Sheet in the North Sea.

The oldest dates of post-glacial sediments in the southern Barents Sea are about 13.5 ka BP in the west and 12.7 ka BP in the east (Fig. 10B, Table 2). However, dates from the central part of the Bear Island Trough are still lacking. Ice-rafted debris studies by Bischof (1994) indicate that it was a marine drawdown of the southern part of the Barents Sea Ice Sheet which gave the main influx in the form of icebergs to cause the meltwater spike dated to about 14.5 ka BP. Jones & Keigwin (1988) estimated the duration of the meltwater spike to be 500 years or less. Based on ice-rafted debris studies, Bischof (1994) found

an initial 500 years long strong pulse derived from the southern part of the Barents Sea Ice Sheet, followed by a lower level input from other sources lasting to about 10 ka BP.

We speculate that the Bear Island Trough during these initial 500 years was deglaciated north-eastward to the position marked by the ice-proximal glaciomarine deposits in the inner part of the trough (Fig 10B). This gives an area of approximately 155 000 km^2 (Fig. 11C). Using an average ice thickness of 1 km for this deglaciated area, this indicates that 155 000 km^3 of ice were drained from the area. In addition, a large amount of ice must have been pulled out from the interior of the ice sheet. Using the same annual ice discharge as estimated for the LGM II (200 km^3/year, see earlier), we suggest as a very tentative approximation, an annual iceberg discharge of (155 000/500 + 200) km^3/year = 510 km^3/year. This is comparable with water discharges from rivers such as the Mississippi (580 km^3/year), Lena (514 km^3/year) or Yenisei (560 km^3/year) (Milliman 1983).

During the drawdown of the Barents Sea Ice Sheet, the Norwegian-Greenland Sea must have received a very large number of icebergs. According to Bischof (1994) most of them drifted southward and 'melted rapidly as they encountered warmer waters at the Vøring Plateau'. The icebergs must have had a cooling effect on the surface water, in turn promoting sea ice preservation through the summer season, and thereby increasing the albedo. This may be the cause for the very low summer temperatures on Andøya during the period 14.4–12.8 ka BP (Fig. 3) following the ice sheet drawdown/meltwater spike.

D Event

During the 14.4–12.8 ka BP cold spell the north-ern Fennoscandian Ice Sheet advanced, in what Vorren et al. (1983) referred to as the D event (13.7–13 ka BP), in the Andøya area where the ice margin probably just reached the inner part of the continental shelf. Judging from the avail-able radiocarbon dates (Fig. 10B) and shore-line stratigraphy, the outer islands in northwest Finnmark were the first to become degaciated (Sollid et al. 1973). The oldest end-moraines in Finnmark are not dated, but it is interesting to note that the easternmost ones tend to turn northeastward into the Barents Sea (Sollid et al. 1973). Most probably the ice margin of the Fennoscandian Ice Sheet followed the outer coast/inner shelf to the eastern Finnmark where it continued into the Barents Sea.

We speculate that the moraine complexes shown by Elverhøi et al. (1993) encircling the shallow Spitbergenbanken (Fig. 10B) may date from this halt/re-advance. In the area between, the ice margin was probably situated on the bathymetric highs in the central Barents Sea (i.e. Thor Iversen Banken and Sentral Banken). Possibly the water depth in this area did not allow a halt, but rather a retardation in the ice margin recession. This gives a tentative reconstruction of the ice sheets during the D event as shown in Fig. 11C.

13–10 ka BP events

The outer fjord areas of northern Norway were deglaciated during the Bølling-Allerød interstadial complex (12.8–11 ka BP). The deglaciation was interrupted by the Skarpnes readvance about 12.5–12 ka BP (Andersen 1968; Vorren & Elvsborg 1979) and the Younger Dryas readvance (Figs 4 and 11D).

In the northern Barents Sea, Polyak & Solheim (1995) have found that the Franz Victoria Trough was deglaciated by 13 ka BP. Probably most of the peripheral troughs and deeper areas of the Barents Sea shelf was deglaciated at that time.

Several radiocarbon dates from Barents Island, the Edge Island, King Karls Land (P. Möller et al. 1992), Bear Island (Hyvärinen 1968) and Franz Josef Land (Forman et al. 1995) indicates that the islands in the northern Barents Sea and the shallow banks, such as the Spitsbergenbanken, must have been deglaciated by 10 ka BP.

Cause of the growth and decay of the ice sheets

The cause of the growth and decay of the Barents Sea Ice Sheet is not fully understood. Jones & Keigwin (1988) viewed this ice sheet 'as a self oscillating system, for which its own increase in mass is largely responsible for its own destruction by isostatic depression of the glacier bed, and for which no external forcing is required to initiate deglaciation'. Elvehøi et al. (1993) suggested that 'the growth was controlled by sea level lowering and exposure of land, while the deglaciation and the pattern of ice recession was a function of sea level rise'. Mangerud & Svendsen (1992) suggested that the 41 ka BP cycle of the tilt of the earth's axis was the main external forcing of the waxing and waning of the glaciers in the Svalbard-NW Barents Sea region.

Not withstanding the importance of relative sea-level fluctuations, either isostatically induced or of global eustatic nature, our results indicate that climatic factors may have played the primary forcing part in the growth and decay of the Barents Sea Ice Sheet as well as for the Fennoscandian Ice Sheet. We have demonstrated that changes in both ice sheets can be related to the air temperature found on Andøya. In partial accordance with this Bond & Lotti (1995) demonstrated that prominent increases in iceberg discharges recurred at intervals of 2000–3000 year during the Last Glaciation. They concluded that the cycles reflect the operation of climate on unstable ice, probably within ice streams or ice shelves. Our results indicate that the reaction of the ice sheets to the changing climate depends on the size of the ice streams; also, a feedback of the iceberg discharge on the climate is indicated.

Conclusions

(1) A close interrelation exists between the summer air temperature on Andøya and the waxing and waning phases of the northwestern Fennoscandian Ice Sheet and the Barents Sea Ice Sheet.

(2) Most of the southern Barents Sea as well as the coastal areas of northern Norway and Spitsbergen were probably deglaciated during the Arnøya Interstadial (about 29 ka BP).

(3) The late glacial maximum extent of the northern Fennoscandian Ice Sheet as well as the southern Barents Sea Ice Sheet can be separated into two maxima, the oldest (LGM I) occurring before 22 ka BP and the youngest (LGM II) after 19 ka BP.

(4) The Andøya Interstadial (22–19 ka BP), separating LGM I and LGM II, commenced with a high arctic climate after which a middle to low arctic climate prevailed. Large areas of the southern Barents Sea were deglaciated (Fig. 11A).

(5) During LGM II the Fennoscandian Ice Sheet probably reached (19 ka BP) and left (15.5 ka BP) its terminal position before the southern Barents Sea Ice Sheet reached (about ?18 ka BP) and left (about 14.5 ka BP) its terminal position at the shelf break. During the LGM II (Fig. 11B) there was probably an ice stream in the Bear Island Trough with an estimated velocity at the front of about 2.5 km/year. An average accumulation rate of 0.3–0.4 m/year is estimated for the drainage area of the Bear Island Trough Ice Stream. The ice stream transported approximately 1500 km³ of sediment to the shelf edge. This sediment cascaded down the fan slope in the form of debris flows.

(6) A warm spell between 16 and 15 ka BP probably caused an elevation of the ELA and thinning of the ice sheets. This in turn triggered a major deglaciation. The smaller outlet ice streams of the northwestern Fennoscandian Ice Sheet may have reacted earlier than the larger ice streams of the Barents Sea Ice Sheet. The latter caused a major drawdown of the marine-based Barents Sea Ice Sheet about 14.5 ka BP.

(7) The huge input of icebergs from the Bear Island Trough Ice Stream (estimated to have been about $510 \, \text{km}^3/\text{year}$) to the northern Norwegian Sea during the marine drawdown cooled the surface water and led to increased albedo and lower summer temperatures. This iceberg induced climatic deterioration resulted in a halt/readvance of the Fennoscandian as well as the Barents Sea Ice Sheet during the D-event (13.7–13 ka BP) (Fig. 11C).

(8) The Spitsbergenbanken and the continental shelf of the northern Barents Sea were probably deglaciated before 10 ka BP. The Younger Dryas glaciers were confined to the land areas with outlet glaciers calving in the fjords (Fig. 11D).

We thank R. LeB. Hooke, J. Mangerud, M. Punkari and J. Sættem for critically reading the manuscript, G. D. Corner for improving the English and J. P. Holm for the drawing work.

References

ALLEY, R. B., BLANKENSHIP, D. D., ROONEY, S. T. & BENTLEY, C. R. 1987. Till beneath Ice Stream B. 3. Till deformation: evidence and implications. *Journal of Geophysical Research*, **92**, 8921–8929.

——, ——, —— & —— 1989. Sedimentation beneath ice shelves- the view from ice stream B. *Marine Geology*, **85**, 101–120.

ALM, T. 1993. Øvre Æråsvatn-palynostratigraphy of a 22,000 to 10,000 lacustrine record on Andøya, northern Norway. *Boreas*, **22**, 171–188.

ANDERSEN, B. 1968. Glacial geology of Western Troms, North Norway. *Norges Geologiske Undersøkelse*, **256**.

ANDREASSEN, K., VORREN, T. O. & JOHANSEN, K. B. 1985. Pre-late Weichselian glacimarine sediments at Arnøy, North Norway. *Geologiska Foreningens Stockholm Forhandlingar*, **107**, 63–70.

BERGER, A. & LOUTRE, M. F. 1991. Insolation values for the climate of the last 10 million years. *Quaternary Science Reviews*, **10**, 297–317.

BISCHOF, J. F. 1994. The decay of the Barents ice sheet as documented in Nordic seas ice-rafted debris. *Marine Geology*, **117**, 35–55.

BOND, G. C. & LOTTI, R. 1995. Iceberg discharges into the North Atlantic on millenial time scales during the Last Glaciation. *Science*, **267**, 1005–1010.

BOULTON, G. S. & JONES, A. S. 1979. Stability of temperate ice sheets resting on beds of deformable sediments. *Journal of Glaciology*, **24**, 29–43.

DOWDESWELL, J. A., KENYON, N. H., ELVERHØI, A., LABERG, J. S., HOLLENDER, F. J. & SIEGERT, M. J. Large-scale sedimentation on glaciated passive continental margins: the Polar North Atlantic. *Geology*, in press.

ECHELMAYER, K. & HARRISON, W. D. 1990. Jakobshavn Isbræ, west central Greenland: seasonal variations in velocity – or lack thereof. *Journal of Glaciology*, **36**, 82–88.

EIDVIN, T., JANSEN, E. & RIIS, F. 1993. Chronology of Tertiary fan deposits off western Barents Sea: implications for the uplift and erosion history of the Barents Sea shelf. *Marine Geology*, **112**, 109–131.

ELVERHØI, A. & SOLHEIM, A. 1983. The Barents Sea Ice Sheet: a sedimentological discussion. *Polar Research*, **1**, 23–42.

——, FJELDSKAAR, W., SOLHEIM, A., NYLAND-BERG, M. & RUSSWURM, L. 1993. The Barents Sea Ice Sheet—a model of its growth and decay during the last ice maximum. *Quaternary Science Reviews*, **12**, 863–873.

——, NYLAND-BERG, M., RUSSWURM, L. & SOLHEIM, A. 1990. Late Weichselian ice recession in the Central Barents Sea. *In*: BLEIL, U. & THIEDE, J. (eds) *Geological History of the Polar Oceans: Arctic Versus Antarctic*. Kluwer, Dordrecht, 289–307.

FORMAN, S. L., LUBINSKI, D., MILLER, G. H., SNYDER, J., MATHISHOV, G. G. KORSUN, S. & MYSLIVETS, V. 1995. Postglacial emergence and distribution of late Weichselian ice-sheet loads in the northern Barents and Kara seas, Russia. *Geology*, **23**, 113–116.

HALD, M., SÆTTEM, J. & NESSE, E. 1990. Middle and late Weichelian stratigraphy in shallow drillings from the southwestern Barents Sea: foraminiferal, aminoacid and radiocarbon evidence. *Norsk Geologisk Tidsskrift*, **70**, 241–257.

HAMBREY, M. J., BARRETT, P. J., EHRMANN, W. U. & LARSEN, B. 1992. Cenozoic sedimentary processes on the Antarctic continental margin and the record from deep drilling. *Zeitschrift für Geomorphologie N.F.*, **86**, 77–103.

HEBBELN, D., DOKKEN, T., ANDERSEN, E. S., HALD, M. & ELVERHØI, A. 1994. Moisture supply for northern ice-sheet growth during the Last Glacial Maximum. *Nature*, **370**, 357–360.

HOOKE, R. LeB. & ELVERHØI, A. 1996. Sediment flux from a fjord during glacial periods, Isfjorden, Spitsbergen. *Global and Planetary Change*, in press.

HYVÄRINEN, H. 1968. Late-Quaternary sediment cores from lakes on Bjrnya. *Geografiska Annaler*, **50A**, 235–245.

JØRGENSEN, I. H. 1994. Late Quaternary evolution of Isfjorden, Central Svalbard, based on evidence from the deglaciation. *Abstract, 5th PONAM Workshop*, Department of Geology, University of Oslo and the Norwegian Polar Research Institute.

JONES, G. A. & KEIGWIN, L. D. 1988. Evidence from Fram Strait (78° N) for early deglaciation. *Nature*, **336**, 56–59.

KOÇ, N. & JANSEN, E. 1994. Response of the high-latitude Northern Hemisphere to orbital climate forcing: evidence from the Nordic Seas. *Geology*, **22**, 523–526.

LABERG, J. S. & VORREN, T. O. 1995. Late Weichselian submarine debris flow deposits on the Bear Island Trough Mouth Fan. *Marine Geology*, **127**, 45–72.

LABERG, J. S. & VORREN, T. O. 1996. The Middle and Late Pleistocene evolution of the Bear Island Trough Mouth Fan. *Global and Planetary Change*, in press.

LAMBECK, K. 1995. Constraints on the Late Weichselian ice sheet over the Barents Sea from observations of raised shorelines. *Quaternary Science Reviews*, **14**, 1–16.

LARSEN, E., GULLIKSEN, S., LAURITZEN, S. E., LIE, R., LØVLIE, R. & MANGERUD, J. 1987. Cave stratigraphy in western Norway; multiple Weichselian glaciations and interstadial vertebrate fauna. *Boreas*, **16**, 267–292.

LEHMAN, S. J., JONES, G. A., KEIGWIN, L. D., ANDERSEN, E. S., BUTENKO, G. & ØSTMO, S. R. 1991. Initiation of Fennoscandian ice sheet retreat during the last deglaciation. *Nature*, **349**, 513–516.

MANGERUD, J. & SVENDSEN, J. I. 1992. The last interglacial-glacial period on Spitsbergen, Svalbard. *Quaternary Science Reviews*, **11**, 633–664.

——, BOLSTAD, M., & 8 others 1992. The Last Glacial Maximum on Spitsbergen, Svalbard. *Quaternary Research*, **38**, 1–31.

MILLIMAN, J. 1983. World wide delivery of river sediment to the ocean. *Journal of Geology*, **91**, 1–21.

MØLLER, J. J., DANIELSEN, T. & FJALSTAD, A. 1992. Late Weichelian glacial maximum on Andøya, North Norway. *Boreas*, **21**, 1–13.

MÖLLER, P., HJORT, C. & INGÓLFSSON, O. 1992. Weichselian and Holocene glacial and marine history of East Svalbard: preliminary report on the PONAM fieldwork in 1991. *LUNDQUA Report*, **35**.

ØSTREM, G. 1964. Ice cored moraines in Scandinavia. *Geografiska Annaler*, **46**, 282–337.

POLYAK, L. & SOLHEIM, A. 1995. Late- and postglacial environments in the northern Barents Sea west of Franz Josef Land. *Polar Research*, **13**, 197–207.

——, LEHMANN, S. J., GATAULLIN, V. & JULL, A. J. T. Two-step deglaciation of the southern Barents Sea. *Geology*, **23**, 567–571.

POOLE, D. A. R., SÆTTEM, J. & VORREN, T. O. 1994. Foraminiferal stratigraphy, paleoenvironments and sedimentation of the glacigenic sequence southwest of Bjørnøya. *Boreas*, **23**, 122–138.

RIIS, F. & FJELSKAAR, W. 1992. On the magnitude of the Late Tertiary and Quaternary erosion and its significance for the uplift of Scandinavia and the Barents Sea. *In*: LARSEN, R. M., BREKKE, H., LARSEN, B. T. & TALLERAAS, E. (eds) *Structural*

and Tectonic Modelling and its application to Petroleum Geology. NPF Special Publications, **1**, 163–185.

ROKOENGEN, K., BELL, G. and 6 others 1977. Prøvetaking av fjellgrunn og løsmasser utenfor deler av Nord-Norge i 1976. *Institutt for kontinentalsokkelundersøkelser*, **91**.

SARNTHEIN, M., JANSEN, E.and 7 others 1992. dO¹⁸ time slice reconstruction of meltwater anomalies at Termination I in the North Atlantic between 50 and 80°N. *In*: BARD, E. and BROECKER, W. (eds) *The Last Deglaciation: Absolute and Radiocarbon Chronologies*. NATO ASI Series, **12**, 183–200.

SEJRUP, H. P., HAFLIDASON, H., AARSETH, I., KING, E., FORSBERG, C. F., LONG, D. & ROKOENGEN, K. 1994. Late Weichselian glaciation history of the northern North Sea. *Boreas*, **23**, 1–13.

SOLHEIM, A. & KRISTOFFERSEN, Y. 1984. Sediment distribution above the upper regional unconformity and the glacial history of western Barents Sea. *Norsk Polarinstitutt Skrifter*, **179 (B)**.

——, RUSSWURM, L., ELVERHØI, A. & NYLANDBERG, M. 1990. Glacial geomorphic features in the northern Barents Sea: direct evidence for grounded ice and implications for the pattern of deglaciation and late glacial sedimentation. *In*: DOWDESWELL, J. A. & SCOURSE, J. D. (eds) *Glacimarine Environments, Processes and Sediments*. Geological Society, London, Special Publications, **53**, 253–268.

SOLLID, J. L., ANDERSEN, S., HAMRE, N., KJELDSEN, O., SALVIGSEN, O., STURØD, S., TVEITÅ, T. & WILHELMSEN, A. 1973. Deglaciation of Finnmark, North Norway. *Norsk Geografisk Tidsskrift*, **27**, 233–325.

SÆTTEM, J., POOLE, D. A. R., ELLINGSEN, L. & SEJRUP, H. P. 1992. Glacial geology of outer Bjørnørenna, southwestern Barents Sea. *Marine Geology*, **103**, 15–51.

THOMSEN, E. & VORREN, T. O. 1986. Macrofaunal palaeoecology and stratigraphy in late Quaternary shelf sediments off Northern Norway. *Paleogeography, Paleoclimatology, Paleoecology*, **56**, 103–150.

VASSMYR, S. & VORREN, T. O. 1990. Clast petrography and stratigraphy in Late Quaternary sediments in the soutwestern Barents Sea. *Norsk Geologisk Tidsskrift*, **70**, 95–110.

VOGT, P. R., CRANE, K. & SUNDVOR, E. 1993. Glacigenic mudflows on the Bear Island submarine fan. *Eos, Transactions of the American Geophysical Union*, **74**, 449, 452–453.

VORREN, K. D. 1978. Late and Middle Weichselian stratigraphy of Andøya, north Norway. *Boreas*, **7**, 19–38.

VORREN, T. O. & ELVSBORG, A. 1979. Late Weichselian deglaciation and paleoenvironment of the shelf and coastal areas of Troms, north Norway – a review. *Boreas*, **8**, 247–253.

—— & KRISTOFFERSEN, Y. 1986. Late Quaternary glaciation in the south-western Barents Sea. *Boreas*, **15**, 51–59.

——, EDVARDSEN, M., HALD, M. & THOMSEN, E. 1983. Deglaciation of the Continental Shelf off Southern Troms, North Norway. *Norges Geologiske Undersøkelse*, **380**, 173–187.

——, HALD, M. & LEBESBYE, E. 1988a. Late Cenozoic environments in the Barents Sea. *Paleoceanography*, **3**, 601–612.

——, LEBESBYE, E. & LARSEN, K. 1990. Geometry and genesis of the glacigenic sediments in the southern Barents Sea. *In*: SCOURCE, J. D. & DOWDESWELL, J. A. (eds) *Glacimarine Environments: Processes and Sediments*. Geological Society, London, Special Publications, **53**, 309–328.

——, RICHARDSEN, G., KNUTSEN, S. M. & HENRIKSEN, E. 1991. Cenozoic erosion and sedimentation in the western Barents Sea. *Marine and Petroleum Geology*, **8**, 317–340.

——, STRASS, I. F. & LIND-HANSEN, O. W. 1978. Late Quaternary sediments and stratigraphy on the continental shelf off Troms and West Finnmark, Northern Norway. *Quaternary Research*, **10**, 340–365.

——, VORREN, K. D., ALM, T., GULLIKSEN, S. & LØVLIE, R. 1988b. The last deglaciation (20,000 to 11,000 B.P.) on Andøya northern Norway. *Boreas*, **17**, 41–77.

Post-glacial environments of the southeastern Barents Sea: foraminiferal evidence

LEONID POLYAK[1,*] & VALERY MIKHAILOV[2]

[1] Research Institute VNII Okeangeologia, St Petersburg, Russia
[2] Research Institute NII Morgeo, Eksporta 5 Riga LV-1226, Latvia
* Present address: Byrd Polar Research Center, The Ohio State University, Columbus, OH 43210, USA

Abstract: Quaternary sediment records from the southeastern Barents Sea were used to reconstruct palaeoceanographic environments since the last deglaciation based on lithology, foraminiferal assemblages and AMS ^{14}C dates. After the ice sheet retreat at 13 ka BP two pulses of glacimarine sedimentation occurred, separated by non-deposition between approximately 12 and 10.5 ka BP. Proximal sedimentation from meltwater over-flows prevailed during the first pulse, whereas the second pulse reflects distal glacimarine environments with some inflow of Atlantic water. Full marine environments were established by 9.3 ka BP, associated with increased Atlantic water advection, intensified currents and reduced sedimentation rates. The maximum Atlantic influence lasted until approximately 5 ka BP, followed by an advance of Arctic surface water with winter sea ice cover.

The Barents Sea is an area of intense interaction of Arctic and Atlantic waters (Fig. 1). As a result, this area is particularly sensitive to climatic changes and has a strong impact on climatic and oceanographic regimes in adjacent regions. During the Quaternary the Barents Sea shelf experienced dramatic environmental changes due to the build-up and decay of ice sheets and associated restructuring of the water circulation and stratification system. Understanding of the Barents Sea development, in particular during the period since the last deglaciation, is necessary for the prediction of possible future changes in the Atlantic sector of the Arctic.

The most informative proxy for palaeoceanographic reconstructions in the Arctic shelf seas are benthic foraminifers (e.g. Osterman 1982; Hald *et al.* 1989; Vilks *et al.* 1989). Several studies describe the post-glacial evolution of foraminiferal assemblages and inferred environmental changes from various areas of the Barents Sea (Fig. 1) (Østby & Nagy 1982; Polyak 1984; Hald *et al.* 1989; Khusid 1989; Spiridonov *et al.* 1992; Polyak & Solheim 1994). However, only two of these stratigraphies are age constrained by AMS radiocarbon dating (Hald *et al.* 1989; Polyak & Solheim 1994). We present a time constrained foraminiferal stratigraphy and palaeoecological interpretation for a complete glacimarine/marine sediment sequence from the southeastern Barents Sea, deposited since the last deglaciation.

Study area

Physiography

The study area is located in the southeastern part of the Barents Sea, bounded by the Kola Peninsula and Pechora coast on the south, and Novaya Zemlya on the east (Figs 1 and 2). It can be divided into a shallow southeasternmost area with prevailing depths <100 m and the Central Deep area with depths >300 m. These areas are divided by a series of banks (Murman, South and North Kanin, and Geese banks) and narrow troughs that stretch in the NW–SE direction (Kanin and Geese troughs).

Oceanography

Water masses in the Barents Sea are represented by Atlantic, Arctic or Polar, coastal, and locally formed waters (Tantsiura 1959, 1973; Loeng 1991) (Fig.1). Warm, high salinity Atlantic water with a temperature >3°C and a salinity of 35‰ is brought by the Norwegian Current. One of the major branches of this current flows counter-clockwise along the southern and eastern margin of the Barents Sea, crossing the study area. Atlantic water gradually transforms by mixing with other water masses and losing heat contents. The transformed Atlantic water often flows as subsurface currents at bathymetric lows. The Arctic water is formed under a strong influence of the northern Eurasian river runoff. A major part of the Arctic water is exported into

From Andrews, J. T., Austin, W. E. N., Bergsten, H. & Jennings, A. E. (eds), 1996, *Late Quaternary Palaeoceanography of the North Atlantic Margins*, Geological Society Special Publication No. 111, pp. 323–337.

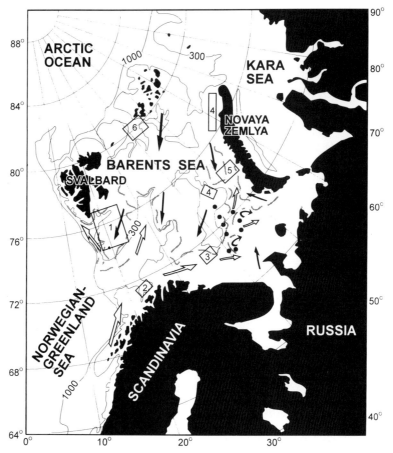

Fig. 1. Map of the Barents Sea with location of present study sites (closed circles) and previous study areas: 1, Østby & Nagy 1982; 2, Hald *et al.* 1989; 3, Polyak 1984; 4, Khusid 1989; 5, Spiridonov *et al.* 1992; and 6, Polyak & Solheim 1994. Bathymetry is shown in 300 and 1000 m isobaths. Major currents are shown by white arrows (Atlantic water) and black arrows (Arctic water). Position of the Polar Front is shown by broken grey line (Tantsiura 1973).

the Barents Sea by southwestward flowing currents from the Kara Sea and the Arctic Ocean. This water mass is characterized by low temperature and salinity, typically of $<0°C$ and $<34.5‰$; its distribution controls the winter limit of sea ice. In summer, owing to ice melting, the surface water temperature increases to 2–3°C, whereas salinity might decrease to $<32‰$. The mixture of transformed Atlantic and Arctic waters forms the local Barents Sea water, typically with temperatures around 0°C and salinity 34.7–35‰. This is the major source of dense bottom water formed during the autumn/winter period due to the atmospheric cooling and subsequent rejection of brines with sea ice formation (Midttun 1985).

The zone of strongest gradients between Atlantic and Arctic waters, the Polar Front, is characterized by intense vertical mixing and increased biological productivity, especially at bathymetric highs. In particular, within the study area, Polar Front processes occur along the slopes of Murman, Kanin and Geese banks, where Atlantic-derived currents interact with Arctic and coastal waters flowing from the north and southeast.

Quaternary geology

Quaternary sediments in the southeastern Barents Sea have been intensively investigated by means of sparker profiling, sea bed coring and shallow drilling (Epstein *et al.* 1983; Krapivner *et al.* 1988; Spiridonov *et al.* 1992; Gataullin *et al.* 1993; Epstein & Gataullin 1993). The Quaternary sequence rests on ancient, mainly Cretaceous

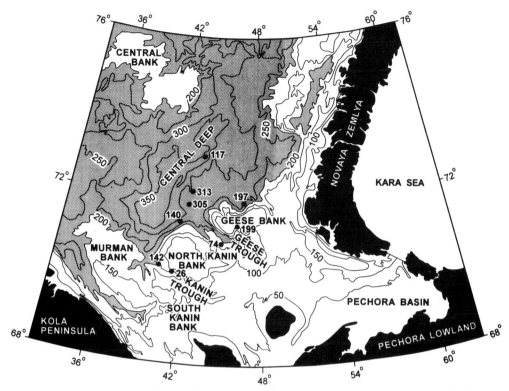

Fig. 2. Map of the southeastern Barents Sea with bathymetry in 50 m isobaths and location of studied borings.

strata with an angular unconformity, known from western Barents Sea as the Upper Regional Unconformity (URU) (Solheim & Kristoffersen 1984). The thickness of the Quaternary section typically ranges from 10 to 50 m in places reaching more than 100 m. This sequence is subdivided into three apparent seismic and lithological units, III–I. There have been different opinions on the age and genesis of the units (Epstein *et al.* 1983; Krapivner *et al.* 1988; Pavlidis *et al.* 1992). Detailed studies of cores, borings and sparker records from the Central Deep and adjacent Novaya Zemlya shelf showed that the sequence of units III to I reflects the succession of the last glacial hemicycle from full glacial to glacimarine and marine environments (Spiridonov *et al.* 1992; Gataullin *et al.* 1993; Epstein & Gataullin 1993). Detailed AMS ^{14}C dating of the glacimarine and marine deposits has finally put them into a reliable chronostratigraphic framework, dating them to ~13–9 and 9–0 ka BP, respectively (Polyak *et al.* 1995).

Materials and methods

This investigation is based on the boring material obtained in the course of geotechnical

exploration of the southeastern Barents Sea in 1986–1991 from the drilling ship *Bavenite*. The technological aspects of drilling are described in Gataullin *et al.* (1993). All the borings were analysed with respect to geotechnical and lithological parameters. Nine borings located roughly along two south–north transects across the Kanin and Geese banks and further north into the Central Deep were chosen for detailed foraminiferal analysis and AMS ^{14}C dating of post-glacial sediments (Figs 2 and 3). Foraminifers were studied in a size fraction of >0.1 mm. AMS ^{14}C dating was performed on 28 samples of benthic foraminiferal tests at the National Science Foundation Arizona Facility and two samples of whole bivalve molluscs at the National Ocean Science AMS facility. The list of ^{14}C dates is presented in Polyak *et al.* (1995).

Results

Lithology

The lower seismic/lithological unit, III, has an average thickness of 5–25 m and is represented by stiff glacigenic diamicton (Fig. 3). This unit is characterized by a chaotic seismic

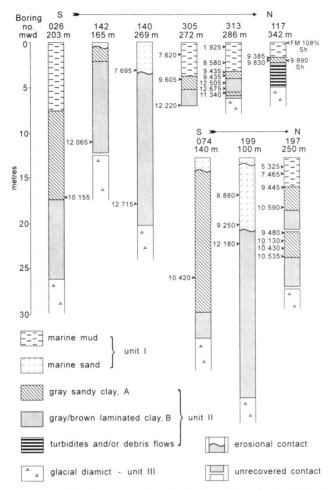

Fig. 3. Lithology and position of ^{14}C dates (in ka) in studied borings above the glacial diamicton (from Polyak *et al.* 1995). Sections are arranged along two roughly south–north transects (see Figs 1 and 2 for locations). FM, percentage fraction modern radiocarbon activity; Sh, mollusc shell; and mwd, water depth in metres.

signature with point hyperbolic reflections (cf. Spiridonov *et al.* 1992; Gataullin *et al.* 1993; Epstein & Gataullin 1993). Its lowermost part often includes detached blocks of Mesozoic bedrock embedded into the diamictic matrix, reflecting the effect of subglacial processes on the substratum.

Unit II overlies unit III, typically filling depressions in its surface. Unit II reaches the thickness of 50–100 m in the southeasternmost Barents Sea and thins to <10 m towards the Central Deep (Fig. 3). Acoustically, this unit is characterized by continuous subparallel reflections, conforming to or slightly smoothing the substratum topography. Unit II can be divided into two subunits, IIB and IIA (Fig. 3; Polyak *et al.* 1995). Sediments of the lower subunit, IIB,

are represented by rhythmically alternating brown and grey muds, the latter typically with a higher silt and sand content. Brown layers of <1 mm to 15–20 cm thickness are fine grained, largely unfossiliferous and are characterized by the precipitation of iron oxides, which presumably provide the brown coloration. Intervening silty grey layers with thicknesses of <1 mm to 2 cm are commonly stained by iron sulphides and contain dropstones and relatively abundant calcareous foraminiferal tests. The laminations can be deformed, acquiring convolute bedding and flow structures. The brown component becomes more prevalent up-section, so that the uppermost part of subunit IIB in some borings is entirely composed of brown clay. In contrast, the basal part of the subunit often includes layers of grey diamictic deposits, interpreted as debris flows and/or turbidites. These sediment gravity flow deposits constitute the entire section of subunit IIB in the Central Deep (Gataullin *et al.* 1993), as exemplified by boring 117 (Fig. 3).

The upper subunit, IIA, is represented by more homogenous, predominantly grey silty/sandy muds with dropstones, abundant calcareous microfossils and iron sulphides. In the direction of the Central Deep this subunit thins and completely loses the brown coloration. The contact between subunits IIA and B in the Central Deep is marked by an oxidized pale brown layer characterized by the precipitation of iron oxides, carbonate dissolution and, in some places, by partial induration (cf. Spiridonov *et al.* 1992; Gataullin *et al.* 1993).

At water depths >200–250 m sediments of subunit IIA grade into strongly bioturbated olive gray muds of unit I, typically less than 2–3 m in thickness. At some sites the transition is marked by a brown layer with signs of carbonate dissolution, similar to the oxidized layer at the IIA–IIB transition in the Central Deep. At shallower water depths unit I is represented by sandier sediments (lag sands on the banks) which truncate units II and III, in places down to the bedrock. As a result of this erosion the upper part of unit II is missing in borings 74, 140, 142 and 199 and the whole unit is completely eroded on top of the Geese and Kanin banks. Another erosional episode is detected within unit I in some sections from the banks (boring 199). At the bottom of bank slopes, unit I has a maximum thickness of 5–10 m due to the downslope redeposition of pre-existing sediments.

Age constraint

Laminated grey/brown muds (unit II) in the area of their maximum thickness southeast of the Kanin and Geese banks are practically barren of microfaunal tests. The most extensively dated sections are therefore located at the margin of the major deposit of unit II, on the southeastern flank of the Central Deep (borings 197, 305 and 313; Figs 2 and 3). They are supplemented by datings from thicker sections in the Kanin and Geese troughs (borings 26, 74, 140, 142 and 199) and from the Central Deep beyond the limit of brown clay distribution (boring 117).

Two age inversions occurred in borings 197 and 313 (Fig. 3). They coincide with section lithology repetitions and are believed to result from the double recovery of the same sections in the process of drilling. Sedimentation rates for

specific environments were calculated where possible between two dating points; otherwise they were estimated between a dating point and lithological boundary, dated in other borings. According to the distribution of dates, the age models are most reliable for subunit IIA and the lower part of unit I in the Central Deep area.

Basal dates from subunit IIB indicate that post-glacial sedimentation had commenced in the study area by approximately 13 ka BP (Fig. 3; Polyak *et al.* 1995). Sediments of subunits IIB and A have high sedimentation rates of over 1 m/ka, which increase toward the southeast, exceeding 10 m/ka in the Kanin and Geese troughs. The two subunits are separated by a halt in sedimentation between approximately 12 and 10.5 ka BP, however. It is difficult to estimate the exact duration of this episode due to the lack of datable material in the upper part of subunit IIB. Deposition of subunit IIA persisted until 9.5–9.3 ka BP, when sedimentation rates dropped significantly to <0.5 m/ka and erosion took place in shallow areas. The highest rates for unit I are found in sandy sediments at the bottom of bank slopes. The end of erosion and commencement of unit I sediment accumulation appears to be time-transgressive depending on the sea bottom topography and current patterns. The second erosional episode represented in boring 199 is not time constrained. Our major effort was aimed at studying the deglaciation sequence and additional dating is needed for the Holocene marine record.

Foraminiferal stratigraphy

The foraminiferal content in the diamicton (unit III) is low, rarely exceeding 1–2/g of dry sediment. The assemblage is dominated by the most common Quaternary Arctic species *Elphidium excavatum* forma *clavatum* and *Cassidulina reniforme*, and occasionally includes 'exotic' taxa of more warm water and/or older faunas. The preservation varies and some of the tests display signs of abrasion and recrystallization. A similar assemblage is recognized in glacigenic diamicts throughout the Barents Sea and is considered to be reworked from older marine deposits (Hald & Vorren 1987; Hald *et al.* 1989; Spiridonov *et al.* 1992).

The most common benthic foraminiferal species in the sediments of subunit IIB overlying the diamicton is *E. e. clavatum* (Figs 4–6). In the sample obtained immediately above the lower contact of subunit IIB (boring 313), *E. e. clavatum* constitutes almost 90%. In addition to extremely low diversity, this assemblage is characterized by the high contents of small-sized and juvenile specimens. The second species in relative abundance for subunit IIB is *Islandiella norcrossi/helenae* (combined), which attains the highest frequencies (at low total abundances) in the fine-grained brown clays characteristic of the upper part of subunit IIB (Figs 4–6). Some intervals in the southeasternmost borings (26, 197, 199, 142) have elevated concentrations of *Haynesina orbiculare*. Calcareous tests from brown muds often bear apparent signs of dissolution, which suggests that part of the assemblage has been dissolved.

Upper subunit IIA is characterized by the highest absolute abundances of calcareous foraminifers (up to 150/g), as well as other calcareous microfossils such as ostracodes and small mollusc shells. *C. reniforme* dominates a high diversity assemblage in the Central Deep (borings 117, 197, 305, 313; Figs 4–7), whereas *E. e. clavatum* and *C. reniforme* co-dominate at shallower water depths. Sections from the Central Deep contain significant numbers of *Cassidulina teretis*, typically accompanied by planktonic foraminifers; a distinct spike of

C. teretis occurs at approximately 9.5 ka BP (Figs. 4–7). The bottom of subunit IIA and, especially, the transition to homogenous muds of unit I (borings 26, 197, 305 and 313) are marked by maxima in concentrations of *Nonion labradoricum*.

The lower part of unit I (apart from lag sands) has a low abundance, partially dissolved calcareous foraminiferal assemblage. The dominant species is typically *Melonis barleeanus* accompanied by *C. reniforme* (Figs 4–7). In the northernmost boring 117, *M. barleeanus* has a distinct maximum at ~6–7 ka BP. A spike in relative abundance of *Trifarina fluens* is detected in borings 197 and 305 at the same level. The upper part of unit I (after approximately 5 ka) is characterized in the Central Deep by the decline of *M. barleeanus*, an increase in total foraminiferal abundance and dominance of *I.norcrossi/ helenae* (borings 117, 197, 305, 313; Figs 4–7). The transition interval is marked in some sections by the spikes of *Cibicides lobatulus* and/or *N. labradoricum*. Another increase in *M. barleeanus*, *T. fluens* or *N. labradoricum* occurs in the Central Deep at ~2.5–4 ka BP.

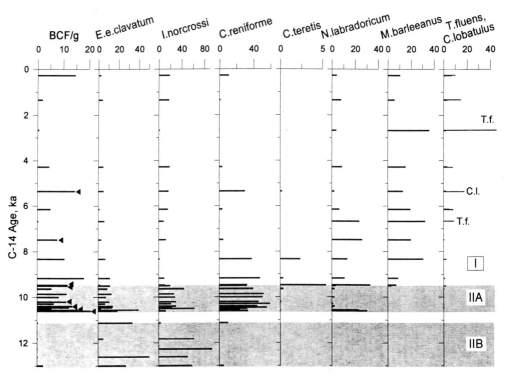

Fig. 4. Benthic calcareous foraminiferal distribution (%) in boring 197. Note the differences in horizontal scales. BCF/g, Number of benthic calcareous foraminifers per gram sediment. The triangles show dated levels. Stratigraphic units are indicated on the right. Age is interpolated between dates, zero for the surface and 13 ka BP for the bottom of post-glacial sequence.

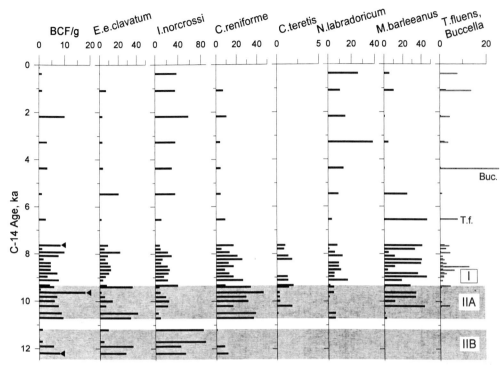

Fig. 5. Benthic calcareous foraminiferal distribution (%) in boring 305. See Fig. 4 for explanations.

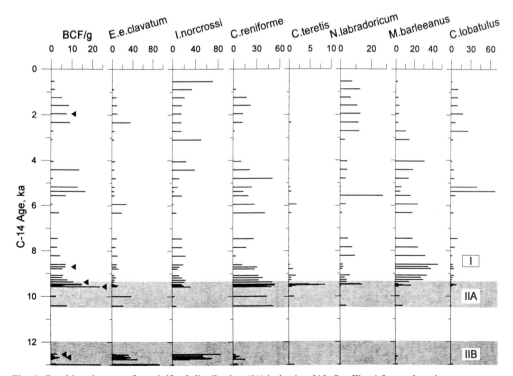

Fig. 6. Benthic calcareous foraminiferal distribution (%) in boring 313. See Fig. 4 for explanations.

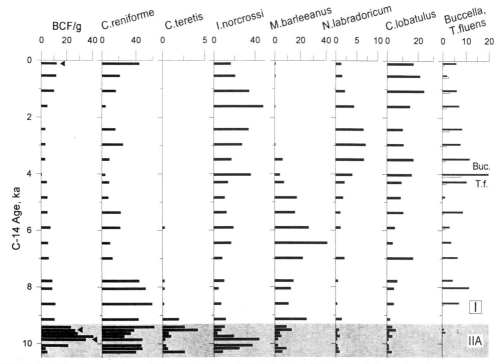

Fig. 7. Benthic calcareous foraminiferal distribution (%) in boring 117. See Fig. 4 for explanations.

After that, *C. reniforme* becomes an important constituent of the *I. norcrossi/helenae* assemblage in the northernmost sites 313 and 117. On the bank slopes, assemblages of the upper unit I are characterized by strong dissolution and predominance of *Buccella* spp. and *T. fluens*, at some levels, with high relative concentrations of *C. lobatulus* and *N. labradoricum*. In the southernmost boring 26, *E. e. clavatum* becomes a dominant species after ~2 ka BP. The surficial sediments contain abundant arenaceous foraminiferal tests, which typically disintegrate soon after burial.

Discussion

Sedimentary environments

Several lines of evidence suggest that unit II was deposited in glacimarine environments established in the southeastern Barents Sea after the major ice sheet retreat at ~13 ka BP. The position of the laminated sediments of subunit IIB immediately above glacial diamictons, the mode of their bedding, acoustic signature, lithology and sedimentation rates make these sediments similar to proximal glacimarine facies, described in detail from recent and Quaternary deposits of Canada, Alaska, Svalbard and Scandinavia (Elverhøi *et al.* 1980; 1983; Powell 1983; Gilbert 1983; Mackiewicz *et al.* 1984; Stevens 1985; 1990; Görlich 1986; Görlich *et al.* 1987). The dominant mechanism of formation appears to be by seasonal or interannual changes in ice sheet melting rate, combined with weak bioturbation. Warm periods imply increased meltwater discharge and the development of a halocline, promoting the separation and long distance transportation of fines, and thus enhanced sedimentation of coarse particles. In contrast, cold and stormy periods reduce meltwater discharge and favour the turbulent mixing of fresh and marine waters, leading to flocculation and deposition of fines. Winter sea ice formation would also promote the mixing process due to the sinking of brines. The offset between the timing of organic productivity blooms and the maximum of clastic sedimentation in summer results in the cyclic accumulation of organic matter in sediments, which causes the diagenetic formation of iron sulphide enriched laminae (Elverhøi *et al.* 1980; Görlich *et al.* 1987). In contrast, the mixing of fresh and marine waters during cold seasons would favor the precipitation of iron oxides, which is a common phenomenon in river estuaries (e.g. Boyle *et al.* 1977).

The more homogenous, dropstone-bearing deposits of subunit IIA presumably reflect an increase in bioturbation and organic productivity, and a change in the dominant sedimentation mechanism from meltwater overflows to iceberg rafting. Such changes commonly accompany the retreat of a glacier front away from the area of deposition (Powell 1983; Görlich 1986) and/or the climatically controlled reduction of sea ice cover in the iceberg-prone areas (Dowdeswell *et al.* 1994). Subunit IIA is therefore interpreted as an ice-distal glacimarine deposit, grading towards the Central Deep into virtually marine sediments with some dropstones. An interval of no or reduced deposition between subunits IIB and A at approximately 12–10.5 ka BP is marked by the prominent oxidized layer with strong carbonate dissolution, a feature typically associated with a drastic decrease in sedimentation rate (Wilson *et al.* 1986; Buckley & Cranston 1988). This episode might be connected with the halt in ice sheet retreat, possibly in combination with permanent sea ice cover during the Younger Dryas cooling (Polyak *et al.* 1995).

Laminated muds commonly overlie glacial diamictons not only in the study area, but also in northern and western parts of the Barents Sea with larger than average water depths (Vorren *et al.* 1984; Hald *et al.* 1989; Spiridonov *et al.* 1992; Polyak & Solheim 1994). However, these laminated muds are thin (typically <5 m), fill only local depressions and lack brown coloration. This difference might reflect the reduced significance of glacier melting processes in the northern/western Barents Sea due to the fast ice sheet decay through iceberg calving. In contrast, the existence of broad shallow areas in the southeastern Barents Sea remote from the shelf edge would favour the stagnation of glacier ice and enhance the importance of melting for deglaciation (Polyak *et al.* 1995). This interpretation explains the thinning of unit II and the disappearance of the brown clay component within the study area towards the Central Deep.

The transition to unit I reflects the establishment of normal marine conditions with the complete retreat of glacier ice from the shelf area by ~9.3 ka BP. This transition lags several hundred years behind the southwestern Barents Sea (Vorren *et al.* 1984), possibly reflecting the influence of lingering glacier ice. The transition is marked by the second oxidized layer, which indicates a reduction in sedimentation rates. The

erosion of pre-Holocene deposits at modern water depths <200–250 m might be associated with the sea floor shallowing due to glacio-isostatic rebound after deglaciation (cf. Piper *et al.* 1983; Henrich, 1990). Alternatively, the winnowing can be entirely attributed to oceanographic factors, such as the impact of the re-established current system and/or ice-free conditions during the Holocene climatic optimum (cf. Lehman & Jones 1989). Late Holocene environments were more favourable for sedimentation, probably due to the advance of Arctic water with sea ice. A second erosional episode occuring on the banks in the Holocene presumably marks the establishment of recent position of the Polar Front.

Foraminiferal assemblages and paleoceanography

Glacimarine environments. The benthic foraminiferal assemblage from the bottom of laminated glacimarine sediments (subunit IIB) is characterized by low diversity and the strong dominance of *Elphidium excavatum* forma clavatum (Figs 4–6 and 8). This species is known to be highly opportunistic, thriving in stressed environments with low and fluctuating temperatures and salinities, high turbidity and a short productivity period (Mudie *et al.* 1984; Hald *et al.* 1993; Hald & Korsun in review). It is thus not surprising that *E. e. clavatum* is commonly found to be the pioneer in postglacial deposits throughout the Barents Sea and other glaciated shelves (e.g. Osterman 1982; Hald *et al.* 1989; Vilks *et al.* 1989; Spiridonov *et al.* 1992; Polyak & Solheim 1994). High contents of small-sized and juvenile specimens, which are typical for *E. e. clavatum* assemblages from glacimarine deposits, also point to stressed conditions (Korsun *et al.* 1995). Elevated concentrations of *Haynesina orbiculare* in subunit IIB indicate low salinities (Khusid & Polyak 1989; Steinsund *et al.* unpublished), which is in good agreement with proximal glacimarine environments. It is more difficult to explain the high relative abundance of *I. norcrossi/helenae* in the brown muds of subunit IIB (Figs 4–6 and 8). The present distribution of *I. norcrossi/helenae* is mainly associated with seasonal sea ice cover and relatively high seasonal productivity (Steinsund *et al.* unpublished), but it is also found as one of the dominant taxa in distal and even proximal glacimarine facies (Jennings 1993; Korsun *et al.* 1995). The rise in *I. norcrossi/helenae* contents up-section within subunit IIB probably reflects the increased distance from a

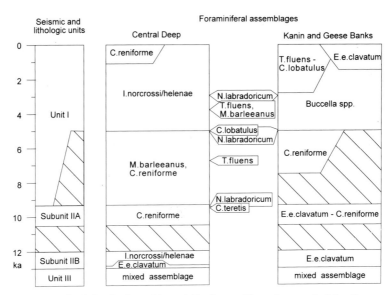

Fig. 8. Schematic generalized distribution of foraminiferal assemblages in post-glacial sediments of the southeastern Barents Sea.

glacier front, although it is possible that this robust species was selectively preserved due to the removal of less resistant calcareous tests by dissolution. The strongest dissolution is associated with the end of glacimarine sedimentation between approximately 12 and 10.5 ka BP. An analogous dissolution event is recorded from the southwestern Barents Sea around 12 ka BP, yet its duration is not dated (Hald *et al.* 1989).

Sediments of subunit IIA are dominated by *Cassidulina reniforme* (Figs 4–8), a typical species for glacimarine and cold water marine soft bottom environments (Mudie *et al.* 1984; Korsun *et al.* 1995; Hald & Korsun in review). In glacimarine successions, *C. reniforme* commonly replaces *E. e. clavatum* at the transition from proximal to distal facies (Osterman 1982; Hald & Vorren 1987; Vilks *et al.* 1989). The *C. reniforme* assemblage is reported for deposits correlative with subunit IIA elsewhere from northern and eastern areas of the Barents Sea (Østby & Nagy 1982; Khusid 1989; Spiridonov *et al.* 1992; Polyak & Solheim 1994). The high abundance of calcareous microfossils in the subunit IIA probably results from the combination of fertile environments at the end of deglaciation with fairly high sedimentation rates, which promote the fast burial of organic remnants and thus prevent calcareous tests from dissolution. The spikes of *Cassidulina teretis* and planktonic foraminiferal abundance in the Central Deep (Figs 4–8) suggest the inflow of Atlantic-derived, probably subsurface waters

during the formation of subunit IIA. The recent distribution of *C. teretis* and planktonics on the Eurasian Arctic shelf is confined to areas influenced by Atlantic-derived water, commonly flowing as a subsurface current (Khusid & Polyak 1989; Jennings & Helgadottir 1994).

Marine environments. The transition from subunit IIA to full marine environments of unit I is accompanied by an increase in the contents of *Nonion labradoricum* (Figs. 4–6 and 8). This species is known to feed on buried organic matter or on fresh phytodetritus (Cedhagen 1991; Corliss 1991) and is potentially indicative of high-productivity environments. The modern distribution of *N. labradoricum* in the Barents Sea shows maximum concentrations in the proximity to the Polar Front zone characterized by high seasonal biological productivity and increased organic matter flux to the bottom sediments (Steinsund *et al.* unpublished). Similar concentrations are often found at the transition from glacimarine to marine environments (Hald & Vorren 1987; Hald *et al.* 1989; Korsun *et al.* 1995), where enhanced organic production and deposition is likely to occur.

The lower part of the homogenous Holocene muds (approximately 9.3–5 ka BP) is characterized by the partial dissolution of calcareous foraminiferal assemblages and dominance of *Melonis barleeanus* (Figs 4–8). The latter is typical of correlative sediments elsewhere in the Barents Sea at depths >200 m (Polyak 1984;

Khusid 1989; Spiridonov *et al.* 1992; Polyak & Solheim 1994). In the southwestern Barents Sea the *M. barleeanus* assemblage seems to occur earlier, sometime between 12 and 8.5 ka BP, although more accurate dating is not available (Hald *et al.* 1989). The highest modern concentrations of *M. barleeanus* are found in fine-grained sediments enriched with organic detritus, which are commonly redeposited from shallow areas (Mackensen *et al.* 1985; Corliss 1985; 1991; Korsun & Polyak 1989). The distribution of *M. barleeanus* on the Arctic shelf is also somehow tied to Atlantic-derived water (Mudie *et al.* 1984; Khusid & Polyak 1989), although not necessarily to increased bottom temperatures (Steinsund *et al.* unpublished). We suggest that the increase in *M. barleeanus* concentrations reflects the strongest advection of Atlantic water to the Arctic shelf during the so-called North Atlantic Optimum (e.g. Haggblom 1982; Bradley 1990). This would intensify the current activity and redeposition of fines and decrease net sedimentation rates over large areas of the Barents Sea (cf. Lehman & Jones 1989). Alternatively, the precipitous drop in sedimentation, marked by the second oxidized layer could be influenced by the furthermost retreat of glaciers onshore. In any case, decreased sedimentation rates in combination with high organic matter flux resulted in intense early diagenetic processes in surficial sediments with concomitant calcite dissolution.

The maximum of *M. barleeanum* contents at ~6–7 ka BP in the northernmost site combined with the spike of *Trifarina fluens* in the southern reach of the Central Deep (Figs 4 5, 7 and 8) points to the furthermost penetration of Atlantic water into the eastern Barents Sea. According to its modern distribution, *T. fluens* is a good indicator of the Polar Front like *N. labradoricum* (Khusid & Polyak 1989; Steinsund *et al.* unpublished), although it is not clear what controls the difference in their distributional patterns. Dating the culmination of the North Atlantic Optimum to 6–7 ka BP is in good agreement with marine records of Atlantic influence in the Norwegian–Greenland Sea and the northern Barents Sea (Lehman & Jones 1989; Koç & Jansen 1992; Polyak & Solheim 1994). On the other hand, coastal records from Svalbard suggest an earlier maximum warming event at 8–9 ka BP (Salvigsen *et al.* 1992). This discrepancy might result from multiple pulses of the North Atlantic Optimum, which only can be tested on high resolution records.

The increase in hydrodynamic activity in the study area is inferred from the spike of *Cibicides lobatulus* at approximately 5 ka BP (Figs 4 6 and 8). This episode is probably responsible for a second erosion of sediments on top of the banks. *Cibicides lobatulus* is a sessile epifaunal foraminifer, which lives in current-influenced environments and has a high probability of post-mortem transportation (Boltovskoy & Wright 1976). Its distribution in the Barents Sea is almost exclusively confined to sea bottom areas exposed to currents (Korsun & Polyak 1990; Steinsund *et al.* unpublished). We presume that the increased current event at the end of the North Atlantic Optimum reflects the intensification of the Polar Front processes southeast of the Central Deep, which is corroborated by the spike of *N. labradoricum* in some sections. This intensification could result from the advance of the Arctic water and the increased hydrological gradients between it and the Atlantic water.

Foraminiferal assemblages in overlying sediments are mainly dominated by *I. norcrossi/helenae* and *Buccella* spp. (Figs 4–8), typical of low Arctic environments with seasonal sea ice cover and relatively high seasonal productivity (Mudie *et al.* 1984; Khusid & Polyak 1989; Steinsund *et al.* unpublished). *Buccella* spp. and *T. fluens* assemblages characterized by strong carbonate dissolution and high relative contents of *C. lobatulus* or *N. labradoricum*, occupy the slopes of Murman (Polyak 1984), Kanin and Geese banks in accordance with recent position of the Polar Front. A spike of *M. barleeanus* and *T. fluens* occurs in the Central Deep at ~2.5–4 ka BP (Figs 4 and 6–8), suggesting a brief migration of the Polar Front northward (second North Atlantic Optimum?). More accurate dating of this episode is not yet possible, and needs additional investigation. Subsequent foraminiferal associations contain notably increased concentrations of taxa with Arctic water affinities (*C. reniforme* in the Central Deep and *E. e. clavatum* in the southeast; Figs 7 and 8), which indicates further advance of the Arctic water and sea ice. Correlative assemblages from the northern Barents Sea are consistently dominated by *E. e. clavatum*, suggesting heavy sea ice conditions (Khusid 1989; Spiridonov *et al.* 1992; Polyak & Solheim 1994).

Conclusions

The last deglaciation of the southeastern Barents Sea began at approximately 13 ka BP. It was followed by the accumulation of laminated brown/grey muds interpreted to be formed in proximal glacimarine environments mainly from overflows with a strong freshwater component.

Foraminiferal assemblages are dominated by *E. excavatum* forma *clavatum*, typical of near-glacier environments, and *I. norcrossi/helenae*.

The non-depositional episode between approximately 12 and 10.5 ka BP is presumed to reflect a halt in deglaciation, possibly associated with the Younger Dryas cooling. This event is marked by carbonate dissolution and the formation of an oxidized layer in sediments from the Central Deep.

Faintly laminated sandy muds with dropstones, abundant calcareous microfossils and monosulphides reflect distal glacimarine environments during the second pulse of deglaciation between approximately 10.5 and 9.3 ka BP. Benthic foraminifers are characterized by a *C. reniforme* assemblage, which is often associated with glacimarine settings. Occurrence of elevated concentrations of *C. teretis* and planktonic foraminifers, with a maximum around 9.5 ka BP, reflect the advection of chilled Atlantic water, probably as a subsurface current.

The transition to full marine environments at 9.3 ka BP is marked by a maximum of *N. labradoricum*, which points to the increased organic flux due to the Polar Front type processes. This transition is followed by a strong decrease in sedimentation rates and erosion of sediments at depths of <200–250 m. Reduced sedimentation in the Central Deep resulted in the formation of a second oxidized layer and carbonate dissolution. This change in sedimentary environment can be explained by a furthermost retreat of glaciers onshore and/or the intensification of currents due to the intrusion of Atlantic water (North Atlantic Optimum). Foraminifers in early Holocene sediments are dominated by *M. barleeanus*, which presumably takes advantage of organic redeposition from highly productive shallow areas subjected to winnowing. A culmination of the North Atlantic Optimum possibly occurred at ~6–7 ka BP with the northernmost position of the Polar Front in the Central Deep.

Another increase in current strength is suggested by a spike of *C. lobatulus* at approximately 5 ka BP, which is probably indicative of the intensification of Polar Front processes due to the expansion of the Arctic water. Subsequent associations are dominated by *I. norcrossi/helenae* and *Buccella* spp., reflecting low arctic environments with seasonal sea ice cover. High percentages of *T. fluens* or *N. labradoricum* on the slopes of Murman, Kanin and Geese banks mark the establishment of the Polar Front at its recent position. A possible readvance of the Atlantic water to the southern Central Deep is inferred at ~2.5–4 ka BP.

Further development of foraminiferal assemblages indicates a final establishment of recent environments with the Arctic water and seasonal sea ice covering most of the southeastern Barents Sea.

The sediment borings were obtained by the Arctic Marine Geotechnical Expedition (AMIGE, Murmansk) and archived at the Research Institute for Marine Geology and Geophysics (NII Morgeo, Riga), former Soviet Union. The ^{14}C dating and part of the foraminiferal study were funded by National Science Foundation Grant OPP-9224471 to S. J. Lehman and L. Polyak. The reviews of A. Jennings and L. Oster-man were very helpful for improving the manuscript. This is a Byrd Polar Research Center Contribution No. 978.

Appendix: faunal reference list

Cassidulina reniforme Nørvang
  Cassidulina crassa d'Orbigny. Feyling-Hanssen *et al.* 1971, plate 7 figs 18 and 19; Østby & Nagy 1982, plate 3 fig. 13.
  Cassidulina reniforme Nørvang: Sejrup & Guilbault 1980, fig. 2F–K.

Cassidulina teretis Tappan
  Cassidulina laevigata d'Orbigny: Østby & Nagy 1982, plate 3 fig. 18.
  Cassidulina teretis Tappan. Mackensen & Hald 1988, plate 1 figs 8–15.

Cibicides lobatulus (Walker and Jacob)
  Cibicides lobatulus (Walker and Jacob). Feyling-Hanssen *et al.* 1971, plate 9 figs 9–14; Østby & Nagy 1982, plate 3 fig. 11.

Elphidium excavatum forma *clavatum* Cushman
  Elphidium clavatum Cushman. Feyling-Hanssen *et al.* 1971, plate 11, figs 10–13.
  Elphidium excavatum (Terquem) forma *clavata* Cushman. Feyling-Hanssen 1972, plates 1 and 2.

Haynesina orbiculare (Brady)
  Elphidium orbiculare (Brady). Loeblich & Tappan 1953, plate 19, figs 1–4.
  Protelphidium orbiculare (Brady). Feyling-Hanssen *et al.* 1971, plate 14, figs 8–11.

Islandiella helenae Feyling-Hanssen and Buzas
  Islandiella helenae Feyling-Hanssen & Buzas 1976, text figs 1–4.

Islandiella norcrossi (Cushman)
  Islandiella norcrossi (Cushman). Loeblich & Tappan 1953, plate 24, fig. 2; Feyling-Hanssen *et al.* 1971, plate 8 figs. 1 and 2.

Melonis barleeanus (Williamson)
  Nonion barleeanum (Williamson). Feyling-Hanssen *et al.* 1971, plate 9 figs 15–18; Østby & Nagy, 1982, plate 3 fig 15.

Nonion zaandamae (van Voorthuysen). Loeblich & Tappan, 1953, plate 15, figs 11 and 12.

Nonion labradoricum (Dawson)
Nonion labradoricum (Dawson). Feyling-Hanssen *et al.* 1971, plate 10, figs 1 and 2; Østby and Nagy 1982, plate 3 fig 17.

Trifarina fluens (Todd)
Trifarina fluens (Todd). Feyling-Hanssen *et al.* 1971, plate 7 figs 12–15; Østby and Nagy 1982, plate 1 fig 21.

References

BOLTOVSKOY, E. & WRIGHT, R. 1976. Recent Foraminifera. Dr W. Junk, The Hague.

BOYLE, E. A., EDMOND, J. M. & SHOLKOVITZ, E. R. 1977. The mechanism of iron removal in estuaries. *Geochimica et Cosmochimica Acta*, **41**, 1313–1324.

BRADLEY, R. S. 1990. Holocene paleoclimatology of the Queen Elizabeth Islands, Canadian High Arctic. *Quaternary Science Reviews*, **9**, 365–384.

BUCKLEY, D. E. & CRANSTON, R. E. 1988. Early diagenesis in deep sea turbidites: the imprint of paleo-oxidation zones. *Geochimica et Cosmochimica Acta*, **52**, 2925–2939.

CEDHAGEN, T. 1991. Retention of chloroplasts and bathymetric distribution in the sublittoral foraminiferan Nonionellina labradorica. *Ophelia*, **33**, 17–30.

CORLISS, B. H. 1985. Microhabitats of benthic foraminifera within deep-sea sediments. *Nature*, **314**, 435–438.

——1991. Morphology and microhabitat preferences of benthic foraminifera from the northwest Atlantic Ocean. *Marine Micropaleontology*, **17**, 195–236.

DOWDESWELL, J. A., WHITTINGTON, R. J. & MARIENFELD, P. 1994. The origin of massive diamicton facies by iceberg rafting and scouring, Scoresby Sund, East Greenland. *Sedimentology*, **41**, 21–35.

ELVERHØI, A., LIESTØL, O. & NAGY, J. 1980. Glacial erosion, sedimentation and microfauna in the inner part of Kongsfjorden, Spitsbergen. *Norsk Polarinstitutt Skrifter*, **172**, 33–61.

——, LØNNE, O. & SELAND, R. 1983. Glaciomarine sedimentation in a modern fjord environment, Spitsbergen. *Polar Research*, **1**, 127–149.

EPSHTEIN, O. G. & GATAULLIN, V. N. 1993. Lithology and conditions of formation of Quaternary deposits in the eastern part of the Barents Sea (Novaya Zemlya side). *Lithology and Mineral Resources (USSR)*, **28**, 84–94.

——, LAVRUSHIN, YU. A., VALPETER, A. P., YUKHNEVICH, K. B. & STEPANOV, Y. F. 1983. Quaternary deposits of the southeastern Barents Sea and adjacent paleoshelf. *Transactions (Doklady) of the USSR Academy of Sciences, Earth Science Sections*, **272**, 180–183.

FEYLING-HANSSEN, R. W. 1972. The foraminifera *Elphidium excavatum* (Terquem) and its variant forms. *Micropaleontology*, **18**, 337–354.

—— & BUZAS, M. A. 1976. Emendation of *Cassidulina* and *Islandiella helenae* new species. *Journal of Foraminiferal Research*, **6**, 154–158.

——, JØRGENSEN, J. A., KNUDSEN, K. L. & ANDERSEN, A. L. 1971. Late Quaternary Foraminifera from Vendsyssel, Denmark and Sandnes, Norway. *Bulletin of the Geological Society of Denmark*, **21**, 67–317.

GATAULLIN, V. N., POLYAK, L. V., EPSTEIN, O. G. & ROMANYUK, B. F. 1993. Glacigenic deposits of the Central Deep: a key to the Late Quaternary evolution of the eastern Barents Sea. *Boreas*, **22**, 47–58.

GILBERT, R. 1983. Sedimentary processes of Canadian Arctic fjords. *Sedimentary Geology*, **36**, 147–175.

GÖRLICH, K. 1986. Glacimarine sedimentation of muds in Hornsund fjord, Spitsbergen. *Annales Societatis Geologorum Polonicae*, **56**, 433–477.

——, WESLAWSKI, J. M. & ZAJACZKOWSKI, M. 1987. Suspension settling effect on macrobenthos biomass distribution in the Hornsund fjord, Spitsbergen. *Polar Research*, **5**, 175–192.

HAGGBLOM, A. 1982. Driftwood in Svalbard as an indicator of sea-ice conditions. *Geographica Annaler*, **64A**, 81–94.

HALD, M. & KORSUN, S. Modern Arctic benthic foraminifera from fjords of Svalbard. *Marine Micropaleontology*, in review.

—— & VORREN, T. O. 1987. Foraminiferal stratigraphy and environment of late Weichselian deposits on the continental shelf off Troms, northern Norway. *Marine Micropaleontology*, **12**, 129–160.

HALD, M., DANIELSEN, T. K. & LORENTZEN, S. 1989. Late Pleistocene–Holocene benthic foraminiferal distribution in the southwestern Barents Sea: paleoenvironmental implications. *Boreas*, **18**, 367–388.

——, STEINSUND, P. I., DOKKEN, T., KORSUN, S., POLYAK, L. & ASPELI, R. 1993. Recent and Late Quaternary distribution of *Elphidium excavatum* f. *clavata* in Arctic seas. *Cushman Foundation Special Publication*, **32**, 141–153.

HENRICH, R. 1990. Cycles, rhythms, and events in Quaternary Arctic and Antarctic glaciomarine deposits. *In:* BLEIL, U. & THIEDE, J. (eds) *Geological History of the Polar Oceans: Arctic Versus Antarctic*. Kluwer, Dordrecht, 213–244.

JENNINGS, A. E. 1993. The Quaternary history of Cumberland Sound, southeastern Baffin Island, Canada: The marine evidence. *Geographie Physique et Quaternaire*, **47**, 21–42.

—— & HELGADOTTIR, G. 1994. Foraminiferal assemblages from the fjords and shelf of eastern Greenland. *Journal of Foraminiferal Research*, **24**, 123–144.

KHUSID, T. A. 1989. Paleoekologiya Barentseva morya v pozdnechetvertichnoe vremya po foraminiferam (Paleoecology of the Barents Sea during Late Quaternary based on foraminifers). *Byullyuten' Komissii po Izucheniyu Chetvertichnogo Perioda (INQUA Bulletin)*, **58**, 105–116 [in Russian].

—— & POLYAK, L. V. 1989. Biogeography of benthic foraminifers in the Arctic Ocean. *In*: BARASH, M. S. (ed.) *Neogenovaya i chetvertichnaya paleookeanologiya po mikropaleontologicheskim dannym* (Neogene and Quaternary paleoceanology based on micropaleontological data). Nauka, Moscow, 42–50 [in Russian].

KOÇ KARPUZ, N., & JANSEN, E. 1992, A high-resolution diatom record of the last deglaciation from the SE Norwegian Sea: documentation of rapid climatic changes. *Paleoceanography*, 7, 499–520.

KORSUN, S. A. & POLYAK, L. V. 1989. Distribution of benthic foraminiferal morphogroups in the Barents Sea. *Oceanology (USSR)*, **29**, 838–844.

——, POGODINA, I. A., FORMAN, S. L. & LUBINSKI, D. J. 1995. Recent foraminifera in glacio-marine sediments from three Arctic fjords of Novaja Zemlja and Svalbard. *Polar Research*, **14**, 15–31.

KRAPIVNER, R. B., GRITZENKO, I. I. & KOSTYUKHIN, A. I. 1988. The Late Cenozoic seismostratigraphy and paleogeography of the Southern Barents Sea region. *In*: MATISHOV, G. G. & TARASOV, G. A. (eds) *Chetvertichnaya paleoekologiya i paleogeografiya severnyh morej* (Quaternary paleoecology and paleogeography of the northern seas). Nauka, Moscow, 103–123 [in Russian].

LEHMAN, S. J. & JONES, G. A. 1989. Shelf sediment accumulation response to Lateglacial–Holocene circulation change in the high Arctic. *EOS, American Geophysical Union Transactions*, **70**, 1146.

LOEBLICH, A. R. & TAPPAN, H. 1953. *Studies of Arctic Foraminifera*. Smithsonian Miscellaneous Collection, **121**.

LOENG, H. 1991. Features of the physical oceanographic conditions of the Barents Sea. *Polar Research*, **10**, 5–18.

MACKENSEN, A. & HALD, M. 1988. *Cassidulina teretis* Tappan and *C. laevigata* d'Orbigny: their modern and late Quaternary distribution in northern seas. *Journal of Foraminiferal Research*, **18**, 16–24.

——, SEJRUP, H. P. & JANSEN, E. 1985. The distribution of living benthic foraminifera on the continental slope and rise off southwest Norway. *Marine Micropaleontology*, **9**, 275–306.

MACKIEWICZ, N. E., POWELL, R. D., CARLSON, P. R. & MOLNIA, B. F. 1984. Interlaminated ice-proximal glacimarine sediments in Muir Inlet, Alaska. *Marine Geology*, **57**, 113–147.

MIDTTUN, L. 1985. Formation of dense bottom water in the Barents Sea. *Deep-Sea Research*, **32**, 1233–1241.

MUDIE, P. J., KEEN, C. E., HARDY, I. A. & VILKS, G. 1984. Multivariate analysis and quantitative paleoecology of benthic foraminifera in surface and Late Quaternary shelf sediments, northern Canada. *Marine Micropaleontology*, **8**, 283–313.

ØSTBY, K. L. & NAGY, J. 1982. Foraminiferal distribution in the western Barents Sea, Recent and Quaternary. *Polar Research*, **1**, 53–87.

OSTERMAN, L. E. 1982. *Late Quaternary history of Southern Baffin Island, Canada: A study of foraminifera and sediments from Frobisher Bay*. PhD Thesis, University of Colorado, Boulder.

PAVLIDIS, YU. A., SHCHERBAKOV, F. A., BOYARSKAYA, T. D., DUNAYEV, N. N., POLYAKOVA, YE. I. & KHUSID, T. A. 1992. New data on the Quaternary stratigraphy and paleo-geography of the southern Barents Sea. *Oceanology (Russia)*, **32**, 633–638 [English translation].

PIPER, D. J. W., LETSON, J. R. J., DE IURE, A. M. & BARRIE, C. Q. 1983. Sediment accumulation in low-sedimentation, wave-dominated, glaciated inlets. *Sedimentary Geology*, **36**, 195–215.

POLYAK, L. V. 1984. Stratigraphy of bottom sediments of the Murman Rise based on Foraminifera. *Byullyuten' Komissii po Izucheniyu Chetvertichnogo Perioda (INQUA Bulletin)*, **54**, 134–139 [in Russian].

—— & SOLHEIM, A. 1994. Late- and post-glacial environments in the northern Barents Sea west of Franz Josef Land. *Polar Research*, **13**, 197–207.

——, LEHMAN, S. J., GATAULLIN, V. & JULL, A. J. T. 1995. Two-step deglaciation of the southeastern Barents Sea. *Geology*, **23**, 567–571.

POWELL, R. D. 1983. Glacial-marine sedimentation processes and lithofacies of temperate tidewater glaciers, Glacier Bay, Alaska. *In*: MOLNIA, B. F. (ed.) *Glacial-marine Sedimentation*. Plenum, New York, 185–232.

SALVIGSEN, O., FORMAN, S. L., & MILLER, G. H. 1992. Thermophilous molluscs on Svalbard during the Holocene and their paleoclimatic implications. *Polar Research*, **11**, 1–10.

SEJRUP, H. P. & GUILBAULT, J. P. 1980. *Cassidulina reniforme* and *C. obtusa* (Foraminifera), taxonomy, distribution, and ecology. *Sarsia*, **65**, 79–85.

SOLHEIM, A. & KRISTOFFERSEN, Y. 1984. The physical environment, western Barents Sea. Sediments above the upper regional unconformity: thickness, seismic stratigraphy and outline of the glacial history. *Norsk Polarinstitutt Skrifter*, **179B**.

SPIRIDONOV, M. A., RYBALKO, A.YE. & POLYAK, L. V. 1992. Late Quaternary stratigraphy and paleogeography of the eastern Barents Sea off central Novaya Zemlya. *In*: SPIRIDONOV, M. A. & RYBALKO, A. YE. (eds) *Osadochnyj pokrov glyacial'nogo shel'fa severo-zapadnyh morej Rossii* (Sedimentary cover of glaciated shelf, North-Western seas of Russia). VSEGEI, St Petersburg, 47–68 [in Russian].

STEINSUND, P. I., POLYAK, L., HALD, M., MIKHAILOV, V. & KORSUN, S. Distribution of calcareous benthic foraminifera in recent sediments of the Barents and Kara Seas. *Unpublished*.

STEVENS, R. L. 1985. Glaciomarine varves in late-Pleistocene clays near Goteborg, southwestern Sweden. *Boreas*, **14**, 127–132.

——1990. Proximal and distal glacimarine deposits in southwestern Sweden: contrasts in sedimentation. *In*: DOWDESWELL, J. A. & SCOURSE, J. D. (eds) *Glacimarine environments: processes and sediments*. Geological Society, London, Special Publications, **53**, 307–316.

TANTSIURA, A. I. 1959. On the currents of the Barents Sea. *Trudy (Transactions) PINRO*, **11**, 35–53 [English translation by the Norwegian Polar Institute, 1983].

——1973. On seasonal changes in currents in the Barents Sea. *Trudy (Transactions) PINRO* [English translation by the Norwegian Polar Institute].

VILKS, G., MACLEAN, B., DEONARINE, B., CURRIE, C. G. & MORAN, K. 1989. Late Quaternary paleoceanography and sedimentary environments in Hudson Strait. *Geographie Physique et Quaternaire*, **43**, 161–178.

VORREN, T. O., HALD, M. & THOMSEN, E. 1984. Quaternary sediments and environments on the continental shelf off northern Norway. *Marine Geology*, **57**, 229–257.

WILSON, T. R. S., THOMSON, J., HYDES, D. J., COLLEY, C., CULKIN, F. & SØRENSEN, J. 1986. Oxidation fronts in pelagic sediments: diagenetic formation of metal-rich layers. *Science*, **232**, 972–975.

Late Weichselian deglaciation of the Barents Sea and low salinity events in the Norwegian Sea

MIKKO PUNKARI

Department of Geology and Geophysics, University of Edinburgh, West Mains Road, Edinburgh EH9 3JW, UK

Abstract: The glacial geomorphology of the northwestern Russian Plain, Pechora lowland, northern Urals and southern Novaya Zemlya was mapped using Landsat satellite imagery. The deglaciation of the ice sheets around the Barents Sea was outlined using geological mapping, published land uplift data and previous observations. The amount of glacial meltwater produced during the deglaciation is compared with other freshwater sources. Freshwater discharges from proglacial lakes are approximated using this ice sheet reconstruction. Variations in precipitation are estimated using ice accumulation rates from an ice core in Greenland.

The ice sheets spreading from the continent and islands surrounding the Barents Sea melted quickly 14–9 ka BP. According to glacial flow patterns and the compilation of ^{14}C dates, the separation of the Scandinavian and Novaya Zemlya ice sheets occurred in the marine zone between the Kanin and Kola Peninsulas at about 13 ka BP. The Dvina–Pechora proglacial lake, which had accumulated south of the confluence zone, drained into the Barents Sea, west of the Kanin Peninsula. The size of the lake was about 350 000 km^2 and the volume of water of the order of 10 000 km^3, equivalent to a 3 cm global sea-level rise.

Low salinity periods at 15–13 ka BP have been reported in the North Atlantic and Norwegian Sea. These have been associated either with active glacier calving and melting or with changes in the oceanic circulation system. The rapid decay of the ice sheets at 14–11 ka BP yielded meltwater about 600 km^3/year, but the greatly increased precipitation during the Bölling interstadial at 12.3 ka BP became the most important source of freshwater entering the sea. The proposed freshwater pulse from the proglacial lake was a short-lasting event, but it may possibly be recorded in the marine stratigraphy by the oxygen isotope signal preserved in calcite from planktonic foraminifera.

Heavy oxygen isotopes (δ^{18}O) enriched in the ocean during the glaciation were depleted to interglacial values during the melting of the continental ice sheets. The Barbados sea level record indicates that glacial meltwater discharge was pulsed, with peaks at 12 and 9.5 ka BP (^{14}C year) (Fairbanks *et al.* 1992). These major oscillations of meltwater discharge represent the global response of the large ice sheets to climate change. In addition to these major events, short-term low salinity events or meltwater spikes at 15–13 ka BP, for example, have been reported in Late Weichselian biostratigraphy of northeastern Atlantic and Norwegian Sea (Sarnthein *et al.* 1992; Duplessy *et al.* 1993; Koç and Jansen 1994). Theories explaining the origin of these low δ^{18}O spikes include collapses or increased melting of ice sheets, discharges of proglacial basins, increased precipitation and changes in oceanic circulation system reducing the production rates of North Atlantic Deep Water (NADW).

Deglacial sea surface salinity in northeastern Atlantic Ocean was lowest (3.3‰ less than the present values) at 13.5 ka BP (Duplessy *et al.* 1993; Labeyrie *et al.* in press). The salinity

variations have been explained as the climate-controlled migration of a boundary separating warm high-salinity from cold low-salinity water masses. These variations are linked with the evaporation–precipitation budget and to the advection of saline subtropical water (Duplessy *et al.* 1993). Changes in the salinity or production rates of NADW may have created δ^{18}O oscillations recorded by foraminifera that are indistinguishable from variations caused by glacial meltwater pulses (Fairbanks *et al.* 1992).

Meltwater events have been associated with active glacier calving and melting in response to increased solar insolation (Koç & Jansen 1994). The surface melting rates of ice sheets were immediately affected by climate change, but the reaction of equally important basal melting rates to warming were delayed up to thousands of years (Whillans 1978). Calving rates were controlled by a complicated system involving subglacial, glaciodynamic and marine boundary conditions and less by direct climatic components (Boulton & Payne 1994). Increased calving and retreat of grounding lines could have been associated with rapid eustatic sea level rise as a result of melting of other ice sheets and the relative sea level rise

From Andrews, J. T., Austin, W. E. N., Bergsten, H. & Jennings, A. E. (eds), 1996, *Late Quaternary Palaeoceanography of the North Atlantic Margins*, Geological Society Special Publication No. 111, pp. 339–349.

caused by glacio-isostatic crustal depression of the Barents Shelf (Jones & Keigwin 1988).

A collapse of a marine-based part of an ice sheet may have occurred as a result of glacio-isostatic crustal depression (Jones & Keigwin 1988) and basal thermal instability of an ice sheet (McAyeal 1993; Boulton & Payne 1994). These theories suggest a sequence where the glacier is initially frozen to its bed and expands and thickens causing crustal depression. The geothermal heat flux then raises the bed to the melting point, and basal melting lubricates the ice–bed interface. The drawdown (fast ice flow in an ice stream) lowers the profile of the ice sheet and the ice margin retreats close to the coastal zone. This allows isostatic uplift and the cycle is then repeated (McAyeal 1993; Boulton & Payne 1994). The rapid retreat of the ice margin may yield icebergs distributing ice-rafted detritus, which could be recorded in the stratigraphy in association with foraminifera indicating a freshwater pulse (Heinrich events) (Bond et al. 1993).

The calculated water volume released by a modelled collapse of the Laurentide Ice Sheet is equivalent to 3.5 m global sea level rise over 250 years at 1.4 cm/a (McAyeal 1993). Based on $\delta^{18}O$ record of foraminifera in North Atlantic, Labeyrie et al. (in press) estimated a sea level rise of about 2 m during each of the Heinrich events.

The $\delta^{18}O$ values of planktonic foraminifera in cores from the northwestern Labrador Sea demonstrate a meltwater pulse at 14 ka BP. Andrews et al. (1994) suggested that such events implicate the Laurentide Ice Sheet as a likely source of major changes in North Atlantic surface water salinity. The effect of collapses in the Laurentide Ice Sheet on the Norwegian Sea was diluted because of the large distance from North America. However, $\delta^{18}O$ values of foraminifera in the Norwegian seafloor sediments suggest that simultaneous meltwater pulses may also have occurred in the Eurasian Ice Sheet (Sarnthein et al. 1992; Koç & Jansen 1994). Such a meltwater pulse at 13–15 ka BP has been associated with a collapse of the Barents Sea Ice Sheet (Jones & Keigwin 1988; Lindstrom & McAyeal 1993).

It has also been proposed that the diversion of meltwater from the Mississippi into the St Lawrence River caused a freshwater pulse in the North Atlantic (Broecker et al. 1990), triggering a change in the thermohaline circulation which may be linked with the cool Younger Dryas stadial. A comparable event was the drainage of the Baltic Sea proglacial lake into the North Sea as a consequence of the generation of a new passage in south central Sweden (Bergsten & Nordberg 1992).

Oceanic circulation models of the North Atlantic have demonstrated that during the deglaciation the conveyor belt circulation system could have been affected by large freshwater perturbations shifting the sites and reducing the depth of deep convection. Disturbance of the ocean conveyor may have reduced the transfer of heat from low to high latitudes and affected the northern hemisphere climate (Lehman & Keigwin 1992; Duplessy et al. 1993; Rahmstorf 1994). Consequently, rapid meltwater events may have had a major impact on the climate change during glaciations and, in particular, during deglaciations.

In this paper, the amount of glacial meltwater produced during the deglaciation is compared with other freshwater sources. The deglaciation of the ice sheets around the Barents Sea is outlined using geological mapping, published land uplift data and previous observations. Freshwater discharges from proglacial lakes are estimated using this ice sheet reconstruction. Variations in precipitation are calculated using ice accumulation rates from an ice core in Greenland.

Methods

Satellite image interpretation of glacial landforms covers the eastern Kola Peninsula, northwestern Russian Plain, Pechora lowland, Ural mountains and southern Novaya Zemlya (Fig. 1). The compilation of previous geological results was extended to the areas of the Svalbard, Franz Josef Land and Novaya Zemlya ice domes of the Eurasian Ice Sheet (Fig. 2).

Hardcopy prints of Landsat MSS imagery (resolution 79 m) were interpreted to produce glacial geomorphological maps of northwestern Russia (1 000 000 km² using the methods described earlier (Punkari 1993). Mapping included flow-parallel features (drumlins, erosional basins), morainic formations (end moraines, transverse moraines), hummocky moraines and glaciofluvial landforms. Quaternary maps published previously show only a few such features. Marginal positions of former ice sheets were interpreted from the maps of youngest relative flow patterns and of end moraines. A compilation of about 50 radiocarbon dates from northwestern Russia were then used to produce isochrones of ice sheet retreat (Punkari 1995).

Holocene relative sea-level data (e.g. Astakhov 1994; Forman et al. 1995) and radiocarbon dates published previously (e.g. Gataullin 1988; Mangerud et al. 1992; Astakhov 1994; Polyak et al. in press) were used to reconstruct the retreat of ice sheets from the northern Barents

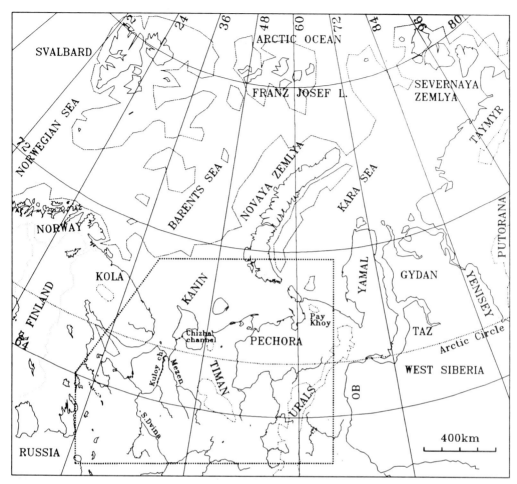

Fig. 1. General map showing eastern Fennoscandia and northwestern Russia including the Barents Sea (depth of 200 m broken line) and the borders of the area investigated (dotted line).

Sea. A calibrated time-scale of radiocarbon dates (Bard *et al.* 1990) was used in the calculations of meltwater volumes, although non-calibrated dates are used in the text.

The reconstruction of the ice marginal positions suggested that major proglacial lakes occurred south of the confluence zone of the Scandinavian and Novaya Zemlya Ice Sheets. The altitude of the drainage channels towards the south, controlling the elevation of the lake surfaces, was measured from topographical maps. Coastlines of the proglacial lakes were digitized to calculate the size of the basins and topographical data were used to estimate the volume of water. Isochrones of ice margins were used to approximate the date of the final drainage of the proglacial lakes into the Barents Sea.

It was predicted that, in addition to the rapid melting of ice sheets and sudden drainage of proglacial lakes, anomalous freshwater pulses may have been caused by increased precipitation. Thicknesses of ice accumulation in GISP2 ice core from Greenland were used to approximate precipitation during the deglaciation (Alley *et al.* 1993). The precipitation changes observed in Greenland are relatively consistent with reconstructions made using palaeobotanic data in La Grande Pile and Les Echets in France (Guiot 1990). It is assumed that similar relative changes also occurred in the Norwegian Sea and Barents Sea.

Probably the biggest uncertainty lies in the estimations of the thickness and deglaciation chronology of the Novaya Zemlya Ice Sheet. Marine data are not available from the Kara Sea and terrestrial observations from the Yamal Peninsula are inadequate for ice sheet reconstructions.

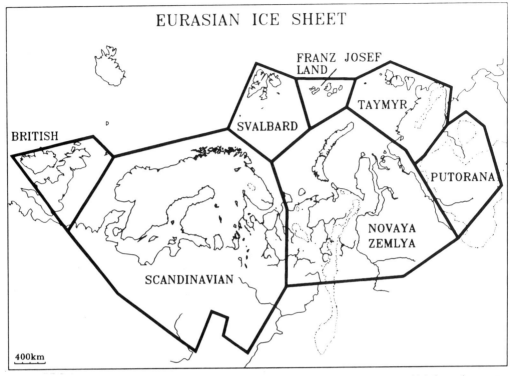

EURASIAN ICE SHEET

400km

Fig. 2. Subdivision of the Eurasian Ice Sheet and the names of the individual ice sheets which formed separate domes during glacial decay and probably also during growth.

Glacial flow and deglaciation in northwestern Russia

The glacial flow-parallel features (Fig. 3) indicate that the Scandinavian Ice Sheet expanded northeastwards into the southern Barents Sea, while the Novaya Zemlya Ice Sheet spread southwestwards into the same area; the two coalesced in the Kanin region and subsequently flowed from the Barents Sea towards the land (Punkari 1993, 1995).

Between 150 and 350 km from the present coastline between Mezen and the Ural mountains, a radical change in glacial morphology approximates the last glacial maximum (Lavrov 1977). North of this line occurs a distinctively 'fresh' landscape of end moraines and hummocky terrain, compared with the eroded glacial deposits south of it. Radiocarbon dates and pollen analyses indicate that the ice margin retreated from this line at about 14 000 years BP (Arslanov et al. 1987). The present data do not allow an interpretation of earlier ice marginal positions of the last glacial, including the global maximum at about 20 ka BP. Ice marginal positions interpreted using youngest flow patterns and end moraines show lobate patterns controlled by topography (Fig. 3).

A compilation of ^{14}C dates (Arslanov et al. 1987; Astakhov 1994; Polyak et al. in press) indicates that deglaciation on the southeastern coast of the Barents Sea was complete at about 10 ka BP. According to ^{14}C dates and glacial flow patterns (Fig. 3), separation of the ice sheets occurred in the marine zone between the Kanin and Kola Peninsulas at about 13 ka BP (16 ka BP, calibrated). Retreat of the ice margin from the southeastern Barents Sea during the Bölling interstadial is supported by the radiocarbon dates of 13 ka BP, which also show that full marine conditions were re-established between 9.6 and 9.4 ka BP (Polyak et al. in press).

Drainage of the proglacial lakes

The reconstruction of ice marginal positions suggests that the Dvina-Pechora proglacial lake was located in the valleys of the Severnyy Dvina, Mezen and Pechora rivers (Fig. 4). Before the

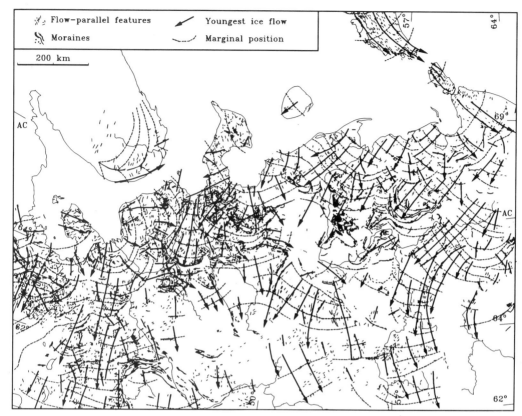

Fig. 3. Glacial flow-parallel features, moraines and glaciofluvial landforms interpreted from satellite images. The successive marginal positions during deglaciations are delineated using end moraines and last glacial flow directions. The landforms in the southern part of the area may originate from the previous glaciation.

final drainage northwards into the sea, the surface elevation of the proglacial lake was 130 m above the present sea level (Arslanov et al. 1987), which was the highest altitude of the Volga river system leading to the south.

The reconstruction shows that the size of the Dvina-Pechora proglacial lake was about 350 000 km^2, comparable in size with the proglacial lakes of the late glacial Laurentide Ice Sheet (Teller & Clayton 1983). The volume of water was of the order of 10 000 km^3, equivalent to a 3 cm global sea level rise. Presumably the drainage of the lake through a passageway generated between the two ice domes would have taken place within a matter of weeks or months. The lake drained into the Barents Sea, west of the Kanin Peninsula, creating the major drainage channels within Kuloy and Chizha (Fig. 1) (Punkari 1995). The Pechora pro-glacial basin was isolated during this drainage and its level dropped stepwise during the period 13–11 ka BP when the receding ice exposed lower passages.

Several observations on high shorelines and lacustrine sediments show that this proglacial lake really existed in the area, and Lavrov (1977), Kvasov (1978) and Arslanov et al. (1987) concluded that the drainage of the lake occurred during the Bölling interstadial (about 12.5 ka BP).

Further east, the meltwater discharge from the Siberian proglacial lakes into the Arctic Ocean may have been even bigger considering the extensive basin between the Ural and Putorana mountains (Fig. 1) (Volkov et al. 1980). However, the chronology and extent of glaciation there are as yet unknown. A meltwater event recorded in the eastern Arctic Ocean sediments at 15.7 ka BP (19 ka BP, calibrated) may be associated with the melting of the Siberian Ice Sheet and with the discharge of the proglacial lakes (Stein et al. 1994).

Deglaciation of the northern Barents Sea

The areal extent, mass distribution of the Eurasian Ice Sheet and timing of the glaciations in

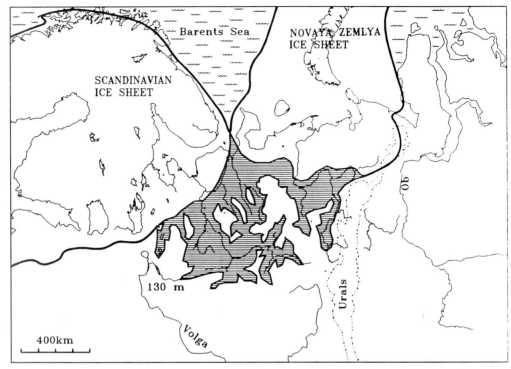

Fig. 4. Inferred limits of the Scandinavian and Novaya Zemlya Ice Sheets at about 13 ka BP. The Dvina-Pechora proglacial lake (hatched) drained into the Volga river system. After the separation of the two ice sheets the lake discharged catastrophically into the Barents Sea.

the area of the Barents Sea are still disputed (e.g. Faustova & Velichko 1992; Elverhøi *et al.* 1993). A new deglaciation reconstruction of the ice sheets in Fig. 5 is based on land uplift data (e.g. Forman *et al.* 1995), maps of glacial landforms prepared by the author (Fig. 3) and previous observations and radiocarbon dates (Punkari 1993, 1995).

Marine terraces have been found at altitudes of 8–10 m in the Yamal Peninsula (Gataullin 1988), 10–20 m at 5 ka BP in Novaya Zemlya (Forman *et al.* 1995), 20–30 m in Pay Khoy, 5–17 m in the Mezen region (see Astakhov 1994) and 80 m in the central Kola Peninsula (Tanner 1915). A continuous terrace, 15–17 m high, has been described in the Pechora coastland (Arslanov *et al.* 1987), although Mangerud *et al.* (1994) reported that no raised beach was discovered during a preliminary survey. The data on shoreline displacement in northwestern Russia are inadequate, but the observations mentioned suggest, together with the geomorphological evidence, that the ice volume here was bigger than proposed in the minimum model, but much less than in the maximum

model of the northern part of the Eurasian Ice Sheet (Hughes *et al.* 1981).

Using Holocene land uplift data, Forman *et al.* (1995) suggested maximum thicknesses of 1500 m for the Novaya Zemlya Ice Sheet and 2500 m for the Svalbard–Barents Sea Ice Sheet. In the case of the Scandinavian Ice Sheet, the contours of the glacier at its max-imum (Boulton & Payne 1994), the isobases (Kakkuri 1985) and the isochrones of the ice marginal retreat are very similar. However, in the Barents Sea area the thickest ice of the glacial maximum was located in the centre of the shelf (Forman *et al.* 1995), but during the deglaciation the marginal islands maintained ice domes for the longest time. These shifts in ice mass distribution make the use of land uplift data difficult.

During deglaciation, rising sea level reduced the effective pressure in the ice sheet and increased sliding and bed deformation, which made the marine ice margins unstable (Elverhøi *et al.* 1993). The drawdown of ice occurred along ice streams located in the topographic basins. The marine-based parts of the ice sheets collapsed first and the ice divides subsequently

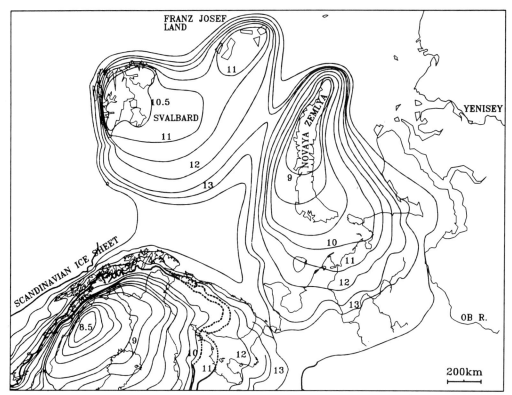

Fig. 5. Isochrones of the marginal positions of the Scandinavian, Svalbard, Franz Josef Land and Novaya Zemlya Ice Sheets around the Barents Sea (14C ka BP). The tentative reconstruction is based on geomorphological maps, land uplift data, and radiocarbon dates.

retreated to the Scandinavian mountains, Svalbard, Franz Josef Land and Novaya Zemlya, the ice flow directions being radially outwards from the land masses (Punkari in press).

Forman *et al.* (1995) concluded, from measurements of raised shorelines, that the retreat of the Svalbard Ice Sheet started at about 13.5–12.5 ka BP (16–14 ka BP, calibrated) and the glaciers reached their present size before 9.5 ka BP (11 ka BP, calibrated). This is consistent with the ^{14}C dates of Mangerud *et al.* (1992). Consequently, the southern part of the Barents Sea was deglaciated a few thousand years earlier than its northern part.

In the estimations of glacial meltwater production it was assumed that the ice sheet was at a steady state at 15 ka (^{14}C years), and that the extent of the ice was that shown in Fig. 5. The maximum thicknesses of ice were deduced from land uplift data (1200 m on average) (e.g. Forman *et al.* 1995). In this reconstruction, the maximum ice volume of the Svalbard, Franz

Josef Land and Novaya Zemlya Ice Sheets is 3 240 000 km^3. The estimation of meltwater production is based on ice marginal retreat shown in Fig. 5 and it excludes possible irregularities in ice volume decay. In reality, however, the strong meltwater event at 13.6 ka BP observed in the Norwegian Sea (Sarnthein *et al.* 1992) suggests an initial rapid collapse of the ice sheets in the Barents Sea area.

Precipitation changes

The present day precipitation is 1000 mm/a in the southern Norwegian Sea and 200 mm/a in the Arctic Ocean. The ice accumulation rates of the Greenland Ice Sheet show that during the glacial period the precipitation was about a half of the interglacial values (Alley *et al.* 1993).

The ice accumulation rates in Greenland show an increase of about 100% in the beginning of the Bölling interstadial at 12.3 ka BP (14.7 ka BP, calibrated), from 100 to 200 mm of ice per year (Alley *et al.* 1993). This approximation is used to infer the average precipitation change at the same period from about 200 to 400 mm/year in the Norwegian Sea. However, the impact of the increased precipitation on sea surface salinity could have been partly suppressed by increased

evaporation caused by the sea surface temperature rise of about 10°C during the same period (Labeyrie *et al.* in press).

The climate of the Younger Dryas stadial at 11–10 ka BP (12.8–11.6 ka BP, calibrated) was cold and precipitation decreased back to a glacial level. During the early Holocene, precipitation

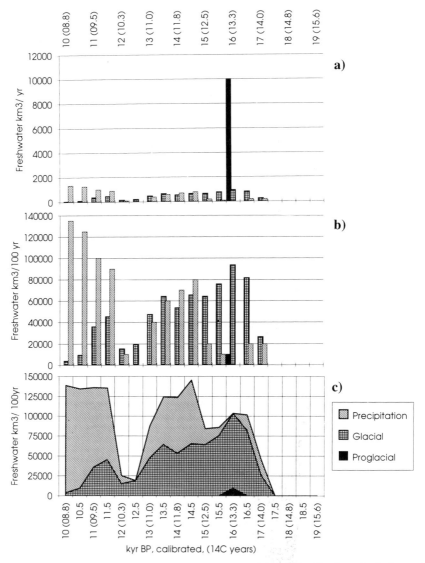

Fig. 6. Comparisons of freshwater inputs into the Barents Sea and Norwegian Sea from the drainage of the Dvina-Pechora proglacial lake, melting of ice sheets, and from the anomalous deviation of precipitation. Deviation of precipitation is presented as water volume in the area of 5×10^6 km², and a value typical of glacial periods (200 mm/year) is used as a base level. The values derive from the ice accumulation data of Greenland. The drainage of the proglacial lake is significant in a one-year cycle (**a**), but becomes suppressed by continuous freshwater sources in a hundred year cycle (**b**). Freshwater input was high before and after the Younger Dryas stadial, but very low during that period (**c**).

suddenly rose again by about 100% to an inter-glacial level (Guiot 1990; Alley *et al.* 1993). The effects of these precipitation changes on the total freshwater volume are evaluated in the next section.

The rapid increase in the sea surface tempera-ture and precipitation could indicate a north-ward shift of the oceanic polar front in North Atlantic (Lehman & Keigwin 1992). The posi-tion of the polar front probably controlled the sea ice cover, evaporation and precipitation (Hebbeln *et al.* 1994).

Results

The importance of the different freshwater sources within time are compared using the statistics described in the previous sections. Volumes of glacial meltwater from the Sval-bard, Franz Josef Land and Novaya Zemlya Ice Sheets and from the part of the Scandinavian Ice Sheet draining into the Barents Sea, and discharge of the Dvina-Pechora proglacial lake are shown as absolute values (Fig. 6). Precipita-tion change means a deviation from the glacial values (200 mm/year) in the Barents Sea and northern Norwegian Sea, in the area of 5×10^6 km². The values derive from the ice accumulation data in Greenland (Alley *et al.* 1993).

Within one year, the drainage of the progla-cial lake forms a drastic spike (Fig. 6a), but in a period of a hundred years, on the scale of bio-stratigraphic sampling, the continuous input of glacial meltwater suppressed this pulse (Fig. 6b). The volume of the discharge was about 16 times larger than the annual meltwater released from the melting ice sheets into the Barents Sea.

The reconstruction of the deglaciation around the Barents Sea suggests that melting of the ice sheets produced freshwater volumes of 2 500 000 km³ in 5 ka. The annual melting rate was more than 600 km³ at 13.7–11.5 ka BP. The melting rates shown include the discharges of up to 200 km³/year from the Scandinavian Ice Sheet into the Barents Sea (Punkari & Boulton 1995).

During the early deglaciation, the melting ice sheets were the main freshwater source (Fig. 6c). The temperature rise during the Bölling inter-stadial at 12.3 ka BP was accompanied by simul-taneous increase in precipitation. The diagrams show that precipitation was at that time a more important freshwater source than the melting of the adjacent ice sheets. The highest freshwater input of the Late Weichselian time took place at 12.2 ka BP because of simultaneous high glacial melting rates and precipitation. This occurred

1.3 ka later than the observed lowest spike of post-glacial sea surface salinity at about 13.5 ka BP connected with a migration of the oceanic polar front (Duplessy *et al.* 1993). Sarnthein *et al.* (1992) demonstrated a major glacial meltwater pulse at 13.6 ka BP, but also another at 12.3 ka BP which coincides with the date of the precipitation anomaly.

The Younger Dryas climate was cold and dry and glacier margins were close to the coastlines; the freshwater input was negligible compared with the preceding warm period. During the early Holocene a sudden increase in precipita-tion caused a freshwater anomaly exceeding the volume of glacial meltwater.

I thank G. S. Boulton for discussions and W. E. N. Austin and anonymous referees for valuable comments.

References

ALLEY, R. B., MEESE, D. A. & 9 others 1993. Abrupt increase in Greenland snow accumulation at the end of the Younger Dryas event. *Nature*, **362**, 527–529.

ANDREWS, J. T., ERLENKEUSER, H., TEDESCO, K., AKSU, A. E. & JULL, A. J. T. 1994. Late Quaternary (stage 2 and 3) meltwater and Heinrich events, Northwest Labrador Sea. *Qua-ternary Research*, **41**, 26–34.

ARSLANOV, H. A., LAVROV, A. S., POTAPENKO, L. M., TERTYCHNAYA, T. V. & CHERNOV, S. B. 1987. New data on geochronology and paleogeo-graphy of the Late Pleistocene and Early Holocene in the northern Pechora Lowland. *New Data on Geochronology of the Quaternary Period*. Nauka, Moscow, 101–111 [in Russian].

ASTAKHOV, V. 1994. *The Last Glaciation in European Russia's Arctic—a Review of Scientific Investiga-tions on Quaternary Stratigraphy and Shoreline Displacement*. SMR Rapport, **13/94**, Universitetet i Bergen.

BARD, E., HAMELIN, B. & FAIRBANKS, R. G. 1990. U–Th ages obtained by mass spectrometry in corals from Barbados: sea level during the past 130,000 years. *Nature*, **346**, 456–458.

BERGSTEN, H. & NORDBERG, K. 1992. Late Weich-selian marine stratigraphy of the southern Kattegat, Scandinavia: evidence for drainage of the Baltic ice lake between 12,700 and 10,300 yrs BP. *Boreas*, **21**, 223–252.

BOND, G., BROECKER, W., JOHNSEN, S., MCMANUS, J., LABEYRIE, L., JOUZEL, J. & BONANI, G. 1993. Correlations between climate records from North Atlantic sediments and Greenland ice. *Nature*, **365**, 143–147.

BOULTON, G. S. & PAYNE, T. 1994. Mid-latitude ice sheets through the last glacial cycle: glaciological and geological reconstructions. *In*: DUPLESSY, J. C. & SPYRIDAKIS, M. T. (eds) *Long-term climatic variations*. NATO ASI Series, **122**, 177–212.

BROECKER, W. S., BOND, G., KLAS, M., BONANI, G. & WÖLFLI, W. 1990. A salt oscillator in the glacial Atlantic? 1 The concept. *Paleoceanography*, **5**, 469–478.

DUPLESSY, J. C., BARD, E., LABEYRIE, L., DUPRAT, J. & MOYES, J. 1993. Oxygen isotope records and salinity changes in the northeastern Atlantic Ocean during the last 18,000 years. *Paleoceanography*, **8**, 341–350.

ELVERHØI, A., FJELDSKAAR, W., SOLHEIM, A., NYLAND-BERG, M. & RUSSWURM, L. 1993. The Barents Sea ice sheet – a model of its growth and decay during the last glacial maximum. *Quaternary Sciences Reviews*, **12**, 863–873.

FAIRBANKS, R. G., CHARLES, C. D. & WRIGHT, J. D. 1992. Origin of global meltwater pulses. *In*: TAYLOR, R. E., LONG, A. & KRA, R. S. (eds) *Radiocarbon After Four Decades*. Springer, New York, 473–500.

FAUSTOVA, M. A. & VELICHKO, A. A. 1992. *Dynamics of the Last Glaciation in Northern Eurasia*. Sveriges Geologiska Undersökning, Ser. Ca, **81**, 113–118.

FORMAN, S. L., LUBINSKI, D., MILLER, G., SNYDER, J., MATISHOV, G., KORSUN, S. & MYSLIVETS, V. 1995. Post-glacial emergence and distribution of Late Weichselian ice-sheet loads in the northern Barents and Kara Seas, Russia. *Geology*, **23**, 113–116.

GATAULLIN, V. N. 1988. *The Upper Quaternary sediments of the west coast of the Yamal Peninsula*. PhD Thesis, VSEGEI, Leningrad [in Russian].

——, POLYAK, L., EPSTEIN, O. & ROMANYUK, B. 1993. Glacigenic deposits of the Central Deep: a key to the Late Quaternary evolution of the eastern Barents Sea. *Boreas*, **22**, 47–58.

GUIOT, J. 1990. Methodology of the last climatic cycle reconstruction in France from pollen data. *Palaeogeography, Palaeoclimatology, Palaeoecology*, **80**, 49–69.

HEBBELN, D., DOKKEN, T., ANDERSEN, E. S., HALD, M. & ELVERHØI, A. 1994. Moisture supply for northern ice-sheet growth during the last glacial maximum. *Nature*, **370**, 357–360.

HUGHES, T. J., DENTON, G. D., ANDERSEN, B. G., SCHILLING, D. H., FASTOOK, J. L. & LINGLE, C. S. 1981. The last great ice sheets: a global view. *In*: DENTON, G. H. & HUGHES, T. J. (eds) *The Last Great Ice Sheets*. Wiley, New York, 263–317.

JONES, G. & KEIGWIN, L. D. 1988. Evidence from Fram Strait (78°N) for early deglaciation. *Nature*, **336**, 56–59.

KAKKURI, J. 1985. Die Landhebung in Fennoscandien im Lichte der heutigen Wissenschaft. *Zeitschrift für Vermessungswesen*, **110:2**, 51–59.

KOÇ, N. & JANSEN, E. 1994. Response of the high-latitude Northern Hemisphere to orbital climate forcing: evidence from the Nordic Seas. *Geology*, **22**, 523–526.

KVASOV, D. D. 1978. The Barents ice sheet as a relay regulator of glacial-interglacial alternation. *Quaternary Research*, **9**, 288–299.

LABEYRIE, L., VIDAL, L. & 9 others. Surface and deep hydrology of the Northern Atlantic Ocean during the last 150 ka. *Philosophical Transactions of The Royal Society*, in press.

LAVROV, A. S. 1977. The Kola-Mezen, Barents-Pechora and Novaya Zemlya-Kolva glacier flows. *In*: CHEBOTAREVA, N. S. (ed.) *Structure and Dynamics of Europe's Latest Ice Sheet*. Nauka, Moscow, 83–100 [in Russian].

LEHMAN, S. J. & KEIGWIN, L. D. 1992. Sudden changes in North Atlantic circulation during the last deglaciation. *Nature*, **356**, 757–762.

LINDSTROM, D. R. & MCAYEAL, D. R. 1993. Death of an ice sheet. *Nature*, **365**, 214–215.

MANGERUD, J., ASTAKHOV, V., SVENDSEN, J. I. & TVERANGER, J. 1994. The Barents ice sheet margin in Arctic Russia. *In*: *First Annual PALE Research Meeting*, Boulder, Abstracts, p. 15.

——, BOLSTAD, M. & 8 others 1992. The last glacial maximum on Spitsbergen, Svalbard. *Quaternary Research*, **38**, 1–31.

MCAYEAL, D. R. 1993. Binge/purge oscillations of the Laurentide ice sheet as a cause of the North Atlantic's Heinrich events. *Paleoceanography*, **8**, 775–784.

POLYAK, L., LEHMAN, S. L., GATAULLIN, V. & TIMOTHY, A. J. 1995. Two-step deglaciation of the southeastern Barents Sea. *Geology*, **23**, 567–571.

PUNKARI, M. 1993. Modelling of the dynamics of the Scandinavian ice sheet using remote sensing and GIS methods. *In*: ABER, J. (ed.) *Glaciotectonics and Mapping Glacial Deposits. Proceedings of the INQUA Commission on Formation and Properties of Glacial Deposits*. Canadian Plains Research Center, University of Regina, 232–250.

—— 1995. Glacial flow systems in the zone of confluence between the Scandinavian and Novaya Zemlya ice sheets. *Quaternary Science Reviews*, **14**, 589–603.

—— & BOULTON, G. S. 1995. Skandinavian mannerjäätikön itäosan dynamiikka ja reuna-asemat Nuoremman Dryaksen aikana (The dynamics and marginal positions of the Scandinavian ice sheet in its eastern part during the Younger Dryas stadial). *Terra*, **107**, 3–14.

RAHMSTORF, S. 1994. Rapid climate transitions in a coupled ocean–atmosphere model. *Nature*, **372**, 82–85.

SARNTHEIN, M., JANSEN, E. & 7 others 1992. $\delta^{18}O$ time-slice reconstruction of meltwater anomalies at termination II in the North Atlantic between 50 and 80°N. *In*: BARD, E. & BROECKER, W. S. (eds) *The Last Deglaciation, Absolute and Radiocarbon Chronologies*. NATO ASI Series, **12**, 183–200.

STEIN, R., SCHUBERT, C., VOGT, C. & FÜTTERER, D. 1994. Stable isotope stratigraphy, sedimentation rates, and salinity changes in the Latest Pleistocene to Holocene eastern central Arctic Ocean. *Marine Geology*, **119**, 333–355.

TANNER, V. 1915. Studier öfver kvartärsystemet i Fennoskandias nordliga delar. *Fennia*, **36**.

TELLER, J. T. & CLAYTON, L. 1983. *Glacial Lake Agassiz*. Geological Association of Canada, Special Paper, **26**.

VELICHKO, A. A. & FAUSTOVA, M. A. 1986. Glaciations in the East European region of the USSR. *In*: SIBRAVA, V., BOWEN, D. Q. & RICHMOND, G. M. (eds) *Quaternary Glaciations in the Northern Hemisphere. Quaternary Sciences Reviews*, **5**, 447–461.

VOLKOV, I. A., GROSSWALD, M. G. & TROITSKIY, S. L. 1980. The discharge of proglacial waters during the last glaciation of Western Siberia. *Polar Geography and Geology*, **IV:1**, 1–14.

WHILLANS, I. M. 1978. Inland ice sheet thinning due to Holocene warmth. *Science*, **201**, 1014–1016.

Palynology as a tool for land–sea correlation; an example from the eastern Mediterranean region

KARIN A. F. ZONNEVELD & KARIN P. BOESSENKOOL

Laboratory of Palaeobotany and Palynology, University of Utrecht, Heidelberglaan 2 3584 CS Utrecht, The Netherlands

Abstract: Sediments from two cores from the Adriatic Sea (Eastern Mediterranean), deposited between 18 and 9 ka BP, have been investigated with respect to their marine (dinoflagellate cyst) and terrestrial (pollen) fossil content. Based on contemporaneous changes in both the dinoflagellate cysts and pollen associations, a paleoclimatic reconstruction of the Adriatic Sea region is constructed for the studied time interval. Several intervals with increased Po River discharge are identified which may be subscribed to melting phases of the glaciers in the Alps and Apennines or increased winter precipitation in the region.

Changes in oceanic circulation and continental environmental changes strongly interact with each other and with changes in climate (e.g. COHMAP 1988; Kutzbach *et al.* 1993). To gain further insight into the causes and effects of climatic change, detailed palaeoclimatic reconstructions and precise correlations between oceanic and continental variations in environmental conditions are necessary. However, current restrictions in, for instance, the dating techniques used to date marine and terrestrial sediments usually make exact correlation difficult. Furthermore, palaeoclimatic reconstructions are often based on either marine or terrestrial (fossil) records, whereas the correlation of these records may provide a more realistic reconstruction. In this paper, an example will be given where palynology is used as a basis for 'land–sea' correlation. By studying both the marine (dinoflagellate cysts) and terrestrial (pollen grains) fossil components of the same sediment samples of a marine core, information can be obtained on contemporaneous changes in both the marine and continental environments. The results are presented here of dinoflagellate cyst and pollen analyses from sediments deposited during the last 18 ka BP in the Adriatic Sea; these provide the basis for a palaeoclimatic reconstruction.

Materials and methods

Sediments from core IN68–9 (IN9) and IN68–21 (IN21; Jorissen *et al.* 1993) in the Adriatic Sea (Fig. 1) have been investigated with respect to their pollen and dinoflagellate cyst content. High sedimentation rates associated with core IN9 provide a sample resolution of 25–50 years (Fig. 2). The age of the samples has been

calculated using linear interpolation between ^{14}C dating horizons, excluding turbidity and ash layers. Six ^{14}C measurements on shells of benthic foraminifera provide index points for the calculation of palynomorph influx data. Complete records of the dinoflagellate cyst and pollen content of core IN9 and a discussion of the age assessments and influx calculations relating to this core can be found in Zonneveld (1995; in press). Relative abundance data for pollen are calculated including all the species in the pollen-sum.

Results and discussion

In core IN9 four intervals with a relatively high pollen influx can be identified: ±14.5–13.5 ka BP

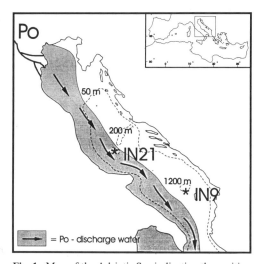

Fig. 1. Map of the Adriatic Sea indicating the position of cores IN9 and IN21.

From Andrews, J. T., Austin, W. E. N., Bergsten, H. & Jennings, A. E. (eds), 1996, *Late Quaternary Palaeoceanography of the North Atlantic Margins,* Geological Society Special Publication No. 111, pp. 351–357.

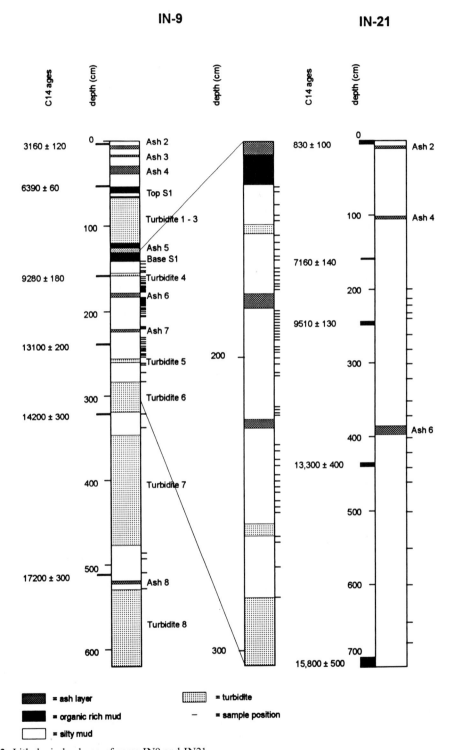

Fig. 2. Lithological column of cores IN9 and IN21.

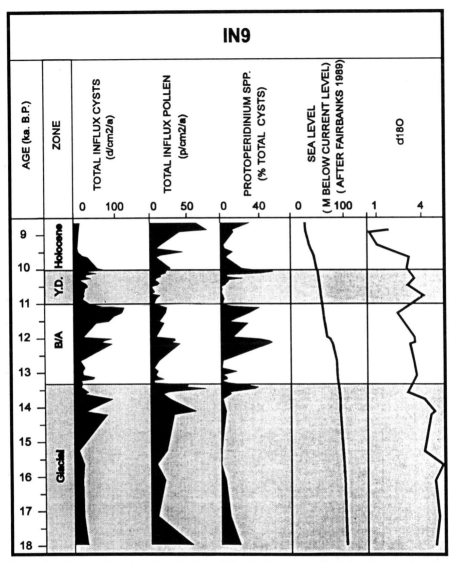

Fig. 3. Comparison between the main sea level height and dinoflagellate cyst, pollen influx data, relative abundance data from *Protoperidinium* cysts and $\delta^{18}O$ values from core IN9 after Zonneveld (in press). d, dinoflagellates cysts; p, pollen grains; cm2, cm²; a, year.

(end glacial), 12.5–12 ka BP (end Bølling), 11.5–11 ka BP (end Allerød) and 10.2–9.3 ka BP (beginning Holocene). All intervals with a high pollen influx are also characterized by a relatively high dinoflagellate cyst influx. As discussed more fully in Zonneveld (1995), variations in the influx of dinoflagellate cysts can be explained in terms of the variation in production of cysts in surface waters and is unlikely to be the result of variations in preservation and/or sedimentation rates, transportation by ocean currents or reworking. Intervals with a high pollen influx generally cor-respond to high relative abundances of *Pro-toperidinium* cysts (Fig. 3). In Recent sediments *Protoperidinium* cysts are found in areas with a high nutrient content and high productivity in surface waters (e.g. Wall *et al.* 1977; Harland 1983; Mudie 1992; Marret 1994) such as upwel-ling areas, ice margins and river plumes. This sug-gests that intervals with a relatively high influx of dinoflagellate cysts and pollen most probably reflect high nutrient availability in surface waters.

High nutrient levels in surface waters can be the result of wind-induced upwelling. At the

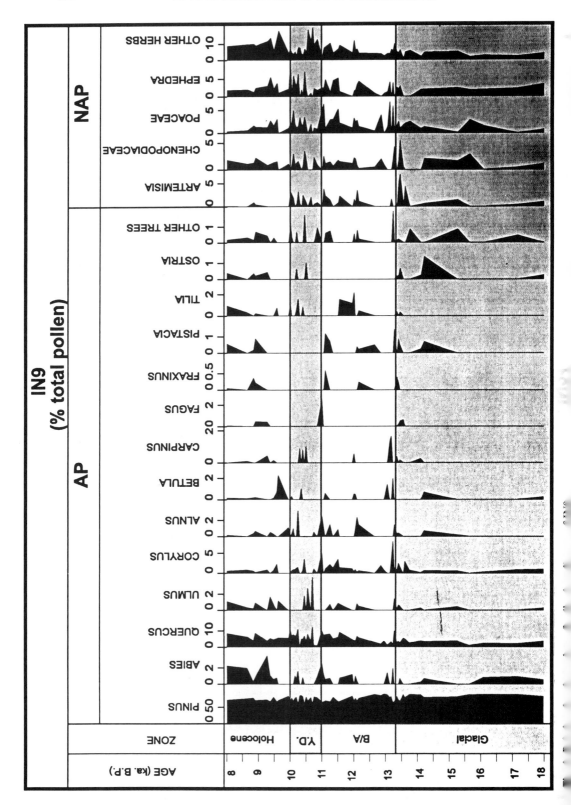

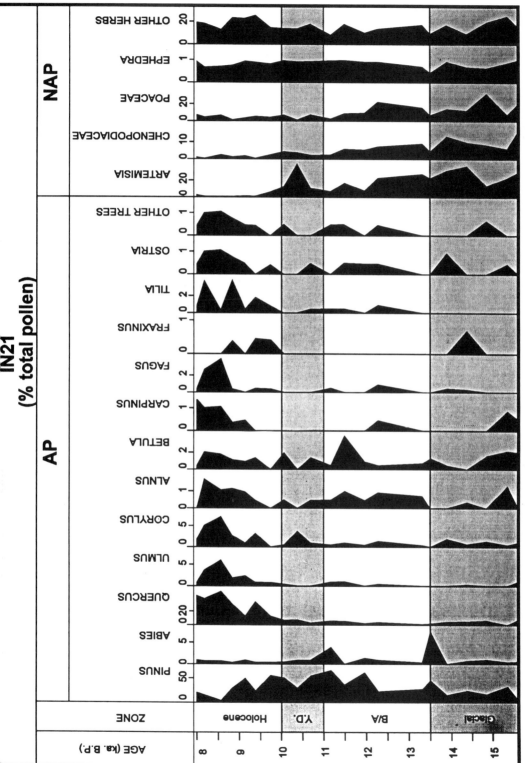

Fig. 5. Relative abundance data of pollen in sediments of IN21.

present time, the wind pattern of the Adriatic Sea and surrounding continental areas is dominated by southeastern and northwestern winds (Orlic *et al.* 1992). Upwelling can only be induced by enhanced northeastern and eastern winds. If the cause of the observed increases in the influx of pollen in these intervals was a change in wind direction, then the pollen rain during these intervals most likely reflects the vegetation cover east and northeast of the Adriatic Sea (Greece and the former Yugoslavia). Vegetation reconstructions based on terrestrial pollen records indicate that during the last glacial period that area was covered with a steppe dominated by *Artemisia, Chenopodiaceae* and *Gramineae* (Wijmstra 1969; Bottema 1974; 1979; Van Zeist & Bottema 1991). Some conifers were present, probably at higher elevations. Other trees were probably confined to limited refugia (Bottema 1974; Tzedakis 1993). Between ±13.5 and 11 ka BP (Bølling and Allerød), coniferous forest colonized the higher elevations of the region around the Adriatic Sea. Between 11 and 10 ka BP (Younger Dryas), however, the vegetation returned to steppe, which in turn was replaced by a mixed forest after 10 ka BP. These changes in vegetation cover are more or less reflected in the records of core IN21 (Fig. 4), but not in those from core IN9 (Fig. 5). No clear trend can be observed in the pollen record of IN9. For instance, an increase in the relative abundance of deciduous tree species is recorded at the end of the glacial stage, including several species characteristic of relatively warm and/or humid conditions (e.g. *Fagus, Fraxinus, Pistacia, Ostrya, Carpinus, Ulmus*). It is therefore unlikely that a change in wind direction was the cause of the increased influx of pollen in the sediments and increased nutrient availability in the surface waters.

The increase in nutrient availability in several periods could also be the result of increased river discharge. At the present time, surface waters of the Adriatic Sea are characterized by an inflow of Mediterranean surface water and an outflow of relatively fresh Po River (discharge) water along the Italian coast (Artegiani *et al.* 1989). Mediterranean surface waters are relatively nutrient-depleted, whereas Po River waters are characterized by a high nutrient content (Jorissen 1988). In the time interval under consideration the current system was probably similar to that of today (Rossignol-Strick 1985; Thunell *et al.* 1987). An increase in discharge would result in a basin-inward extension of the Po River discharge water plume along the coast of Italy, resulting in increased nutrient availability in the surface waters at the position of

IN9. Furthermore, the Po River waters contain high amounts of organic material (including pollen) which is deposited below the current (Jorissen 1988). Extension of the Po River plume would therefore result in the increased deposition of organic material and influx of pollen in the more central parts of the basin. Pollen grains transported by the Po River either originate from the vegetation in areas adjacent to the river or are reworked from eroded sediments. The pollen from deciduous tree species which prefer warm/humid conditions (found in the Adriatic Sea sediments that date between 14.5 and 13.5 ka BP) therefore probably originate from older interglacial deposits. This seems to be confirmed by the pollen assemblages recovered from core IN21. This core was obtained from a location below the Po River discharge plume, a location that was likely to have been affected by the Po discharge throughout the last 18 ka. In all samples from IN21, low amounts of pollen from trees that are characteristic of more warm humid conditions have been recorded, indicating the continuous deposition of these pollen types beneath the Po discharge plume.

Intervals with increased influx of pollen and dinoflagellate cysts can consequently be characterized as periods with increased river discharge. The first of these periods (14.50–13.5 ka BP) corresponds to the melting of the glaciers in the Alps and Apennines at the end of the last glacial (Maisch 1982), which provides a mechanism for the increased Po River discharge during this period. The increased Po River discharge around 12 and 11 ka BP cannot be subscribed to melting phases of the glaciers in Alps and Apennines. Vegetation reconstructions based on pollen indicate increasing temperatures, but no increase in precipitation during these periods (Bottema 1974; Schneider 1978). However, the vegetation is mainly influenced by spring and summer precipitation. The increased discharge could therefore be the result of increased winter precipitation.

This is a paper of the Netherlands Research School for Sedementary Geology, NSG No 950710.

References

ARTEGIANI, A., AZZOLINI, R. & SALUSTI, E. 1989. On dense water in the Adriatic Sea. *Oceanologica Acta*, **12**, 151–160.

BOTTEMA, S. 1974. *Late Quaternary vegetation history of northwestern Greece.* PhD Thesis, Rijksuniversiteit Groningen, Groningen.

——1979. Pollen analytical investigations in Thessaly (Greece). *Palaeohistoria*, **21**, 19–40.

COHMAP PROJECT MEMBERS 1988. Climatic changes of the last 18,000 years: observations and model simulations. *Science*, **241**, 1043–1052.

HARLAND, R. 1983. Distribution maps of recent dinoflagellate cysts in bottom sediments from the North Atlantic Ocean and adjacent seas. *Palaeontology*, **26**, 321–387.

JORISSEN, F. J. 1988. Benthic foraminifera from the Adriatic Sea; principles of phenotypic variation. *Utrecht Micropaleontological Bulletin*, **37**, 1–174.

——, ASIOLI, A.& 8 others 1993. Late Quaternary central Mediterranean biochronology. *Marine Micropaleontology*, **21**, 169–189.

KUTZBACH, J. E., GEUTTER, P. J., BEHLING, P. J. & SELIN, R. 1993. Simulated climatic changes: results of the COHMAP climate-model experiments. *In*: WRIGHT, H. E., KUTZBACH, J. E., WEBB III, T., RUDDIMAN, W. F., SREET-PERROT, F. A. & BARTLEIN, P. J. (eds) *Global Climates Since the Last Glacial Maximum*. University of Minnesota Press, London, 24–93.

MAISCH, M. 1982. Zur Gletscher- und Klimageschichte des alpinen Spätglazials. *Geographica Helvetica*, **37**, 93–104.

MARRET, F. 1994. Distribution of Dinoflagellate cysts in recent marine sediments from the east Equatorial Atlantic (Gulf of Guinea). *Review of Palaeobotany and Palynology*, **84**, 1–22.

MUDIE, P. J. 1992. Circum-arctic Quaternary and Neogene marine palynofloras: paleoecology and statistical analysis. *In*: HEAD, M. J. & WRENN, L. H. (eds) *Neogene and Quaternary Dinoflagellate Cysts and Acritarchs*. American Association of Stratigraphic Palynologists Foundation, Dallas, 347–390.

ORLIC, M., GACIC, M. & LA VIOLETTE, P. E. 1992. The currents and circulation of the Adriatic Sea. *Oceanologica Acta*, **15**, 109–122.

ROSSIGNOL-STRICK, M. 1985. Mediterranean Quaternary sapropels, an immediate response of the African monsoon to variation of insolation. *Palaeogeography, Palaeoclimatology and Palaeoecology*, **49**, 237–263.

SCHNEIDER, R. E. 1978. Pollenanalytische Untersuchungen zur kenntnis der spät- und postglazialen Vegetationsgeschichte am Südrand der Alpen zwischen Turin und Varese (Italien). *Botanischer Jahrbücher Systematik*, **100**, 26–109.

THUNELL, R. C., WILLIAMS, D. F. & HOWELL, M. 1987. Atlantic–Mediterranean water exchange during the Late Neogene. *Paleoceanography*, **2**, 661–678.

TZEDAKIS, P. C. 1993. Long-term tree populations in northwestern Greece through multiple Quaternary climatic cycles. *Nature*, **364**, 437–440.

VAN ZEIST, W. & BOTTEMA, S. 1991. Late Quaternary vegetation of the Near East. *Beihefte zum Tübinger Atlas des Vorderen Orients*, **Reihe A/18**, 1–155.

WALL, D., DALE, B., LOHMAN, G. P. & SMITH, W. K. 1977. The environmental and climatic distribution of dinoflagellate cysts in the North and South Atlantic Oceans and adjacent seas. *Marine Micropaleontology*, **2**, 121–200.

WIJMSTRA, T. A. 1969. Palynology of the first 30 metres of a 120 m deep section in northern Greece. *Acta Botanica Neerlandica*, **18**, 511–527.

ZONNEVELD, K. A. F. 1995. Palaeoclimatical and palaeo-ecological changes during the last deglaciation in the Eastern Mediterranean; implications for dinoflagellate ecology. *Review of Palaeobotany and Palynology*, **84**, 221–253.

—— Palaeoclimatic reconstruction of the last deglaciation (18 ka BP–8 ka BP) in the Adriatic region; a land–sea correlation based on palynological evidence. *Palaeogeography, Palaeoclimatology and Palaeoecology*, in press.

Earth rotation, ocean circulation and palaeoclimate: the North Atlantic – European example

NILS-AXEL MÖRNER

Paleogeophysics & Geodynamics, Stockholm University, S-10691 Stockholm, Sweden

Abstract: The glacial eustatic rise in sea level after the 20 ka BP glaciation maximum led to an increase in the equatorial radius and hence a general deceleration in the Earth's rate of rotation. The sea-level rise can be approximated by two superposed exponential curves with a transitional period about 13–10 ka radiocarbon years BP. This period is known to cause high-amplitude climatic changes and regionally irregular changes in sea level. This is interpreted as a break down in the Earth–Moon adjustment to the post-glacial deceleration, which was instead compensated by rapid re-distributions of oceanic water masses and interchanges of angular momentum between the hydrosphere and the solid Earth. At about 6000 years BP the glacial eustatic rise in sea level ended and a new set of circumstances began, which were characterized by feedback interchanges of angular momentum between the solid Earth and the hydrosphere. It is proposed that the palaeoclimatic changes on a decadal to millennial time-scale are primarily driven by the causal connection between the Earth's rotation, oceanic circulation, ocean/atmosphere heating, atmospheric (wind) heat transport and continental palaeoclimatic changes.

It is often claimed that the ocean circulation is driven by thermohaline forces. The interchange of angular momentum between the hydrosphere and the solid Earth is another fundamental factor, however. This can be demonstrated for the ENSO events, for the last centuries' instrumental data, for decadal to century scale changes during the Holocene, for the high-amplitude climatic–eustatic changes about 13–10 ka BP, and for the main glacial–interglacial cycles (Mörner 1984a; 1984b; 1988; 1989; 1993a; 1993b; 1993c; 1995).

The oceans have a remarkable heat-storing capacity. Any change in the distribution of the water masses will therefore have strong effects on the global climatic temperature distribution. The oceans contain huges masses of water (of a reasonably high density) that are constantly circulating both horizontally and vertically over the globe. Any irregularity in the circulation leads to a redistribution in the total mass, which affects the sea level and has to be compensated by an interchange of angular momentum between the hydrosphere and the solid Earth.

Our palaeo-records indicate a very strong linkage between changes in the ocean surface circulation – heating or cooling the wind passing over the ocean surface – and changes in past continental climate and coastal sea level. This applies for the high-amplitude changes about 13–10 ka BP (i.e. the Bölling–Alleröd warming and the Younger Dryas cooling over northwestern Europe) as well as Holocene and Historical decadal to century scale changes and ENSO events (Mörner 1993a; 1995).

In between the Milankovitch time variability and the annual changes, we have the decadal to millennial scale changes in climate. For our future life on Planet Earth, these changes are of primary significance because they will set the frame of the living conditions in the near future. Their driving mechanisms, however, are poorly understood and much debated. Do they represent changes in the total energy budget, the redistribution of energy within a more or less fixed terrestrial budget, or a combination of both?

In 1984, I proposed that most of the short-term changes in climate and sea level are, in fact, the function of the redistribution of energy and water masses over the globe via variations in the main oceanic circulation system (Mörner 1984a; 1984b), in contrast with the general idea of globally more or less uniform changes due to solar variability and glacial eustatic changes in level. This was further analysed in a number of papers (Mörner 1988; 1993a; 1993b; 1993c). In this paper, we analyse the North Atlantic–European situation during the deglaciation phase with comparative discussions for the period of the last glaciation maximum and the period in the Holocene when the deglaciation was over and full interglacial climatic conditions were established.

Gulf Stream and the Polar Front

The Gulf Stream sets the characteristics of the oceanography of the North Atlantic (Stommel 1965). The Gulf Stream (like the Kuroshio Current in the Pacific) brings warm equatorial water to high latitudes in the northeastern North

From Andrews, J. T., Austin, W. E. N., Bergsten, H. & Jennings, A. E. (eds), 1996, *Late Quaternary Palaeoceanography of the North Atlantic Margins*, Geological Society Special Publication No. 111, pp. 359–370.

Atlantic in an eastwards branching-up current system (Fig. 1). There are two main branches: the southern branch (SB) and the northern branch (NB), each of which consists of sub-branches. The water of the Gulf Stream is driven by strong forces causing the dynamic sea surface to rise about 4–5 m above the geoid (Fig. 1). Any change in these driving forces will affect the total amount of water transported along this, such as like the distribution of this transport via the various sub-branches of the main Gulf Stream.

At the last glaciation maximum around 20 ka, the Polar Front was displaced southwards to the northern margin of the southern branch of the Gulf Stream (i.e. a latitude corresponding to central Portugal). Today, it is located slightly off the coasts of southern Greenland. During warm periods, the Gulf Stream penetrated far up into the north (into the Barents Sea and up to the Fram Strait). During cold periods, Arctic water penetrated far south, displacing the Polar Front accordingly (e.g. Lamb 1979).

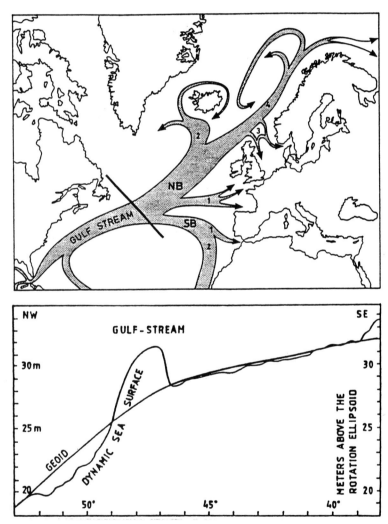

Fig. 1. Upper panel: the Gulf Stream and its division into a southern branch (SB) consiting of two arms, one towards Gibraltar (1) and one back to the equatorial region (2; the Canaries Current), and a northern branch (NB) consisting of four arms; one towards the Bay of Biscay (1), one towards Iceland (2), one into the North Sea (3) and one up into the Arctic (4). Lower panel: Satellite profile (from autumn 1978) of the sea surface topography across the Gulf Stream (as given by a line in the upper panel), indicating that the dynamic sea surface due to the current velocity, is forced to rise by 4–5 m above the geoid level (Menard 1981; Mörner 1983).

Effects of changes in the Earth's rate of rotation

The Earth's rotation around its spin axis has two main effects on the hydrospheric distribution of the oceanic water masses.

(1) The oceanic water forms an equatorial bulge (i.e. a little too much water is concentrated to this region where the centrifugal forces are strongest).

(2) The equatorial surface water lags behind the solid Earth so that strong equatorial currents from the east to the west are formed in all the ocean basins, with compensational back-currents not only via the equatorial counter currents but primarily via the Circum-Antarctic Current in the southern hemisphere and the Gulf Stream and the Kuroshio Current in the northern hemisphere. This surface circulation is, of course, linked to the deep-water circulation. This is, for example, easily seen in the areas of coastal upwelling.

The Earth's rate of rotation may change by means of two different mechanisms (both following the physical law of the conservation of angular momentum).

(1) The total terrestrial angular momentum may change (in response to radius changes and mass dislocation). These changes are compensated by changes in the Earth–Moon distance so that the total angular momentum of the Earth–Moon motions around the barycentre is constant (Marsden & Cameron 1966; Dieke 1966; Mörner 1993a).

(2) The different sub-units of the Earth (core/solid Earth, solid Earth/hydrosphere, solid Earth/atmosphere) may change their individual rates of rotation by interchanging angular momentum between each other to keep the total terrestrial angular momentum constant (Mörner 1984a; 1988; Rochester 1984). This is known as 'differential rotation'. The instrumental records cover about 300 years (Stephenson & Mossison, 1984). The Earth/ocean (hydrosphere) interchange is of decadal to century duration (Mörner 1988) with components (ENSO events) as short as a few years (Mörner 1989; cf. Eubanks et al. 1986). The core/mantle interchange is of decadal duration (e.g. Rochester 1984; LeMouël et al. 1986). The Earth/atmosphere interchange is of inter-annual to annual duration (e.g. Barnes et al. 1983; Rosen & Salstein 1983; Hide & Dicky 1990).

The effects on the oceanic circulation of these two types of changes are very different (cf. Mörner 1993a; in press).

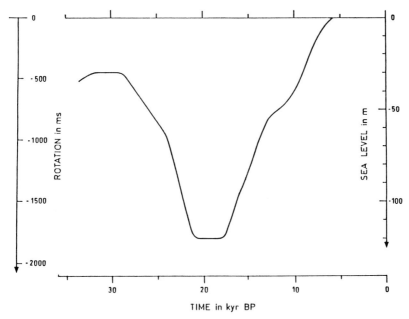

Fig. 2. Generalized eustatic curve of the last 35 ka BP (based on a combination of the Barbados and northwest European records). The corresponding rate of rotation is given in milliseconds to the left.

The glacial eustatic changes in oceanic water volume directly alter the radius of the Earth and hence must affect the total rate of rotation. During the maximum glaciation, eustatic sea level fell by about 100–120 m, which would generate a speeding up in spin velocity of about 1500–2000 ms (ignoring the compensational effects due to the accumulation of ice masses at high latitudes). During the post-glacial rise in sea level from about 18 up to about 6–5 ka BP, the earth must have experienced a corresponding slowing down (deceleration). When the sea level stopped rising for glacial eustatic reasons about 6000–5000 years BP, the terrestrial system seems to have become very sensitive to the interchange of angular momentum between the solid Earth and the hydrosphere (the distribution of oceanic water masses), between the solid Earth and the atmosphere (the distribution of atmospheric air masses) and between the solid Earth and the core.

This means, in fact, that the Earth went through different stages or modes: the glacial mode with stable low sea level; the main deceleration mode when the sea level rose from 18 to 6–5 ka BP; and the interglacial Holocene mode with stable high sea-level and dominance of

the interchange of angular momentum. This is illustrated in the Fig. 2 sea-level graph where the radius-changing sea-level curve has been converted to corresponding rotational scale (letting 1 m in sea level equal 15 ms in rotation).

Figure 2 records an important fact. The post-glacial sea-level rise does not form an exponential curve as would have been expected, but two superposed exponential curves with a transitional period around 13–10 ka BP. It is exactly during this period that the Earth experienced a series of high-amplitude climatic changes (Mörner 1993a).

The 20 ka BP glaciation maximum

Because of the low sea level, the Earth's total rate of rotation was very much increased. This speeding up caused: (1) the equatorial bulge to increase, (2) the equatorial current to increase (transporting more water westwards and most probably switching-off ENSO events; Mörner 1993c); (3) the Gulf Stream and Kuroshio Current to bend towards the equator and the Gulf Stream to concentrate the transport of water along its southern branch, allowing the

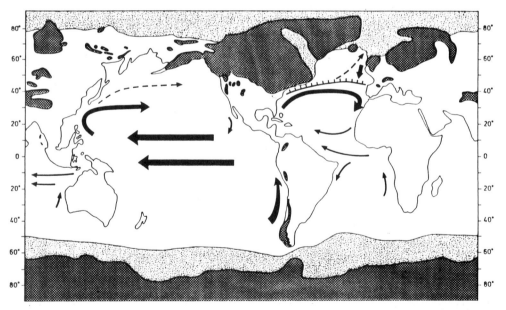

Fig. 3. Changes in the ocean current system (arrows) as a function of increased spin rate during the 20 ka BP glaciation maximum (dark areas, main glaciated areas; dotted areas, sea ice cover). The transport of hot equatorial water by the Kuroshio Current and Gulf Stream were displaced significantly more towards the equator (thick arrows compared with broken arrows). In the Atlantic, Arctic water penetrated far down, displacing the Polar Front to much lower latitudes (dentated line). The warm main equatorial westerly currents were strongly increased. The cold Humboldt and Benguela Currents (also the West Australian Current) were intensified, generating strongly increased coastal upwelling and oceanic productivity.

Polar Front to migrate southwards, which in combination with the effects from the glacial built-up meant as far down as to about latitude 40° N; and (4) increasing the coastal upwelling (via the cold currents feeding the equatorial currents in the east). Therefore the ice age conditions in northwest Europe correspond to conditions 'as warm as today' (Fatela *et al.* 1994) in the Azores–Gibraltar region.

This situation is illustrated in Fig. 3. It is important that the Kuroshio Current also bent down because this was a direct effect of ocean circulation in response to the speeding up and not a glaciation effect (as, we may argue, was the dominant factor in the Atlantic).

The Polar Front/Gulf Stream distribution at the glaciation maximum is illustrated in Fig. 4A.

The 18–13 ka BP first deceleration period

When the sea level started to rise as a function of the onset of glacial melting about 18 ka BP, the terrestrial system came into a new mode of general deceleration (because of the successively increasing equatorial radius). This slowing down caused: (1) a decrease in the equatorial bulge; (2) a decrease in the equatorial currents; (3) a northward migration of the Gulf Stream and Kuroshio Current with more water sent to higher latitudes, forcing the Polar Front to migrate northwards; and (4) a decrease in coastal upwelling. This leads to a warming in north-western Europe. The Azores–Gibraltar region, on the other hand, was likely to experience a cooling.

The Polar Front/Gulf Stream distribution at about 15 ka BP is illustrated in Fig. 4B. The Gulf Stream warming and the glaciation cooling competed in the north. In the region off south-west Iberia and Gibraltar, cooling conditions are recorded, however (Cachão 1994; Fatela *et al.* 1994).

When the Gulf Stream began to flow north-wards again, this was, of course, at the expense of transport along the southern branch, which allowed cold water to penterate south along the Iberian coast. This is why maximum cold conditions off Iberia occurred, not at 20 ka BP, but later during the deglaciation phase (Cachão 1994; Fatela *et al.* 1994). In association with this period, there are coarse-grained deposits of the Heinrich 1 event present (Lebreiro *et al.* 1994), indicating that icebergs from intensive calving in the Hudson Striat region in northern Canada were transported to the European side along the northern margin of the southern branch of the Gulf Stream (cf. Fig. 4B).

The 13–10 ka BP transitional period

The period around 13–10 radiocarbon ka BP is anomalous in two ways; (1) the glacial eustatic general sea-level came into a transitional mode (separating two periods of exponentially rising sea-level, Fig. 2) characterized by the regional redistribution of water masses; and (2) this period is characterized by a number of high-amplitude climatic oscillations.

The change in sea-level rise must have led to a corresponding adjustment in the response to changes in rotation. The climatic changes recorded during this time interval have such amplitudes and frequencies that they must be driven by some special process. The interfacing of Milankovitch variables has sometimes been proposed, but this would never produce the type of signals that are recorded. It must be a process capable of inducing rapid changes, like the swings of a cord in response to a beat (Fig. 5c). Only the oceans seem to have enough heat-storing capacity and the right order of magni-tude of circulation time.

I therefore proposed (Mörner 1993*a*) that this period is characterized by rapid geographical displacements of oceanic water masses due to corresponding interchanges of angular momen-tum between the solid Earth and the hydro-sphere in a desperate way to compensate for the sudden change in general deceleration. This means that we are dealing with a relation between sea-level rise and deceleration that at about 13 ka BP came into a crisis situation and had to be compensated by rapid mass redis-tributions. This led to a series of compensational swings – like beating a cord.

Figure 5 illustrates the sea-level rise according to the northwest European eustatic base curve of Mörner (1969; 1976) and the Barbados eustatic curve of Fairbanks (1989), the corresponding rates of changes and the Dye-3 oxygen isotope record from Greenland. The sea-level data show the transitional period and the irregular mass distributions within the period. The Greenland isotope record shows very nicely the 'beat on a cord' type signal at 13–10 ka BP.

With respect to my proposal of an oceano-graphic origin – rather than global effects on solar insolation changes – to the high-amplitude changes within this period, I note the following statements; 'responses to some kind of threshold or trigger in the North Atlantic climatic system' (Alley *et al.* 1993); 'large-scale changes in oceanic circulation in the north Atlantic region' (GRIP 1993); 'instabilities in the North Atlantic thermocline circulation' (Stuiver & Braziunas 1993); and 'we have to look for

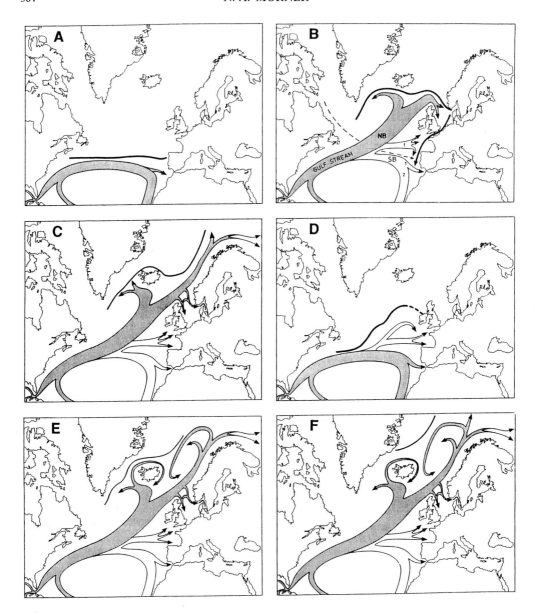

Fig. 4. Migration with time of the Gulf Stream and Polar Front in the North Atlantic. (**A**) At the 20 ka BP glaciation maximum when the Gulf Stream was restricted to its southern branch giving conditions 'as warm as today' off southwest Iberia. (**B**) During the deglaciation phase about 15 ka BP when a northward flux caused a corresponding decrease along the southern branch of the Gulf Stream so that maximum cold conditions occurred off southwest Iberia. (**C**) At the Bölling warm swing about 13.0–12.5 ka BP when the Gulf Stream suddenly penetrated all the way into the Barents Sea and a new marine biota rapidly was established along the northwest European coasts. (**D**) At the Younger Dryas cold phase 11–10 ka BP when very severe climatic conditions returned and the northern branch of the Gulf Stream was cut off increasing the southern flux so that warm and moist conditions occurred along the southwestern coast of Iberia. (**E**) In early Holocene time when there was a second intensive flux of the Gulf Stream far to the north. (**F**) During the Holocene climatic optimum when the Gulf Stream reached further north than today and the southeast Greenland coast was ice-free.

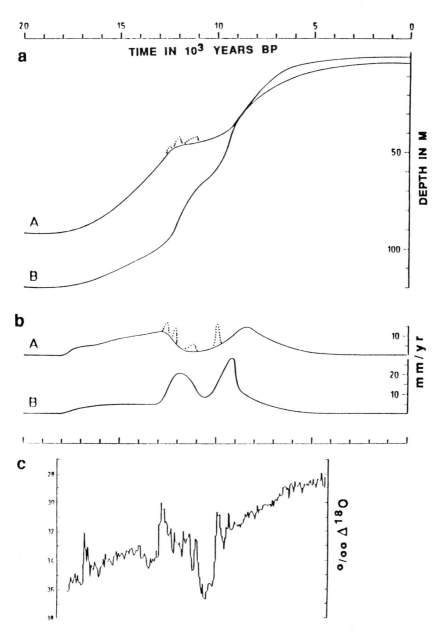

Fig. 5. Upper panel: eustastic sea level curves for northwestern Europe (**A**) and for Barbados (**B**), and, at the base, corresponding rate curves in mm/year. Both curves show the superposition of two exponential rises with a transitional period at about 13 000–10 000 BP, during which period the rate curves exhibit heavy fluctuations that primarily are out of phase and opposed (dotted lines on the two A curves refer to actual oscillations on the eustatic base curve which, for simplicity, was drawn to exclude the recorded oscillations). Lower panel: oxygen isotope records from the Greenland Dye-3 ice core (redrawn from Dansgaard & Oeschger 1988). A sequence of high-amplitude swings between colder and warmer climate are recorded and stands our as an anomaly – a 'beat on a cord' signal – to the gently rising curve of low-amplitude variability before and after.

oceanographic events' (Duplessy this volume). I can see no other mechanism than the rapid redistribution of water masses via surface circulation (and related deep water motions) in a feedback coupling with the interchange of angular momentum. The sea-level data records this like the 'beat on a cord' signal in the isotope record.

A completely different type of information telling us about a change in Earth's mode of rotation comes from palaeomagnetism (Mörner 1991). At about 13.2 ka BP there was a trans-polar VGP shift (i.e. a shift that followed a meridional lope). Such a shift can only be understood in terms of the displacement of the symmetry axis of two rotation bodies; in this case the core and the mantle. Consequently, we know that Earth's rotation really was upset. The first change came at 13.2 ka BP and the main oceanic effects began at about 13 ka BP. Because the Fennoscandian uplift suddenly started at around 13 ka BP for reasons other than glacial thinning, we may suspect that the Earth's general J2 gravity shape was deformed (Mörner 1991), a fact that need not be considered here, but helps to understand the rotational/gravitational crisis that occurred at about 13.2–13.0 ka BP

Bölling warm event

At around 13 ka BP (which, as a matter of fact, is a rounding-off of lots of radiocarbon shell dates of about 12 700 years BP), there was a drastic change in marine biota along the northwest European coasts. This is recorded as a sudden change in malacological fauna in the Kattegatt (Mörner 1969), along the Norwegian coast (Mangerud 1977) and around Scotland and in the North Sea (Peacock this volume).

This change in biota signifies a suddan and drastic increase in the transport of warm Atlantic water along the Gulf Stream to the north (cf. Ruddiman & McIntyre 1981; Duplessy *et al.* 1981). It penetrated all the way up into the Barents Sea (Polyak this volume). The Gulf Stream penetration seems to have been restricted to a corridor along the Norwegian coast, the remaining part of the Norwegian–Greenland Sea beeing cold and ice-covered (cf. Koç this volume). As is evident from the Greenland isotope record, this was a very drastic warming event (Fig. 5c). The Polar Front/Gulf Stream situation at the Bölling warm peak is illustrated in Fig. 4C.

Figure 6 illustrates the interpretation of available Bölling (13 ka BP) data with respect to the present day oceanic circulation system of the

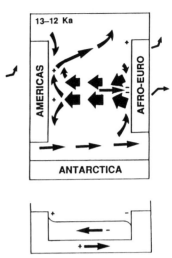

Fig. 6. Changes in ocean circulation and regional sea level during the Bölling warm phase. Decreased water masses off West Africa (−) and increased water masses off Brazil and Barbados as in northwest Europe (+) together with a northward shift of the Gulf Stream (upper panel) can only be interpreted (lower panel) in terms of differential rotation between the solid Earth (speeding up) and the hydrosphere (slowing down).

Atlantic (cf. Mörner 1993*a*). Off equatorial West Africa, the sea level stopped rising (Tastet 1989). Off Brazil and at Barbados, the sea level began to rise rapidly (Fig. 5A; Fairbanks 1989). Along the coast of northwest Europe, sea level experienced a rapid rise (Mörner 1969) and at the same time the Gulf Stream sent a strong pulse of increase far up to the north. This can only be understood in a strongly increased lagging behind of the water masses with respect to the solid Earth; i.e. a speeding-up of the solid Earth and a slowing down of the hydrosphere as illustrated in the lower graph of Fig. 6.

Younger Dryas cold event

The Younger Dryas period refers to the time of 11–10 ka BP when southern Scandinavia (like much of the rest of Europe) experienced a final tundra period and when the ice recession slowed down drastically, stopped or even reverted to re-advance. The isotopic record from Greenland (Fig. 5c) provides a good illustration of the dimension of this cold swing. Both the onset and the end of this period were drastic and rapid.

Such an event could never be the function of solar variability nor phasing of the Milankovich variables; the origin must be looked for in other mechanisms (e.g. Mörner 1993*a*).

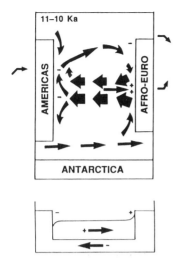

Fig. 7. Changes in ocean circulation and regional sea level during the Younger Dryas cold phase. Increased water masses off West Africa (+) and decreased water masses off Brazil and Barbados like in northwest Europe (−) togeter with a strong southward shift of the Gulf Stream (upper panel) can only be interpreted (lower panel) in terms of differential rotation between the solid Earth (slowing down) and the hydrosphere (speeding up).

During the Younger Dryas, the whole system rapidly and drastically reversed; the Polar Front was displaced far south (the northern branch of the Gulf Stream ceased to exist), the warm

surface water was predominantly transported along the southern branch of the Gulf Stream, generating warm and humid conditions off Gibraltar and along the southwest coast of the Iberian Peninsula, where peat and humus soils of Younger Dryas age were formed (Zazo *et al.* 1996). This strongly speaks of oceanic circulation changes as the driving factor for the Younger Dryas event. The Polar Front/Gulf Stream situation at the Younger Dryas cold peak is illustrated in Fig. 4D.

Figure 7 illustrates the interpretation of available Younger Dryas data with respect to the present day oceanic circulation system in the Atlantic (cf. Mörner 1993a). Off equatorial West Africa, the sea level started rapidly to rise (Tastet 1989). Off Brazil and at Barbados, the rate of sea level rise dropped significantly (Fig. 5A; Fairbanks 1989). Along the coast of northwest Europe, sea level dropped (Mörner 1969). The northern branch of the Gulf Stream was cut off at the same time as the Polar Front moved down. This can only be understood in terms of a reversal of the main equatorial currents, i.e. a slowing down of the solid Earth and a speeding up of the hydrosphere as illustrated in the lower graph of Fig. 7.

Because there, in the North Atlantic, is competition between the Polar Front displacement and the Gulf Stream distribution, it is interesting and significant to note that the Kuroshio Current in the Pacific (where the Polar Front was far to the north) also experienced a southward

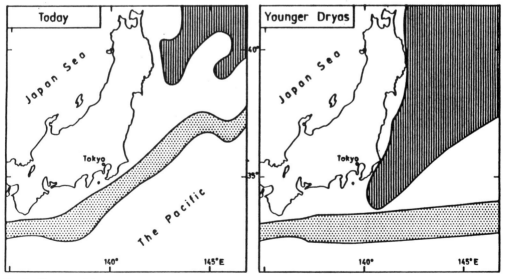

Fig. 8. Changes of the warm Kuroshio Current (dotted) and the cold Oyashio Current (hatched) of today and in the Younger Dryas period. The southward displacement of both currents must be a function of the speeding-up in oceanic angular momentum (cf. Fig. 7).

displacement during the Younger Dryas period (Fig. 8). This can hardly be caused by anything else than an oceanic speeding up (in full agreement with the interpretation given in Fig. 7).

The 10–6 ka BP final deceleration period

At around 10 ka BP, a second period of rapid sea-level change began. This pushed the terrestrial system into a second mode of general deceleration. This resulted in a strong northward flush of the Gulf Stream. A new marine fauna and flora was suddenly established along the coasts of northwest Europe (Mörner 1976; 1984*a*; Björklund *et al.* 1985). The Atlantic water penetrated far up into the Barents Sea (e.g. Polyak this volume) and the Norwegian Sea (e.g. Hald this volume; Koç this volume). The Gulf Stream in Early Holocene time is illustrated in Fig. 4E.

The post-5–6 ka BP interglacial Holocene period

At around 5–6 ka BP ago, the glacial eustatic rise in sea level stopped and the terrestrial system came into a new mode of unchanged total angular momentum. This period was, on the other hand, characterized by a dominance of interchange of angular momenum between the Earth's different sub-layers and in particular between the solid Earth and the hydrosphere (the oceanic circulation of water masses). This interchange was in the form of a feedback coupling. Mörner identified 16 such pulses (or 'Super-ENSO events') plus some Historical events (Mörner 1984*a*; 1988; 1993*b*; 1995). As an analogy, he used present ENSO events (Mörner 1989; 1993*c*).

At the Holocene Optimum (in Mid Holocene time), the Gulf Stream reached far up into the Arctic and the southeast Greenland coast was free of pack ice. This situation is illustrated in Fig. 4F.

The Subatlantic period (from 2500 a BP onwards) is characterized by cooler and wetter climatic conditions in Scandinavia and less influence of the Gulf Stream in the Barents Sea. In view of ocean circulation changes, it may be significant that, in the northwest of Spain, it is characterized by warmer and dryer conditions. At around AD 950, the Vikings could sail along southeast Greenland and establish a colony in southwest Greenland. One century later this route was no longer possible because of a general weakening of the northward penetration of the Gulf Stream

(Mörner 1993*b*; 1995). Similarly, the cold periods 1440–1460 (within the Spörer Minimum time period), 1687–1703 (within the Maunder Minimum time period) and 1808–1821 (within the Dalton Minimum time period) seem to be driven primarily by ocean circulation changes with a strong southward penetration of cold Arctic water (Mörner 1995).

These young Historical changes are outside the theme of this paper. They are important in this context, however, because they also tell about the strong influence on European climatology that comes from ocean circulation changes (all of which can be related to changes in the Earth's angular momentum budget).

Conclusions

There is a linear relation between sea level and Earth's rate of rotation. This means that the Earth went through different stages or modes: (1) a glacial mode with low and stable sea level; (2) a main deceleration mode when the sea level rose from about 18 ka BP to Mid-Holocene time which, from 13 to 10 ka BP, was interrupted by a transitional period when rapid differential rotation took over; and (3) an interglacial mode of stable sea level for the last 5000–6000 years with a switch to differential rotation.

We have tried to show that there, indeed, is a very strong linkage between Earth's rate of rotation – total as well as differential – and the changes in ocean circulation. The ocean circulation changes are, in their turn, strongly linked to the palaeoclimtic evolution on the bordering land masses. This is due to the high heat-storing capacity of the oceans, the ocean/atmosphere heat flux, and the ocean/land interaction via wind heat transport.

Consequently, we see a causal connection between Earth's rotation, oceanic circulation, ocean/atmosphere heating, atmospheric (wind) heat transport and continental palaeoclimatic changes. We propose that the palaeoclimatic changes on the decadal to millennial timescale are primarily driven by this mechanism. The most outstanding examples are, of course, the high-amplitude swings in the period 13–10 ka BP – i.e. the Bölling warming of 13–12 ka BP and the Younger Dryas cooling of 11–10 ka BP. Figures 6 and 7 illustrate the driving mechanism in view of observed changes in oceanic water masses and palaeoclimate.

Our observations, interpretation and proposed mechanism for palaeo-climatic changes on the decadal to millennial basis imply that the oceanic system has a much more important role than previously appreciated (e.g. Rind in press). This should significantly affect our modelling of corresponding past and future climatic changes.

References

ALLEY, R. B., MEESE, D. A. and 9 others 1993. Abrupt increase in Greenland snow accumulation at the end of the Younger Dryas event. *Nature*, **362**, 527–529.

BARNES, R. T. H., HIDE, R., WHITE, A. A. & WILSON, C. A. 1983. Atmospheric angular momentum correlated with length of the day changes and polar motion. *Proceedings of the Royal Society, London*, Series. **A387**, 31–73.

BJÖRKLUND, K. R. ET AL. 1985. Evolution of the Upper Quaternary depositional environment in the Skagerak. A synthesis. *Norsk Geologisk Tidsskrift*, **65**, 139–149.

CACHÃO, M. 1994. Quaternary calcareous nannofossil assemblages and time series from Iberian Occidental margin. *In: Abstracts, 1st Symposaium on the Atlantic Iberian Continental Margin, Lisbon*, 9–10.

DANSGAARD, W. & OESCHGER, H. 1988. Past environmental long-term records from the Arctic. *In*: OESCHGER, H. & LANGWAY JR, C. C. (eds) *The Environmental Record in Glaciers and Ice Sheets*. Wiley, Chichester.

DIEKE, R. H. 1966. The secular acceleration of the earth's rotation and cosmology. *In*: MARSDEN, G. B. & CAMERON, A. G. W. (eds) *The Earth–Moon System*. Plenum Press, New York, 98–164.

DUPLESSY, J. C., DELIBRIAS, G., TURON, J. L., PUJOL, C. & DUPRAT, J. 1981. Deglacial warming of the northeastern Atlantic Ocean: correlation with palaeoclimatic evolution of the European continent. *Palaeogeography, Palaeoclimatology, Palaeoecology*, **35**, 121–144.

EUBANKS, T. M., STEPPE, J. A. & DICKEY, J. O. 1986. The El Niño, the Southern Oscillation and the Earth's Rotation. *JPL Geodecy and Geophysics Preprints*, **143**.

FAIRBANKS, R. G. 1989. A 17,000-year glacio-eustatic sea-level record: influence of glacial melting rates on the Younger Dryas event and deep-ocean circulation. *Nature*, **342**, 637–642.

FATELA, F., DUPRAT, J. & PUJOS, A. 1994. How southwards migrated the polar front, along the West Iberian margin, at 17,888 years BP?. *GAIA, Revista de Geociencias, Universidade de Lisboa*, **8**, 169–173.

GRIP (GREENLAND ICE-CORE PROJECT MEMBERS) 1993. Climate instability during the last inter-glacial period recorded in the GRIP ice core. *Nature*, **364**, 203–207.

HIDE, R. & DICKEY, J. O., 1990. Earth's variable rotation. *JPL Geodecy and Geophysics Preprints*, **285**.

LAMB, H. H. 1979. Climatic variations and changes in the wind and ocean circulation: the Little Ice Ages in the Northeast Atlantic. *Quaternary Research*, **11**, 1–20.

LE MOUËL, J. P., GIRE, C. & JAUPART, C. 1986. Sur le corrélation entre la figure de la terre et les mouvements animant les couches externes de son noyau. *Compt Rendu Academie Scientifique, Paris*, **B303**, 613–618.

LIBREIRO, S. M., MORENO, J. C., ABRANTES, F., WEAVER, P. P. E. & MCCAVE, I. N. 1994. Late Quaternary palaeoceanography off Iberia: Tore Seamount (39° N, 12° W). *Abstracts, 1st Symposaium on the Atlantic Iberian continental margin, Lisbon*, 28.

MANGERUD, J. 1977. Late Weichselian marine sediments containing shells, foraminifera, and pollen, at gotnes, Western Norway. *Norsk Geologisk Tidsskrift*, **57**, 23–54.

MARSDEN, G. B. & CAMERON, A. G. W. (eds) 1966. *The Earth–Moon System*. Plenum Press, New York.

MENARD, Y. 1981. Ètude de la variabilité de la topographie dynamique des océans liéé à la circulation océanographique, l'ouest de la dorsale médio-Atlantique entre 30° N et 55° S en latitude. *Annales Géophysique*, **37**, 99–106.

MÖRNER, N. A. 1969. The Late Quaternary history of the Kattegatt Sea and the Swedish West Coast; deglaciation, shorelevel displacement, chronology, isostasy and eustasy. *Sveriges Geologiska Underskning*, **C-640**, 1–487.

—— 1976. Summary and conclusions. *Boreas*, **5**, 247–256.

—— 1983. Sea levels. *In*: GARDNER, R. & SCOGING, H. (eds) *Mega-Geomorphology*. Oxford University Press, Oxford, 73–91.

—— 1984a. Planetary, solar, atmospheric, hydrospheric and endogene processes as origin of climatic changes on the Earth. *In*: MØRNER, N. A. & KARLÉN, W. (eds), *Climatic Changes on a Yearly to Millennial Basis*. Reidel, Dordrecht, 483–507.

—— 1984b. Climatic changes on a yearly to millennial basis. Concluding remarks. *In*: MÖRNER, N. A. & KARLÉN, W. (eds) *Climatic Changes on a Yearly to Millennial Basis*. Reidel, Dordrecht, 637–651.

—— 1988. Terrestrial variations within given energy, mass and momentum budgets; paleoclimate, sea level, palaeomagnetism, differential rotation and geodynamics. *In*: STEPHENSON, F. R. & WOLFENDALE, A. W. (eds) *Secular Solar and Geomagnetic Variations in the last 10,000 years* Kluwer Academic, Dordrecht, 455–478.

—— 1989. Changes in the Earth's rate of rotation on an El Niño to century basis. *In*: LOWES, F. J., COLLINSON, D. W., PARRY, J. H., RUNCORN, J. H., TOZER, D. C. & SOWARD, A. (eds) *Geomagnetism and Palaeomagnetism*, Kluwer Academic, Dordrecht, 45–53.

—— 1991. Trans-polar VGP shifts and Earth's rotation. *Geophysics and Astrophysics Fluid Dynamics*, **60**, 149–155.

—— 1993a. Global change: the high-amplitude changes 13–10 ka BP ago – novel aspects. *Global and Planetary Change*, **7**, 243–250.

—— 1993b. Global change: the last millennia. *Global and Planetary Change*, **7**, 211–217.

——1993c. Present El Niño–ENSO events and past Super-ENSO events. *Bulletin de l'Institut Francais d'Etudes Andines*, **22**, 3–12.

——1995. Earth rotation, ocean circulation and paleoclimate. *Geojournal*, **3714**, 419–430.

RIND, D. 1996. The potential for modelling effects of different forcing factors on climate during the past 2000 years. *In: Proceedings NATO conference on climate changes during the last 2000 years*. In press.

ROCHESTER, M. G. 1984. Causes of fluctuations in the rotation of the Earth. *Philosophical Transactions of the Royal Society, London*, **A313**, 95–105.

ROSEN, R. D. & SALSTEIN, D. A. 1983. Variations in atmospheric angular momentum on global and regional scales and the length of the day. *Journal of Geophysical Research*, **36**, 5451–5470.

RUDDIMAN, W. F. & McINTYRE, A. 1981. The North Atlantic during the last deglaciation. *Palaeogeography Palaeoclimatology Palaeoecology*, **35**, 145–214.

STEPHENSON, F. R. & MORRISON, L. V. 1984. Longterm changes in the rotation of the Earth: 700 BC to AD 1980. *Philosophical Transactions of the Royal Society, London*, **A313**, 47–70.

STOMMEL, H. 1965. *The Gulf Stream*. University of California Press, Berkley.

STUIVER, M. & BRAZIUNAS, T. F. 1993. Sun, ocean, climate and atmospheric $14CO_2$: an evaluation of causal and spectral relationships. *The Holocene*, **3**, 289–305.

TASTET, J. P. 1989. Continental shelf and sea-level evolution during the last 120,000 years on the northwest African margin: Ivory Coast example. *In: International Symposium, Global Changes in South America during the Quaternary, São Paulo 1989, Special Publications*, **1**, 213–215.

ZAZO, C., GOY, J. L., LARIO, J. & SILVA, P. 1996. Littoral zone and rapid climatic changes during the last 20,000 years BP. The Iberia. *Zeitschrift für Geomorphology N.S., Suppl-Bd.*, **102**, 119–139..

Index